KU-682-779

Practical
Knowledge for All

Our Colour Plates

(1) COLOURS OF THE SPECTRUM

The language of colour is one which we all understand in some measure, but we may never appreciate its more subtle nuances unless we have some grasp of the theoretical basis of the science of colour. Who would suspect, for instance, that a ray of sunlight is composed of all the colours of the rainbow—a fact beautifully demonstrated by the simple experiment, illustrated in the colour plate opposite, of passing a narrow beam of sunlight through a glass prism? The beam, it will be seen, is "bent", and broadens out until it emerges in the rainbow hues of red, orange, yellow, green, blue, and violet. This band of colours was called the "spectrum" by Sir Isaac Newton, who first made the experiment.

(2) PRIMARY AND SECONDARY COLOURS

Then in the colour plate overleaf we have in the clearest possible form the "primary" colours distinguished from the "secondary". Red, yellow, and blue, shown in the outer parts of the three circles on the left, are "primary" colours, i.e. they cannot be made from mixtures of other colours. Where two of the circles overlap, a "secondary" colour is produced—green, orange, or purple. Where all three overlap, in the middle, black results. Just as there are three primary colours for pigments, so there are three primary colours of light—blue-violet, yellow-green, and red-orange —and where these overlap we have the secondary colours of light. Where all three primaries overlap, white is the result.

PHYSICS 17

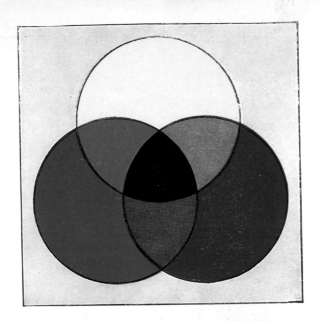

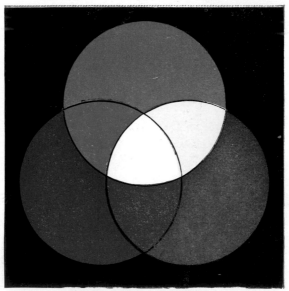

PRIMARY COLOURS OF PIGMENT (above)
AND OF LIGHT (below)

PRACTICAL KNOWLEDGE FOR ALL

Sir John Hammerton

**Comprising Easy Courses in Literature Language
History Geography the Arts and Sciences Written
by Experts and Arranged for Home Study**

NEWLY REVISED EDITION

In Six Handy Volumes with over 360 Special
Plates including Twelve in Full Colours
and about 1300 other Illustrations

FIFTH VOLUME

LONDON

THE WAVERLEY BOOK COMPANY LTD.

A5

Printed in Great Britain by The Amalgamated Press, Ltd., London.

LITERARY CONTENTS

OF VOLUME V

COMPLETE LIST OF COURSES

ACCOUNTANCY	ECONOMICS	LATIN
AERONAUTICS	ENGINEERING	MATHEMATICS
ART & ARCHITECTURE	ENGLISH LANGUAGE	MODERN HISTORY
ASTRONOMY	ENGLISH LITERATURE	PHILOSOPHY
BIOLOGY	FRENCH	PHYSICS
BOTANY	GEOGRAPHY	PHYSIOGRAPHY
BRITISH HISTORY	GEOLOGY	PHYSIOLOGY
CHEMISTRY	GERMAN	SHORTHAND
DRAWING & DESIGN	HISTORY : ANCIENT &	SPANISH
ECONOMIC GEOGRAPHY	MEDIEVAL	ZOOLOGY

LIST OF SPECIAL PLATES
IN VOLUME V

Frontispieces in Colour:

Colours of the Spectrum ;　Primary and Secondary Colours

Maps and Plans in the Text

(8)

Multiple-Shop Accounts

MANY concerns have more than one place of business, and a large multiple-shop undertaking may operate several hundred branches. In such cases, it is important that separate records should be kept for each branch, in order that the management may be able to control the activities of the local staff, and to make comparisons between one branch and another. Not every branch is equally profitable, and the accounts must be kept in such a way that the trading results of each individual branch may readily be ascertained. The books kept at the branch are in no way different from the books of any other business. Records of purchases and sales, cash received and paid, are kept on the usual lines. It is necessary, however, for these records to be summarized in the books of the head office, which is the centre of administration and control; it is with the accounts of the branches, as they appear in the head office books, that we are concerned. The subject is a large one, and it will only be possible to refer briefly to the more important features.

In the usual type of organization, all purchases, or nearly all, are made at headquarters, the goods being issued thence to the branches. The branch is frequently simply a selling agency, and, if this is the case, the books kept locally will be confined to a record of goods received from the head office, together with details of sales, cash received and remitted to head office, debts outstanding from customers, and any petty expenses that may have been disbursed. Periodically—usually at the end of each week—the branch will forward to the head office a summary embodying these figures, which will form the basis for the entries in the head office ledger. The records kept at the branches are not, therefore, part of the double entry system of the head office. It should be understood that the entries made in the head office do not record details, but only the totals, as shown by the periodical branch returns.

When the goods are issued by the head office to the branches, they may be invoiced at any one of three figures: (1) at cost price; (2) at a percentage above cost; (3) at selling price.

If the goods are invoiced at cost price, an account is opened for each branch in the head office ledger, to which the cost of the goods is debited, an account termed Goods to Branches being credited. As the weekly branch returns are received, the branch is credited with the sales, both for cash and on credit, for the period. A Branch Cash account is debited with the cash sales, and a Branch Debtors account with the credit sales ; the weekly return will also include the amount of cash received from debtors during the period, and this sum is credited to Branch Debtors account, and debited to Branch Cash account. The Branch Cash account is credited with sums remitted to the head office, the General Cash account of the concern being debited ; the Branch Cash account is also credited with expenses paid by the branch, and Expense accounts are debited. Separate Expense accounts are kept for each branch, in order that the net profit earned by each individual branch may be ascertained. Balances are brought down on the Branch account, the Branch Debtors account, and the Branch Cash account, representing stock on hand, debts due by customers to the branch, and Cash in hand at the branch. These accounts may be illustrated by a simple example.

The stock on hand at the Liverpool branch of a concern on January 1 was £500 ; goods are invoiced by head office at cost. £3,000 worth of goods are sent to the branch during the month of January. Cash sales, £2,000 ; credit sales, £2,500 ; stock January 31, £700 ; cash received from debtors, £2,300 ; cash remitted to head office, £4,000 ; sundry expenses paid by the branch, £250. The accounts in the books of the head office will appear as follow :

Branch Account

Jan. 1				By—		
To—						
Balance, c/d	..	..	£ 500	Cash Sales	.. ..	£2,000
Goods	.. ..	..	3,000	Credit Sales	.. ..	2,500
Gross Profit to Branch				Stock, c/d (Jan. 31)	..	700
P. & L. %	..	..	1,700			
			£5,200			£5,200

| To Balance c/d | .. | .. | £700 | | | |

Goods to Branches

To—				By—			
Trading %c	..	..	£3,000	Branch	..	..	.. £3,000
			£3,000				£3,000

Branch Debtors Account

To—				By—			
Credit Sales	..	..	£2,500	Branch Cash %c	..	..	£2,300
				Balance, c/d	..	..	200
			£2,500				£2,500

To Balance, c/d £200

Branch Cash Account

To—				By—			
Cash Sales	..	..	£2,000	Cash	..	..	.. £4,000
Branch Drs.	..	..	2,300	Sundry Expenses		..	250
				Balance. c/d	..	..	50
			£4,300				£4,300

To Balance, c/d £50

Branch Sundry Expenses

To—				By—			
Branch Cash %c	..	£250	Branch P. & L.	..	..	£250
		£250				£250

Branch Profit and Loss Account

To—				By—			
Sundry Expenses	..	£ 250	Branch %c	..	..	.. £1,700
Net Profit to General							
P. & L.	..	..	.. 1,450				
			£1,700				£1,700

It will be observed that the Goods to Branches account has been closed off to the General Trading account of the head office. It is probably more suitable to make the credit direct to Purchases account. The Branch account constitutes the Trading account of the branch.

A more complicated system is necessary when goods are invoiced to the branch at selling price. This is the method most commonly employed. The advantage of this procedure is that it affords an excellent check on the accuracy of the branch returns, since the two sides of the Branch account should agree ; if the Branch account is debited with all goods received by the Branch at selling price, and credited with sales and closing stock, also at selling price, it is clear that the two sides of the account are equal. If there is any discrepancy, there has been a mistake or inaccuracy in the returns supplied by the branch to the head office, and the cause should at once be investigated. Of course, a certain small margin of error may be normal, since, in some businesses, small losses of stock due to breaking bulk, fractional errors in the turn of the scale, etc., are unavoidable. Where the shortage, however, exceeds the normal, the fact is at once evident.

The following example illustrates the accounting procedure. A trading concern sends to a branch goods costing £1,000, and invoices them at selling price, which is 25 per cent above cost. The branch soon afterwards returns £50 worth of goods (selling price). The branch sales (all credit) for the period under review amounted to £800, while customers had returned £60 worth of goods to the branch. The value of the stock on hand (at selling price) at the end of the period amounted to £450. £650 was received from debtors, and was remitted in total to the head office. The accounts of the head office will appear as follow :

Branch Account

To—		By—	
Goods	..£1,250	Returns to Head Office £ 50	
Returns from Cus-		Sales 800	
tomers	60	Stock, c/d 450	
		Shortage 10	
	£1,310		£1,310
To Stock, c/d £450			

Goods to Branches

To—		By—	
Returns .. .. .. £ 40		Branch £1,000	
Purchases 960			
£1,000		£1,000	

Branch Debtors Account

To—		By—	
Sales £800		Returns .. .. .. £ 60	
		Cash 650	
		Balance, c/d 90	
£800		£800	

To Balance, c/d £90

Branch Adjustment Account

To—		By—	
Returns .. .. .. £ 10		Branch £250	
Shortage 10			
Reserve, c/d 90			
Gross Profit 140			
£250		£250	

By Reserve, c/d £90

Under this system, the Branch account ceases to be a Trading account, as it was when the goods were invoiced at cost. The account in which the gross profit appears is the Branch Adjustment account, while the Branch account itself resembles a personal account, since it is debited with the selling price of the goods received, just as the personal account of a customer would be debited. The corresponding credit entry is split into two parts, the part which is equal to the cost price of the goods being credited to the Goods to Branches account, and the part which is equal to the gross profit being credited to the Branch Adjustment account. Goods to Branches is closed off, as in the previous illustration, to Purchases account, thus eliminating the cost of these goods from the Trading account of the head office ; this is clearly equitable, since, when the goods are sold, the Sales account of the head office does not receive the credit.

The Branch Adjustment account has been credited with the full gross profit on all the goods sent to the branch, but not all of this can be credited to the Profit and Loss account for the period, since a part of the goods remain unsold at the end of the period, and a corresponding proportion of the gross profit has not, therefore, been earned.

A debit entry is, consequently, made in the Branch Adjustment account, the amount of the debit being the gross profit on the unsold goods (i.e. closing stock) ; the balance of the Branch Adjustment account now clearly represents the gross profit on the goods which *have* been sold (G.P. on total goods minus G.P. on unsold goods = G.P. on goods sold), and this amount is transferred to the Branch Profit and Loss account. The double entry is completed by crediting the gross profit on the unsold goods in the Branch Adjustment account, after the account has been ruled off. This is the item termed Reserve in the illustration. In other words, the gross profit on the goods sold is transferred to the Profit and Loss account, while the gross profit on the unsold goods is brought down as a balance. The ingenuity of double entry book-keeping is shown by the effect of considering the credit balance (reserve) on the Branch Adjustment account in conjunction with the debit balance on the Branch account (stock). The stock appears at selling price, yet, for balance sheet purposes, it must be valued at cost. If the credit balance on the Adjustment account, which is equal to the difference between the cost price and the selling price of the closing stock, is deducted from the selling price of the closing stock, the net figure is clearly the cost price of the closing stock.

Perhaps the Goods Returned require some explanation. The principle is to reverse the original entry ; for instance, when the branch receives goods from the head office, Branch account is debited, and Goods to Branches and Branch Adjustment are credited. When the branch returns goods to head office, the Branch account is credited, and Goods to Branches and the Branch Adjustment account are debited. When goods are sold, Branch account is credited, and Branch Debtors account is debited ; when customers return goods, Branch account is debited, and Branch Debtors credited.

We have now considered two methods of recording branch transactions. In practice, a combination of the two methods is frequently employed. Goods are, in most cases, invoiced to branches at selling price, for purposes of control, but the Branch account, in which the selling price is debited, is sometimes purely a memorandum account. In the financial accounts, it is more usual to treat the Branch account as a Trading account, and to debit it with the cost price of the goods.

LESSON 14

Instalment and Hire Purchase

A CONTRACT of hire purchase and an agreement to pay by instalments are in law two entirely different things. In a contract of hire purchase the goods do not become the property of the purchaser until the final payment has been made, but in a contract for payment by instalments, the goods become the property of the purchaser immediately the contract has been signed. The effect of this distinction is that, in the event of the purchaser defaulting in payment, then, if the contract is one of hire purchase, the vendor can recover the goods, but if the contract is one for payment by instalments, he is unable to seize the goods, since they now belong to the buyer.

If this legal view were to form the basis of the treatment of these transactions in the books of the seller, then, in the case of instalment contracts, the correct procedure would be to credit the full sales value immediately to the sales account, since, as the property has passed, a sale has taken place ; in the case of hire purchase, however, the property does not pass until the final payment has been made, and it would therefore be incorrect to credit sales with the full selling price immediately the contract has been signed, since no sale has taken place. The correct procedure would be to spread the credit to sales over the full period of payment.

It is a cardinal principle of accountancy that profits should never be anticipated and never overstated. An understatement of profits, or a very cautious provision for all possible losses, is sound and prudent finance. Now, if the legal view were to determine the accountancy treatment of hire purchase and instalment contracts, a more cautious policy would be adopted in the case of hire purchase than in the case of instalment purchase. In point of fact, however, the risk of loss is greater in the case of instalment contracts than in the case of hire purchase contracts.

The legal distinction should not be allowed to obscure the fact that the two types of contract are, from the financial point of view, similar and should therefore receive similar treatment in the books of account.

The fundamental difference between the purchase of goods on deferred payments and a normal purchase for cash or payment in the immediate future lies in the fact that the instalments include interest. The vendor first ascertains the normal selling price of the article and adds a certain sum for interest ; the total so calculated is divided into a number of equal instalments. The mathematical calculation is somewhat complicated, since the balance outstanding on which interest is payable gradually diminishes as the instalments are paid. Therefore each successive instalment includes a diminishing amount of interest, although the total payment remains fixed.

For instance, if an article, which would be sold for cash for £372, were sold under an instalment agreement by which four equal annual instalments were to be paid, the first being due immediately the contract is signed, and the remaining three at yearly intervals, then, assuming the vendor to charge interest at 5 per cent, the amount of each instalment would be £100. The calculation may be shown by the following schedule :

Year	Principal at commencement of year	Interest for year	Total	Cash paid
		£	£	£
I	£272 (i.e. £372 less deposit)	14	286	100
2	£186	9	195	100
3	£95	5	100	100

Since the first £100 is paid immediately, the balance on which interest runs during the first year is only £272 ; interest on £272 at 5% is £14, making a total of £286 owing at the end of the first year. £100 is then paid, leaving £186 owing, upon which interest runs for the second year ; the interest upon £186 is £9, making a total of £195 owing. £100 is then paid, leaving £95 owing, upon which interest runs for the third year; interest on £95 is £5, making £100, which is discharged by the final payment of £100. The figures are approximated, for the sake of clarity.

In the books of the buyer the above transactions would appear as follow:

ASSET ACCOUNT

To Vendor	.. ..	£372	Depreciation is written off in the ordinary way.

VENDOR

		£			£
To Cash	.. .. ..	100	By Asset	.. .. ..	372
„ Balance c/d ..	..	272			
		£372			£372
To Cash	.. .. ..	100	By Balance b/d ..	..	272
„ Balance c/d ..	..	186	„ Interest ..	..	14
		£286			£286
		£			£
To Cash	.. .. ..	100	By Balance b/d ..	..	186
„ Balance c/d ..	..	95	„ Interest	..	9
		£195			£195
		£			£
To Cash	.. .. ..	100	By Balance b/d ..	..	95
			„ Interest ..	..	5
		£100			£100

INTEREST

		£			£
To Vendor ..	.. ..	14	By P. & L. a/c ..	..	14
To Vendor ..	.. ..	9	By P. & L. a/c ..	..	9
To Vendor ..	.. ..	5	By P. & L. a/c ..	..	5

The buyer does not debit his asset account (the asset in question may be, for instance, a machine) with the total payable to the vendor, but only with the price which he would have paid had he bought the machine for cash. This is the true cost of the machine. The balance simply represents interest on a debt due. The vendor is credited with the interest due to him, and an interest account is debited. The interest is transferred to the debit of Profit and Loss account. In this way, a correct distinction is made between the acquisition of an asset and the incurring of an expense. The cash price of the machine is the cost of acquiring an asset ; the interest charge is an expense.

From the point of view of the vendor, there are, broadly, two principal methods of treatment. Under the first method, the accounts are similar to the accounts of the purchaser which have just been demonstrated, with, of course, the sides reversed. The vendor credits " Hire Purchase Sales " account with the cash selling price, and debits the personal account of the customer ; at periodic intervals, the customer is debited with the interest accrued, and interest account is credited, the balance of interest account being transferred to Profit and Loss account at the end of the accounting period. The precise form of the accounts under this method is subject to several variations, but the principle is the same in each case.

There is, however, another method of dealing with hire purchase accounts in the books of the seller which is entirely different in principle from the foregoing. Under this method, a special form of day book is kept, in which there are columns provided for (a) the cost price of the goods sold, (b) the total sum payable by the purchaser, (c) the number of instalments. The sales ledger, containing the personal accounts of customers, is purely memorandum. This is of primary importance. The customer is debited with the full total payable, including interest, and is credited with the cash which he pays, but these entries do not form part of the double entry in the financial books. In the financial books, a Hire Purchase Trading account is debited with the total of the cost price column of the Day Book, that is, with the cost price of the goods sold under hire purchase agreements, and Purchases account is credited. The Hire Purchase Trading account is credited in total with the cash received from customers. At the end of the accounting period, it becomes necessary to examine the memorandum sales ledger in detail. Each individual personal account is separately considered, and the cost price of the goods sold to each customer is multiplied by a fraction equal to the proportion between the number of unpaid instalments and the total number of instalments payable. The aggregate of all balances outstanding in the memorandum sales ledger, valued on this basis, is credited to the Hire Purchase Trading account, and debited to an account termed " Stock of Goods out on Hire Purchase," or some equivalent designation.

It will be observed that the effect of this method is to postpone the taking of profit, since the Profit and Loss account is not credited with the cash selling price when the contract is signed. The credit to Profit and Loss account is only made as and when the instalments are received.

A simple illustration may make this method clearer : Assume the cost price of an article to be £100, and the total payable under a hire purchase agreement to be £150, in six instalments of £25 each. By the end of the accounting period in which the contract is signed, four instalments have been paid. In the memorandum sales ledger, the personal account of the purchaser would appear as follows :

MEMO.

PURCHASER

	£		£
To Total due	150	By Cash	25
		,, ,, ...	25
		,, ,, ...	25
		,, ,, ...	25

If we assumed this to be the sole hire purchase transaction for the period, the following would be the form of the Hire Purchase Trading account :

HIRE PURCHASE TRADING a/c

	£ s. d.		£ s. d.
To Cost price	100 0 0	By Cash received ..	100 0 0
,, Profit	33 6 8	,, Stock out on Hire	
		Purchase	33 6 8
	£133 6 8		£133 6 8

The value of " Stock out on Hire Purchase " is calculated by reference to the account of the buyer in the memorandum sales ledger. Two instalments out of six remain unpaid ; the original cost of the article was £100 ; $\frac{2}{6} \times 100 = £33$ 6s. 8d. The double entry is completed by a debit to a " Stock on H.P." account, which appears in the balance sheet as an asset.

It is important to understand that this method is not scientifically accurate. The total profit on the whole transaction, *including interest*, is £50. If each instalment included an *equal* proportion of profit, the profit included in each instalment would be $£\frac{50}{6} = £8$ 6s. 8d., and the profit included in the four instalments which have been paid would be $4 \times £8$ 6s. 8d. $= £33$ 6s. 8d., which is the amount of profit shown in the Hire Purchase Trading account. It is not, in fact, however, true that each instalment includes an equal proportion of the profit, since, as we have seen, the total profit includes interest and, as was demonstrated in the example illustrating the buyer's accounts, the interest charge gradually diminishes as instalments are paid and as the balance outstanding grows less. The effect of this method is, therefore, not only to postpone profit-taking until cash is actually received, but to understate the profit on the earlier instalments, that is, to postpone profit-taking even more.

LESSON 15

Joint Stock Company Accounts

THE distinctive features of company accountancy are due to the special character of the ownership of joint stock undertakings and to the law governing their constitution. The law of joint stock companies has been consolidated by the Companies Act of 1929. It will, therefore, be necessary to outline briefly the provisions of this Act, in so far as they affect the accounts. The capital of companies, unlike the capital of sole traders or partnerships, is divided into shares of fixed amounts. The value of each share is generally small, and the most usual denomination is £1. The vast majority of joint stock companies are limited liability companies ; that is to say, the liability of members is limited to the amount they have agreed to pay on their shares. In contrast, sole traders and partners are liable for the debts of their undertakings to the full extent of their private possessions.

The security and relative freedom from anxiety which the limited liability type of ownership affords accounts for its popularity. Furthermore, the division of capital into shares facilitates changes in the ownership of the undertaking, since shares are transferable by private contract from one person to another. This is a great convenience to persons who wish to dispose of either the whole or part of their interest in an undertaking without being involved in cumbersome legal procedure. On the other hand, joint stock companies are bound to comply with the numerous regulations of the Companies Act, the provisions of which are designed to prevent the obvious abuses which the principle of limited liability would otherwise make possible. There are two kinds of limited liability company—public and private. Private companies are exempt from many of the regulations which bind public companies.

Memorandum and Articles. The first step in the formation of a company is to draw up a document termed the Memorandum of Association, which must be signed by at least seven persons, who each agree to take up at least one share in the company. The Memorandum is the document which defines the nature and objects of the company. It must state : the name of the company ; the situation of the registered office ; the objects of the company ; that the liability of the members is limited ; and, finally, the amount of the share capital.

A second document, termed the Articles of Association, is usually prepared. The Articles contain the regulations for the internal management of the company and deal with such matters as the classes of shares into which the capital is to be divided, procedure at meetings, voting rights, powers and duties of directors, transfer of shares, dividends, and audit. A public company is not bound to have Articles (though a private company must), but, if no Articles are prepared, Table " A," which is a set of model Articles contained in a schedule to the Companies Act of 1929, automatically applies. Broadly speaking, the Memorandum defines the relationship of the company with the outside world, while the Articles define the rights and duties of members and officers of the company *inter se*, and govern internal procedure.

The Memorandum and Articles, together with a list of the names and addresses of the directors, and a statutory declaration that the requirements of the Companies Act have been complied with, must be filed with the registrar of joint stock companies at Somerset House. Certain fees, including a stamp duty of 10s. per cent on the authorized share capital, must be paid, and the registrar will then issue a Certificate of Incorporation. The legal existence of the company commences from the date of the issue of the certificate.

If the directors apply to the public for subscriptions to the share capital, they must publish a document termed a prospectus, which must contain very full information of the company's affairs. In particular, details of the manner in which the shareholders' money is to be used must be given. If the company is formed to acquire an existing business, a report on the past profits of the undertaking, certified by the auditors, must be included in the prospectus. The nature of any assets to be acquired, and the price to be paid, particulars of all underwriting commission, and any payments to the promoters, must be disclosed.

The share capital authorized by the Memorandum is not usually issued at once in total; the business of the company may expand in the future, and it is convenient for the directors to have the power to issue further capital without altering the constitution of the company.

Types of Shares. Shares may be of several classes, of which the following are typical examples: pre-preference, preference, participating preference, preferred ordinary, ordinary, deferred ordinary, and founders' shares.

Fundamentally, there are two types of shares. The investor may choose security both of capital and dividends, combined with a small return on his money, or he may decide to take a greater risk of losing his capital in whole or in part, combined with the *possibility* of receiving a relatively high return on his money. If he makes the first choice, he buys preference shares, which carry the right to receive dividends in priority to the ordinary shareholders. If the profits are only sufficient to pay the guaranteed preference dividend, this dividend will be paid, and the ordinary shareholders will receive nothing. But if the profits are high, the preference shareholder receives nothing beyond his guaranteed dividend, and the ordinary shareholder may receive a dividend as high as the profits of the company and the prudence of the directors will allow. Of course, if the company makes no profits at all, the preference shareholder cannot be paid, but if the shares are cumulative, the unpaid dividend is carried forward, and is a first charge against the profits of subsequent years. The preference shareholder is relatively certain of a small return on his investment, while the ordinary shareholder takes the chance of making handsome profits, but he takes a greater risk of getting nothing at all.

The seven classes of shares mentioned above are arranged in order of security. The pre-preference shares rank prior to all others, but the rate of dividend is lowest ; the deferred shares rank after all other classes, and are therefore subject to the highest degree of risk, but they claim the largest dividends, if large profits are earned. Participating preference shares are in the nature of a compromise. A minimum dividend, at a lower rate than the preference share dividend, is guaranteed, and, in addition, these shares carry the right to a certain minimum share of the surplus profits remaining after all preference dividends have been paid. The right of participation is usually small ; the ordinary shares carry the right to the greater part of the surplus. When deferred shares are issued, the dividend on ordinary shares is restricted to a certain maximum, and the whole of the balance goes to the deferred shareholders.

The expression " share capital," if used without qualification, may refer to any one of the following varieties of " capital " :

1. Authorized capital is the *maximum* capital of the company as defined in the Memorandum.

2. Issued capital is equal to the nominal value of all the shares for which the public and other persons have been invited to subscribe.

3. Subscribed capital is equal to the nominal value of all the shares subscribed ; all shares issued are not necessarily subscribed.

4. Paid-up capital is the total paid up on the shares issued and subscribed, which is frequently less than their nominal value. For instance, the directors may require the shareholders to pay 10s. per share on shares of £1 each, and defer the payment of the balance until it is required. A certificate is issued to each shareholder when he has paid the amount due on his shares, and his name, with particulars of the shares, is entered in the share register of the company.

LESSON 16

Share Issues in Company Accounts

THE published prospectus of a company usually includes a form of application for shares. All applications received are listed on a document termed an application and allotment sheet. If the public apply for more shares than the directors propose to issue, the directors will usually make allotments uniformly proportional to applications, though they are entitled to use their discretion. The amount due on application (frequently 2s. 6d. or 5s. on a £1 share) is entered in detail in the Shareholders' Cash Book, and in total in the General Cash Book ; the Shareholders' Cash Book is a memorandum record. An Application and Allotment Account is opened in the ledger, which is debited with the total amount due on application and the total amount becoming due when the directors proceed to allotment. Share Capital Account is credited with both these amounts. The cash received on application and allotment is credited in total to the Application and Allotment Account ; if the issue is over-subscribed, the credit to the Application and Allotment Account will, obviously, exceed the debit. The excess application moneys are, however, returned to the subscribers, and Application and Allotment Account is closed by a debit of this amount.

The accounts may be illustrated by the following example :

On January 1st a company makes an issue of 100,000 ordinary shares of £1 each, 5/- being payable on application, 5/- on allotment, and 10/- on 1st April. Applications are received for 120,000 shares ; the directors return the excess application moneys, and proceed to allotment on 8th January, all sums due on allotment being received. On April 1st, the directors make the first and the final call of 10/- per share, and all the shareholders pay the amounts due from them, except John Smith, who holds 500 shares.

The entries in the financial books are as shown in pages 25 and 26, but it must be remembered that the detailed work is dealt with in subsidiary memorandum records ; the Shareholders' Cash Book has been referred to, and a similar book is used for calls. From these subsidiary books, the entries in the Share Ledger (also memorandum) are made. The Share Ledger contains a folio for each member, and shows the number and value of shares held by each, the amount paid on the shares, the dates when payments are due, and the dates when the cash is paid.

So long as shares are not fully paid, the liability of the shareholder remains, and in the event of the company becoming insolvent, the liquidator can call upon the shareholders to pay up to the nominal value of their shares.

In the illustration below, the debit balance on Call Account (calls in arrear) is a debt due from the shareholder ; any balance of this nature will be shown in the Balance Sheet as a deduction from Share Capital Account, and not upon the assets side.

Shares may be issued to the public at a price greater or less than their nominal value. If the price is greater than the nominal value, the excess is termed a premium. There are no restrictions upon the issue of shares at a premium, but a company may not issue shares at a discount until one year after it commences.

A company, for instance, issues 50,000 shares of £1 each at a premium of 1s. per share, 11s. being payable on application and allotment, and 10s. one month later. Subscriptions were received for the amount of the issue.

Application and Allotment Account

Jan. 5th			Jan. 5th			
To Ordinary Share Capital A/c	..	£50,000	By Cash	.. .. ..	£55,000
„ Cash (application moneys returned)		5,000			
		£55,000			£55,000

Call Account

April 1st			April 1st			
To Ordinary Share Capital A/c	..	£50,000	By Cash	.. .. ..	£49,750
			„ Balance c/d	.. ..	250
		£50,000			£50,000

April 1st
To Balance brought down (Calls in arrear) £250

Cash Book

Jan. 5th			Jan. 5th		
To Application and			By Application and		
Allotment A/c ..	£55,000		Allotment A/c ..	£5,000	
April 1st					
To Call A/c	£49,750				

Ordinary Share Capital Account

April 1st		Jan. 5th		
To Balance c/d ..	£100,000	By Application and		
		Allotment A/c ..	£50,000	
		April 1st		
		„ Call A/c	50,000	
	————		————	
	£100,000		£100,000	
		April 1st		
		By Balance b/d	£100,000	

Application and Allotment Account

To Share Capital A/c	£25,000	By Cash	£27,500
„ Premium on Shares			
A/c	2,500		
	————		————
	£27,500		£27,500

Call Account

To Share Capital A/c	£25,000	By Cash	£25,000

Share Capital Account

	By Application and	
	Allotment A/c ..	£25,000
	„ Call A/c	25,000

Premium on Shares Account

	By Application and	
	Allotment A/c ..	£2,500

There is no legal objection to the premium being credited to the Profit and Loss Account, but this procedure is unusual. In practice, the premium is usually regarded as being part of the capital of the company, and the balance of the Premium Account appears on the liabilities side of the Balance Sheet.

If we assume that the 50,000 shares in the above illustration were issued at a discount of a shilling, the Application and Allotment Account would appear as follows :

Application and Allotment Account

To Share Capital A/c	£25,000	By Cash	£22,500
		„ Discount on Shares	
		A/c..	2,500
	£25,000		£25,000

An Account for " Discount on Shares " would be opened, to which the £2,500 would be debited.

Discount on Shares Account

To Application and	
Allotment A/c ..	£2,500

The discount is usually written off to the Profit and Loss Account over a period of years, by the same method as wasting assets are depreciated.

The articles of a company usually give the directors power to forfeit shares for the non-payment of calls. For example, suppose a final call of 5s. per share on 1,000 shares of £1 each remains unpaid. There will be a debit balance of £250 on the Final Call Account, representing the debt due from the shareholder. If the directors decide to forfeit these shares the accounts necessary to record this transaction, assuming the full value of the issued share capital to be £50,000, would appear as follows :

Share Capital Account

To Forfeited Shares		By Balance	£50,000
A/c	£1,000		
„ Balance	49,000		
	£50,000		£50,000
		By Balance	£49,000

Forfeited Shares Account

To Final Call A/c ..	£250	By Share Capital A/c	£1,000
„ Balance	750		
	£1,000		£1,000
		By Balance	£750

Final Call Account

To Balance	£250	By Forfeited Shares A/c	£250

The credit balance of £750 remaining on the Forfeited Shares Account is the amount paid up on the shares. The Share Capital Account is reduced by the *full* nominal value of the shares forfeited, since this is the amount that is included in the original credit to Share Capital. The balance of the Forfeited Shares Account is a profit, since the shares have been cancelled, and the cash is not returnable. Balances of this nature, however, are more usually shown on the liabilities side of the Balance Sheet.

Forfeited shares may be re-issued at a price not *less* than the amount unpaid by the defaulting shareholder. In this way, the company receives the full nominal value of the shares in cash. If the shares were issued to a new subscriber at a figure below— in this example, 5s. per share—this would be equivalent to issuing shares at a discount, which is illegal except in the circumstances referred to above. But if the shares are re-issued at less than their nominal value, the difference must be made good by transfer from the Forfeited Shares Account, since otherwise the credit balance on this account could be treated as a profit, and the full nominal value of the shares would not be capitalized.

It is assumed that the 1,000 shares are re-issued at 5s. per share.

Share Capital Account

	By Balance	£49,000
	„ Forfeited Shares re-issued A/c ..	1,000
		£50,000

Forfeited Shares Account

| To Forfeited Shares Re-issued A/c .. | £750 | By Balance .. .. | £750 |

Forfeited Shares Re-issued Account

To Share Capital A/c	£1,000	By Forfeited Shares A/c	£750
		„ Cash (5/- per share)	250
	£1,000		£1,000

The Share Capital Account is now brought up to its correct figure of £50,000, all the shares being now fully paid up.

LESSON 17

Profits and Income Tax in Company Accounts

WE have seen that when a sole trader withdraws money from his business for his private purposes, a drawings account is debited, and that the balance on this account is transferred direct to the debit of the trader's capital account. The net profit is credited to the capital account, and the final effect of these entries is that the balance of the capital account is increased by the profit but reduced by the withdrawals of the cash representing either the whole or part of the profit.

For a number of reasons this procedure cannot be followed by joint-stock companies. The Share Capital Account must always remain in the books at its original figure ; it can only be increased by a new issue and can only be reduced in exceptional circumstances. The balance of the Profit and Loss Account cannot be added, and drawings (or dividends) cannot be deducted.

The Appropriation Account is, in form, a continuation of the Profit and Loss Account. The net profit is brought down to the credit of the Appropriation Account. The purpose of this account is to show what becomes of the profit—how much is to be used for paying dividends, and how much for dividend purposes.

The directors may decide that the business will be strengthened by a retention of part of the profits within the business. It must always be remembered that a profit is represented by an increase in net assets, and if the directors wish to increase permanently the assets of the business, it follows that the whole of the assets which represent the net profit cannot be used for paying dividends. In order to make this clear, an entry is made debiting the Appropriation Account and crediting an account termed " General Reserve," thus indicating that the assets representing this part of the profits are reserved, and are not to be used to pay dividends.

To the Appropriation Account is also debited the balance of the Income Tax Account. Income Tax should not be debited to the Profit and Loss Account proper, since it is not an expense which reduces the amount of the net profit ; it is a payment made *out of* profits. The purpose of the Profit and Loss Account is to show expenses which reduce the amount of the gross profit, while the Appropriation Account shows what is done with the net profit which remains after charging all expenses incurred in earning it.

The amount of the dividend which has been agreed upon is debited to the Appropriation Account, and a dividend account is credited ; this credit represents a liability to the shareholders. If any balance remains on the Appropriation Account, this balance appears as a separate item on the Balance Sheet as " Profit and Loss Account." This represents profits which have not been used for dividends, but which may still, unlike the General Reserve, be used for dividends in subsequent years. Of course, the directors are quite at liberty, if they think fit, to declare dividends out of General Reserve, but such a course is unusual. It will be observed that there will now be three balances in the Balance Sheet of a Limited Company, which together correspond to the single capital account of the sole trader, viz. Share Capital Account, General Reserve Account, and Profit and Loss Account. The General Reserve and the final balance of Profit and Loss are, of course, equal to the original net profits, less dividends and Income Tax (i.e. the sole trader's Drawings).

For example, a Limited Company has a net profit of £20,000. The directors propose to declare a dividend of 6% on 50,000 Preference Shares of £1 each, and of 5% on 100,000 Ordinary Shares of £1 each, both fully paid up. £10,000 is to be transferred to General Reserve, and the balance carried forward.

The accounts necessary to record these transactions will appear as follows :

Appropriation Account

To	£	By	£
Preference Dividend	3,000	Net Profit brought	
Ordinary Dividend ..	5,000	down	20,000
General Reserve ..	10,000		
Balance carried			
forward	2,000		
	£20,000		£20,000

General Reserve

By Appropriation
Account £10,000

Limited Companies (and other businesses) are assessed to Income Tax upon the amount of their profits, calculated according to certain rules. When the tax in respect of these profits is paid, an Income Tax Account is debited with the amount of the payment. Limited Companies are required by law, however, to deduct Income Tax from dividends before making payment to the shareholders, who do not, therefore, receive the full amount of their dividend in cash. The reason for this procedure is that the profits of the Company are, in final analysis, the income of the shareholders, who are liable for tax upon the amount they receive. The tax is collected by the Revenue authorities from the company for the sake of convenience, because it is simpler to make one assessment upon the company rather than several thousand assessments upon several thousand shareholders. Furthermore, a company rarely distributes the whole of its profits in dividends. A certain proportion is usually retained by the company as a reserve, and, if the company were not taxed, the profits carried to reserve would escape taxation. No profits, however, are taxed twice over ; in so far as profits are distributed as dividends, the company is simply the channel through which shareholders pay their Income Tax. The company pays the tax and deducts the amount from the amount due to the shareholders.

Assuming Income Tax to be at 5s. in the £, the individual shareholder receives in cash 15s. for every £1 of dividend due to him. But the Appropriation Account is debited with the full amount of the dividend, and the dividend account must be "credited" with the same amount. When the cash is paid to the shareholders, Dividend Accounts are debited ; the balances are closed by a transfer to the credit of Income Tax Account.

6% Preference Dividend Account

To		£	By		£
Cash ..	..	2,250	Appropriation		
Income Tax	..	750	Account ..	..	3,000
		£3,000			£3,000

Ordinary Dividend Account

To		£	By		£
Cash ..	..	3,750	Appropriation		
Income Tax ..	..	1,250	Account ..	..	5,000
		£5,000			£5,000

Income Tax Account

		By	
		Preference Dividend	£750
		Ordinary Dividend	£1,250

When the Income Tax (which is assessed upon the *whole* of the company's profits) is paid, the total payment will be debited to the Income Tax Account. Since the credit to this account represents tax on only that part of the profits which have been distributed as dividends, the debit will be greater. The final balance of Income Tax Account will be transferred to the debit of the Appropriation Account of the following period.

Over any given period of time, the total of Income Tax which is debited to the Appropriation Account should be exactly equal to tax on undistributed profits. In any practical case, however, any exact reconciliation is impossible to achieve, owing to the fact that the net profit for Income Tax purposes may not be quite the same figure as the net profit appearing in the Profit and Loss Account. Furthermore, the assessment for a given year is based upon the profits of the previous year ; Income Tax rates change, and the rate at which tax is deducted from dividends may be quite different from the rate at which Income Tax is paid, in respect of the profits out of which the dividend has been declared.

ARCHITECTURE IN MODERN LONDON. Essential notes in recent architecture are economy of means to an end and the utilitarian aspect of design based on functional requirements. Shell-Mex House (top) and Broadcasting House, Portland Place, are typical expressions of such construction. ART AND ARCHITECTURE 25

Photos, courtesy of "Architectural Review" and B.B.C.

TWO MODERN LONDON BUILDINGS. Left, the Masonic Peace Memorial building stands at the junction of Great Queen Street, Wild Street, Long Acre and Drury Lane. It shows the classic order and with majestic dignity fulfils the functions of headquarters to the Craft and of monument in memory of the Brethren who fell in the Great War. Right, the offices of the London Passenger Transport Board, a modified type of skyscraper with a stepped top. ART AND ARCHITECTURE 25

Right photo, courtesy of London Passenger Transport Board

Plate 2

Volume V

THE FREEMASONS' HOSPITAL. The Masonic Hospital and Nursing Home at Ravenscourt Park, which was opened in July, 1933, is here seen in a general view from the air. A striking feature is the shape of the open-air balconies, thirty-five feet in diameter, which constitute a remarkable engineering achievement. The design of the whole building expresses its requirements as a hospital. ART AND ARCHITECTURE 25

LIVERPOOL'S MODERN GOTHIC CATHEDRAL. Situated on St. James' Mount, Liverpool, the first Anglican Cathedral to be constructed in the Northern Province since the Reformation will, when finished, be the largest church in England. In harmony with modernist architecture the surfaces of the red sand-stone walls are unbroken, without recourse to niches, arcading or diaper work; elaborate decoration is reserved for wood and metal work. An essential part of the design, the central tower, more than twice the height of the existing roof, is not yet completed. An interior view is given in Plate 5. ART AND ARCHITECTURE 26

Photo, Stewart Bale

Plate 4

Volume V

LESSON 18

Preparation of the Balance Sheet

THE Balance Sheet is a list of all the balances remaining in the ledger after the nominal accounts have been closed off to the Profit and Loss Account. The debit balances which appear on what is usually termed the assets side of the Balance Sheet consist of assets and also of any expenses which have not been written off to the Profit and Loss Account. An example of the latter is a discount on the issue of shares, which was mentioned in Lesson 16 (page 24). Another example is the preliminary expenses incurred in the formation of a limited company. These expenses are usually so heavy that a false impression would be created if they were charged in total to the Profit and Loss Account of the first year, and the usual procedure is to apportion Preliminary Expenses over a period of five years. Any part not written off remains in the ledger as a debit balance, and must therefore appear on the " assets " side of the Balance Sheet, although not really an asset.

Assets are divided into two classes—fixed and floating. Floating assets include cash and assets which will be eventually converted into cash. Fixed assets are those which are *not* held with a view to resale or conversion into cash but which are necessary in order to enable the business to be carried on, and the typical example of this class is plant and machinery. Fixed assets are, in final analysis, nothing more or less than revenue expenditure paid in advance.

The essential point of difference between fixed assets and current working expenses is that the benefit derived from the expenditure upon fixed assets is of longer duration. By the time a fixed asset has worn out, its cost is just as much an expense as any other Profit and Loss item, such as wages or rent. It will be seen that the difference between fixed assets (such as plant and machinery) and expenses not written off (such as preliminary expenses of a limited company) is not so great as a first impression might lead one to suppose. Both appear on the asset side of the Balance Sheet, and both represent an expense incurred in the conduct of the business, the benefit from which is not yet

B5

exhausted. The fact that fixed assets represent something solid and tangible, something which has a market value, while unexpired expenses have no realizable value at all, is not so important as it might appear. It is true that if the company were wound up the distinction would be of the utmost importance. The Balance Sheet, however, is a statement of the position of a going concern, not of a business about to be wound up. In the latter case, the expression " Statement of Affairs " is used ; in the " Statement of Affairs," but not in the Balance Sheet, all assets are shown at realizable values.

The " liabilities " side of the Balance Sheet includes liabilities in the true sense, that is, liabilities to external creditors, and also the liability of the business to its proprietor or proprietors. The amount due to the proprietors is the original capital plus undistributed profits ; in the case of the sole trader these are merged in one account—the Capital Account. In the case of the limited company, undistributed profits must be shown separately, apart from the original capital. Since the two sides of the Balance Sheet agree, it follows that the total of assets minus liabilities to external creditors must be equal to original capital plus undistributed profits.

A Balance Sheet can be drawn up in such a way as to disclose the true position of the business, or it can be drawn up in such a way as to conceal the true position. The first principle to be observed in the preparation of a Balance Sheet which is to serve its true purpose, is to show dissimilar items separately. For example, it has been quite common to read on a Balance Sheet " Freehold Land, Plant and Machinery, and Goodwill," only one total figure being shown. It is clearly impossible to appreciate the true position of the concern if the values of these three assets are not shown separately. Freehold land is a valuable asset, while the goodwill may be unsalable, and in the absence of any information it is impossible to know what proportion of such a total figure represents a valuable asset, and what proportion represents something of little or no value.

The second principle is that assets should be shown in some logical order, and not merely listed indiscriminately. Floating assets and fixed assets should be separately grouped, and all assets should be shown in order of realizability. It is of no importance whether the most liquid or the least liquid assets come first, so long as a logical sequence is preserved. If liquid assets are shown first, the following is typical of the order in which a list of assets might appear in the Balance Sheet:

A. Floating Assets.
1. Cash.
2. Investments.
3. Bills Receivable.
4. Sundry Debtors.
5. Stock in Trade.

B. Fixed Assets.
6. Furniture.
7. Plant and Machinery.
8. Land and Buildings.
9. Patents and Trade Marks.
10. Goodwill.

C. Unexpired Expenditure.
11. Preliminary Expenses.
12. Discount on Debentures.

The third principle to be observed is that the basis upon which assets are valued should be clearly indicated. Plant and machinery, at cost, is a very different thing from plant and machinery, less 20 per cent depreciation. True values may be understated or overstated, and, for a correct estimate of the position of business to be formed, the disclosure of the method of valuation is essential. Furthermore, the valuation of the assets determines the profit, as shown by the Profit and Loss Account. The gross profit will be higher or lower, according as the value placed upon the closing stock is higher or lower. The greater the amount of depreciation written off fixed assets, the lower the net profit, and vice versa. The greater the reserve against bad and doubtful debts (i.e. the lower the value placed upon sundry debtors), the lower the net profit.

It will be seen that the Balance Sheet and the Profit and Loss Account are intimately linked up. The Balance Sheet is, in a sense, the more important document, since it is the key to the whole position of the business. The Profit and Loss Account shows how the profit for the period has been earned, while the Balance Sheet shows what has become of it, i.e. by what assets it is represented. What considerations should determine the values to be placed upon the assets?

Since floating assets are held with a view to conversion into cash, they should be valued having regard to the amount they may be expected to realize. Thus debtors should be stated, not at their nominal value, but at a figure which makes allowances for all losses from bad debts. Stock in trade should be valued at cost, or, if the market price is lower than cost, at the market price ; but if the market price is above cost, the higher value should be disregarded, since otherwise a profit would be anticipated. It is a principle of accounting that no credit should be taken for a profit that has not been earned (and a profit can only be said to be earned when the goods are sold) ; but, on the other hand, all provision should be made for expected losses. The profit of a business should never be overstated, since, if the proprietors withdraw too much from the business, its financial position will be weakened. An understatement of profit, though equally incorrect in theory, strengthens the position of the business, since it reduces proprietors' withdrawals.

Fixed assets should be written off over a period equal to their working life. In the case, for instance, of leases, the exact life of the asset is known. In the case of furniture and machinery, it must be estimated. It is not usually necessary to depreciate freehold land, since it is not a wasting asset ; but, on the other hand, if the market price rises, it should never be written up. Loose tools are not usually depreciated by a fixed percentage, since it is difficult to keep an exact record of a large number of small items. The method employed is to revalue the stock of loose tools at the end of each accounting period. Thus, if new tools are purchased during the year, the cost will be added to the balance brought forward from the previous period. The value placed upon the whole at the end of the year will be credited to Loose Tools Account, and brought down as a balance, and the difference will be written off to the Profit and Loss Account.

Our Course in Accountancy is continued in Volume 6.

Modern Trend in London Architecture

(See plates 1–3)

LONG before the War concrete and steel had begun to take the place of brick and stone as materials for large buildings of an industrial character. Since concrete and steel are primarily engineering materials, and the good architect always thinks in terms of his material, the engineer's aesthetics and architecture now follow one from the other. It would be very little use if they did not. In London and in other cities far bigger buildings than were dreamt of formerly are demanded by the economic necessities of the time. Huge business combines embracing a number of firms, which in the old and easier days would have had their separate sets of premises, now seek a building large and spacious enough to accommodate the lot under one roof ; and the same tendency towards concentration is observable in the increased size of miscellaneous modern offices which spring up in every business quarter of London as soon as an old lease falls in. Only a strong combination of architect, practical builder and engineer could cope with the complex problem connected with the solidity and safety of these greatly enlarged units.

The approximation of architecture and engineering does not imply any disregard of style. The highest aim of the latter has always been the creation of perfect, and therefore beautiful, efficiency. The Roman engineers built magnificent bridges, aqueducts and baths. They treated each problem on its merits. Aiming at stability and use rather than at outward effect, their massive structures gain in grandeur by strict economy of design. They used simple instruments invented by the Greeks ; working largely by rule of thumb, there was not much advance in technical skill, but great advance in practical utility.

In the second century B.C. concrete was manufactured. This development made possible the roofing of vast palatial buildings and public baths. By the end of the second century A.D. almost every city in the Roman empire had an ample water supply for domestic, civic and industrial purposes. By the fourth century still further advance had been made in engineering feats, but architecture was vulgar and grossly over-decorated with forms of embellishment which had lost all inherent meaning.

A modern writer has observed that most of the ancient Greek temple buildings could have been produced by machinery in so far that their architectural effect depends largely upon the repetition of certain features in the right places. That mechanism is not the death of artistry may be proved by some of our recent bridges, in which the professional architect had no hand. Mass, rhythm and proportion are sufficient for beauty.

In modern building we have to fight against that Gothic or Tudor picturesqueness which made a bad use of space. Space is immensely valuable in London ; the price of building has greatly advanced ; incoherent planning of interiors, which results in space cramping and wasting, can no longer be allowed.

In our own day the use of reinforced concrete has brought about a development in roof construction just as it did with the Romans. Though architects still continue to design slanting roofs of tiles or slates on large buildings, there is no need for this extravagant wastage of space. Roofs no longer require to be pointed for the purpose of throwing off water. By replacing the roof with terraces, as has been done in some of the newer blocks of flats and office buildings, beauty of design as well as enjoyment of space is served. The various set-backs and recessions promote the play of light and shade, which is a necessary feature of architectural expression. Instead of vertically, the accent runs horizontally from left to right. These horizontal lines correct an undue appearance of height in a tall building, and also give it an air of greater stability. Of practical advantage in a big city, terraced formation is a protection from street noises.

While the conventions of Greek, Roman and Renaissance styles are still with us in portico, arch and colonnade, there is an endeavour by many architects to forget such traditions in modern designs ; to remember the scientific spirit of experiment in the ages with which these styles are associated, rather than to imitate their actual achievements ; to formulate our own ideal of construction and synthesis, guided by a clear conception and sense of organization. It is no use being surprised or dismayed at the first results ; they will not continue to present such a lack of harmony as the experiments in modern Regent Street. A recognition in law, apart from the operations of the London Building Act, that architecture is no longer a matter for purely private speculation, but requires some form of public control, has already occurred with regard to the river-front in the case of new buildings in Adelphi Terrace, designs for which required approval by the Crown Lands Advisory Committee.

The useful thing proved in Regent Street was that the shop is no longer, as in Nash's time, a ground-floor feature of the building, but requires the whole building to be subordinated to its needs, the chief among which is daylight and, therefore, windows. Shops are designed now to consist almost wholly of glass, with a structure of steel and an impervious material to resist damp and dirt from fog.

Architecture planned for sunny climates is probably out of place in London. Villas based on classical models may look lovely in the south of France or in Italy, but most unsuitable in our suburban districts ; skyscrapers after the manner of New York or Chicago are impracticable against English skies. That Renaissance expression, Britannic House (architect, Sir Edwin Lutyens), would grace Florence harmoniously, but looks out of place in Finsbury Square.

Aligned as decoration, sculpture occupies a place on public buildings. Modern architects and sculptors unite in believing that such sculpture should be part of the building and as far as possible carved by the hand of the sculptor in position on the edifice. With regard to all decoration they are in some agreement with John Evelyn, the famous diarist of the 17th century, who, complaining of the over-elaboration of ornament in his period (when Palladian classical architecture was the style), observes : " a judicious Spectator is rather distracted and quite confounded than touched with that Admiration, which results from true and just Symmetrie, regular Proportion, Union and Disposition."

In England we have always been influenced by foreign contemporary styles and yet gone our own way, emphasizing our individuality even at the expense of harmony. The new buildings in London, therefore, present a great variety. Perhaps the most successful type is seen in the frankly commercial, examples of which are Shell-Mex House (Messrs. Josephs) and Adelaide House, where the point at issue has been how to obtain the most utility ; materials employed and the construction adopted are subservient to the idea of direct relationship between building and purpose.

In Adelaide House (Sir John Burnet), at the City end of London Bridge, the utilitarian problem was to provide on each floor the maximum unimpeded space for the subsequent division into suites of offices of various sizes as required by the tenants. There is emphasis of vertical lines in this building, and the sculptured cornice is the only external decoration.

Imperial Chemical House at Millbank, one of the largest of the " combine " business houses, also had to face a cross river frontage. Architecturally, this building has not the unity of Adelaide House ; the colonnaded upper portion provides more contrast than is necessary to the stark bareness of the lower storeys. On the whole, however, like Unilever House (near Blackfriars Bridge), it takes its place with dignity on the river front scheme, and shows that fitness of purpose which is the controlling force of new London in general. Bush House, in Aldwych, designed by an American architect, Harvey Corbett, viewed along the wide vista of Kingsway, arrests the eye, but, with its classical portico, is less frank in structure than other commercial buildings and lacks their dignity of simplicity.

The Underground Building, over St. James's Park Station, is referred to in connexion with Epstein's sculpture in Lesson 24, (volume 4, page 83). It is a successful example of the modified London type of skyscraper with a stepped top. New bank buildings spring up in all localities. The London Architectural Medal for 1932 was given in favour of Lloyds Bank headquarters, Lombard Street elevation, designed by Sir John Burnet and Partners, with Messrs. Campbell Jones, Sons and Smithers.

The new Masonic Temple in Great Queen Street, the result of the Million Masonic Peace Memorial Fund, was opened and dedicated in July, 1933. In architecture of this type it is necessary to sink commercial utilitarianism (without losing sight of purpose) in a dignified and austere classicism, and the new temple forms a majestic addition to London's great buildings. It was designed by H. V. Ashley, F.R.I.B.A., and Winton Newman, F.R.I.B.A. The Masonic Hospital and Nursing Home (designed by Sir John Burnet, Tait and Lorne) at Ravenscourt Park, also opened in July, 1933, possesses a novel feature in the shape of its sun balconies. The design of the building is a departure from traditional forms, being largely functional.

Classical buildings on a more modest scale are the Auctioneers' and Estate Agents' Institute at the north-east corner of Lincoln's

Inn Fields, and the Friends' House at Euston, with its two façades and main portico stretching the height of three floors to a boldly projecting cornice. Fitness of purpose has not been lost sight of in these two quiet buildings of essential sobriety.

Adelphi House, built on the site of Adelphi Terrace, belongs to the functional style of architecture in which broad, simple lines are employed without ornamentation.

In the West End, particularly in Park Lane, where site values are inflated, hotels and blocks of flats have reached high altitudes for London, and on the whole achieve a balance between utilitarianism and that organization of formal relations which is the architect's work. New blocks of flats have arisen in many districts, and extensive building of this kind has greatly changed the architectural character of St. John's Wood and parts of Hampstead during recent years.

Broadcasting House (architect, Lieut.-Col. G. Val Myer, in association with M. T. Tudsbery, civil engineer), in Portland Place, contains a massive brick tower, enclosing studios isolated from exterior noise ; it is one of the finest broadcasting buildings in the world.

Cinema houses have called into being what may be termed a new branch of commercial architecture. The problems of seating very large audiences, of complex lighting and the effective projection of films and sound, have been well solved. Unfortunately, the buildings are often marred by sensationalism in the desire for a conspicuous façade. The Leicester Square Odeon is an example that seeks to impress by size and eccentricity.

LESSON 26

Recent Provincial Architecture

(See plates 4–7)

OF all the provincial buildings in course of erection during this century none has been watched with greater interest than the new cathedral at Liverpool. Part of the romance attached to this notable undertaking was, doubtless, due to the fact that its designer, Giles Gilbert Scott, was only twenty-one years old when he was selected from more than a hundred competitors to carry out the work. Another interesting feature of the commission was that when the foundation-stone was laid in 1904, nobody could guess how long the building would take to complete. That was to depend on the amount of money available from time to time. The design itself is a free interpretation of Decorated Gothic, as free as Westminster cathedral is a free adaptation of Byzantine. The scheme is being carried out with but little modification, and the vast size of the structure, together with its commanding site, makes it easily the most striking achievement in the ecclesiastical architecture of the 20th century.

In his modernist interpretation of Gothic principles Sir G. G. Scott set an example that has been followed since by several builders of smaller churches in the provinces. Certainly none of them expresses the same degree of " freedom " that can be claimed by some of the new concrete churches on the Continent. Nevertheless, there have been one or two buildings, such as, for example, Queen's Cross church at Maryhill, Glasgow, by Messrs. Honeyman, Keppie and Mackintosh, wherein the Gothic has been combined with modern simplicity in the structural lines.

A similar caution has been observed with most provincial civic buildings, in order to preserve harmony with existent architecture. The group of municipal buildings in Cathays Park, Cardiff, comes under the convenient heading of English Renaissance, though the City Hall and Law Courts are stamped with the individuality of their architects, Messrs. Lanchester and Rickards. This heading also covers the rather less ambitious County Hall at Glamorgan, the Free Library at Lincoln and the Central Reference Library and Royal Infirmary at Bristol, although the last, on its hill site, is rather strikingly modern in its reliance on mass and proportion. It is also, perhaps, a sign of the times that its material is Portland stone, thereby differing markedly from most of the public buildings in that city, which are constructed of the warmer-tinted Bath stone.

The architect (Arnold Thornely, F.R.I.B.A.) of the new Parliament House at Belfast was fortunate in the isolated plateau site selected for the structure, since this enabled him to design and plan without having to consider the question of architectural harmony with neighbouring buildings ; he had only to study the requirements of a dignified Parliament House, and his conception has resulted in a structure that is definitely Palladian in character. The almost mathematical spacing and repeated forms of the four tiers of windows, the colonnaded portico, and the sculptural group in the tympanum symbolizing the presentation of the lighted torch of Freedom to Northern Ireland, are all in the neo-classical Greek temple tradition. Structurally, however, the Parliament House is modern ; a steel frame supports a brick shell strengthened by a good deal of reinforced concrete and faced with Portland stone.

In every provincial town, and in many villages, a tribute has been erected to the men who fell in the Great War ; some of the permanent shrines are well worthy of the architectural student's attention. The Scottish National Memorial on the Castle Hill, Edinburgh, is significant architecturally because, apart from its own merits, its erection eliminated some drab and mean buildings on a famous and prominent site, converted the rectangular block of barracks into a Gallery of Honour, and transformed the entire group on the summit, giving it a unity and impressiveness it had not previously possessed. The materials in this instance are of almost equal importance with the design ; the walls of the shrine, between their tall and handsome buttresses, are constructed of local red and brown rubble stones, roughly fashioned in harmony with the old stones of the existing building. Sir Robert Lorimer was the architect.

Nottingham's classic Arch and Colonnade of Remembrance in the rock garden and recreation grounds overlooking the river Trent are in harmony with their landscape setting. Equally fine is the circular colonnade at Cardiff, the three porches of which stand for the three ways of war—by sea, land and air. Also classic in design is the Memorial Hall at Stockport. Built of stone, it serves the purpose of an art gallery and educational centre, and was specially fortunate in the street-corner site obtained. The Roman Doric Hall of Memory at Birmingham, built of Portland stone upon a base of Cornish granite, also benefits from its isolated position.

Cinema theatres have sprung up during the last two decades by the hundred in every county and shire. More interesting architecturally is the Shakespeare Memorial Theatre at Stratford-on-Avon, opened by the Prince of Wales on April 23rd, 1932. On July 2nd, 1929, the foundation-stone was laid. As a result of an appeal sponsored by the *Daily Telegraph* in 1926, funds were forthcoming to build a theatre in place of the old one, which had been burnt down—a theatre worthy of Shakespeare's town. A competition open to architects of the British Isles and of the

United States resulted in the selection of the work of Miss Elisabeth Scott, a young English architect, then practically unknown. She refused to be fettered by traditional period or by the architecture of the town, and boldly followed functional requirements in her monumental design. The exterior is entirely of brick. Access to the main foyer is by five beautifully conceived and executed bronze doors. High up on the façade are the series of brick carvings by Eric Kennington (*see* Lesson 24, volume 4, page 83), which bring the eye to the upper line of the front elevation. The sculpture is thus of perfectly legitimate use, and without any extravagance it decorates harmoniously. No thought was given to the exterior until the interior of the building had been perfectly planned for the adequate production of plays. Messrs. Maurice Chesterton and John C. Shepherd were the architects associated with Miss Scott in this building.

In every provincial resort new hotels mark the note of modernism, and efforts have been made, more or less successfully, to erect buildings which enhance the town and provide the benefits of first-class hotel life. An imposing building of this type is the Midland Hotel at Morecambe, designed by Oliver Hill, R.I.B.A., and built to conform to the line of the new sea wall and promenade. The glistening exterior is due to a polishing process which achieves on a surface of white cement and carborundum an effect of white marble.

Roadhouses, the new type of one-night or casual entertainment hostelries for motorists, have been erected on most of the main roads. In some cases country houses have been adapted, but recent constructions show more of the new style than the old in architecture. A chain of these in the Midlands are known as " the Knights on the Road," and are planned with economy of design ; they are mainly brick-built and cream-rendered.

Architectural interest attaches to the new buildings of Merchant Taylors' School—removed from the City, after 372 years of educational life there, to Sandy Lodge, near Rickmansworth— since the dignified form of the place has been largely conditioned by the desire for a maximum of air and sunlight in all the classrooms. This has meant that the two long arms of the main school building face each the same way with their corridors on the northern side. The architects, Professor William G. Newton and Partners, have successfully combined in their design scholastic serenity with modern scholastic requirements.

Foreign Buildings of a New Era

(See plates 8–10)

ARCHITECTS today may very generally be divided into two groups, periodists and modernists. The English architect Sir Edwin Lutyens is a foremost exponent of the first group with his successful adaptations of English Renaissance, and his example has been freely followed in certain directions in the United States. There, in spite of the wonders of modernist American architecture, reverence for the classic ideal still persists in most official buildings—State capitols, museums, colleges and art galleries—while country-house architecture usually reveals national period styles determined more or less by the dominant element in the population of a State or province ; thus California exhibits the Spanish love of ornamentation, while Virginian country houses may still be Georgian " colonial." The advantage of period designs in building is that they fit into existing settings ; the disadvantage, that no progress is made towards a new architecture. They win popular approval the world over, chiefly because they are safe and easy to understand.

Many of the modernists make use of novelties in materials and the latest technical and engineering discoveries without logical development of design ; others are functionalists who believe that beauty arises out of perfect adaptation to the assigned end ; others, again, are brilliant individualists whose works are sound in construction, yet novel both in technique and design. If the new form has real justification it soon ceases to be repugnant ; if, on the other hand, it is merely fantastic it has no influence on architecture or affinity with fine buildings ; its design is not worth repetition, adaptation or standardization. Le Corbusier, the famous French architect, has pointed out in his book, " Towards a New Architecture," that style is unity of principle animating all the work of an epoch, the result of a state of mind which has its own special character. He states : " It may be accepted that the great epochs of architecture depend upon a pure system of structure." He is at one with the functionalists when he says : " The plan proceeds from within to without. The exterior is the result of an interior." He stresses, however, that architecture goes beyond utilitarian needs ; that it is a plastic art of contour and profile. It has the spirit of order, a unity of intention ; it deals with quantities and the sense of relationships ; its elements are light and shade, walls and space.

Skyscraper Masterpieces. During the last fifty years the use of steel and concrete has overturned various decrepit architectural beliefs. Nowhere is this more plainly seen than in New York, with its famous skyline ; here unity of principle has been created by the necessity which at first forced American architecture to build skyscrapers with the utilitarian motive of accommodation for vast business enterprise and population, and afterwards by an aesthetic sense of the loveliness that these aspiring buildings can possess against the background of the sky. Skyscraper architecture in New York is concentrated more or less in the downtown financial district, in the Fifth Avenue shopping district south of Central Park, and in the residential Riverside Drive district over the Hudson to the north-west. With little tradition of their own, New York architects collected a few European ideas to play with. Some of the Wall Street buildings, for instance, are like gigantic Georgian mansions ; one or two houses on Fifth Avenue vaguely recall Venetian palaces, while there is a French atmosphere about others. In the main, however, the architecture has now achieved a harmony which is American—modern American, with clear-cut lines and fine proportions combining drama and fantasy in the strangest and most exciting fashion with functionalism.

New York is still a city of rapid growth and constant change. Arresting among its buildings are the Chanin Tower, fifty-six storeys in height ; the famous Woolworth Building, the tower of which soars 792 feet into the sky (the top of its spire is often cloud-enfolded) and imparts a wonderful grace to the massiveness of the main structure ; the thirty-one-storeyed Telephone Building, a majestic masterpiece of commercial architecture with stepped façades ; the fantastic Chrysler Building, which comprises sixty-eight storeys ; and the Metropolitan Insurance Company of New York's Office, which has solved the problem of the hundred-storey structure, and accommodates 30,000 workers.

Between Fifth and Sixth Avenues, from Forty-eighth to Fifty-first Streets, the huge Rockefeller Centre includes the R.C.A. building, housing 70,000 workers, the International Radio City Hall, and the British Empire Building. This vast block forms an important addition to New York's architec-

tural skyline. The Empire State Building, the highest building in the world, provides a supreme example of commercial
architecture.

The World's Fair (1939), containing two hundred buildings,
was an astonishing achievement, and the variety of architectural
styles exemplified in the various Pavilions of the Nations augurs
well for the future. They involved an extensive use of glass,
though it is impossible to say whether the architectural designs
will effect a radical change in the art, since the buildings were
primarily intended as temporary structures. The Main Hall of
the British Pavilion was a model of graceful design.

While most of the school and college architecture in the United
States is academic, the new " Cathedral of Learning " at Pittsburg
is of skyscraper persuasion. One of the most striking railway
stations in the world is the Hollywood Terminal, an all concrete
building, the front of which is decorated in accordance with
Spanish tradition. The United States may also be said to have
specialized in the architecture of the stadium. Harvard University
was the first to build one of these enclosures on modern lines with
claims to architectural dignity. The circular " bowl " at Yale
University and the more recent Coliseum at Los Angeles are both
modern adaptations of the Roman amphitheatre.

France, both in Paris and the provinces, has been slow to break
with tradition ; the true Parisian hates change, and architecture
is subject to the strong influence of the École des Beaux Arts.
Already, however, the work of the modernists is emerging, and the
face of Paris is gradually changing. The suburbs have much need
of improvement, as they have never possessed a dignity worthy of
their city. In spite of her artistic reputation, the taste displayed
in provincial and suburban villas has been worse in France than
anywhere else in Europe. Fine blocks of apartment houses and
workmen's flats are being erected on the outskirts of Paris.

The modernist architecture of Paris itself is chiefly concerned
with shops and business houses. The Champs Elysées, with its
magnificent vista, is in process of transformation into a street
of fine showrooms and shop fronts, to be enhanced by such
buildings as the handsome National City Bank of New York.
The new Berlitz building on the site of the Pavillon de Hanovre
breaks with tradition, and the functionalist ideal is well expressed
in the latest typical Parisian commercial building, the offices of the
Messageries Hachette.

Swedish architects possess a masterly understanding of the technique of materials. Their work, however, is linked to the past—the people set great store by the romantic past of their country—and the handicraft rather than the mechanical spirit pervades their designs. Whatever forms they use, the architects are romanticists rather than modernists. The Town Hall, Stockholm, is a fine new-old style building.

Germany has gone more whole-heartedly for modernist architecture than either England or France. The Nazi regime undertook the construction in Berlin and Munich of grandiose public buildings which were intended to express the spirit of Greater Germany. An abundance of light and air is characteristic of the modern apartment buildings in Berlin and other large cities in Germany ; some blocks are designed with solid balconies in horizontal strips the length of the façade ; other blocks are constructed on purely geometrical principles, in which small rectangular balconies are fitted into the angles of the façade, like shelves into a corner. In many of the larger commercial buildings graciousness has been entirely sacrificed to dynamic energy. An example is the Karstadthaus, the huge department store with a subway station, in the Berlin district of Neuköln, designed with uncompromising verticality. A certain lack of humanity characterizes some of these buildings, which repel rather than attract, as if German seriousness had over-concentrated on the logical and functional requirements of the plan and ruled out all charm. The new workmen's dwellings are a bright side of Berlin and other big German city architecture ; in this type of building frank utilitarianism is humanly expressed in terms of comparative spaciousness and comfort.

Holland uses brick or concrete with equal success in domestic architecture. Large plate glass ground-floor windows, bedroom windows running from wall to wall, and flat roofs are very usual in Dutch country houses. The national love of colour is expressed in brightly painted doors and window frames. The slum campaign is proceeding practically in Holland. In the chief Dutch cities, the local authorities provide colonies for undesirable tenants, where the buildings are of simple construction, and where the families registered by the police as destructive, dirty or quarrelsome can be housed under supervision and not allowed to destroy the harmony of the better types of workmen's flats or Council dwellings.

It is quite impossible in the space of one short Lesson even to touch on the wonders of such amazing new cities as Polish Gdynia or Magnitogorsk, that Russian expression of architectural modernism. The trend of architecture in the U.S.S.R. is towards an uncompromising functionalism. Moscow is being rebuilt on the most modern lines. Factories, flats, and restaurants are usurping the older-style buildings. The student who wishes to read further concerning the problems of modern architecture may consult the following works: "Modern Architecture," Howard Robertson; "The Architecture of a New Era : Revolution in the World of Appearance," R. A. Duncan; "Modern Architecture : Romanticism and Re-integration," Hitchcock.

LESSON 28

Practical Work of the Architect

THE architect's drawings are only a means to an end; he expresses his art in buildings which have some utilitarian purpose, buildings executed not by himself but by the builder. The drawings are only part of the architect's work; he must equip himself for dealing with a continuous series of problems arising out of the construction of his designs. Some of this knowledge can be gained in schools, such as the Architectural Association School in London, the largest training centre for architects in England, or the School of Architecture in connexion with Liverpool University ; more can be acquired in the office of a good architect, and the rest only in the school of experience.

A thorough knowledge of the practical side of building is necessary before an architect can supply his specifications. The specification is a written description of the work, dealing in detail with the operations of each individual trade employed in the building. It forms, with the drawings, an expression of his instructions to the contractor and his workmen, and it describes materials, methods of work and so on which cannot be explained in the drawings. It should be precise, and all vague terms like " of good quality " should be avoided, a definite quality or money value being stated wherever possible. The beginner may take the specification of a similar building as a model, so far as general arrangements of trades, customary phraseology of, and detailing of works in each trade are concerned, being careful not to transfer portions of the old specification bodily into the new, unless they fully apply.

In the pressure under which modern work has often to be conducted, especially in the big cities, it is quite usual for the quantity surveyor to write the specification from the architect's notes and drawings as the quantities are " taken off." The only danger of this procedure is that the surveyor may not in some matters exactly express the architect's intentions. The architect, therefore, should always read through the document after completion, in case of such misunderstanding.

Methods of Estimating Cost. The architect must provide his client with an estimate of the probable cost of the building. It is often necessary that this estimate should be given before the design and plans have been fully worked out. This requires experience, but with certain types of buildings, the accommodation of which is more or less standardized, it is possible even without plans to give a fairly reliable estimate based on the cost per person or item. In a hospital, for example, so much per bed, in a church or school, so much per sitting, may be taken from a building of the same class as a basis of cost. But even in these rough estimates judgement and experience are necessary, owing to the wide range in cost.

A usual method of estimating is known as cubing. This consists of calculating the actual cubical contents of the building. Measurements are taken to the outside of all walls horizontally, and vertically from the top of the footings to half-way up all inclined roofs and to the parapets of flat roofs, allowance being made for any special features rising above this level. The cubical contents being ascertained, the cost of erecting the building at so much per foot cube is calculated, the cost per foot cube being based on the similar cost of a similar building or group of buildings averaged.

A more exact method, but one involving some expense, is to have the quantities for the general " carcass " work taken out by the surveyor and priced, and then a percentage added for the finishing trades. This will very often give very accurate results. Whatever the method employed, the architect who is going to invite tenders for the work should be careful not to underestimate. Should his estimate be considerably exceeded by the lowest tender, it is sure to lead to unpleasantness.

PRACTICAL WORK OF THE ARCHITECT

When definite estimates from builders are required, it is generally necessary that bills of quantities should be prepared either by the architect or by the surveyor he usually employs in works of importance. Briefly, bills of quantities consist of a summarized statement of the whole quantity of the work in a building, divided into trades. The amount of brickwork, for example, is measured from the drawings and reduced to a definite number of rods, and any special work is dealt with separately. The work in each trade is thus dealt with by the process known as " taking off "—that is, by measuring from the drawings—and " billing," which is collecting the various items and tabulating them in bills. Any special work that cannot be dealt with by measuring, such as the setting of a stove in a fireplace, is made the subject of a *provision*. In this case the work done is actually measured or accounted for as daywork on completion. Alternatively, it may be made the subject of an *allowance*, in which case the builder inserts a sum which he considers will suffice to meet it. In either case a stipulation should be made for deducting the full amount if the work is not carried out.

Whether the builder's tender be private or public (invited through public advertisement, as is generally done in important works), the client's interests should be protected by the insertion of the following clause : " The owner (or my client) does not bind himself to accept the lowest or any tender, or to pay the cost of preparing any estimate." There may be good grounds for not accepting the lowest tender—grounds connected with the standing and reputation of the builder. A legal contract is created by a letter from the architect, on his client's instructions, to a builder, accepting his tender.

The scale of professional charges is subject to revision ; particulars are published by the Royal Institute of British Architects. The amount of actual supervision by the architect depends greatly on the character of the work and the reliability of the builder and his foreman. For most buildings of any magnitude a clerk of works is appointed, preferably by the architect himself. He is the architect's representative on the job, and it is his business to furnish the latter with a weekly report of the state of the weather, number of men employed, materials received, drawings received and wanted. Above all, he must constantly supervise the work and materials.

This Lesson completes our Course in Art and Architecture.

LESSON 28

Stellar Motions and Magnitudes

(See plate 11)

ALTHOUGH the stars are apparently fixed, they have a real motion of their own in addition to the apparent diurnal motion due to the earth's rotation, and the apparent annual motion across the sky, as a body, due to the earth's revolution round the sun. This latter, we saw in Lesson 27 (volume 4, page 110), produces yet another motion, only apparent in stars sufficiently near—the minute circle which they appear to perform relative to the more distant stars.

In addition to these apparent motions the stars change their positions slightly from year to year ; this is known as their *proper motion.* It is imperceptible to the naked eye even during a lifetime, but is very apparent in modern instruments of precision. There are two ways in which this motion can be measured. One is by the actual displacement of the star on the celestial sphere—but most of this is found to be due to *precession, nutation* and *aberration,* which are also due to terrestrial influences and are shared by all the stars in any particular section of the sky.

After all these minute quantities have been allowed for, there remains the gradual shift of each star relative to the others. Not many more than a hundred stars are known which thus move a second of arc or more in a year. So small an amount is this that it would take about 2,000 years for a star with such a *proper motion* to move over a distance equal to the apparent diameter of the full moon. It was discovered by Halley, 200 years ago, that Sirius had travelled southward to about this extent, that is, half a degree, since the time of Ptolemy. The largest proper motion known is that of Barnard's star of the tenth magnitude ; it amounts to 10·25 seconds in a year and would, therefore, travel over half a degree in 176 years.

A large proper motion is generally an indication that the star is among the nearest to us and, therefore, likely to reveal a parallax when measured. If we know the distance of such a star from the earth or, as is usually reckoned, from the sun, then it becomes possible to calculate the star's actual velocity. It is, however, necessary to know also its radial velocity, to be obtained from the angle at which the star is travelling relative to the line of sight. Thus a distinction must be drawn between the star's apparent angular rate of motion and its actual velocity, since a star travelling direct towards us in the line of sight would possess no perceptible proper motion.

Döppler's Principle. The spectroscope has enabled astronomers to solve this problem, to measure a star's motion in the line of sight and decide whether it is approaching or receding, with remarkable accuracy. This is in virtue of *Döppler's principle*, which may be briefly explained as follows :

Each of the series of lines in the spectrum has a precisely defined space according to the gas from which it originates ; this is due to the fact that light of any particular wave length is refracted to a certain definite extent. Now suppose the source of the light is a star travelling towards the spectroscope, the light which it emits will reach the spectroscope with its own speed added to that of the star. Consequently, a greater number of light waves will reach the refracting prism of the spectroscope in a second than would be the case if the star were at rest, while a lesser number of light waves will arrive if the star be receding. Thus there is revealed a shift in the lines in the spectrum through a distance which, though very minute, is capable of being measured with sufficient accuracy to show the direction and extent of stellar velocity. If the star is receding, the lines will be shifted toward the red end of the spectrum ; if it is approaching, the lines will be shifted toward the violet end. Thus is the *radial velocity* obtained.

The speed of stars was thus obtained, visually at first, by Huggins in 1867 ; but for the last 45 years photographic records of the star's spectrum have replaced the visual, and the *radial velocity* of several thousand stars is now known. This, together with the star's angular *proper motion*, which gives us by a simple calculation the star's *tangential velocity*, enables its actual speed to be calculated and also the direction in which it is travelling. It is found that the stars generally appear to be speeding in different directions, though there are some which form groups and travel like a vast flock all in one direction. There is no such thing as rest in the universe, for all the bodies within it are travelling at immense speeds. Our own sun is moving at the rate of about $12\frac{1}{2}$ miles per second towards a certain point, called the solar apex, in the constellation of Hercules at approximately right ascension 271°, or 18 hours, and declination + ·31°.

An effect of this motion is to cause the stars to open out in the direction of the sun's motion and to close in toward the *antapex* or opposite point. Sir William Herschel noticed this effect, and concluded that it was caused by the motion of the sun and, of course, the whole solar system, which is travelling through this never-ending stellar vista.

Absolute and Apparent Magnitude. The *absolute magnitude* of a star may now be arrived at, since its parallax, i.e. distance and *apparent magnitude*, is known. It thus becomes possible to deduce the brightness and real magnitude a star would present if it were removed to a standard distance. For suppose all stars were at this standard distance, then their apparent magnitude would represent their absolute magnitude ; but they are, as we have seen, at vastly different distances. Now to know the absolute magnitude of a star is of great importance to its study.

While a star's absolute magnitude may be computed from its apparent magnitude, it is necessary to have some standard of comparison. The sun used to serve this purpose as magnitude 0·0, but since 1922 the standard has been defined by the International Astronomical Union as the magnitude a star would have if it were at a distance of 10 parsecs, which corresponds to a parallax of 0·1″ and represents about 33 light-years. The absolute magnitude M is, therefore, expressed in terms of the apparent magnitude m, and parallax p, in seconds of arc thus :
$$M = m + 5 + 5 \log p.$$

We may thus visualize our sun, which is the nearest star and has an apparent magnitude of − 26·6 ; but at a distance of 10 parsecs or 33 light-years this would be reduced to + 5·0 of apparent magnitude. In other words, it would be classed as about fifth magnitude and be only visible as a faint star. Now, since Vega, for example, at a distance of 8·1 parsecs, and Capella, at 13·5 parsecs, appear as brilliant first magnitude stars at this distance, it becomes obvious how much greater their absolute magnitude must be as compared with the sun, Vega being 0·6 and Capella much greater, with − 0·4. The minus sign indicates that it is above the standard 0·0, and, therefore, the greater the − magnitude the greater the luminosity ; on the other hand, the greater the + sign the less is the luminosity and the smaller the absolute magnitude.

It has of late years been found possible to determine the absolute magnitude of a star without taking into account its parallax. Differences in the intensities of certain lines of the spectra of dwarf stars, as compared with corresponding intensities of certain lines of giant stars' spectra, had long been noticed; it was ultimately found, from an investigation of individual stars whose parallax, and therefore absolute magnitude, was known, that there was a relation between the intensities of the lines and the absolute magnitude of the stars. A calibration curve of intensities was eventually constructed from numerous stars of known parallax and absolute magnitude, and from this it became possible to deduce the absolute magnitude of numerous stars of *unknown* parallax simply by comparing the relative intensity of the particular lines in their spectrum with those of the standardized curve of spectroscopic intensities for various absolute magnitudes. This done, it became possible to determine a star's parallax from the absolute magnitude thus obtained. As a consequence, the distances of some thousands of stars whose parallax was too small to be reliably measured trigonometrically or which, owing to vast distances, possessed no parallax at all, were able to be calculated with a precision comparing favourably with many distances obtained trigonometrically with far more labour. Parallaxes obtained by this method are termed *spectroscopic*, and many more have been acquired thus than by trigonometry. Photography of the star's spectrum is obtained with great precision, and the *spectrograms* provide other valuable data for microscopic investigation.

LESSON 29

The Light of the Stars

(See plate 12)

MOST of our knowledge concerning the stars has been obtained by analysing the light they emit. This light varies enormously both in quantity and character. Luminosity as observed visually is no absolute criterion of the particular star's mass or immensity, since a relatively small mass may accompany an immense volume and a surface of comparatively poor luminosity—in which case a relatively small star of great luminosity will far outshine and radiate more light than its much greater rival. These differences are found to be associated with the surface temperatures of the stars.

The luminosity of the stars has been very precisely ascertained from their distances and absolute magnitudes. This luminosity is usually expressed in terms of the sun by the symbol ☉. The differences are tremendous, the most luminous, as far as is known, being Canopus, which has been calculated to radiate 91,000 times the light of the sun, but from a distance of 652 light-years. On the other hand, Proxima Centauri, which happens to be the nearest known sun to our own and which is invisible except through powerful telescopes, radiates 11,000 times *less* light than our sun. It is a small sun which appears to have nearly " burnt itself out " or, in other words, exhausted its luminous radiation.

We find that Canopus has the greatest absolute magnitude of —7·4 ; Rigel, a brilliant star which radiates 18,000 times the light of the sun, follows with —5·8. Sirius, which owing to its proximity appears the brightest star in the heavens, with an *apparent* magnitude of —1·58, actually radiates only 30 times more light than our sun ; its *absolute* magnitude is +1·3.

It is obvious to the naked eye that the stars exhibit different colours, from the reddish Antares and Betelgeuse to the orange Arcturus, the pale yellowish Capella, brilliant white Sirius and Vega, the bluish Rigel and many other Orion stars. Spectroscopic study of these differences in light has revealed astonishing differences in the surface conditions and in the constitution of the stars. The various tints indicate different spectra.

Classification of Stellar Spectra. A spectroscopic analysis has now been made of about 250,000 stars. The spectra have been arranged in *classes*, each designated by a letter : O, B, A, F, G, K, M, N, R, and S. They were originally in alphabetical order, but subsequent discoveries have necessitated the changed sequence. Since these types blend one into another, various subdivisions by decimal numbers are used, such as B2 and B5, the latter indicating a star of spectral *type* midway between the *classes* B and A. Subdivisions are indicated by letters, as Oa, Ob, Ma, and so on.

This classification, while indicating a spectral type, reveals at the same time a period in the life of a star or sun when it is at about a certain surface-temperature and in a definite known physical condition associated with either youth or age. The light when analysed is seen to consist of a continuous emission spectrum, upon which appear different lines of absorption characteristic of the various spectral classes. The lines of hydrogen appear in all, but the lines of other elements appear with different intensities in each spectral class, and are variously absent in certain classes.

The following are the general characteristics of each class. Class O spectra consist of bright bands superimposed upon a faint continuous background. This class represents the Wolf-Rayet stars. New or temporary stars which suddenly blaze up and then die down to faintness also frequently belong to it, when they are expressed as either Oa, Ob or Oc. The subdivisions Od and Oe represent spectra which contain dark lines chiefly of hydrogen, ionized helium and ionized calcium. The star λ Cephei is typical of these. The surface temperatures of stars of Class O are considered to range between 35,000° and 40,000° Centigrade ; Novae (new) or temporary stars doubtless reach much higher temperatures. Thus the greenish-white Class O represents the hottest type of star known.

Class B spectra contain only dark lines, chiefly of helium. Stars in this class are called helium stars, being largely enveloped in incandescent helium, together with ionized oxygen and nitrogen. Surface temperatures range from about 23,000° C. for class Bo to about 15,000° C. for sub-class B5. Several of the stars of Orion, including δ, ε and ζ of the " Belt," are of class Bo. Achernar and δ Persei are notable examples of B5 sub-class.

Class A spectra consist of very intense hydrogen and increased calcium lines ; magnesium and numerous lines of ionized metals appear in A5. Surface temperatures range from about 11,000° C. for Ao to about 8,500° C. for A5. Sirius and Vega are good examples of Ao stars and Altair of the A5 sub-class. All are a brilliant white.

Class F spectra display a great increase in the intensity of the metallic lines and a decrease in those of hydrogen. Surface temperatures of about 7,500° C. are attained for Fo, to which class Canopus belongs. The temperature declines to about 6,500° C. for F5. Procyon is a good example of this class.

Class G spectra have numerous metallic lines present, together with reduced hydrogen lines. Those of iron and ionized calcium are very strong, and there is a band representing a carbon compound. Surface temperatures are about 6,000° C. for class Go, to which our sun and Capella belong. For the intermediate class

G5 the surface temperature declines to about 5,500° C. The stars μ Cassiopeiae and κ Geminorum are of this class. All G type stars are yellowish owing to the greater absorption at the violet end of the spectrum.

Class K spectra are noteworthy for bands due to the presence of hydrocarbons; surface temperatures are about 4,200° C. Arcturus is a good example of " giants " of this type. In the intermediate class K5 bands due to titanium oxide appear, and there is a reduction of temperature to about 3,400° C. K stars are orange, deepening to K5.

Class M spectra exhibit broad absorption bands with low temperature metallic lines intense, and solar lines faint and few in number; titanium oxide bands become strong and increase toward the intermediate classes M5 and M8. Surface temperatures range from about 3,000° C. for Mo to about 2,700° C. for M5. Betelgeuse and Antares are typical examples of Mo class This type have a reddish-orange tint. The subdivision class M8e have spectra similar to M8 but with *bright* hydrogen emission lines, a remarkable feature peculiar to long-period variable stars ; Mira or o Ceti is a notable example. Temperatures vary between 2,300° C. and 1,700° C.

Class N spectra have broad absorption bands very intense at the red end of the spectrum ; these are chiefly caused by the presence of carbon monoxide and cyanogen. All stars of this class are small and very red, owing to the absence of violet in the spectrum. They are apparently " dying suns," and the surface temperatures are low—about 2,600° C. The star 19 Piscium is typical of this class.

Class R spectra are similar to class N, but with the cyanogen line very intense. These stars, though very faint, are not so red as N, and have surface temperatures of about 2,300° C.

Class S spectra exhibit bands of zirconium oxide and strong low temperature lines, indicating that they are not much above 2,000° C. They are faint and red, being all telescopic, and mostly variable stars of long period.

Stages of Stellar Decay. It will be seen from this short survey that the stars decrease in temperature through a well-defined series of gradations indicated by their spectra. That the details of the spectrum reveal the temperatures and, therefore, the conditions existing on each star or sun has been proved from laboratory experiments in physics. It is, however, not to be supposed, because, for instance, B stars exhibit a spectrum rich in helium lines and A stars one well supplied with hydrogen that, therefore, these elements are exceptionally plentiful in such stars. It means that these stars are in that degree of incandescence which causes these elements, helium and hydrogen, to be in such a condition as to produce the effect recorded in the star's spectrum.

Every star goes through most of the stages indicated by the above classes during successive periods of its existence. Long ages ago our sun was an F star ; before that it was an A, in still more distant aeons a brilliant B, and possibly even an O5 type of star at the apex of heat and light radiation ; still more remotely it was a *giant* K star, and from thence to near its birth stage a super-*giant* M star like Betelgeuse. On the other hand, long ages hence our sun will dwindle to a *dwarf* M type, and thence probably pass through the N stage, or through R to N, ultimately to its final extinction, when its radiant energy is expended. Such is the accepted theory of the normal life of a star—barring collisions, convulsions, or stellar conflagrations, when the series may begin all over again.

LESSON 30

More About Stellar Measurement

(See plate 13)

WE have seen how the distance, magnitude and temperature or colour index of a star are arrived at, and how a fairly accurate conception of its size may be estimated as a consequence. Where it has subsequently been possible to measure giant stars, the calculated dimensions have been found remarkably in accord with the measured diameters. It is obvious that when the intrinsic brilliance of a star's surface is known, its actual total output of luminous energy will depend upon the area of surface presented, a large surface pouring out a much greater volume than a small one. This can be measured mathematically ; thus, when it and the star's distance, colour index and temperature are taken into account, the star's actual size may be calculated.

We know that our sun, whose size has been precisely measured, possesses a certain absolute magnitude, and from this its apparent magnitude at certain distances can be calculated ; therefore any other star possessing a similar spectrum and absolute magnitude, at the same assumed distance, will be of similar proportions to the sun. Any variations therefrom, either as to spectra, absolute magnitude and distance, become a sure indication of the size of a star by comparison with the sun. It is, therefore, usual to express a star's radius in *radii* of the sun—the sun's radius is 432,000 miles —easily converted into diameter by doubling the figures.

Stellar Interferometer. Measurement of the angular diameter of the larger stars, if not too distant, has of late years become possible by means of the stellar interferometer. This is a most ingenious appliance—developed by Michelson, but originally conceived by Fizeau in 1868—which may be attached to great telescopes, such as the 100-inch telescope at Mount Wilson Observatory in California.

By means of four plane mirrors placed at M_1, M_2, M_3, and M_4 in the illustration in Plate 13, the capacity of the telescope becomes greatly increased by the two outer mirrors, M_1 and M_4, which are placed at an angle of 45° to the horizontal, reflecting the light of the star to the two inner mirrors, M_2 and M_3, which are also at an angle of 45° and which are so placed that the star's light is thence sent down the tube of the telescope to its great concave mirror. Thus two beams or " pencils " of light from the star reach the magnifying mirror, which passes them on to the focal plane of the eyepiece. The effect is to produce a series of interference fringes, which at a certain but varying distance apart of the plane mirrors, M_1 and M_4, will cause the interference fringes to disappear. Now the *distance apart of these two plane mirrors bears a definite and measurable relationship to the angular diameter* of the particular star under consideration.

The smaller the angular diameter of the star to be measured the greater is the telescopic aperture necessary ; to effect this, the two outer plane mirrors M_1 and M_4 are placed farther apart, the two inner ones M_2 and M_3 remaining fixed at a distance of four feet, and each pair of mirrors being equidistant from the long axis of the telescope.

Theoretically, there is no limit to the distance at which the plane mirrors M_1 and M_4 may be placed apart, and therefore there need be no limit to the stars which might be measured, providing the mechanical difficulties can be overcome ; for the utmost precision in using the instrument is necessary.

Changes in the distance are effected by a long girder (G) which is placed across the end of the open tube of the telescope ; along this the plane mirrors M1 and M4 can be moved to its full extent. Thus it becomes possible to have the equivalent of a telescope over 20 feet in diameter for the production of the interference bands, which is all that matters in this case, but not, of course, for normal observation.

When Betelgeuse had this interferometer applied, it was found that the interference fringes produced by the two beams of light vanished when the plane mirrors were 10 feet apart. Mathematical calculations based upon a standard derived from the known angular distances apart of certain double stars, notably Capella, gave for Betelgeuse the angular diameter of 0·047 of a second of arc, an amount quite beyond the possibility of measurement by direct vision on account of the minute spurious disks presented by the stars when observed telescopically ; these are due to optical causes and cannot be eliminated.

Giant Suns. At the distance of Betelgeuse, that is, 58·80 parsecs or nearly 192 light-years, this angular diameter of 0·047″ would represent an actual diameter of 300 times that of the sun, or 259,200,000 miles. Thus Betelgeuse was found to be a colossal sun with a diameter much larger than the earth's orbit ; if the earth were as near to the centre of Betelgeuse as it is to the centre of our sun it would be 123,000,000 miles below the surface of that giant sun. Betelgeuse has long been known to vary irregularly in its brightness, and the above measurement was taken near its maximum. Since then, the star having become less brilliant, it was remeasured ; it required a spacing of 14 feet between the plane mirrors M1 and M4. This proved that Betelgeuse now had an angular diameter of 0·034″, and had therefore shrunk to 210 times the sun's diameter, or 181,440,000 miles. Thus the irregular variations in the light of the " pulsating suns " was proved to be due to expansion and contraction of the bodies in question.

Arcturus, another giant sun, required an extension of the interferometer to 24 feet before the interference fringes vanished. This spacing indicated an angular diameter of 0·020″, which at the distance of Arcturus, that is, 12·50 parsecs, represented a diameter 27 times greater than that of our sun, or 23,382,000 miles. Aldebaran also gave an angular diameter of 0·020″, but owing to its much greater distance of 17·54 parsecs this represented an actual diameter 38 times that of the sun, or 32,928,000 miles. Aldebaran belongs to the gK5 class, while Arcturus is gK0; the letter g prefixed to the class signifies "giant," to distinguish them from the "dwarf" types, which, exhibiting similar spectra, are in a much later stage of stellar evolution.

Antares is another of these colossal giant suns which have already been thus measured. It required a spacing of 12 feet between the plane mirrors; from this was calculated an angular diameter of 0·040", actually less than Betelgeuse. But Antares is much farther off, and at a distance of about 38·5 parsecs; therefore this angular diameter represented the stupendous actual diameter of about 232 times that of the sun, or nearly

Name of Star	Apparent Magnitude	Absolute Magnitude	Distance in Parsecs	Spectral Class	Light radiated	Proper Motion in Seconds
Sirius	−1·58	+1·3	2·7	A0	30	1·315
Canopus ..	−0·86	−7·4	200·0	gF0	91,000	0·022
Vega	0·14	0·6	8·1	A0	50	0·348
Arcturus ..	0·24	−0·2	12·5	gK0	130	2·287
Rigel	0·34	−5·8	167·0	B8	18,000	0·005
Procyon ..	0·48	3·0	3·2	F5	6·5	1·242
Achernar ..	0·60	−0·9	20·4	B5	240	0·093
β Centauri	0·86	−1·36	27·8	B1	340	0·039
Altair	0·89	2·4	4·9	A5	11	0·659
Betelgeuse ..	0·90	−2·9	58·8	gM0	1,500	0·032
Aldebaran ..	1·06	−0·2	17·5	gK5	112	0·205
Pollux	1·21	1·2	9·9	K0	28	0·623
Spica	1·21	−4·0	111·0	B2	4,100	0·051
Antares ..	1·22	−1·7	38·5	gM2	3,400	0·032
Fomalhaut ..	1·29	2·0	7·3	A3	16·3	0·367
α Cygni ..	1·33	−5·2	200·0	A2	12,000	0·004
Regulus ..	1·34	0·2	17·2	B8	86·7	0·244
β Crucis ..	1·50	−3·98	125·0	B1	3,930	0·054
Barnard's Star	9·70	13·4	1·86	M5	0·0005	10·250
van Maanen's Star	12·30	14·3	3·92	F0	0·0002	3·010

200,000,000 miles. The circumference of Antares is thus much greater than the orbit of the planet Mars.

While α Herculis remains the largest *known* sun, it is probable that Canopus exceeds it. Canopus is too far south for the Mount Wilson interferometer to measure it.

Dwarf Stars. The dwarf type of star, to which our sun, Sirius, Vega, Altair, Procyon, and most stars belong, is much farther advanced in stellar evolution, and much more massive in proportion to its volume. Though usually of greater intrinsic brilliance and greater apparent magnitude, yet owing to the smallness of their angular diameter it will not be possible to measure most dwarf stars until means are found of greatly extending the spacing of the plane mirrors of the interferometer.

There remains, however, the method of *calculating* diameters which was described above. Now, in the case of those stars which it was subsequently found possible to measure, it was seen that the calculated diameters were remarkably in accord with the measured diameters, notwithstanding the difficulties and delicacy of such measurements. For instance, Arcturus was calculated to have an angular diameter of 0·023″, while it was found by interferometer measurement to be 0·020″. Betelgeuse was calculated to be 0·048″, while the interferometer revealed it as 0·047″, and Antares, which was calculated to be 0·042″, proved to be 0·040″.

The calculated diameters are as follow for the most prominent stars, in proportion to the sun—Sirius, 1·8 times ; Vega, 2·4 ; Altair, 1·4 ; Procyon, 1·9 ; Barnard's Star, 0·16 ; van Maanen's Star, 0·007 ; β Centauri, 11·0.

The table in the previous page applies the facts elucidated in the four previous Lessons to the most noteworthy stars. The column of " Light radiated " is in terms of our sun.

The last two stars in the table are introduced for comparison from the other end of the scale. Betelgeuse is variable. Double stars with large components are not included, as these are specially dealt with in our next Lesson.

LESSON 31

Double Stars and Binary Systems

(See plate 13)

DOUBLE stars when viewed telescopically are found to consist of two suns with an angular separation of usually not more than 30″ ; a few exceptions, however, have been discovered in which such stars have a physical connexion at distances greater than this. The first star found to be double was Mizar or ʃ Ursae Majoris, when Riccioli noted it in 1650. In 1874, Sir William Herschel, who had for some years been giving close scrutiny to the subject, produced a catalogue with about 700 double stars, describing their relative positions. Now about 21,000 have been catalogued and more are being added every year. This includes many triple and some multiple stars.

It will be obvious that because two stars appear close together they may, in some instances, be thus seen in the line of sight only and one component may actually be nearer to us than to the other. When there is thus no physical connexion they are described as *optical doubles*. When, instead, they are connected by gravitational attraction or common proper motion they are known as *physical doubles* or pairs. There is a further and important distinction which originated with Sir William Herschel. By the beginning of the last century he had noted changes in the relative positions of the components of some of the double stars which he had catalogued many years before. The fact was consequently revealed that several pairs were sufficiently close to influence one another gravitationally and so produce orbital motions. To such a star he gave the name of *binary*.

The probability of two stars being binaries when appearing very close together is much greater than that they are merely optical doubles ; this is particularly the case when they are both of similar brilliance, or if the brighter component is yellowish and the fainter either greenish, blue or purplish in tint. These complementary colours prevail in binary systems and are the direct consequence of their stellar evolution.

A few binaries or double stars are perceptible with good field glasses, and these are examples which are much more than 30″ apart. Nearly all require telescopic aid and usually high powers, since so many appear not more than a second or two apart. A great telescope will reveal double stars down to 0·2″ of separation, but the interferometer, which has been such a valuable aid in measuring the diameters of stars, has been useful in proving suspected stars to be double. It was, in fact, first used upon the star Capella, which Greenwich observations had indicated as appearing elongated in its spurious disk, thus suggesting that the star might be double ; the interferometer not only proved it to be so, but also gave the angular distance apart of the components. As a consequence it has become possible to measure the angular distance of separation between stars down to 0·08″.

At the distance of many double stars this small amount represents thousands of millions of miles, and even in the case of the nearest it will mean hundreds of millions, but numbers of binaries are much nearer together even than the earth is to the sun. This

ECCLESIASTICAL ARCHITECTURE AND A FAMOUS SCHOOL. Above, view of the choir of Liverpool cathedral, showing the sanctuary, the great east window and the carved oak organ case and stalls. Below, part of Merchant Taylors' School at Sandy Lodge, Herts, whither this ancient foundation removed from Charterhouse Square in the City. The buildings are planned to admit the maximum of air and sunlight.

ART AND ARCHITECTURE 26
Upper photo, Stewart Bale

DESIGN OF FUNCTIONAL EXCELLENCE. The monumental Shakespeare Memorial Theatre dominates the river bank at Stratford-on-Avon. The practical requirements of a theatre as a place in which to produce plays have governed the design of the building, expressed in brick of six different colours—brindle, buff, blue, brown, red and silver grey. Access to the main foyer is gained through five magnificent bronze doors.

ART AND ARCHITECTURE 26

Photo, Dixon-Scott

Plate 6

Volume V

MODERNISM IN HOTEL AND ROADHOUSE. The Midland Hotel, Morecambe (top), with its glistening white surface resembling fine marble, its sun balconies and conformity with the line of the sea-wall in front, marks a new phase in English seaside hotel construction. The " Nottingham Knight " roadhouse (bottom) is one of the " Knights on the Road " which exhibit an interesting application of economy in planning. All of these roadhouses are practically identical in design, arrangement and equipment and are thus advertised by their uniform appearance. ART AND ARCHITECTURE 26

Photos, (above) courtesy of L.M.S.; (below) Messrs. Davis & Knight, Architects, and Crittalls Ltd.

UTILITARIAN CONTINENTAL BUILDINGS. Berlin's huge department store, the Karstadthaus (left) on the Hermannplatz, presents a striking impression of verticality with its pilasters, unbroken by any decoration, ascending to the sky. In complete contrast is the emphasized horizontalism of the offices of the Messageries Hachette (right) in Javel, south-west of Paris. ART AND ARCHITECTURE 27

Photos, Wide World, The Times

Plate 8

Volume V

has been found out by means of spectroscopy ; for instance, if two stars close together and of similar brightness are revolving in an orbit appearing more or less edgewise, as seen from the earth, then at certain times one of the stars will be moving along the line of sight towards the observer, while the other star at the opposite side of this stellar orbit will be moving away from the observer. The result will be that the lines of the spectra of each component star will be displaced, upon the same principle, i.e. Döppler's (*see* Lesson 28, page 52), as obtained in the case of stars advancing and receding from us.

There will also be the additional peculiarity that the spectral lines will appear doubled. This appearance is greatest when the perspective presents the stars widest apart, while, when both stars are together in the line of sight, the duplicated spectral lines close up and appear single. If there are great differences in the respective magnitudes of the components, or if they are of different spectral types, the problem becomes more complex, but can nevertheless be accurately solved. The variations are always periodic and repeat themselves at intervals of perhaps a few hours, a few days or, occasionally, after the lapse of years. In the case of orbits presented more or less circular, other methods, involving the orientation of the spectroscope to the stars, have to be adopted ; thus precision may be attained even as to the position of *periastron* and *apastron ;* in the instances of stars which are also visually double, additional data becomes available, while one method may be used to check the accuracy of the other.

These stars are known as *spectroscopic binaries* ; over a thousand are known, and from the number tested about one star in five proves to be a spectroscopic binary, on an average, though in some spectral classes the proportion is greater, notably the B type of star. From this calculation we see what a large number of stars must be spectroscopic binaries. The details are obtained photographically from five, or preferably more, spectrograms taken at different times in order to record various positions of the component stars and thus compute their orbit

With their parallax known it subsequently becomes possible to calculate their mass, luminosity, distance apart, and even their actual dimensions in miles. Thus it is found that many spectroscopic binaries are composed of suns only a few million miles apart. Curiously enough, the first to be discovered, as in the case of double stars, was again Mizar of Ursa Major, when Pickering, in 1889, found that the spectrum of the brighter of these two stars possessed lines that were doubled at regular periods of 20½ days. Subsequent research explained the cause, and showed this star to be composed of two suns 25,300,000 miles apart, with an average orbital velocity of 43 miles a second and revolving in a period of 20·54 days ; their united mass being 1·67 of the sun's with an absolute magnitude of 1·4 at a distance of 22·22 parsecs, or nearly 72½ light-years.

It has been calculated that about 56 per cent of spectroscopic binaries have periods of less than 20 days, and 26 per cent between 20 and 100 days, the remainder being longer. Of these the most noteworthy is Capella, one of whose visual components, as revealed by the interferometer, is a spectroscopic binary, whose suns have a period of 104 days, and a mass somewhat larger than our sun. The star β Arietis is a spectroscopic binary whose suns average about 29,000,000 miles apart, and the period of their revolution 107 days. The brighter star of ξ Ursae Majoris is composed of two suns averaging 36,500,000 miles apart, with a period of revolution amounting to 665 days, their orbital motion averaging only 4½ miles a second. An exceptionally long period is that of β Capricorni, its two suns taking 1,375¼ days to complete the revolution of their immense orbit, the diameter of which averages no less than 470,000,000 miles.

Noteworthy examples of close spectroscopic binaries with very short periods are the following : Spica Virginis, a brilliant star of the first magnitude, being composed of two suns whose mass is 9·6 and 5·8 that of our sun, and whose distance apart of their centres averages only 7,000,000 miles ; from this we see that their surfaces must be almost in contact, consequently their period of revolution is only 4 days, the smaller sun travelling over the larger orbit at the terrific average rate of 130 miles a second. ψ Orionis has a period of only 3 days, while the components of μ Scorpii revolve in only 1¾ days, speeding round their common centre of gravity at the terrific rate of about 300 miles a second. The centres of these suns being only about 7,000,000 miles apart, their surfaces must be close together.

Similar details have been obtained regarding *visual binaries,* and in many instances one or more of the components of visual binaries have been found to be themselves *spectroscopic binaries.* Thus steller systems are gradually revealed to be composed of several suns, some with pairs of almost equal mass and volume like ε Lyrae, with two pairs of visual suns and one spectroscopic companion to the brightest of the four ; their periods are hundreds of years in duration. Again, Castor is a splendid example of a multiple system of suns. It is a visual binary (particulars of which are given in the following list) ; these components, known, as is usual with double stars, as A and B, according to their relative brightness, have a distant companion star known as C. Now all three, A, B, and C, are spectroscopic binaries with short periods of revolution, thus providing six suns to this system of Castor.

Other binaries consist of a large primary with one or more lesser suns revolving round it, usually in elliptical orbits ; they

Name	Distance in Parsecs	Period of Revolution years	Apparent Distance apart in "	Actual Distance apart in astro. units	Mass of each Component
α Centauri ..	1·32	78·8	17"·65	23·3	1·10 and 0·94
" Proxima "	1·30	—	131"·0"·00	—	Very small
Sirius	2·70	50·0	7·57	20·4	2·44 and 0·96
Procyon ..	3·21	39·0	4·05	13·0	1·10 and 0·40
Capella.. ..	13·30	0·285	0·054	0·85	4·20 and 3·30
Castor	13·16	340·00	6·06	80·0	Spectro. bin.
εHydrae ..	50·00	15·3	0·23	11·5	3·50 and 3·0
ζHerculis ..	9·00	34	1·35	12·2	1·10 and 0·5
ξUrsae Majoris ..	7·00	60·8	2·51	17·0	0·7 and 0·7
γ Coronae Borealis ..	45·45	87·8	0·73	33·0	4·7 (combined mass of both)
η Cassiopeiae	5·60	526	10·10	55·0	0·8 and 0·6

are probably " glowing worlds in the making," such as were once Jupiter, Saturn, and our earth, when their volume and intrinsic radiance were much greater than now.

The accompanying table shows the brightest and most noteworthy *visual binaries*. The period of revolution is given in years and decimal fractions of the same. The apparent angular distance apart is given in seconds of arc, while the actual distance is in terms of the sun's distance or astronomical units, as, for example, the companion of Sirius, which is nearly 20½ times 93,000,000 miles. The mass of each component is given in terms of the sun's mass ; for example, one component of α Centauri has a slightly greater mass than the sun.

LESSON 32

Principal Classes of Variable Stars

ALTHOUGH the great majority of stars shine with a luminosity apparently steady and without perceptible variations, there are between 5,000 and 6,000 known stars whose fluctuations are a characteristic and very instructive feature as to stellar conditions. These are termed *variable stars*. There are many types, the different variations in their light being due to different causes. The various peculiarities, both in their periods, light curves or intensities and in their spectra, have been closely studied. As a result, distinct varieties and classes, with characteristics common to each class, have been revealed, with minor differences in each class.

The four classes are: eclipsing variables; short-period variables; irregular variables; and long-period variables. To these are added by some a fifth class, the *Novae* or so-called new stars.

Variable stars are designated by a Roman letter, one from R to Z, which is placed in front of the name of the constellation. Thus we get S Persei for Algol, Z Herculis and Y Cygni. When all the letters down to Z have been applied and there are still more variables in the constellation to be designated, the letters are doubled progressively from RR, RS, RT, and so on to ZZ. Thus are obtained TV Cassiopeiae, RT Persei, TX Herculis and RZ Ophiuchi. No letters above R are used for this purpose, and no methods are at present adopted to distinguish the four classes.

Eclipsing Variables. This class consists of *binary* stars whose components revolve at such an angle relative to the earth that the planes of their orbits are presented edgewise or almost so; consequently, one or other periodically passes in front of its companion, and there occurs an observed diminution of the light during the time that one is being eclipsed. The resulting variations in magnitude differ according to the relative brightness of the two components and the inclination of the planes of their orbits. When this reaches 90° the orbits appear as straight lines, and one star passes centrally across the other in eclipse.

Between 200 and 300 eclipsing variables are known. More are discovered each year, mainly through photography, because none of the separate components is perceptible visually—even through the most powerful telescopes, in which they always appear as one star ; but through the spectroscope their binary character is proved.

The most noteworthy and easily observed eclipsing variable is Algol or β Persei, also known under its variable star title of S Persei. Algol decreases from 2·3 to 3·7 magnitude in about 4½ hours, during which time a large and much less luminous body passes in front of Algol until the minimum is reached, when only one-sixth the light of the star reaches us. After a few minutes it is perceived to be brightening up, until after another 4½ hours Algol has resumed its normal brilliance and the obscuring body has passed. The whole process is repeated after an interval of 2 days 20 hours and 49 minutes, but about midway between each minimum there occurs a slight diminution of Algol's light : this happens when the bright orb of Algol passes in front of the much less luminous disk of its companion. This is known as the secondary minimum and is a frequently observed feature of eclipsing variables, as is theoretically to be expected. The above phenomena, together with spectroscopic and mathematical considerations, indicate that Algol consists of two bodies, one very brilliant and radiating about 200 times the light of the sun, while the other is much less luminous and, though nearly as large, or perhaps larger, possesses far less mass. Algol is a B type of star, and the distance of its centre from that of its faint companion is, according to Vogel, about 3,250,000 miles.

Another type of eclipsing variable is represented in a bright star by β Lyrae ; in this case the secondary minima are much more pronounced, each being separated by two equal maxima. The whole cycle of change takes 12 days, 21 hours, 47 minutes, and ranges from 3·4 to 4·5 magnitude at greatest minima, and to 3·8 at secondary minima, which occurs exactly midway between the greatest minima. Spectroscopic investigation into this curious variation has shown that it is due to two very ellipsoidal bodies, one much brighter than the other, revolving round a central point of gravity, between two centres, and with their surfaces almost touching. The resultant tidal effect of such proximity is sufficient to account for their oval shape. The brightness of one is about 9½ times greater than that of the other, so when it is the turn of the brighter one to pass in front of the fainter, the secondary minima occur. Another bright variant is

that of β Aurigae, in which both stars are of nearly equal brightness and size ; in this case the minima are of equal intensity and
the whole cycle of variation 3 days 23 hours 2½ minutes. Most
other eclipsing variables are very faint or telescopic.

Short-Period Variables. This class of variable star consists of
those whose brightness varies in consequence of periodical
physical changes in the star itself ; they are therefore true
variables and are now usually referred to as *Cepheid* variables,
from the star δ Cephei, which typically represents them. This
star varies between 3·7 and 4·6 magnitude in a period of 5 days
8 hours 48 minutes, so it is easily observable. It is of type gF8,
with a mass 10·5 times that of our sun, but with the very low
density of only 0·0006 that of our sun. With a mean absolute
magnitude of 2·2 it becomes obvious that δ Cephei is a sun of
enormous size. This has been calculated to amount to an average
diameter of 22,500,000 miles, or about 26½ times that of our sun.

Now spectroscopic and mathematical research has established
the fact that the great variations in the light of this star are due
to a periodic change in its diameter amounting to about 1,600,000
miles. At maximum this huge gaseous sun has risen to a great
increase of surface temperature amounting to about a thousand
degrees Centigrade, resulting in an immense increase in light and
heat radiation. After this terrific expansion, which occupies
little more than a day, it shrinks less rapidly during the course of
the next four days to minimum, in preparation for the next
outburst of energy. As distinct from the eclipsing variables,
the increase from minima to maxima is always much more rapid
with Cepheids than is the decrease.

While δ Cephei is typical of short-period variable stars, of which
several hundred are known and are being added to every year,
there are the following differences. The periods of pulsation
range from a few hours to about 36 days, though the average is
about 7 days. While the light variation usually amounts to about
1 magnitude it may be nearly half a magnitude more or less. The
Cepheids are all giant suns, some attaining 5 or 6 times the
diameter of δ Cephei, but they are all of very low density, which
is lower in proportion to the increase in the star's diameter and
absolute magnitude.

Certain varieties of short-period variables, such as RV Tauri,
possess light curves which suggest, according to Jeans, that they
may be composed of two bodies very close together or in a state

approaching fission, in which the variations in their light would be produced largely by their rotation and tidal oscillations, thus accounting for the complicated light curves.

Long-Period Variables. This class exhibits periods of variation ranging from about 150 days to 400, though a few of the stars belonging to it extend to 600 days ; rarely are they less then 150. There is thus a wide separation from the Cepheids and eclipsing variables. In the long-period variables the variation is very great, often amounting to a difference of 9 magnitudes.

A typical example is the easily observed o Ceti, popularly termed Mira, the " Wonderful." While known from ancient times, Fabricius, in 1596, first noted its periodic variations. These take a cycle of between 320 and 370 days to complete ; at maxima it will reach magnitude 2 on occasions, but is usually about magnitude 3, less frequently 4, and more rarely only 5. At minima it usually descends to magnitude 9, and has reached 9·6. As this star is most of the time below 6th magnitude its absence from the sky is readily noted. It is also perceptible for between 80 and 90 days after maxima, from which it will be seen that, like the Cepheids, the decrease is not so rapid as the increase ; but the ascending light curve is not so steep and much less regular than in those of the Cepheids, thus suggesting spasmodic and explosive outbursts, which are spectroscopically shown to be chiefly incandescent hydrogen ; these produce the colossal eruptions, which may amount on occasion at maximum to 10,000 times the star's luminosity at minimum.

The star χ Cygni is another notable example, in which the light has been known to increase 35,000 times, from a minimum of 13·7 to a maximum of magnitude 4·8, in about 8 months. Its light curve shows varying maxima and minima, and with the ascent nearly twice as rapid as the descent, or decline in brilliancy.

Over 1,000 of these long-period variables are known, and it has been found impossible to formulate any theory fully to explain all their variations and to ascribe them to any one cause. Some undoubtedly pulsate, as in the case of the famous Betelgeuse. A probable solution in many instances is that clouds of less luminous material envelop these giant gaseous M stars, increase during quiescent minima, are then subsequently rent and temporarily dispersed by the great uprush of super-heated gases from below in which hydrogen chiefly figures. Then the star appears as a great blaze of light.

Irregular Variables. One type of this class is the U Geminorum type. These are faint stars which have periodic outbursts at irregular intervals of a month or two lasting but a few days. In the case of U Geminorum two different maxima occur at intervals of between 40 and 150 days, when it will increase from magnitude 13½ to nearly 9 in 3 to 4 days, then diminishing like a Cepheid, and later, after a varying interval, rise to perhaps magnitude 8·8. The stars SS Cygni vary similarly from magnitude 12 to 8·5, and SS Aurigae from 14·7 to 10·5.

Another singular type of irregular variable is that of R Coronae Borealis. While normally of magnitude 5·5, at irregular intervals its light decreases to 7 or, maybe, down to magnitude 15 ; it then remains so for a few months or several years subject to slight variations.

Finally there are a number of generally faint and red stars, chiefly of the types Me, N and S, whose variations are less than 2 magnitudes. With but few exceptions they appear to be suns approaching the end of their luminous radiation. Normally they are very faint, of 13 magnitude or below ; then at irregular and usually long intervals they will temporarily brighten up by 1 or 2 magnitudes, and then revert to their former faintness. Their temperatures are low, about 2,000° Centigrade. The explanation of their variability would appear to be that more or less solid surfaces are forming which get periodically broken up by outbursts of incandescent material from below these less luminous molten or solid surfaces. The star U Hydrae is a notable example of this type, varying from magnitude 4·5 to 6·1-6·3, and with an Nb spectrum devoid of violet light.

LESSON 33

Stars that Wax and Wane

(See plate 14)

THE novae or " new stars " are new only in the sense that they blaze up and present the spectacle of a brilliant star where nothing before was perceptible to the naked eye. By means, however, of the higher telescopic powers and the more complete methods of stellar photography now available it has been found that a faint star originally existed where the outburst occurred, and that what was observed was not actually a new star, but an old one which had become subject to some celestial catastrophe. The brilliance rapidly fades and the star slowly dwindles to a faint telescopic visibility again, after sundry oscillations in brightness. Such is the normal life of so-called novae, or " temporary stars " as they are sometimes called.

The method of nomenclature adopted is the word Nova, followed by the name of the constellation in which it appeared and the year, as indicated in the following list. This includes only the prominent novae visible to the naked eye which have appeared during the present century, and about which much is known through spectroscopy and stellar photography.

In addition to these novae a number of faint and telescopic stars of this type have been discovered, largely by photography, chiefly in the Milky Way and in star clusters, but of these but little is known.

Nova Persei 1901	inc. from mag.		13·5 to	—0·8
Nova Lacertae 1910	,,	,, ,,	13·5 to	5·0
Nova Geminorum 1912	,,	,, ,,	15·0 to	3·7
Nova Aquilae 1918	,,	,, ,,	11·0 to	—1·0
Nova Cygni 1920	,, below	,,	15·0 to	1·8
Nova Pictoris 1925	,, from	,,	12·7 to	1·2

Nova Persei 1901 was discovered by Anderson on February 22 of that year. It was the first to provide visual evidence through powerful telescopes of what had happened. This star increased over eight magnitudes in 28 hours, finally exceeding Capella in brilliance. So colossal was the outburst that in four days its light had increased 20,000 times. It soon diminished ; after 24 hours its brilliance had decreased by one-third, and in about a year it had dwindled to twelfth magnitude.

Stellar Conflagrations. In the meantime the ordeal of the star had been revealed, for a cloud of faint light was subsequently seen to be enveloping Nova Persei ; later it was found to be expanding at a great rate. This continued until, after about 8 months, it had attained the enormous apparent distance of about a minute of arc from the star. When the distance of Nova Persei from us—about 111 parsecs—was taken into account, it became obvious that the luminous clouds, if they were travelling, were doing so with the speed of light. Since this was an impossibility, the true solution appeared to be that what was observed was the light of the colossal conflagration on Nova

Persei travelling outwards and illuminating clouds of nebulous matter in its path long after the outburst itself had died down.

The importance of the revelation was great, because the phenomenon proved the truth of one of the supposed causes of these outbursts, namely, that they were due to a faint and relatively small sun rushing into a nebula or cloud of dark matter and consequently blazing up into a terrific incandescence, on much the same principle that causes a great meteor to blaze on entering the earth's atmosphere—though with this difference, that in the star the conflagration is relatively only superficial, for after passing through the nebula it again settles down to the condition of an apparently faint star, but at a higher temperature and magnitude than it was before. In some cases, as with Nova Persei, for instance, the star is later on found to be surrounded by a vast nebulous envelope or gaseous shell as the result of the outburst ; this is revealed both visually and spectroscopically.

Nova Aquilae 1918 was the brightest nova of modern times, exceeding all stars in apparent brilliance expect Sirius and Canopus. Its rise from eleventh magnitude to — 1·0 took only about four days, from June 5 to 9, during which time its luminosity had increased about 3,000 times. Having attained maximum, it immediately began to diminish, and a fortnight later was of only third magnitude, while six months afterwards it had diminished to sixth magnitude.

It was one of the most exhaustively studied of all novae, particularly its spectroscopic changes. By a fortunate chance it was photographed on June 5 at Heidelberg, when the star was of only 10·5 magnitude, and at the beginning of its stellar conflagration. Another fortunate chance provided a photograph of this celestial region on June 7, when Nova Aquilae had attained sixth magnitude ; by the next evening it was of first magnitude and its true character was realized.

Meanwhile many spectrograms had been obtained indicating the terrific convulsions the star was undergoing, far exceeding in magnitude and velocity any other known celestial phenomena. The absorption lines of the spectra indicated immense radial velocities of approach, reaching to over 1,400 miles per second, thus revealing the explosive force of the gases which expanded in all directions outward from the star. This subsequently became *visible* as a vast shell of luminous vapour or nebulosity, and then became a luminous disk, which continued to expand for several years until it attained the immense diameter of 16". While the light curve was very similar to that of Nova Persei, and exhibited minor fluctuations as it decreased, there was no evidence that Nova Aquilae had become immersed in a dark nebula (as had happened to Nova Persei), which could be accounted a possible cause of the outburst. The evidence rather suggests that the luminous nebulosity was due to a colossal explosion of Nova Aquilae itself.

Nova Cygni 1920 was discovered by the veteran astronomer Denning, on August 20, when its magnitude had increased to about 3·5. By August 22 it had reached magnitude 2·8, and on August 24 it attained 1·8. Its total increase of luminosity must have been far greater than that of either Nova Persei or Nova Aquilae, since photographic plates taken before the outburst and registering stars down to 15 magnitude show no trace of the star ; therefore the increase must have been stupendous, and the catastrophe the greatest known. The decrease was most rapid, the nova declining to magnitude 4 in a week and magnitude 9 in a couple of months. It appears to have been originally a small star at a distance of 38½ parsecs, and much nearer than the other novae. Though no shell or disk of expansive gases was observed, yet its spectrum indicated terrific radial velocities, amounting to as much as 1,100 miles a second ; so, apparently, Nova Cygni 1920 was of the same type as Nova Aquilae 1918.

Mystery of Nova Pictoris. Nova Pictoris 1925 provided a somewhat different spectacle and a unique problem. This star, which was only observable from southern latitudes, blazed up to about 60,000 times its original brilliance, being first noticed in May of that year. Its increase took several days, and it also remained bright for a longer period than is usual with novae, being still of third magnitude in the following September and remaining visible to the naked eye for over three years.

A singular feature of this outburst—which was obviously a different convulsion from those already considered—was the appearance of a nebulous ring, not seen until January, 1928, which continued to expand ; then in March, 1928, the unprecedented spectacle was revealed that Nova Pictoris had apparently divided into two separating stars. Bearing in mind the immense distance and date of the convulsion, it would have taken quite three years for the separation to have become perceptible even in powerful telescopes, that is, supposing the stars to have burst asunder with speeds of several hundred miles a second.

The nebulosity had by this time attained a diameter of about 6' and exhibited condensations similar to those of Nova Persei 1901. In view of the stupendous diameter represented by this nebulous ring, and the presence of two inner rings, it became obvious that what was being witnessed was the progress of the light of three successive outbursts through a vast and otherwise invisible nebula. Whether this stellar catastrophe was actually caused by a star being rent asunder by some terrific explosive force within itself, or through becoming immersed in the dark nebulous matter, it is impossible to say. An attractive alternative theory was that the conflagration might have been caused by two suns or a sun and a dark world colliding. This theory is generally discounted because of the immensity of space between independent stars. In Nova Pictoris it would not account for the presence of the vast nebula. It is possible that the two stars of Nova Pictoris were originally there, that one of them was becoming a dark world, and that the whole was rejuvenated by the nebulous immersion.

Records of novae go back for over 2,000 years. The first was noted in Scorpius in 134 B.C. and another in Ophiuchus in 123 B.C. ; one in Centaurus in A.D. 173, and the next in Aquila in A.D. 389. All these were of about first magnitude, and, as is usual with novae, in or near the Milky Way. Scorpius again had novae in A.D. 827, 1006 and 1203, all about first magnitude ; while Ophiuchus had another nova in A.D. 1230.

The famous nova of 1572 was the most brilliant known ; it appeared in Cassiopeia, and was generally known as Tycho's star. It was brighter than Venus at her greatest brilliance and reached -4 magnitude, being visible during the day. After 16 months it became invisible. Another very bright nova appeared in Ophiuchus during 1604, and has been known as Kepler's star ; it reached -2 magnitude, that is, brighter than Sirius.

Novae usually appear in constellations of the Milky Way, and in the nebulous areas within 10° of the galactic equator, the median line of the Milky Way. Numbers of the fainter telescopic novae occur in Scorpius and Sagittarius, while Aquila, Perseus, Cygnus, Ophiuchus and Gemini follow closely in the occurrence of these stellar outbursts.

Our Course in Astronomy is continued in Volume 6.

LESSON 31

Man's Vestigial Structures

IN the bodies of many of the higher animals are found structures that appear to be quite useless to their owner, but resemble the organs of some other animal. The splint bones of the horse's leg (*see* Lesson 27, volume 4, page 130) are almost useless to the modern horse, but they recall the toes of the horse's ancestors ; the whale shows its descent from a land animal in the vestigial bones of the hip girdle and thigh which are found in many whales of today. Again, in the embryos of the whale-bone whale, and in the baby duck-mole, small teeth are formed, although the adults are toothless. These embryonic teeth correspond to the teeth developed in the embryonic state in other mammals. The vestige of the hip girdle is present in some of the larger snakes (Pythonidae), and also the vestige of a hind limb— obvious relics of the amphibian ancestors of the reptiles. Many flightless insects show vestigial wing structures, and fish and lizards living in underground lakes have vestigial eyes.

Vestigial structures are also found in the plant world. The desert cactus has developed leathery outgrowths from the stem, so that the sun can act upon the chlorophyll without occasioning much loss of water ; useless vestiges of *true* leaves, however, still appear on the plant.

As might be expected, since the human body is the most complex and one of the most recently evolved organisms, it exhibits some of the weightiest of this vestigial evidence for evolution. Anatomists have discovered, in the body of man, nearly two hundred vestigial organs. Many features which occur in the human embryo are merely temporary structures which disappear during ontogeny, but others persist into the adult stage, although they serve no useful purpose. The presence of these useless relics can be explained on no other assumption than that the human body has evolved from other and simpler organisms which led a different life and required a different structure to cope with their environment

Vestiges in the Human Embryo. One of the most striking vestiges in the human embryo is the presence from the fourth to the eighth week of an external tail, containing from eight to eleven vertebrae. These vertebrae are progressively reduced and, as growth continues, the surrounding parts cover the tail tip. In a newborn child there is always a depression at the bottom of the back which indicates where the tail receded and was bent under. In a few instances, these caudal bones have not receded, and a child has been born with a tail. The reason for this vestigial tail is fairly clear ; man's small arboreal ancestors needed a tail as a prehensile organ, but, as bulk increased, it became useless for this purpose, and the caudal bones and muscles have been converted to support the pelvic girdle, upon which a greater weight is thrown by the erect position of the great apes.

Another vestigial structure appears in the wrist of the embryo. The lower primates, the gibbon and orang-utan, have nine wrist bones, while the gorilla, chimpanzee and Man have only eight. The extra bone (the os centrale) appears as a knob of cartilage in the human foetus, but, later, usually fuses with other bones.

The notochord, or primitive spine (*see* Lesson 22, vol. 3, p. 130), is an early feature of the human embryo. This structure persists throughout life in the lancelet, lamprey and some fish and newts, but it is replaced by the vertebral column in adult mammals. The notochord in the mammal embryo resembles the notochord in the embryo lancelet and, indeed, in most embryo fish.

Vestiges in the Adult. In animals that walk on " all fours," there is what is known as the azygos lobe of the lung, that is, a structure at the base of the right lung which intervenes between the heart and the diaphragm. In Man and the upright apes, the heart rests upon the diaphragm itself, but a rudiment of the azygos lobe persists.

At the top of the human shoulder blade there is the hook-like, bony structure process known as the coracoid (crow's beak) process. It is the vestige of a bone which, in the Australian duck-mole and in reptiles and birds. stretches from the shoulder blade to the middle of the shoulder girdle, where it is joined by a bone called the episternum (above the breast bone). If the finger is pushed in between the ends of the collar bone, the notch, into which the episternum fitted, can be felt at the top of the breast bone. In some men, vestiges of the episternum are also present.

There are many vestigial muscles in the human body. In the wrist, for example, there is the rudiment of a muscle which, in the monkeys, passes from the forearm to the hand and acts upon the skin and pads of the palm to tighten the grip. In the apes and Man this muscle is either absent or vestigial. Monkeys and lower mammals have a set of muscles with which they can twitch and pivot the ear ; these muscles are also present in the anthropoid apes and Man, but may be considered vestigial, as they do not function. Only a few human beings can twitch their ears. The greater freedom with which Man can rotate the head, and his greater reliance upon sight, render these ear muscles useless.

Many men have a little conical tip (known as Darwin's point) on the inner edge of the helix or fold of the ear—a vestige of the pointed tip of the animal ear. The hair on the human body is useless today, but the muscles which, in the furry animals, raise the fur on a cold day to prevent loss of heat still contract the skin into a gooseflesh state. And there is a third eyelid—a fleshy fold in the inner corner of the human eye. The cat cleans its eyeball by rapidly drawing this curtain across it and back, but in the human eye this fold is a useless vestige.

Vestiges Due to Retardation. If we refer back to the theory of heterochrony, described in Lesson 30 (volume 4, page 140), we may explain the persistence of these vestiges as a negative result of neoteny. In neoteny, it will be remembered, the somatic cells develop at a relatively slower rate than the gametic and, therefore, the body becomes sexually mature before all the embryonic features have fully developed, while some features which appeared only in the larval or embryonic stage of the ancestor appear in the adult stage of the descendant. The original adult features, that is, those appearing in the adult stage of the ancestor, appear too late to be fully formed by the time the descendant reaches sexual maturity. They tend, therefore, to be pushed off, as it were, from the end of the ontogeny, and, if they appear at all in the adult descendant, they appear as vestigial features. Characters, then, become vestigial owing to the relative retardation of the factors which control them. The third molar, or wisdom tooth, for example, is very late in its appearance in Man ; the retardation is, indeed, so great that it often does not appear at all.

The Hormones. In vertebrates, the rate of growth of many structures is controlled by the secretions from the endocrine glands, and the development of these glands is in turn controlled by genes. Thus it is proved that a tadpole will not metamorphose into a frog if the thyroid gland has been extracted, because the thyroid hormone controls the growth of the necessary lungs, tongue and limbs. The pituitary hormone regulates the growth of the face, and it is owing to the retarded action of this hormone that the heavy brow ridges of the adult ape and early Man do not appear in the modern face.

Occasionally, however, these glands do not, for some pathological reason, exert this retarding influence. The rate of development is altered and a man appears with ape-like characters : over-developed hair, heavy brow ridges, very large jaws, precocious sexuality ; or the sutures of the skull may close prematurely. These " throw-back " features cannot be considered as vestiges, although, like them, they prove Man's affinity to, and evolution from, other animals. They are termed atavistic features and are merely the effect of a capricious reversion to the same set of genetic circumstances as those in which the ancestor was developed.

LESSON 32

Lamarck's Theory of Inheritance

So overwhelming is the accumulated evidence for evolution that evolution is generally accepted as a fact today. Its acceptance as a fact immediately provokes the inquiry, why and how there arose this vast diversity of organisms that exist today and have existed in the past. Mendelian inheritance produces variations of existing types, but does not give rise to new characters.

Lamarck (1744–1829), Professor of Zoology, held a post at the Paris Museum of Natural History during the years of the French Revolution. In his day the current belief was that the different species of organisms were created once and for all, and that no changes had occurred since the beginning of the universe. Only advanced thinkers, e.g. Kant, Goethe, Buffon, had hitherto questioned this belief. Lamarck, in classifying the animal kingdom, was struck by the infinite gradations of forms. He declared in his " Zoological Philosophy " that life arose spontaneously in the most elementary forms, and that these forms evolved into forms of greater and greater complexity. He recognized, too, the probability of the common origin of animals and Man, but, possibly in deference to the prejudices of his age, he did not proclaim it.

LAMARCK AND INHERITANCE

Lamarck considered that there were two causes of evolution : the first, the fact that organisms possessed an innate tendency to evolve towards greater complexity : the second, the inheritance of acquired characters. He encountered perplexities in classifying animals. For example, he placed snakes higher in the scale than frogs, because the latter pass through a fish-like stage ; on the other hand, frogs have legs, which, in Lamarck's opinion, should place them above the snakes. To account for this discrepancy, Lamarck produced his famous theory of inheritance. The snakes, he argued, burrow and squeeze their bodies through narrow openings ; their bodies, accordingly, become long and narrow. Had they long legs they could not burrow or hide, while short legs would not support their long bodies. Hence, by disuse, they have lost their legs. These modifications (longer bodies and loss of legs) would only take place gradually, the slight effects in one generation of squeezing the body and ceasing to use the legs being handed down to, and intensified in, the next generation.

The following are some of the examples taken by Lamarck to illustrate his theory. Birds have acquired webbed feet by their constant effort to swim ; others (the waders), their long necks and legs by their efforts to reach their submerged food without wetting their bodies. Giraffes have long necks because ancestral giraffes, in time of dearth, stretched their necks to browse upon trees, and, so we must suppose, each extra milli-metre of neck so acquired was inherited by the descendant. The ai, or sloth, at first an animal of normal activity, took to climbing trees, and found food there in such abundance that ordinary movement was no longer a necessity. This acquired restfulness was handed down, being intensified in the process, until the sloth has almost lost the power of movement on the ground.

This theory of the inheritance of acquired characters has exercised the minds of biologists and other thinkers from Lamarck's day to this. It has been violently attacked by some, and as strongly upheld by others. It is an attractive theory since, if it be true, efforts at social advancement, such as state education, will affect not only the present generation but its descendants. Moreover, like many other biological theories, it appears to explain how evolution occurred. But to gain acceptance it must be capable of proof, and this is exceedingly difficult to obtain. Here are some of the objections to which the theory is exposed. In the first place, a large number of acquired characters are obviously not inherited. There is no evidence that the juggler's manual dexterity is handed on to his children, or that a baby of French lineage brought up in England is slower at learning to speak English or quicker at learning French than the average English child. Again, it is difficult to understand how some characters, such as blue eyes, the placenta, black or red hair, tall or short stature, could have been acquired.

Thirdly, modifications of the body due to environment or to the use or disuse of some particular organ affect the body or somatic cells. Weismann has pointed out that the hereditary factors or, as they are now called, the chromosomes and genes, are screened from the influences that affect the rest of the body. Therefore, modifications of the body, that is, characters acquired during the life of the individual, would not affect the genes, which are the only factors in inheritance.

Many experiments have been conducted with a view to proving or disproving Lamarck's theory, with inconclusive results. Pavlov, a Russian physiologist, claimed that he had taught mice to come for food at the peal of a bell, and that the number of peals needed to train their descendants to do the same decreased with each generation. He has since withdrawn this claim. Weismann cut off the tips of the tails of generations of mice, but their descendants obstinately produced tails of the normal length. Kammerer claimed that black salamanders bred in a yellow box became yellow, and that their descendants inherited this colour even when the yellow box was not used. Further research has done much to discredit Kammerer's experiments.

The examples which were cited by Lamarck as proof of his theory are not convincing. The ancestors of the wading birds, for instance, must have been very persistent in the search for a fish diet, to have sought it in vain for thousands of years, while they were developing their long legs and necks and their spreading toes. The evolution of the legless snake, the web-footed bird, the long-necked giraffe, etc., can be better explained by the theory of natural selection, which is the subject of the next Lesson. Most modern biologists consider, therefore, that Lamarck's theory has not yet been established as fact.

The following books are useful : Lamarck's " Zoological Philosophy," Elliott's translation (Macmillan) ; " The Biological Basis of Human Nature," H. S. Jennings (Faber & Faber).

LESSON 33

Darwin's Theory of Natural Selection

LAMARCK published his "Philosophy of Zoology" in 1809, but the scientists of his day, notably Cuvier, refused to entertain the idea that species had evolved, and it was not until after "The Origin of Species" was published by Charles Darwin in 1859 that the idea of evolution met with general acceptance. The theory of natural selection, which Darwin expounds in his book "The Origin of Species," arose from the consideration of two facts. The first of these facts is the amazing fecundity of life, every species producing far more individuals than do, or can, survive; the second, the universal variability of life.

There is no need to emphasize these two points. With regard to the first, it has been calculated that the one-celled Paramoecium alone would, in a few years, fill the known universe with its offspring, did they all survive and continue their geometrical rate of reproduction. The second is equally obvious; no two plants or two animals have been known to be exactly alike. Since, then, the large majority of individuals perish in the struggle for existence, the minority which survive will be those most fitted and adapted to their environment. These individuals are endowed with favourable variations in virtue of which they survive. Although the variations may be slight, they will be handed on to the next generation, in which there will be further accentuation of these variations, and so on, until a new species appears with these variations fully developed.

Natural Selection. The gardener and the animal breeder produce wide variations by selecting parents which show some of the characters they are anxious to develop, and then, from the descendants of these parents, again selecting for mating those individuals which possess the required characters in the fullest degree. In this way, for example, animals as diverse as the carthorse and the racehorse, and the greyhound, bulldog, and King Charles spaniel, have been produced from the same original stocks. Much more slowly, but quite as effectively, Nature has selected those organisms which are best fitted for survival. In the preceding Lesson the giraffe's long neck was taken as an example of a character which, according to Lamarck, had been acquired by the ancestral giraffe through stretching up to browse on trees. This elongation of the neck, slight at first, had, in Lamarck's view, been inherited and accentuated by posterity.

The theory of natural selection, however, accounts for the long neck in a different way. Among the ancestors of the giraffe there were, thrown up by the chance variability of Nature, individuals that were taller and had slightly longer necks than others. These individuals, in time of dearth, would be able to browse, while their short-necked brothers starved. Moreover, the taller, long-necked individuals would be the first to see and to flee from lions which might be stalking the herd. They would thus survive and reproduce offspring which also would have long necks, or would at least show a tendency to vary in this way.

Selection or Disuse. Some modifications in structure which would be attributed by Lamarckians to the inheritance of the acquired effects of disuse are explained more simply by the theory of natural selection. More than 200 species of beetles on the island of Madeira are wingless or have only vestigial wings ; they also have the habit of sheltering under stones, etc., during a storm. These facts might well be attributed, as in Lamarck's view, to inheritance of a character acquired through disuse, but Darwin pointed out that many species of beetles which depend on their wings for their livelihood and which flourish elsewhere are absent on these islands. He suggests that the wingless state of so many beetles is due to the fact that, for generations, beetles which flew least, through indolence or wing deficiency, would have the best chance of survival in a storm, as they would not be blown out to sea. Their wing deficiency (caused, as we now know, by gene mutation) or indolent habit would be inherited, and natural selection would continue to favour those of weak flying habit. This is an interesting example of the survival value of the loss of organs.

Meaning of Mimicry. Darwin also explains the occurrence of the wonderful phenomenon of mimicry in plants and animals by his theory of natural selection. The well-known stick insect can be scarcely distinguished from a dead twig. Other insects no less closely resemble leaves. Harmless flies (*Syrphidae*) have the significant coloration of the bee or wasp, and are left alone by the insect-eaters in consequence. An Australian fish

(*Phyllopteryx*, cousin to the sea horse) has appendages of ragged skin which enable it to sidle up to its prey, or to escape from its enemies, in the guise of a bunch of seaweed.

The green tree frog, the striped zebra and tiger, the twig-like caterpillars, the poisonless snakes which have the same markings as the adder and cobra, are all examples of the survival value of mimicry. To test the protective value of colour, 45 green mantises (praying insects) were tethered to green herbage, and 65 of a brown-coloured variety to brown withered grass. At the end of 17 days all had survived. But when 25 green insects were tethered to brown herbage, all were eaten by birds in 11 days, and of 45 brown insects tethered to green grass, 10 only survived after 17 days.

Lamarck accounted for the variability of life by postulating in every organism " an innate tendency towards progress," and an outgrowth of this theory—the theory of the *Élan Vital* of Bergson and the " life force " of latter-day thinkers—is still suggested as an explanation of the motive force behind evolution. But mimicry can hardly be interpreted as an exhibition of the " innate tendency towards progress " when it is remembered that these stingless bee-mimics—the *Syrphidae* mentioned above —are particularly numerous in southern Japan, where the bee and wasp are unknown. Consequently, if some mysterious " life force " has produced the striped abdomen of this fly, it would seem that in this locality it has exerted itself in vain. This Neo-Lamarckian theory of a " life force" will be reviewed, with other possible causes of evolution, in a later Lesson. Meanwhile, we must return to Darwin, who was much perplexed by the universal variations in Nature. For his attempt to explain them by the theory of pangenesis, the reader is referred to his books.

Darwin knew nothing of Mendelian inheritance or of the modern discoveries of chromosomes and genes. In particular, the evidence which modern biologists are accumulating to show that the causes of variation must be located in the genes, was denied to him. Indeed, he dismissed sudden and large variations as " sports " and of no significance. Today these variations caused by transmutation of chromosomes are known to be the basis of evolutionary development. What Darwin did was to insist that all variations are tested and must, in order to survive, pass through the sieve of natural selection. Selection is made in three ways : by (a) the struggle between friends, such as the known tendency of locusts to become cannibals when other food fails, or the disappearance of the English black rat when the brown rat invaded our country about A.D. 1700 ; (b) the struggle between foes—between carnivores and herbivores, wolf and stag, cat and mouse ; (c) the struggle with environment in which (for examples see Lesson 26, volume 4, page 126) whole genera (e.g. the reptiles at the end of the Mesozoic era) have " gone under." Thus, natural selection is the arbiter of the evolutionary fate of variations.

In addition to " The Origin of Species," Darwin's " Descent of Man " should be read. His theory is further developed and defended in Wallace's " Darwinism " (Macmillan).

LESSON 34

Sexual Selection in Bird and Beast

THROUGHOUT the world of living organisms the basic and ultimate unit of life is the gene. The viruses which cause diseases such as typhus, small-pox, trench fever, distemper, influenza and foot-and-mouth disease, and which are the smallest known particles of living matter, behave in ways suggestive of the action of genes. Such microscopic and ultra-microscopic particles are measured in microns: a micron equals $\frac{1}{25000}$ inch; ultra-microscopic organisms range from $\frac{1}{10}$ of a micron to $\frac{1}{100}$ of a micron across. In the larger bacteria there are no chromosomes, but genes appear to be present in the free state. As we leave this lowest rung of the ladder of living matter we find on each higher rung a gradually increasing complexity of the gene and chromosome mechanism.

The beginnings of sexual union appear in the Protozoa among the simple flagellates (*see* Lesson 4, volume 1, page 87), although in their case there is no definite distinction between male and female organisms, and reproduction is asexual only. Sex distinction becomes more pronounced in multicellular organisms, until in the higher mammals the sole method of reproduction is bisexual. Midway between these two extremes there are examples of every kind of variation, from asexual to bisexual reproduction. Most plants, snails, and some worms are hermaphrodites, the same individual functioning both as a male and as a female. In insects, among the lowest mammals and in the higher plants sexual and asexual reproduction are coexistent ; the oyster is unique in that the same individual may perform the functions of male and female at different stages of its growth.

Coincident with the evolution of form there has been evolution of sex, leading to bisexual reproduction with its infinite possibilities of recombination and perpetuation of new characters.

Darwin lacked our later knowledge of Mendelian inheritance and of the XY chromosome mechanism of sex (*see* Lesson 17, volume 3, page 112). He was, nevertheless, impressed by the evolutionary significance of bisexual union, although he viewed the matter from a different standpoint from that taken today.

In Lesson 17 it is explained that sex differentiation is due to the presence of two X chromosomes in the female and of only one X chromosome in the male. This is true for all mammals, and for fish (in so far as they have been examined) and for many insects. The male in these cases is di-gametic (producing two kinds of sperm gametes, X and Y), and it is the sperm, therefore, and not the egg which determines the sex of the offspring. The reverse is the case in birds and some moths—the female, and not the male, being di-gametic. As the body develops, organs arise which produce secretions or hormones that influence the growth of the body. The testes of the male secrete a sex-hormone which controls the development of what are known as secondary sex characters, two of which (in Man) are growth of the beard and voice " breaking." The ovaries also produce a hormone which governs the appearance of secondary female characters. If anything happens to alter the normal growth of these organs (testes and ovaries) the secondary sex characters are also altered. Hens, after successfully bringing up broods of their own chickens, have been known to lose their femaleness, and to begin to crow and in some cases become the father of chickens. On examination it was found in every case that the ovary had become diseased and was not therefore secreting the hormone for secondary female characters, and that male tissue had grown in its place. Similarly, castrated male animals lose some of their male characteristics. The eunuch is usually beardless and his voice alto.

Secondary Sex Characters. In some species these secondary sex characteristics are developed much more strongly than in others, and Darwin considered that they have been so developed as a result of sexual selection. For example, such secondary sex characters as the beautifully coloured plumage of the male pheasant, bird of paradise and the peacock are displayed before the female to influence her choice of a mate. Although, perhaps, the female does not deliberately select her mate, her pairing instinct is aroused by the display ; thus, the brighter the plumage and the greater the virility of the male the more likely is he to be successful and produce offspring, while his less decorated brother may be doomed to celibacy. These secondary sex characters are thus handed on by parents in which they are most fully developed.

Secondary sex characters sometimes become so exaggerated in the course of many thousands of years that they appear to menace the existence of the species. The peacock's lovely but overwhelming train is a heavy handicap to flight, and it is doubtful whether it would survive as a species were natural selection allowed full sway in deciding its fate.

Many birds produce startling results during courtship by inflating their windbags. The great bustard inflates an air sac which lies under the skin of its neck and breast, and at the same time draws its neck downward and backward, until its head is almost hidden by the projecting air bladder. In this strange attitude and with its tail thrown up the cock parades before its mate. The pouter pigeon is another example of windbag courtship. This bird has been bred by artificial selection from wild pigeons which inflate their neck when amorously excited.

Courtship by display is not confined to birds. The roaring of the gorilla and the inflating of the windbags encircling the neck of the orang-utan are examples of display by the males of the great apes. Among the lower apes the mandrill gives a most vivid colour display during courtship. The bare skin of his face becomes suffused with a brilliant " blush " of cobalt blue, and he endeavours to ingratiate himself with the female by alternately presenting to her his highly-coloured face and no less vivid hinder end, the naked skin of which is a brilliant scarlet and blue.

Another form of sexual selection—selection by battle between rival males—has given rise to secondary sex characters of a different type. In addition to the brilliant colour of male birds, the scent spray of the male butterfly, or the scent gland of the male deer, sexual selection has fostered the growth of offensive weapons such as horns, tusks and spurs ; also defensive features such as the mane of the horse and lion, the beard of Man and ape and the thickened folds of skin in the hippopotamus.

Sexual selection appears strongly to have influenced the evolution of the seal tribe, and especially of that species known as the sea lion or eared seal. In the breeding season the older bulls arrive first at the " rookeries " or breeding grounds, and when the cows follow each bull endeavours to drive as many as he can to his own breeding ground. Fierce battles ensue, the largest and strongest bulls being the most successful. The breeding season lasts for over two months, and during that time the bull dare not leave his harem for fear that it may be raided by the other bulls. For two months he fights and fasts, and fat and lusty as he may be when he arrives, he leaves the ground lean and wound-scarred. But he passes his virility to his offspring, and the bull seal is usually much larger than the cow.

This recurrent amorous excitability pervades all the higher species of organisms. Among the arthropods, the spiders, the beetles, the grasshoppers, and the butterflies all show sexual excitability. Even some of the coldblooded reptiles (the crocodiles, for example) make a nuptial display.

Bisexual reproduction has affected profoundly the course of evolution, and the theory of sexual selection is an important corollary to Darwin's main theory of natural selection. Darwin's " Descent of Man " and " The Courtship of Animals " by Pycraft (Hutchinson & Co.) are recommended for additional reading.

LESSON 35

Environment's Part in Evolution

LIFE, as we know it, can exist only within a relatively narrow environment. If the temperature of the earth rose 50° C. above or fell 50° C. below the average world temperature, or if the oxygen content of the atmosphere were quadrupled, life would cease to be. Life is also dependent on the moisture and carbon dioxide in the atmosphere, and any big variation in atmospheric pressure would be fatal.

Jeans estimates the age of the earth at 2,000 million years, half of which elapsed before the conditions of atmosphere, temperature, etc., were such that life could appear. Moreover, we are assured that very few of all the myriads of stars are associated with planetary systems, and that within such systems as there may be it would be only by a very rare combination of circumstances that an environment such as ours could be repeated. Life, then, so far as we know, exists precariously on the thin crust of a small satellite of the sun, which is a comparatively insignificant star.

Geologists believe that this thin crust of the earth's surface is subject to slowly recurring periods of submergence and emergence. Six periods of emergence are known, during which great mountain chains have been thrown up and the climate has become dry and extreme (see Schubert's " The Earth and Its Rhythms "). This change of climate has caused the partial extinction of dominant phyla, the members of which had become specialized and also bulky during the long periods of moist and equable climate which preceded such terrific upheavals. These phyla were replaced by smaller and more adaptable species, which in turn became dominant groups. The earth's crust is near the peak of emergence at the present time, but if the rhythm of a rising and falling surface persists as before, from one-fifth to one-third of the present land world will be submerged in 150 million years' time, causing a corresponding change of climate and a consequent change in present-day fauna and flora. Thus climatic environment has profoundly influenced, and continues to influence, evolution.

Genes and Environment. From the very beginning the life of an individual is conditioned by environment. The part of the fertilized egg which happens to come to the surface of the ovary determines the position of the future head of a tadpole, say, while the back of the future tadpole develops in the frog's egg on the side opposite to that on which the sperm happens to penetrate. If in the earliest stage of development a group of cells which would normally become an eye is transplanted to the animal's leg, the cells fall in with their environment and become skin or muscle cells. This environmental influence, however, is only operative for a short time. There is a special region of activity where the embryo's back will appear, known as the "dorsal lip." When this region has developed, it regulates the future growth of the organism, so that a grafted group of cells is no longer influenced by its environment. If, when the dorsal lip is formed, a limb bud is transplanted, it now persists in forming a limb, whether it be grafted on to the back or flank.

ENVIRONMENT AND EVOLUTION

Thus in the earliest stages of development the chemical properties of the genes in the cell are influenced by their interaction with those in neighbouring cells, but after a certain stage of development has been reached this plasticity is lost and the destiny of a group of cells becomes fixed. A group of cells which may at first become either a fore or a hind limb can, later, only form a fore limb, and of these fore limb cells some, which could earlier have formed any part of the palm or wrist or hand, can, finally, form only the finger. Environment is now powerless to alter their development.

Effect of Isolation. One of the most striking effects of environment on evolution is to be found in island life. In Lesson 33 the wingless insects of Madeira were cited, but on many islands it is not only the insects but the birds which have lost the power of flight. Galapagos has a flightless cormorant ; in New Zealand are found the kiwi and a flightless owl-parrot. In prehistoric times the moa, a giant flightless goose, also existed there. Many flightless birds, notably marsh rails, live in the South Sea Islands, and the dodo was a large flightless pigeon which inhabited Mauritius until it was exterminated by Man, for whom it was an easy prey. These islands were cut off from the mainland before the mammalian beasts of prey had spread to them, and in this isolated environment flight was not a necessity.

Again, the giant tortoises and lizards of Galapagos have become extinct on the mainland owing to the fiercer struggle for existence. The same fate has, for the same reason, overtaken the egg-laying mammals in all parts of the world except in Australia and Tasmania. New Zealand has only one native mammal, a mouse. Thus in these isolated environments evolution has either taken a divergent course or has marked time.

Another striking result of environment is seen in the case of cave-dwelling animals. In the Mammoth Cave of Kentucky cave fish are found in various stages of bleaching and eye degeneration. A newt, *Proteus*, lives in the limestone caves of the eastern Alps ; it is blind and pinkish-white, with vestigial legs. These acquired characters have not been transmitted in the Lamarckian sense. If a young newt is exposed to white light, it develops a dark pigmented skin, and continued exposure to red light develops the eyes, although for many generations its ancestors were blind and white. Hence it possesses the genes for eye and pigment formation, but its environment has overshadowed its heredity.

Heredity or Environment ? The relative importance of these two factors—heredity and environment—can never be decided. The Victorians stressed the importance of environment ; many biologists of today are equally emphatic in urging the importance of heredity ; each is, however, essential if we are to account for the facts. On this point the study of identical twins is instructive. Ordinary or " fraternal " twins are produced in consequence of two eggs being fertilized at the same time ; as each egg contains a different set of genes such twins differ in many respects. But it may happen that a single egg divides into two, and in this case identical twins are produced, formed from the same set of chromosomes and genes. Such twins are always of the same sex.

Environment steps in during the early stages of development and sometimes makes one twin right-handed and the other left-handed, and sometimes one is stronger than the other. On the other hand, heredity settles that they shall both have the same coloured eyes and hair and that the individual hairs of each will be of the same shape in section, that is, either round or oval. There is less resemblance between the finger marks of the right and left hands of twin A than there is between the finger marks of one hand of twin A and one hand (right or left) of twin B.

Their mental and emotional characters are also remarkably similar. In one case identical twins were separated when very young babies and brought up in extremely dissimilar environments for seventeen years. One was well educated and lived in town ; the other had but slight education and lived in the country. At the end of seventeen years their intelligence quotient (obtained by intelligence tests, which do not demand education) was nearly the same, while their emotional reactions were identical. Heredity, too, decreed that each should have the same childish diseases, and at the same time, but the better environment of the one mitigated the effects of these while the other suffered their full virulence.

The influence of environment may be further studied in " Heredity and Environment," by E. G. Conklin (Oxford University Press) ; " Biological Basis of Human Nature," by H. S. Jennings (Faber & Faber).

Our Course in Biology is continued in Volume 6.

LESSON 28

Study of the Lowly Algae

(See plate 15)

THE group of phanerogams which has now been described in the Lessons of this Course includes plants with which everyone is familiar on account of their abundance, their size, often their conspicuous flowers, and, not least, their economic importance. We will now turn straight away to consider some of the lowest forms of plant life, leading from the simplest to those of increasing complexity, and so gain some idea of the enormous range of structure and mode of life exhibited by members of the vegetable kingdom.

The group of lowest plants, thallophytes, embraces an enormous number of species, which are so varied in kind that some are to be found almost everywhere. The plant-body is technically known as a *thallus*, namely, an expansion which is not divided into root, stem and leaf. Thallophytes are conveniently divided into three great groups—algae, or green thallophytes; fungi, or non-green thallophytes; and lichens, plants of a mixed nature consisting of an alga and a fungus living together.

Though all green thallophytes, or algae, possess the green colouring matter chlorophyll, this is in many cases obscured by the presence of brown or red pigment. The group, therefore, may be conveniently divided into the " green," " brown " and " red " algae, according to which pigment is dominant. The seaweeds which cover the rocks between tide-marks are the best-known brown algae, while the red algae are the red seaweeds which frequent deeper waters. Green algae are abundant in fresh water, nor is free water their only habitat, for many of them can thrive on any damp surface, such as soil, rocks, tree-trunks and wooden fences. Generally speaking, the larger and more complex forms are marine; the fresh water and terrestrial representatives are both smaller and simpler. Among the brown seaweeds there are forms which rank with the most gigantic members of the vegetable kingdom, one (*Macrocystis pyrifera*), native to the non-tropical southern seas, attaining the length of several hundred feet; in contrast, other algae are entirely invisible as individuals to the naked eye. The whole plant body of these most minute forms consists merely of one single isolated cell. We will consider two types as illustrations of these very simple unicellular plants, both of which belong to the green algae.

Everyone must have noticed how frequently the trunks of trees, palings, etc., are covered by a bright green powdery layer, which is particularly conspicuous in damp winter weather. This green substance is chiefly made up of vast numbers of the unicellular green alga called *Pleurococcus viridis*. Each plant is a single rounded cell, bounded by a thin cell wall and containing dense protoplasm, a nucleus, and a large chloroplast. The plant reproduces itself by simple division of the original cell, and the resulting cells often remain densely grouped together in clusters for some time. On account of its chlorophyll it is able to form starch in the presence of sunlight, and, therefore, given adequate water supply, this single-celled organism is perfectly capable of leading an independent life.

As our second illustration, we will take a plant which passes its ordinary vegetative life in a state of active movement. This state of affairs is found in the single-celled green alga, *Chlamydomonas*, which occurs in ponds and puddles, often in such quantity as to give a bright green colour to the water, though the single cells are invisible to the naked eye, being only about $\frac{2}{100}$ millimetre long. The cells are usually oval and rather pointed at one end ; to this end are attached two *cilia* or fine threads of protoplasm, by means of which the plant swims about. Within the cell wall at the pointed end there is a little red spot called the " eye-spot," which is considered to be sensitive to light and possibly influences the plant to swim to conditions where illumination is best for it. Most of the cell is occupied by a large cup-shaped chloroplast ; in this is embedded a special protein mass called a pyrenoid, whose function is not definitely known, but round which starch is deposited as it is formed by the chloroplast. The cell contains a nucleus and two small vacuoles near the pointed end. The plant multiplies by its contents dividing up into two, four, or eight exactly similar " daughter cells," which are set free by breaking through the cell wall.

In addition to this method, this very simple plant shows a definite sexual method of reproduction, important differences being shown by different species. As before, the cell contents divide up, but this time to as many as 64 individual units, which, except for their smaller size, are very similar to the vegetative cell. They swim about by means of their cilia, and when two meet they get entangled by their cilia and ultimately fuse together. These little cells which fuse in pairs are called the gametes, and the cell which results from their fusion, the zygote. The latter forms a thick wall round itself and can resist cold or drought. When conditions are suitable its contents divide up to form two, four or more new individual *Chlamydomonas* plants. In some species the gametes which fuse are all of similar size ; in others, however, e.g. *C. Braunii*, there is a definite size difference ; a large and a small sexual cell always fuse together, the contents of the smaller one passing into the larger. The smaller, more active, cell is the male element, and the larger receptive one the female. We see, then, that even the simple one-celled plant is highly specialized as regards sex.

Plants Like Animals. It is not easy to draw a hard-and-fast line between the motile unicellular algae such as *Chlamydomonas* and a somewhat similar group known as the *Flagellata* (*see* Lesson 4 in Zoology, volume 1, page 613). Some of these show wholly animal characteristics, while others show a mixture of plant and animal characters. Such forms probably indicate that both plants and animals have had a common origin in the very remote past, and their common ancestors were possibly very similar to the flagellate forms which abound in water today. According to this suggestion plant life began in the water, and there passed through the earliest stages in its evolution, acquiring the essential green pigment and developing forms of many different kinds, all minute, free-swimming and relatively simple in structure. *Chlamydomonas* may be a present-day survivor of this stage. As we consider plants which come higher in the evolutionary scale, we see that many of them reflect the habits of their aquatic ancestors in that the presence of water is essential for fertilization to occur.

Many thread-like green algae live in ditches and ponds, some attached by one end, and others floating freely. One of the commonest of the latter is *Spirogyra*, which consists of a row of cylindrical cells each bounded by a cell wall. The whole filament is enclosed in a sheath of mucilage, which makes the alga feel slimy to the touch. Each cell is lined with protoplasm, and the nucleus is suspended by delicate strands of protoplasm in the centre of the cell. The large chloroplast is in the shape of a spiral band, and has embedded in it many pyrenoids.

During spring and summer *Spirogyra* is constantly increasing in length by division of the constituent cells, and pieces are frequently separated to form new and distinct plants. On approach of autumn a sexual reproduction takes place, though with no structural difference between male and female cells. The process is known as " conjugation." Two filaments lie together, and their adjacent cells send out processes which fuse together at the tips and form a conjugating tube or canal between the two cells. Meanwhile, the cell contents have rounded up to form the gametes. One of these (the male) passes through the connecting tube and fuses with the other (the female) to form a " resting spore." This forms a thick wall and remains dormant through the winter ; in the following spring it germinates.

If, during spring or summer, some of the mud from the bottom of a pond is examined under the microscope, it will almost certainly be found to contain some of the remarkable little plants known as desmids, each of which consists of a single cell. The desmids show great diversity of form, and include some of the most beautiful of microscopic objects. Many of them are of complex outline, and present a formidable exterior of spines and processes which serve as a means of defence against small aquatic animals. Some of them possess the power of movement. The usual method of multiplication is by cell-division, but occasionally the cells conjugate in pairs to form resting spores, which tide over the unfavourable winter season like those of *Spirogyra*.

LESSON 29

Seaweeds—Large and Small

(See plate 16)

THE seaweeds which cover the rocks between tide-marks are the best-known brown algae, and attract the attention of every visitor to the seaside. The popular name for them is " wrack," and there are many common species round our coasts. One of the most abundant is bladder-wrack (*Fucus vesiculosus*), the forking thallus of which is attached at one end, and, when covered by the tide, is buoyed up by numerous air-

HOUSING THE ARTISAN IN HOLLAND. Tenements erected by a Dutch
public utility society in a southern suburb of Amsterdam ; the design shows
austerity tempered by national love of the picturesque. ART AND ARCHITECTURE 27

Photo, B. S. Townroe

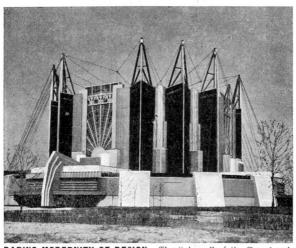

DARING MODERNITY OF DESIGN. The " dome " of the Travel and
Transport Building at Chicago's World's Fair (1933) contained the first
important application to architecture of the principle of the suspension
bridge, the roof of metal plates being hung from " sky hooks." The
" dome " was 200 feet high and had an interior diameter of 206 feet.
ART AND ARCHITECTURE 27

Courtesy of the Century of Progress Exhibition Chicago

AN ASTONISHING SKYSCRAPER. The Chrysler
Building in New York is an example of American
architecture charged with singular grace and imaginative fancy. Comprising 68 storeys, its height, 809
feet above the street level, is effectively emphasized
by the pointed cupola at the summit.
ART AND ARCHITECTURE 27

Plate 10   *Volume V*

RELATIVE DISTANCES OF THE NEARER STARS. This diagram shows thirty of the nearest stars at their proportionate distances from the earth, but not in their relative positions. The number of years against each star represents the time its light takes to reach the earth. The sun's light takes about 8 minutes to cover the 93 million miles that separate the sun from the earth. ASTRONOMY 28

'PROPER MOTION' OF THE STARS
As a result of the earth's annual revolution, the stars *appear* to move through the heavens. They do actually move, however; and a way of determining this "proper motion" of an individual star is shown in these diagrams prepared by Dr. Smart. The star at A, in the photo at the top, taken at Cambridge Observatory in 1903, is "Groombridge 34," a double star with a large proper motion. From photographs taken 23 years later, this proper motion was accurately determined, so that it is possible (*see* bottom diagram) to estimate the position (B) it will occupy 500 years hence. The proper motions of the other stars are relatively small.
ASTRONOMY 28

Plate 11

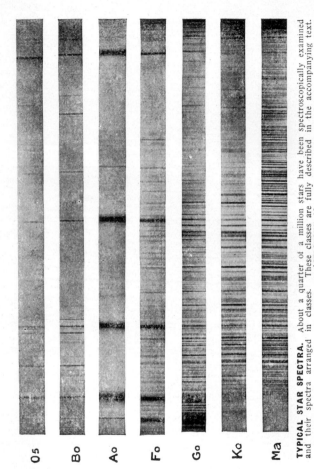

O5

B0

A0

F0

G0

K0

Ma

TYPICAL STAR SPECTRA. About a quarter of a million stars have been spectroscopically examined and their spectra arranged in classes. These classes are fully described in the accompanying text.
ASTRONOMY 29

Photos taken by Curtiss at Michigan, with 37½″ Reflector

Plate 12

Volume V

containing swellings. If a small piece of this or any other brown seaweed is placed in alcohol, the brown pigment will rapidly dissolve out, and a green hue will be assumed, i.e., the chlorophyll will become visible. In winter and early spring the tips of wrack branches swell up and assume a yellow or orange tint. If such a swelling be held up to the light, a number of little round dots of darker tint will readily be perceived. Each of these is in reality a pit, or "conceptacle," lined with hairs, some of which are modified into egg-organs, sperm-organs, or both (according to the species). In a female conceptacle, containing only egg-organs, each of these is an ovoid body on a very short stalk, containing eight egg-cells. The sperm-organs are minute bladder-like structures borne on branched hairs, and giving rise to large numbers of excessively minute sperms. When a ripe egg-cell is liberated, numerous sperms are attracted to it, and one actually fuses with it, thus bringing about fertilization.

Beginning near low-water mark and extending some distance into shallow water we find the "Laminaria zone," so called after brown seaweeds of that name. They are larger and broader than the wracks, and the thallus is smooth or corrugated, according to the species. It is these plants which are so often taken home by seaside visitors to serve as "weather-glasses," as, owing to the salt which clings to them, they become damp on the approach of rain.

Large masses of seaweed are to be found drifting about in the ocean, especially in the Sargasso Sea, a huge eddy occupying several thousand square miles of the North Atlantic. The most notable form to be seen here is the "gulfweed" (*Sargassum bacciferum*), which is buoyed up by stalked floats resembling berries in appearance. A huge brown seaweed (*Macrocystis pyrifera*), with pear-shaped floats, native to the non-tropical parts of southern seas, attains the astonishing length of several hundred feet. Fucus and Laminaria are largely used as manure, and under the name of "kelp" were formerly employed in the manufacture of potash. As a source of iodine they (especially Laminaria) are still valuable.

Diatoms. The almost infinitely varied microscopic forms known as diatoms, which possess flinty coverings of great beauty and exquisite geometrical symmetry of pattern, may be reckoned as the humblest of the brown seaweeds. They are to be found in both salt and fresh water, and even on the surface of damp

earth. Large tracts of the ocean floor, especially in the Antarctic regions, are covered with fine " ooze " principally composed of their remains. Some diatoms are stalked and immobile,
but most of them are free, and, like many of the lowest plants,
possess the power of movement. When examined under a microscope they may be seen gliding along in a very interesting and
curious fashion.

The surface layers of the sea and of lakes are inhabited by
countless myriads of diatoms, which constitute the chief food
of innumerable minute animals, especially the lowly cousins of
shrimps and prawns. These little creatures in their turn are
devoured by herrings and many other sorts of fish, so that Man
himself is indirectly indebted to diatoms for an important part
of his diet. And this becomes still more obvious when we remember that oysters, cockles, and mussels feed upon these lowly
plants wholesale.

Large numbers of fossil diatoms are known. Not only are
these minute plants actively engaged at the present time in
forming deposits on the ocean beds, but similar " diatomaceous
earths," found associated with rocks of Tertiary age, are a proof
of their activities in former eras. Such earths are white or grey
in colour, often so soft as to crumble readily in the fingers, and
they are composed almost entirely of the flinty remains of diatoms. Some of the deposits are of economic importance, being
used as polishing powders and in the manufacture of dentifrices.

Red Seaweeds. Most red seaweeds inhabit moderate depths
in the sea, and are unsurpassed for their beauty of form and
colour. Many of them are torn from their moorings and cast up
on the shore by storms. The reproductive processes are too
complex to be discussed here. Some of the red seaweeds are
strengthened by calcareous matter, and are represented on our
own coasts by branching forms and pinkish crusts which are
to be found on rocks between the tide-marks. " Carrageen
moss " (*Chondrus crispus*) is a stoutly built, forking red seaweed which grows on the coast of Britain, and has been used in
much the same way as isinglass. " Laver " is another edible
species, with a fairly broad, branching thallus. It is exposed
for sale in Scotland, and in South Wales is mixed up with dough
and baked into a sort of bread.

Though the majority of the red algae are seaweeds, a few
genera are found only in fresh-water streams. These do not

usually possess the striking red colour of the marine forms, but appear nearly black or even green on account of far less red pigment being present to mask the chlorophyll.

Blue-Green Algae. These plants of very simple structure resemble the algae in their habit and mode of life, but their real relationships with the group are still open to doubt. As their name indicates, they have characteristic colouring. Some are terrestrial, some aquatic, occurring both in the sea and in fresh water. These plants must rank amongst the lowest members of the vegetable world, the only others which are equally simple being the *bacteria*. The unicellular forms usually occur as colonies united by a mass of mucilage ; a large number of forms have the habit of simple or branched filaments also surrounded by mucilage. The facts that the cells have no well-defined nucleus and that sexual reproductive organs are entirely absent are both features indicating extreme simplicity.

The blue-green algae possess a very marked power of existence under adverse conditions. They form the principal vegetation of hot springs, and have been stated to occur at as high a temperature as 87° C. In contrast, they can flourish in Antarctic lakes. Certain of the algae are active in rock formation by precipitating carbonate of lime from the water in which they live. The brightly-coloured deposits found around hot springs in different parts of the world owe their beauty to the presence of coloured algae within the deposit.

Ancestors of Land Plants. It is now commonly supposed that plant life began in the sea, and there went through the earliest stages of evolution. Many different minute and simple forms, all containing chlorophyll, were developed, and all were free to swim or float in the water. Such free microscopic plants are known collectively as plant " plankton," and Chlamydomonas (*see* Lesson 28) serves to illustrate the kind of plants they were, not far removed from organisms with animal characteristics, and yet with green pigment and cell-walls.

In the earliest phases of the plankton period there was probably no distinction into plant and animal kingdoms, but in the later plankton phase organisms with plant or animal characteristics had been evolved and were present in the seas together. How long the primitive world of life consisted only of plankton cannot possibly be known, but it must have been for a very long period. In time, however, the plant world developed a new kind of organism. Some of the primitive plankton plants gave up their free-swimming mode of life and became fixed organisms, or " benthos," with a specially developed holdfast at their lower ends which anchored them firmly to the rocks or ooze. With these benthos plants lay the future : the free end grew out into a thallus of threads, or a mass of tissue composed of many cells ; in some cases it even became differentiated into an axis bearing lateral expansions, perhaps the first foreshadowings of stem and leaves, which later became fixed in the higher plants. The plants of the benthic phase must have grown in the sea much as their possible descendants, the seaweeds of today.

This phase in which plankton and benthos shared the marine world must also have lasted for a long period, until land surfaces appeared for plants to inhabit. As portions of the earth's crust emerged from the water, the benthos would be exposed to the air, and if desiccation were not too severe, the survivors would become the forerunners of the present-day vegetation of the land.

LESSON 30

Fungus Forms and Their Effects

(See plate 17)

THE Fungi group is a subdivision of the Thallophyta, and contains an enormous number of forms, being by far the largest group of the non-flowering plants. Up to the present time about 50,000 species have been described. All the members of this vast and heterogeneous group are distinguished by the absence of chlorophyll, hence all fungi are incapable of assimilating the carbon dioxide of the air and must obtain their carbonaceous food ready-made from other sources. The parasitic fungi obtain their organic carbon food from other living organisms, the saprophytic forms from dead organic matter.

In addition to the fungi of essentially parasitic and saprophytic habit (so-called *obligate* parasites or saprophytes) there are intermediate forms which are capable of changing their method of nutrition according to circumstances. A form which is usually saprophytic but capable of a parasitic existence is called a facultative parasite, and one in which these habits are reversed a facultative saprophyte.

Symbiosis. Fungi may also establish a symbiotic relation-ship with another organism, i.e. a relationship in which the two associated organisms derive mutual benefit from each other. The lichens are an example of such a partnership, the entire lichen plant being composed of the cells of a green or blue-green alga and those of a fungus. The term " mycorrhiza " is given to the structures formed by the association between a fungus and some organ (usually the roots) of the higher plants. When associated with the roots it is probable that the fungus in some way assists the plant to obtain nourishment from the soil.

An interesting case of dependence of the higher plants on fungal infection is shown by many orchids. Under natural conditions the germination of the seeds of these plants depends on the presence of the appropriate fungus. It is found that sterilized seeds can germinate if supplied with fairly concentrated solutions of sugars, which indicates that, in Nature, the fungus probably influences the uptake of nourishment by the seeds. Members of the heath family (*Ericaceae*) show fungal infection in all parts of the plants, and here again the germination of the seeds to healthy and vigorous seedlings is checked if the seeds are deprived of the fungus by sterilization. The Japanese orchid, *Gastrodia elata*, contains no chlorophyll and obtains all its nourishment from a fungus. Without association with the fungus the orchid produces no flowers and weak tubers, and if isolation is maintained for several seasons the plant dies.

Importance of Fungi. Many of the fungi are of great practical interest, and the study of their physiology and mode of life is one of the most important branches of Botany. Very many of them are destructive parasites, and cause the worst diseases of field and garden crops, and forest trees. The rust, smut and bunt of wheat, apple scab and potato blight are examples of fungal diseases of great economic significance ; to these innumer-able others might be added. Some, such as the dry-rot fungus, do harm by injury to the timber in buildings ; others destroy articles of food, which are attacked by " mould."

Fungi, however, must not be regarded as entirely injurious to higher organisms. Those which live in symbiotic union with other plants are obviously beneficial to their associates ; several of the larger kinds are good for food, and the saprophytes are extremely useful in bringing about decay and thus ridding the earth of the dead remains of animals and plants. The microscopic yeasts, owing to their power of forming carbon dioxide and alcohol from sugar, play an important part in the brewing and breadmaking industries.

General Structure. The vegetative plant body of a fungus is known as the *mycelium*, and is made up of a tangled weft of colourless filaments or *hyphae*, which may be divided by cross-walls into many cells, or may be completely devoid of cross-walls in the lower forms. In the protoplasm of these hyphae are contained numerous small nuclei, which have the same structure as the nuclei of other plants and animals. Reproduction is brought about by *spores*, of which there are many kinds, some being formed without any sexual process, others as the result of fusion of male and female cells. In the case of moulds the actual mycelium is visible as the white or coloured downy mass described as mould ; in the larger fungi (e.g. mushrooms, puffballs, bracket fungi) the part popularly called the fungus is in reality only the fruit body concerned with spore production, whereas the mycelium is obscured beneath the ground or other substratum.

Diseases Caused by Fungi. The fungus *Pythium de Baryanum* causes " damping off " of seedlings, attacking them at ground-level and softening the tissues so that the seedlings fall over. The disease is favoured by excessive moisture and overcrowding of the seedlings. The branched mycelium of the fungus produces spherical swellings (*sporangia*) in which spores are formed. These spores are known as zoospores, as, like animals, they possess the power of movement, being provided with two minute cilia by means of which they can swim in a drop of moisture. In dry conditions the sporangium can germinate directly to a new mycelium without the formation of zoospores. We have here an example of the way in which an organism, accustomed to aquatic life, might adapt itself to a terrestrial environment. *Pythium* also has well-differentiated sexual organs, the male and female being known as the *antheridia* and *oogonia* respectively. The *oospore* which results from fertilization is a thick-walled resting-spore, and can tide over unfavourable periods till it germinates either with or without the formation of zoospores according to the conditions. *Pythium* is a fungus which starts life as a parasite and continues as a saprophyte after the death of the infected seedlings.

The disease of potato blight is caused by *Phytophthora infestans*. It first became notorious in 1845–6, when it caused the potato famine in Ireland. The mycelium is widely distributed within the host plant, causing black blotches on the stems and leaves, and rotting of the tubers. Branched hyphae protrude from the host tissues into the air, and bear egg-shaped sporangia, which are readily detached and carried away by the wind to spread infection. These sporangia may produce numerous motile zoospores, or germinate directly to a new mycelium, when the term *conidium* is usually applied instead of sporangium.

Moulds. It is a familiar fact that jam, cheese, bread, fruit and many other articles of food, as well as leather, etc., are liable to become " mouldy " if kept in a damp place. This is due to infection by the spores of various forms of the lower fungi.

The common form of green mould (*Penicillium glaucum*) is often to be seen on oranges and bread, among many other things. The mycelium is made up of excessively delicate branching threads, some of which grow into the air and give rise to rows of spores that are disseminated by the least breath of air. A more complicated process of reproduction, involving fertilization, has already been mentioned. The blue mould (*Aspergillus*) of cheese is broadly similar, but the spore-bearing branches end in swellings, from which numerous long chains of spores radiate.

White mould (*Mucor*) is often to be seen on bread and horse-dung. The mycelium is made up of whitish, cobwebby hyphae, from which long spore-bearing branches rise into the air. Each of these ends in a rounded sporangium, within which numerous spores are produced. There is also a process of conjugation between specialized mycelial branches, by which resting-spores (zygospores) with firm investments are produced. These are able to remain dormant for some time, and thus enable the fungus to combat unfavourable surroundings.

Moulds of Two Sexes. Of recent years it has been shown that some species of mucor and its near relatives have two kinds or strains of mycelium. These, when grown apart, produce only sporangia, but when the mycelia of two strains are brought into contact, zygospores are produced. Species in which conjugation depends on the interaction of two strains of mycelia are said to be *heterothallic*, while those which can form zygospores in a single mycelium are described as *homothallic*. The distinction between the unlike strains is equivalent to the difference of sex in other plants and animals, but must be regarded as a physiological rather than a morphological difference, as the sexual organs of the heterothallic mycelia appear alike. The distinction of sex is thus expressed in its simplest form, as the capacity to produce zygospores with a different individual only.

The mould fungi may be regarded as definitely higher in the evolutionary scale than such types as *Pythium* and *Phytophthora*. They are adapted to a terrestrial mode of life, for at no stage in their life history are motile zoospores produced.

LESSON 31

Edible and Harmful Fungi

(See plates 17 and 18)

THE leaves of a number of common plants, e.g. strawberry, gooseberry and hop, are subject to attacks by species of fungi, which cause the condition popularly known as white or powdery mildew or blight. As our illustration we will take the fungus *Sphaerotheca mors-uvae*, which causes the highly destructive disease known as American gooseberry mildew. A spore, on germination, forms a white web-like coating over the leaf and sends hold-fasts into the epidermal cells. During summer infection is spread by the liberation of large oval spores (conidia) which are produced in rows on the external hyphae. In the late summer sex organs are formed on the mycelium and, as a result of fertilization, thick-walled spherical fruit bodies arise. When mature, these are dark brown or black, and may easily be seen with a hand lens on infected leaves. Within each fruit body are egg-shaped spores which spread the infection in spring.

The details of the formation of the sex organs and growth of the fruit body are too complicated to be given here, but it should be mentioned that the immediate outcome of fertilization is the formation of a large sac-like cell which is called the *ascus* ; in this the *ascospores* (usually eight in number) are produced. The formation of an ascus is one of the important features in the classification of the fungi, and a large number (over 15,000 species) are grouped together as the *Ascomycetes*. These vary greatly in habit, but all develop the characteristic mother cell or ascus in which the spores are formed. Some of the more familiar Ascomycetes are the edible morels and truffles, and the common coral-spot so frequently seen on dead sticks.

Yeast (*Saccharomyces*) is a very simple type of fungus which belongs to the Ascomycetes, though its relationship to other members of the group is somewhat obscure. Unlike other members of the group, it possesses no well-developed mycelium, but occurs as separate cells. They are found naturally on the surface of fruits, e.g. grapes and apples, and on other plant tissues. Some forms have been " domesticated," notably those used in the manufacture of beer and in bread-making.

If a little yeast is examined under the high power of a microscope it will be found to consist of innumerable ovoid yeast plants, each of which is a single cell. These reproduce by the process known as " budding," in which a cell gives rise to a small protuberance or bud which gradually grows until it is as large as the mother cell, and is then cut off. Occasionally separation is delayed, and by repeated budding colonies of loosely joined cells are temporarily built up. Under certain conditions some yeasts are able to form spores. The mother cell functions as an ascus, and the protoplasm divides up to form four thick-walled ascopores. The cells and spores are so small and light that they are easily carried long distances by the wind.

Alcoholic Fermentation. The most remarkable fact in regard to the vital processes of yeast is that, when placed in a solution containing glucose sugar, it is able to break up the sugar molecules and form carbon dioxide and alcohol, as expressed by the equation :

$$C_6H_{12}O_6 \rightarrow 2CO_2 + 2C_2H_5OH.$$

As with normal respiration, this process of decomposition of sugar results in the liberation of energy which is sufficient for growth of the yeast plant.

It has been shown that this decomposition of sugar by yeast is due to several enzymes (collectively known as *zymase*), which are present in the yeast cells. These can be extracted from the cells, and the extract brings about fermentation exactly as do the living yeast plants. The enzyme *invertase* is also present in yeast cells, and if the latter are placed in a solution of cane sugar ($C_{12}H_{22}O_{11}$) this enzyme must transform the cane sugar into fruit sugar and grape sugar (glucose) before fermentation can start. This process is known as *inversion*. The chemical reactions which take place during fermentation are extremely complex, and many other substances in addition to carbon dioxide and alcohol are formed as by-products.

Rust Fungi. These fungi, together with the larger familiar forms (mushrooms, puff-balls, etc.), are classified as the *Basidiomycetes* and include over 13,000 species. Their characteristic spores are produced very differently from those of the Ascomycetes. The spores are known as *basidiospores* and are produced externally on little stalks from the mother cell or *basidium*. At present there is no member of the Basidiomycetes known in which normal fusion of male and female elements takes place.

The rust fungi are, without exception, obligate parasites on the leaves and stems of higher plants. They cause very destructive diseases of cereals and grasses, their name being derived from the fact that at a certain stage they are revealed by the appearance of rust-red streaks on the stems and leaves. We will take as our example *Puccinia graminis*, the black rust of wheat, which, although not the commonest, is one of the most interesting of its kind. The delicate mycelium grows within the host tissues, and in summer produces pustules of rust-red spores which break through the epidermis and are exposed to the air. These spores (*uredospores*) are easily detached from their stalks by the wind and rapidly infect other plants.

Later on in the season the diseased patches turn black, owing to the production of dark-walled spores (*teleutospores*) in the place of the uredospores. These represent the resting stage of the fungus, in which it passes through the winter. These spores germinate in spring while still attached to the straw. Each sends out a small hypha (the basidium) which produces four minute basidiospores. These are incapable of infecting any cereal or grass plant, but depend on a totally different host, the barberry, for further development. When the mycelium is established on a barberry leaf, small orange-coloured " cluster cups " appear as swellings on the lower surface. In these still another type of spore (*aecidiospore*) is produced in large numbers. These spores will grow no farther on the barberry, but, when transferred by wind or rain to wheat or grasses, will produce a mycelium from which the uredospores are formed, the life cycle being thus completed.

In addition to the cluster cups on the lower surface of the barberry leaf there are minute yellow specks formed on the upper surface. These produce spores (*pycnospores*) which are very much smaller than any other kind formed by the rust. Until quite recently it was thought that these were functionless male cells, but it is now known that they play an important part in the life history of this *Puccinia*. Like certain of the mucors, the black rust fungus is heterothallic (*see* Lesson 30, page 100), and unless the two physiologically different strains are united, aecidiospores are not produced. It is found that the pycnospores are carried about by flies and other insects and when deposited by a mycelium of opposite strain, infect it, and so establish the growth of a fertile mycelium.

The fact that barberry was connected with the appearance of black rust of wheat was well known to farmers long before it was explained by botanists. In 1760 a law was passed in Massachusetts ordering the destruction of all barberry bushes in the province, but it was not until 1865 that all stages in the life history of the parasite were demonstrated by the German botanist De Bary.

For the full normal life cycle of *P. graminis* two entirely different hosts are necessary. This phenomenon is known as " heteroecism," and is displayed by several other rusts. Many, however, pass all their life cycle on one host (autoecism), and many have a far simpler life history than the black rust through certain spore stages being omitted altogether.

Mushrooms and Toadstools. These popular names denote representatives of a group of over 11,000 species. The mushroom is a saprophyte growing in pastures and in richly manured soil, but some of its near relations are parasitic on trees, to which they do great damage. Some toadstools are very poisonous to human beings if eaten, hence great care should be taken in the selection of mushroom-like fungi for food. The mycelium (popularly known as " spawn ") is very inconspicuous and remains hidden in the soil. This gives rise to the stalked spore-producing body, which is seen above ground, and which is made up of closely interwoven and compacted hyphae. When fully developed, the underside of the expanded top of a mushroom or toadstool will be seen to possess a large number of radiating plates or " gills," on the surface of which the minute basidiospores are produced in great numbers. From spore counts it has been calculated that a fruit body of the edible mushroom (*Psaluota campestris*) of 8 centimetres diameter produces about 1,800,000,000 spores. The gills vary in colour with the species, being, in the edible mushroom, pink in the young specimen and turning brown and then black with age.

A thin section through part of a gill, when seen under the microscope, shows that the surface layer consists of closely packed club-shaped cells (basidia), each with four little stalks at its tip, and a small spore borne on each stalk. The spores are readily dispersed by wind and germinate into new mycelia.

Bracket Fungi and Puff Balls. Many of the bracket fungi do considerable harm to trees. The mycelium ramifies in the wood and the fruit bodies project as semicircular plates from the trunk. Instead of the under surface being composed of gills, in some of these fungi (and also in some toadstools) it consists of tissue studded with minute holes. These are the ends of little tubes which are lined with spore-bearing basidia. The spore-producing body of the puff ball is a structure in which spores develop, to be liberated later by the bursting of the mature wall.

LESSON 32

Lichens, Bacteria and Slime Fungi

(See plate 18)

THE familiar plants known as lichens are found in the form of various coloured crusts on rocks, roofs and walls, or tufted growths on the trunks of trees and so forth. A lichen is a compound plant consisting of an alga associated with a fungus, both of which can clearly be seen in a thin section under the microscope. The algal cells containing chlorophyll appear healthy and are capable of vegetative multiplication : but the fungus alone is concerned in the development of a definite fruit-body, which indicates that the fungus is the dominant partner in the association. It is the fungus, indeed, which forms the framework of the plant, and, with the captive green algal cells, grows into a definite and often conspicuous thallus very different from the body of any ordinary fungus or alga.

A lichen, as a whole, is neither a parasite nor a saprophyte. The green cells of the alga are capable of carbon assimilation in the light, and, being surrounded by the fungal hyphae, are protected from desiccation. The fungus obtains its carbon foods from the alga, and in turn passes to the algal cells water and dissolved mineral salts, which are absorbed all over the surface of the fungal threads. Many of these plants can withstand extreme conditions of drought, and can exist on barren rocks and other unfriendly strata ; on this account they are valuable pioneers for higher vegetation.

Nearly all lichen-fungi belong to the class of fungi called *Ascomycetes*, and produce a fruit-body, often cup-shaped and brightly coloured, in which many asci and ascospores are embedded. The ascospores on germination form a new fungal filament, which must come in contact with the appropriate algal cells to build up a new lichen thallus. In some members of the group special little masses of both fungal and algal cells become isolated for reproduction, and when detached from the parent thallus serve at once to reproduce the necessary constituents of alga and fungus.

The characteristic colours which many lichen possess, e.g. yellow, orange or red, are due to acids formed in the thallus as a result of vital activities of the constituent partners. Over 140 different acids are known to occur in these plants, and from them are obtained litmus and many other pigments used in dyeing. Two lichens especially are of value as food substances : one the so-called Iceland " moss," which is eaten in that country ; the other the reindeer " moss " of high latitudes, which during the winter forms the almost exclusive food of the reindeer.

Structure of Bacteria. Familiar by name to everyone, the bacteria are an extensive group of minute and structurally simple organisms. Most are unicellular and have no well-defined nucleus. They are destitute of chlorophyll, as are the fungi, and are, as a rule, adapted to a parasitic or saprophytic mode of life ; on this account they may be regarded as a subdivision of the fungi, though, being quite different in structure and development, they really constitute a wholly distinct class of organisms.

Both as saprophytes and parasites, the bacteria are important in the life of the world. Certain parasitic members are known to be the cause of many of the infectious diseases of men, animals and plants. As saprophytes, they are the great agents of decay of all kinds, owing to the fact that they set up rapid chemical changes in the organic substances on which they feed. For example, when meat becomes putrefied, or milk turns sour, or wine is converted into vinegar, the change in each case is due to the action of a definite species of bacterium bringing about chemical alterations. The whole subject of the fermentations set up by these organisms has of recent years become of the greatest practical importance both to medicine, regarding the parasitic forms, and to innumerable branches of industry in which the saprophytic forms are involved. The science of bacteriology has grown up on these subjects, but they lie beyond the scope of this Course.

The average-sized bacterial cell is only about one-thousandth mm. in diameter, and a convenient classification is based on the shape of the individuals. Some are rod-shaped, and are termed *bacilli ;* others spherical, the *cocci ;* others comma-shaped, the *vibrios ;* and, again, others appear as a spiral, the *spirilli.* By means of prefixes the arrangement of the cells can be indicated ; thus a *coccus* type in which the cells are attached together in a chain is a *streptococcus ;* if the *coccus* cells are grouped together as a bunch of grapes they are referred to as *staphylococcus.*

Bacterial Reproduction. Each cell is surrounded by a cell-wall, not, however, of cellulose, but of a substance resembling protein. As already mentioned, there is no definite nucleus, but the application of suitable stains reveals the presence of granules of nuclear material scattered throughout the protoplasm. Some species of bacteria possess cilia (protoplasmic threads protruding through the cell-wall) which enable them to swim about in a liquid medium. Others are non-motile, possessing no cilia.

When in suitable conditions bacterial cells multiply by the simple process of dividing into two parts, i.e. by *simple fission.* In some species the daughter cells do not readily separate, so that dense masses of dividing cells become aggregated together in colonies known as *zoogloea* masses. Fission can go on with great rapidity, and many bacteria divide every twenty minutes or half an hour. A calculation shows that no less than 17,000,000 individuals will be produced from a single organism in twenty-four hours by fission occurring once an hour. In practice, however, this population is limited by the available food supply.

Under certain conditions, usually unfavourable ones, bacteria produce spores. A single thick-walled spore is formed from the protoplasm within the cell, and possesses extraordinary powers of resistance. Some will resist a dry heat of 100° C. for a long time, and may even withstand boiling. Both the spores and the vegetative cells are so minute that millions are suspended in the air by the faintest air currents.

Nutrition of Bacteria. The principal food of bacteria is found in the substances excreted by living animals, or in the complex organic matter resulting from the decomposition of the dead bodies of animals and plants. Nutrition of all plants and animals has a twofold aspect ; the material taken in must supply (1) substances for growth of the organism, (2) a source of energy for vital processes, i.e. it must be respiratory material. In animals organic food supplies both these needs, and in the green plant the process of photosynthesis yields carbohydrates which are used for both purposes. In certain diseases of bacteria, however, the case is quite different, and two entirely distinct classes of material are necessary, one type for body-building, the other for respiration and release of energy. Examples of these are the *nitrifying bacteria* (*see* Lesson 14, volume 2, page 103), one of which, *Nitrosomonas*, oxidizes ammonia to nitrites, and another, *Nitrobacter*, oxidizes the nitrites to nitrates. The *sulphur bacteria* utilize sulphuretted hydrogen for the purpose of obtaining energy, and oxidize the substance to water and sulphur. This reaction takes place within the cells wherein granules of sulphur are deposited. The *iron bacteria* oxidize ferrous salts to ferric salts, and *hydrogen bacteria* oxidize marsh gas or even free hydrogen for the same purpose. In all these reactions sufficient energy is set free for synthetic processes to take place without the organism depending on the radiant energy of sunlight. Such synthesis is termed *chemosynthesis*, as opposed to *photosynthesis*.

Some bacteria will only thrive in the presence of oxygen ; these are called *obligatory aerobes*. Others, on the contrary, only grow in the absence of free oxygen (*obligatory anaerobes*), such as the *denitrifying bacteria* described in Lesson 14. Various experiments have proved that direct sunlight is very harmful to the growth of bacteria, and, if sufficiently intense, will kill the cells outright. The rays in the violet end of the spectrum and the ultra-violet rays are most effective in checking the growth of these organisms.

Invisible Bacteria. Organisms are known to exist which are so small as to be invisible under the microscope. They are sometimes called " filter-passers," for, on account of their size, they are able to pass through porcelain filters. Such organisms are responsible for diseases such as yellow fever and foot-and-mouth disease.

Slime Fungi. This group of organisms lies on the borderland of the animal and vegetable kingdoms, and their place in Botany may be questioned. They are certainly of great scientific interest, for in them the behaviour of living protoplasm can be studied more conveniently than in any other creatures. Unlike the fungi and bacteria, the majority are of no practical importance. A few are parasitic on plants, and cause such diseases as the finger-and-toe or club-root disease of turnips and cabbages.

In the vegetative state a typical slime fungus, or *Myxomycete*, is a naked mass of protoplasm, sometimes several inches in extent, which creeps slowly about on moist, dead leaves, bark or wood. In dry conditions the protoplasm passes into a resting stage by being partitioned up into numerous hard-walled cysts. When moistened the walls of the cysts are absorbed and active movement recommences. When reproduction is about to take place the character of the organism is completely changed. Activity ceases, and the protoplasm is converted into a mass of rather complex sporangia, in which the spores are produced. From these spores new, active protoplasmic masses originate.

LESSON 33

Mosses and Moss-like Plants

THE next subdivision of the vegetable kingdom to be considered is that of the *Bryophyta*, or moss-like plants. It includes two great classes, the true mosses and the liverworts. The mosses, the general appearance of which is familiar to everyone, have a vegetative growth much like that of small higher plants, with well-formed stems and leaves, which, however, as we shall see in a later Lesson, are not directly comparable with those organs of flowering plants. The liverworts, perhaps less generally known to those who are not botanists, sometimes have a habit not unlike that of the true mosses ; but many have a much simpler organization, consisting merely of an undifferentiated green thallus. They are commonly found on wet banks or walls, or may actually live under water. One of the commonest is *Pellia epiphylla*, the structure and life history of which will be described.

Liverworts. The plant of *Pellia epiphylla* in its vegetative condition is a green, flat, lobed thallus, repeatedly branched, the lobes often overlapping one another. The plants grow together in masses and may cover a considerable patch of ground. The thallus has an upper and an under surface, the former being the darker green, while from the latter emerge numerous brown hairlike *rhizoids*, which fix the plant to the ground. The cells of the thallus show scarcely any differentiation; all are thin-walled, except, possibly, a few central ones, and there are chloroplasts in the superficial cells.

The thallus produces both male and female sex organs on its upper surface. The male organs are known as *antheridia ;* when mature, they are globular bodies attached to the thallus by a very short stalk. They may be seen with the naked eye as little dots on the thallus near its centre. Each antheridium is enclosed singly in a sheath of thallus tissue, which leaves only a small opening at the top.

The female organs, or *archegonia,* as they are called, are found in a group just behind the tip of the thallus, and are almost covered by an overlapping sheath of thallus tissue. The archegonia are flask-shaped organs. When mature, there is a long neck consisting of many cells, down the centre of which a canal passes to the swollen basal portion. In this basal part is the egg cell awaiting fertilization.

As in the lower plants generally, fertilization must take place under water. After rain or dew the surface of the thallus is wet enough for this to be accomplished. When moist, the antheridium bursts, and its contents, a mass of male cells, are set free. Each male cell (*spermatozoid*) is provided with two cilia, and can therefore swim through the liquid towards the archegonia. It is probable that the neck cells of the archegonium secrete substances which attract the spermatozoids in the right direction. These swim down the canal between the neck cells, and one of them effects fertilization by uniting with the egg cell. The result of this union is the development of a spore-producing fruit called a *sporogonium.*

This structure appears as a dark green ball, about one-sixteenth of an inch in diameter, attached to the thallus by a light green stalk which is fixed tightly in the thallus tissue. The length of the stalk varies greatly according to the habitat of the plant, and may attain several inches. The mature fruit body rather resembles a long, thin pin with a round, almost black, head. In this head, or capsule, numerous spores are developed, and with them some curious elements called *elaters,* which are long narrow cells with spiral thickening. The wall of the capsule splits open to release the spores, and the elaters are of use in loosening the mass of spores so that they are more readily dispersed by the wind. On germination a spore develops into a new thallus.

In many liverworts there are special organs for vegetative reproduction. Small green cups appear on the thallus, and in these are born minute *gemmae* or buds, which are capable of growing into distinct plants.

Mosses. The true mosses are more highly organized plants than the liverworts, possessing a perfectly distinct stem bearing spirally arranged leaves. We will base our description on the

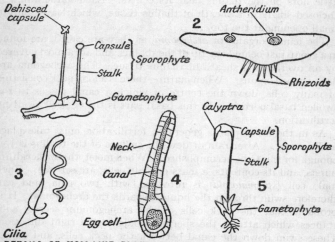

DETAILS OF MOSS-LIKE PLANTS. 1. Plant of Pellia bearing sporogonia. **2.** Cross-section of Pellia thallus showing male organs. **3.** Spiral-shaped spermatozoid with two cilia. **4.** Archegonium (female organ). **5.** Fruiting plant of Funaria.

common moss *Funaria*, which usually grows on the ground and is especially abundant in places where there has been a fire. The moss grows in close, bright green tufts, each single plant consisting of a slender, erect stem densely clothed with small, simple leaves. At the base of the plant are a number of brown rhizoids, which fix the plant in the soil and absorb water. True roots do not exist in any of the *Bryophyta*.

The tissues of the stem show a simple but well-marked differentiation into three regions : the epidermis, the cortex, and a central cylinder of long, thin-walled cells for water conduction. In some of the larger mosses the tissues are more complex and are possibly analogous to the xylem and phloem of the higher plants. The leaves of *Funaria* are very thin, being only one cell thick, except in the position of the conspicuous mid-rib. The cells are densely packed with chloroplasts. The conducting tissue in the stem is not continuous into the leaves ; this is compensated for by the fact that the leaves themselves can absorb water. On this account, mosses which may be completely dried up in hot weather revive very rapidly when rain falls.

Male and female organs are borne on the same plant in *Funaria*, but this is not the case with all mosses. The antheridia are borne terminally on a shoot in a dense cluster surrounded by a tight rosette of reddish or orange leaves. The rosette strikingly resembles a flower, especially in the larger mosses, such as *Polytrichum*, common on heaths. The antheridia are club-shaped, and produce a vast number of motile spermatozoids.

The archegonia are formed terminally on branches below the male rosette. When mature they have the same form as the archegonia of the liverworts. Here again fertilization depends on the presence of water, and is effected by the motile spermatozoids swimming down the neck canal and one uniting with the egg cell. In the mosses cane-sugar is secreted in the neck cells of the archegonium to lure the male gametes towards the egg. The result of fertilization is the development of the sporogonium.

This, the moss fruit, consists of a long, thin, red-brown stalk attached to the plant and bearing at its top a nodding pear-shaped capsule, which is first green, but finally turns brown. On the top of the capsule is a conical membraneous hood, the *calyptra*. This hood is really the upper part of the archegonium which has ruptured and had its tip carried up by the developing sporogonium. When the calyptra is removed, the top of the capsule can be seen as a neat conical lid.

The internal structure of the capsule is rather complicated and need not be fully described here. The upper part is fertile and produces the spores, while the more solid basal portion performs the nutritive function of carbon assimilation. This is rendered possible by the presence of stomata in the epidermis and the layers of cells containing chloroplasts just within the epidermis.

As the spores ripen the capsule begins to dry up, and the lid at its apex becomes detached. The spores, however, are not all set free at once. Beneath the lid there has developed a double row of little teeth (formed from thickened pieces of cell wall), which partly close the mouth of the capsule. These teeth are sensitive to moisture and only open to allow escape of the spores in dry weather.

A spore does not germinate at once into a new moss plant, but forms a very simple branched filamentous growth somewhat like a green alga. This is called moss *protonema*. It is attached to the ground by colourless rhizoids, and the young moss plants arise from it as lateral buds. In this way a large number of new moss plants is produced from the germination of a single spore.

The leaves of the bog moss (*Sphagnum*) contain large, empty cells as well as the green assimilating ones. The empty cells have small holes communicating with the exterior, and can readily fill with water. Dry *Sphagnum* can suck up a great deal of moisture and is employed as an absorbent in surgery.

From our description of the life cycles of *Pellia* and *Funaria* we see that the life story of the *Bryophyta* includes two distinct phases : the one concerned with the production of the sexual organs (the moss or liverwort plant) ; the other concerned with the production of asexual spores (the sporogonium). The plant which produces the sexual organs is relatively highly specialised compared with the *Thallophyta*. It is also self-supporting, absorbing its own water and mineral salts and performing carbon assimilation. The sporogonium is always in some way dependent for nourishment on the plant to which it remains attached. In most liverworts it is entirely parasitic, and in mosses partly parasitic, obtaining water and dissolved salts from the sexual plant while the capsules form their own carbon foods. The sexual phase is technically called the *gametophyte* and the spore-producing phase the *sporophyte*. These two phases normally alternate with one another and arise from one another, and a similar alternation is encountered in all the higher groups of plants, with the sporophyte becoming the dominant phase.

Our Course in Botany is continued in Volume 6.

LESSON 13
The Civil War and Its Fruits
(See plate 19)

THE Declaration of the Lords and Commons, dated June 6, 1642, in defence of the Order of Parliament of three months earlier for mustering the militia, is the first practical usurpation of sovereignty by the British Parliament. The king had become a fiction, and the constitutional issue was decided by the arbitrament of war. On August 22, 1642, Charles set up his standard at Nottingham, hoping to end the war speedily. The gentry could collect such of their tenants as they could arm and drill, and it was on these that the Royalists were mainly dependent, the militia machinery being for the most part in the hands of Parliamentarians, as also was that for the collection of taxes and for the fleet. The bulk of the gentry were Royalists (Cavaliers); the bulk of the townsmen Parliamentarian (Roundhead). The strength of the Roundheads was in London, the eastern counties, and the ports; that of the Cavaliers in the north and west. The division was made by the antagonism of two loyalties which ought never to have been in conflict—loyalty to Church and king, or to civil and religious liberties.

For the first year the balance of military successes was with the Royalists. Then Parliament allied itself with the Scots, who had hitherto held aloof, in the Solemn League and Covenant on a religious basis; and Colonel Oliver Cromwell raised, organized, and trained by his own methods, in the eastern counties, the troops who were presently to be known as the Ironsides, who, with the Scots, routed the Royalists under the king's nephew, Prince Rupert, in the north at Marston Moor (July, 1644). The tide turned. Montrose raised the Highland clans for the king, and seemed likely to carry the Royalist cause to victory in Scotland; but Cromwell in England organized the New Model Army, and in June, 1645, Sir Thomas Fairfax, in command of the Parliamentary forces, won the decisive victory at Naseby. The king's army dissolved into a number of scattered detachments; Montrose was overwhelmed at Philiphaugh; the Royalists could make head nowhere. In the May following, Charles placed himself in the hands of the Scots army in the north of England, and then began a long series of negotiations.

Trial and Beheading of Charles I. The king's object was to induce one or other of the groups among his enemies to accept his own terms, which proved unacceptable to any of them. The Scots, discontented at his refusal to support Presbyterianism, accepted payment for their recent military services in alliance with Parliament and deserted the king, leaving him in the hands of the Parliamentary commissioners. The " Puritan " army, however, wanted freedom for a host of sects, mistrusted Parliament, kidnapped Charles, and kept him virtually in their own custody at Hampton Court. The negotiations went on, till he attempted flight to France, was caught, and imprisoned at Carisbrooke. In 1648 there were Royalist insurrections ; in August a Scots army invaded England for the king, and was shattered by Cromwell at Preston ; the effect was to convince the army that peace was impossible while the king lived. While Cromwell was away, the army in London under Colonel Pride " purged " the Parliament by forcibly excluding from it all the members who took the side of the king ; and the remnant—the Rump—assumed absolute authority.

For the subsequent proceedings there was no legal warrant whatever. It appointed a court to try " the man Charles Stewart " for treason. Charles refused to plead before a court which had no legal jurisdiction. He has the credit of standing up for the law, which he had formerly employed in an attempt to gain absolutism. His assailants accused him on merely technical grounds. The court pronounced the death-sentence, half its members refusing signature, and the king of England and Scotland was publicly beheaded at Whitehall, manifestly by the fiat of the irresistible Puritan army, whose leader—in fact, but not officially—was Oliver Cromwell, the country submitting only because it had no choice (January 30, 1649).

Cromwell in Ireland. The Rump proclaimed a republic under the name of the Commonwealth, and the abolition of the monarchy and the House of Lords, and ruled as the sole sovereign authority. Such an arrangement could not have been enforced but for the support of the army. For nearly three years Cromwell himself, who was only its general and, at first, not even general-in-chief, was rarely present in London, being away on campaign most of the time. Most of Ireland was in arms for the restoration of the monarchy. Cromwell was sent to establish the new government, which he did by force, acting on the strictest Puritan principles. The Royalists were pronounced rebels, the Roman Catholic priests combatants, and himself, as the instrument of the " righteous judgement of God," elected to inflict slaughter " to prevent the effusion of blood for the future." After Cromwell's departure in 1650 his work was carried on with equal ruthlessness by Ireton and Ludlow ; colonies of Puritan soldiers were planted in Ulster, and the property of Catholic landowners confiscated in all parts of Ireland, with the exception of the wilds of Connaught, in which the Royalists sought refuge from the savage fury of the conquerors.

In 1650 the Scots government, indignant because their king had been beheaded by the English, recalled Charles II, the exiled heir, to the throne on their own terms. This act the English government had no sort of right to forbid, but could not afford to permit. Cromwell was no sooner back from Ireland than he was dispatched—now as Lord General—to bring the Scots to reason. He snatched a remarkable victory out of the jaws of defeat at Dunbar (Sept. 3, 1650) ; but when, in the following campaign, he left the way to England open, Charles II with the Scots army marched south, to be trapped at Worcester and decisively crushed by the pursuing and converging forces on the anniversary of Dunbar, though Charles after many hairbreadth escapes made his way to France. Scotland could no longer offer effective resistance, and was next year incorporated with the Commonwealth, but with General Monk as military governor.

England under Cromwell. Meanwhile the Rump was becoming increasingly unpopular. Royalists, to keep their estates, were forced to pay down a sum of money. This would have been fair enough from the Parliamentary point of view had the system been fairly carried out. But members of Parliament were bribed to let certain persons off easily, and used their power to promote personal interests. Parliament's great work, however, was the reorganization of the navy, which had been neglected ever since Elizabeth's death, and was at this time surpassed by that of Holland. England sought alliance with Holland both as a republic and as a leading Protestant power, but her overtures were rejected, and trade rivalry brought on a great maritime war with the Dutch (1652–4), from which England emerged definitely the equal if not the superior of Holland.

After Worcester, Cromwell was indisputably the most powerful man in the country. But the Rump wanted to remain in permanent control, and to disband the army of which he was the trusted commander ; and when it was engaged in passing a bill in the new Parliament for which everyone else was calling, he went down to the House with a body of troopers and dissolved it by his own authority—backed by the army (April, 1653). Although Parliament had done well in some things, Cromwell declared that they were polluted by self-interest and that it was not fit for them to " sit here any longer."

From that time he ruled as a military dictator, a Caesar maintained by the power of an irresistible Puritan army, which in December made him Lord Protector with almost absolute powers, and with a single-chamber Parliament pledged to maintain the new constitution. That experiment failed. In 1657 a new Parliament was called. It made him Protector for life, after offering him the crown, which he reluctantly refused. But when it met again it fell to discussing the constitution instead of attending to pressing business. No other was called before his death on September 3, 1658, and then followed a chaos for which General Monk found the only possible solution—the recall of Charles II (May, 1660) and his establishment on the throne. As an experiment or series of experiments in constitution building, the Commonwealth had proved a complete failure, while it had implanted in the English mind a permanent loathing for anything like a military dictatorship, and for any kind of government which interferes, as the Puritan government did throughout, on moral or religious grounds, with the private lives of its citizens. The domination of Puritanism was followed by the inevitable reaction. But for the time a very strong dictatorship was the only possible alternative to anarchy, and Cromwell was the only man capable of shouldering the burden, which wore him out. Inevitably his rule was arbitrary, harsh, exasperating ; but it gave probably more security and less injustice than the country would have had to endure without him. His foreign policy was in one respect unfortunate, because it helped to give France a dangerous predominance in Europe, which paved the way for the aggression of Louis XIV during the next fifty years ; but it also enabled England ultimately to be the insuperable obstacle in the path of that aggression, and restored the prestige lost almost from the moment of James I's accession.

LESSON 14

English Politics in the Reign of Charles II

(See plate 20)

THE recall of Charles II in 1660 was hailed with joy by three-quarters of the country and accepted as the best available course by nearly all the rest. After enthusiastic greetings at Dover, on his thirtieth birthday he entered London, also amidst joyous, shouting crowds. His return did not represent the triumph of any political principle, but it meant that the country was thoroughly sick of two things—military dictatorship and the official interference with the private lives and occupations of the citizens which Puritanism regarded as a proper function of government.

In effect, the terms of the agreement between what may be called Monk's Parliament and the exile-king were that the legislation passed by " the king in Parliament " in the last reign was to be the recognized law of the land, all later legislation being invalid ; that there was to be no vindictive action taken against those who had opposed the late king, even in arms, except as concerned the actual regicides ; that the question of taxation was to be no longer disputable—the crown was to receive a fixed annual revenue without power to add to it, anything additional being procurable only by Act of Parliament. The settlement by agreement of the religious problem was to be postponed till a regular Parliament could be summoned, with a king on the throne. Scotland was again to be a separate kingdom. The restoration was really more a restoration of Parliament than of king.

Restoration of the Establishment. Those were the terms which Charles—a man of far greater intellectual ability than his father—accepted with a light heart. The settlement was duly made on those lines. When Parliament was summoned, it proved to be Royalist and fervently Anglican in religious sentiment, but as tenacious of its own rights and privileges as any of its predecessors, and as hostile to Rome as to Puritanism, though the king did not fully realize this till half-way through his twenty-five years' reign. On the religious question Parliament took its own way, which was not the king's. While the old penal laws against Papists remained in force, it passed a series of laws, including the Act of Uniformity (1662), penalizing Protestant Nonconformity, or Dissent as it now began to be called. By this act every clergyman and schoolmaster who was not in accord with everything contained in the Prayer Book was to be precluded from holding benefice. About 2,000 clergy resigned, and Nonconformists now abandoned the idea of Church unity and petitioned for toleration.

Charles himself had his own reasons for wanting to restore Romanism, accompanied by toleration of Protestant dissent; but he did not choose to gain his ends by fighting. He assented to the repressive legislation, but later tried a risky experiment; by royal prerogative he " suspended " the penalties for Nonconformity. But when Parliament met, it not only forced him to withdraw this " Declaration of Indulgence," denouncing it as illegal, but also passed the Test Act (which continued in force for more than a century and a half), excluding from all public offices any person who could not pass the test of membership of the Church of England (1673). The Act inflicted no penalty on the holder of a special belief, but led, in particular, to every Roman Catholic being driven out of office.

For the next eight years Charles was fighting a duel of wits with Anthony Ashley Cooper, earl of Shaftesbury (1621-83), who, with the exception of Charles himself, was the cleverest politician in England. A born party leader, whose sense of justice was acknowledged by even his worst enemies, Shaftesbury was in fact loyal to two principles only, his love of Parliamentary government and his desire for toleration based on hatred of clerical interference.

Origin of the Whig Party. Hitherto he had imagined that he was in the king's confidence, together with the other members of the so-called ministry of Cabal. (This word was used to denote the king's group of advisory ministers, being formed from the first letters of their names, Clifford, Arlington, Buckingham, Ashley—created earl of Shaftesbury later—and Lauderdale.) In 1673 he discovered the contents of the secret articles of the Treaty of Dover, signed in 1670 between Charles and Louis XIV, by which, in return for his assistance against the Dutch and the restoration of Catholicism in England, Charles was to become the pensioner of Louis, who undertook to supply troops to enforce Catholic domination and the revival of the royal prerogative to the

English crown. Shaftesbury, accordingly, realized that toleration for the Catholics in Charles's intention was connected with a scheme for the overthrow of English independence ; he, therefore, now remained faithful to his principle of toleration only for Dissenters, and, supporting the Test Act, incurred Charles's great anger. He was dismissed from the ministry and set himself to form a Parliamentary opposition, which developed into the Whig party, the Court party being known as Tories.

Scare of the ' Popish Plot.' Henceforward it became the primary object of Shaftesbury's own policy to procure the exclusion of the heir presumptive, the king's brother James, for in James's creed not only was " Divine Right " the first article, but as a zealous Roman Catholic he was firmly determined to Catholicize the government. A few years later the country went crazy over a monstrous fabrication, the " discovery " by the notorious liar Titus Oates of a (wholly fictitious) Popish Plot (1678). The king himself did not dare to stand up against the unreasoning panic ; nor did the judges. According to Oates's announcement the king was to be murdered, James set on the throne, Protestantism to be ruthlessly suppressed.

In his duel with Shaftesbury Charles had a weapon in reserve. Louis XIV, who feared lest Parliament should, by keeping Charles short of money, eventually drive him into alliance against France, in 1678 provided him with a pension, sufficient to make him independent of supplies from Parliament. Till that pension had been secured Charles could only stand on the defensive with Shaftesbury.

The religious panic wore itself out ; Parliaments had met, fought, and failed to pass the Exclusion Bill (1679), which excluded James from the throne, and were prorogued or dissolved.

Charles as Autocrat. A new Parliament met early in 1681. Shaftesbury and the Whigs gathered to it confident of winning a crushing victory ; but it had met only to be immediately dissolved, and no other Parliament was called in the remaining four years of the reign. Charles was independent, having secured his pension, and the succession for his brother. Armed rebellion was not even in sight. The horror of a Catholic successor to the throne was not equal to the horror of anything which might threaten a second civil war. Charles's personal popularity increased with the violence of his Whig opponents. During the next two years he acquired, by an ingenious but strictly legal remodelling of the corporations, the crown's control over the borough elections to the House of Commons ; so that James, when he duly became king at Charles's death in 1685, was able at once to summon an enthusiastically Tory Parliament.

Charles never defied Parliament as his father had done ; he did not ignore the lesson of his ill-fated Declaration of Indulgence—while the Exclusion Bill never passed the Lords. He got his own way by relying not on force but on intellectual dexterity veiled under a mask of frivolity. Only towards the end of his reign had he succeeded in making himself independent. Apart from the French king's pension, he had rallied round the throne all those who were anxious at all costs to maintain order and avoid civil war. On the other hand, Parliament had defeated toleration ; it had definitely acquired the right of " appropriation of supply," that is, of voting supplies for specific purposes, with the concomitant right of controlling the expenditure ; it had established the principle of ministerial responsibility, so that a minister could not escape punishment even by proving that he had acted under the king's orders ; and its Habeas Corpus Act (1679) had at last made it impossible to detain an accused person in prison for any long time without bringing him up for trial.

Social Life in Caroline London. Charles's extravagance in Court expenditure increased trade and prosperity in certain directions, though his finances during the earlier part of his reign were often in hopeless confusion. The growth of London, after the fire in 1666, was a sign of renewed prosperity. The Court and meetings of Parliaments meant that many rich families had new town houses, and there was much building round the districts known now as Lincoln's Inn and Soho Square. While painting was in the hands of foreign artists, English architecture flourished. The disaster of the great fire gave Sir Christopher Wren (1632–1723) his opportunity. Though many of his plans for a vast scheme of rebuilding for London were rejected, he was chosen as architect for the new St. Paul's, and, in addition, designed many other London churches and buildings throughout the country.

The coffee house and the theatre were great features of the day. The former owed its existence to the introduction of chocolate and coffee as beverages. The latter had added an interest by the introduction, about 1659, of actresses for the women's parts, hitherto played by boys. Pepys' Diary is the most authentic account of London life in the first nine years of Charles's reign.

LESSON 15

The 'Glorious Revolution' of 1688

(See plates 21 and 22)

WHEN James II (1685–89) came to the throne, the country was well disposed towards him and somewhat ashamed of its Popish Plot panic; Charles had ensured him a Tory House of Commons. With tact and a moderate policy he might have recovered comparative practical toleration for his co-religionists, short of actual repeal of the Test Act. In theory, though not in fact, the doctrine of divine right was triumphant after the Restoration—so triumphant as to deceive James and tempt him to ruin; the characteristic political philosophy of the period was that expounded in Sir Robert Filmer's " Patriarcha " (1680), wherein is traced the divine right of kings from the power granted to Adam by God. James, more conscientious but far less astute than Charles, flung away his chances by reverting to arbitrary methods, and alienating the Crown's strongest supporters, the High Anglicans, clerical and lay.

The Whigs, led by Shaftesbury (who had fled to Holland and died in exile in 1683), when working for the Exclusion Bill, had fixed upon Monmouth, an illegitimate son of Charles II, as the Protestant candidate for the succession. Monmouth headed a revolt, easily crushed at the battle of Sedgemoor (1685), but with a vindictive savagery large numbers of the rebels were executed without trial, and Jeffreys, the cruellest of judges, was sent to hold the " Bloody Assizes " in the western counties, hanging 320 persons and transporting more than twice as many to be slaves in the West Indies. As a reward for his efficiency he was made Lord Chancellor on his return to London. The unfortunate Monmouth's own execution united all parties in recognizing as heir to the throne the king's Protestant daughter Mary, the wife of his nephew William, Stadtholder of Holland. Monmouth's death brought the whole Opposition into line, making caution and moderation on the king's part the more necessary.

But James blundered into the conviction that he was master of the situation. He created alarm by demanding the repeal of the Test and Habeas Corpus Acts. Finding the issue of that demand doubtful, he prorogued and then dissolved the loyal

Parliament. He went on to appoint Roman Catholic officers in the army, substituted Roman Catholics for Protestants in civil and even in ecclesiastical offices, packed the Bench with judges who affirmed the legality of these proceedings, and appointed by prerogative a new arbitrary Court of Ecclesiastical Commission. The alienation not only of the most moderate constitutionalists, but also of the Anglican sentiment, which was the Crown's most valuable asset, was completed by the issue of a new Declaration of Indulgence in 1687, suspending all laws against Romanists and Dissenters alike, and by the ejection in the same year of the Fellows of Magdalen College, and their replacement by Roman Catholic priests.

James obstinately shut his eyes to the rising tide of hostility. He renewed the unconstitutional Declaration of Indulgence, and in a moment of madness ordered the clergy to read it from their pulpits. Seven of the most revered and most loyal among the bishops presented a petition against the order ; whereupon he arrested them for publishing a " seditious libel." While they were awaiting trial a son was born to James. The boy would succeed in priority to the two Protestant daughters by his previous marriage. Hitherto it had been assumed that, whatever James himself might do, a Protestant successor could be counted upon. The whole world believed, quite erroneously, that the boy was a supposititious child, procured from some poor woman to provide an heir who would be brought up as a Catholic. A few days later the trial of the seven bishops took place ; their unexpected acquittal was hailed with uproarious popular rejoicings, in which even the soldiers whom James was reviewing at Hounslow joined with enthusiastic shouts. That night a secret message was dispatched by leading Whigs, Tories and bishops acting together, to William in Holland, urging him to intervene, unless he wished his wife to be robbed of the succession.

William and Mary. Four months later (November 5th, 1688) William landed at Torbay with a small force, not to depose James, but in answer to the appeal from all parties that he should bring the king to reason. James set out with troops to meet him, but they and their officers deserted him and joined William ; amongst them was John Churchill, afterwards duke of Marlborough. James returned to London, but after riots, and with William's connivance, he fled secretly to the court of his cousin Louis XIV in France, while William and Mary were invited, on terms, by a provisional government to occupy the throne vacated by his flight. On their acceptance of this " Declaration of Right " the reign of William and Mary began (1689). The Declaration was then embodied in a statute always known as the Bill of Rights, This ensured that, while people had believed James was a king by divine right, no one could think that of William. It affirmed in favour of Parliament every doctrine which had been in dispute between Crown and Parliament since the days of James I. The sovereign from henceforth owed his position to a Parliamentary vote. A corresponding arrangement with the Scots provisional government gave William and Mary the crown of Scotland, still an independent kingdom. The political revolution of 1689 was successful, while that of 1641 was a failure ; the policy of setting Parliament above king in the latter case was not a clear issue ; the dispute between Church and Puritans had complicated matters.

For James and his supporters, henceforth known as Jacobites, he was still the lawful sovereign ; the government was a rebel government and William a usurper. In England no large body of Jacobites was ever ready to risk armed rebellion against the *de facto* government. In Scotland, John Graham of Claverhouse, " Bonnie Dundee," raised the Jacobite clans, but when he fell at Killiecrankie (1689) the cause was lost. Ireland had never been consulted ; the Ulster Protestants were for long in danger of being crushed by the Jacobites. James tried to make Ireland the military base for recovery of his crown, with help from French troops ; but after meeting a far from decisive defeat by William at the Boyne Water he fled to Kinsale and embarked for France (June, 1690), though his followers held out gallantly for a year more. The victors took an iniquitous revenge by ignoring their pledges and imposing drastic penal laws on the Catholics, which left them absolutely helpless for resistance to the small Protestant minority.

After the end of the Irish war there was no more serious risk of Jacobite insurrection, though there were periodical assassination plots and constant private intriguing with the exiled court. The menace of a French invasion on behalf of James disappeared with the naval battle of La Hogue in 1692.

The Stadtholder of Holland did not desire the English crown for itself ; but, because he wanted England on the Dutch, not the French side in his lifelong battle with Louis XIV, he was willing to accept the responsibility and to discharge it conscientiously. He was unpopular in England not only because of his taciturnity and cold manner, but also because he was a continental rather than an insular statesman. As time went on he found the Whigs more inclined to support him than the Tories. He agreed with them in advocating a wide toleration for Dissent, the more because High Church doctrines were difficult to reconcile with loyalty to the Revolution ; so that he tended more and more to draw his ministers from the Whigs. But to the end of the reign the ministries were still mixed, though the Tory opposition grew stronger.

In 1694 queen Mary fell a victim to an attack of smallpox. William, who was deeply devoted to her, never really recovered from her loss. She left as a memorial Greenwich Hospital, designed by Sir Christopher Wren, which her uncle Charles II had begun to build as a palace, but which she completed as a home for disabled sailors.

From 1691 to 1697 William had been engaged with the French war of the Augsburg League, and had been reasonably but not enthusiastically supported, chiefly because Louis posed as the champion of the exiled James ; but at the peace of Ryswick Louis had formally recognized William. When in 1700 Louis tore up his agreement with William and accepted the entire Spanish inheritance for his grandson Philip, and William set himself to organize a new European coalition to procure a partition between Philip and the Emperor Leopold's younger son, Charles, it seemed that the Tories could see no good reason for English intervention. But in 1701 James II died, and Louis could not resist making at his bedside the lordly gesture of acknowledging his son James Edward as the true heir to the English throne. Forthwith the whole country was ablaze with indignation ; Whigs and Tories vied in acclaiming the war.

William was accidentally thrown by his horse early in 1702. His collar-bone was broken, and his exhausted frame did not survive the shock many days. The succession had already been settled on his sister-in-law Anne, and after her (by a Tory Parliament) on a cousin, Sophia, Electress of Hanover, the nearest Protestant descendant of the house of Stuart.

Taxes under William and Mary. During his reign William had stedfastly devoted himself to the domestic and constitutional interests of England. From Holland were introduced better

INTERFEROMETER FOR MEASURING STARS. In this combined photograph and diagram the star's light, as shown by the arrows, reaches the plane-mirrors M1 and M4 direct from the star; it is then reflected on to plane-mirrors M2 and M3. From these it is projected down the long open tube of the telescope in two slender beams to the great 100-inch mirror, whence the beams are passed to the focus of the eyepiece in the usual manner of a reflecting telescope. ASTRONOMY 30

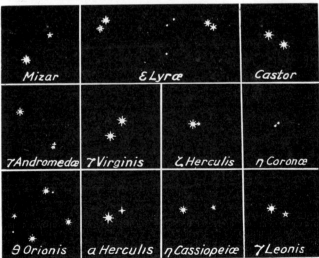

VISUAL BINARIES. Famous examples of visual double, triple, quadruple and multiple stars such as are described in the text. ASTRONOMY 31

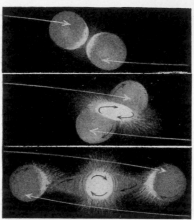

WHEN A STAR SPLITS. These diagrams, prepared by Professor A. W. Bickerton, purport to show how two stars colliding with one another may split and produce a third. ASTRONOMY 33

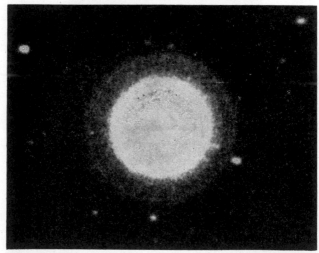

NOVA PICTORIS. First observed in May, 1925, this star suddenly attained to an extraordinary degree of brilliance (as seen in this photo) and then slowly waned, until in January, 1928, observers noticed the appearance of a nebulous ring. This continued to expand until in March, 1928, two stars were seen where one had been before. It has been suggested, therefore, that in 1925 Nova Pictoris was split in two, as the result either of an internal convulsion or of the impact of another star. ASTRONOMY 33

Courtesy of H. E. Wood, Union Astronomer, Johannesburg

Plate 14   *Volume V*

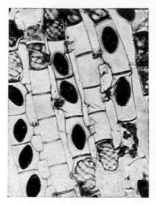

TYPES OF ALGAE. Left, Spirogyra nitidia (× 45); the parallel filaments have formed the spores, which are seen as oval shapes. These are
later released and lie dormant through the winter, but in the spring they
burst the cell wall and grow to form new plants. Right, Closterium
(× 80), a desmid with smooth outline which lives in water at high levels.
BOTANY 28

Photomicrographs, H. S. Cheavin

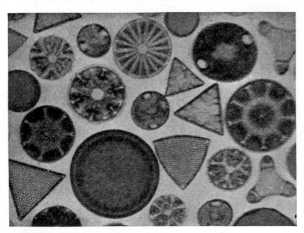

DIATOMS. Microscopic forms of brown seaweed, the coverings of
which show varied and intricate geometrical patterns, highly magnified.
BOTANY 29

Photomicrograph, John J. Ward

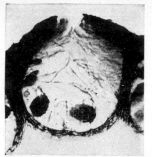

FUCUS VESICULOSUS: REPRODUCTIVE ORGANS. Left, female conceptacle : right, male conceptacle (× 40 approx.). BOTANY 29
Photomicrographs, H. S. Cheuvin

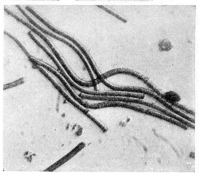

TYPES OF SEAWEED. Top left, Fucus vesiculosus or bladder-wrack, the common brown seaweed of the seashore (much reduced). Top right, Laminaria, another large brown seaweed (much reduced). Bottom left, Chondrus crispus, or carrageen moss, a red seaweed (about actual size). Bottom right, Oscillaria, a filamentous blue-green alga (magnified approx. 90 times). BOTANY 29

Plate 16   *Volume V*

agricultural methods—in particular, the cultivation of grasses and root crops for the winter feeding of cattle. Dutch architects increased the comforts of the smaller domestic buildings. In 1694 the first stamp duties were imposed on legal documents, and the Bank of England was founded as a sort of monopolist in the state money-lending business. A company was formed with a capital of £1,200,000, which was lent to the government, who guaranteed the interest of £100,000, but not to repay the principal. This foundation of the Bank of England was the beginning of the National Debt. On the accession of William and Mary, the chief direct tax was a hearth tax (imposed by Charles II on every hearth except those in labourers' cottages), for which, afterwards, the window tax was substituted. Indirect taxation included customs and excise.

LESSON 16

Domestic Politics Under Anne and George I

(See plates 23 and 24)

SOME account of the War of the Spanish Succession is given in Lesson 12 in Modern History (volume 2, page 551). Here we must be content to note that the really decisive turning point in favour of the Grand Alliance was Marlborough's victory at Blenheim (1704), which definitely forced the French behind the Rhine. Almost at the same moment, an Anglo-Dutch squadron under Admiral Rooke captured Gibraltar, to become a permanent British naval base for control of the Mediterranean. Blenheim was capped by Ramillies in 1706, and Gibraltar by Port Mahon (Minorca) in 1708, when Marlborough also won the third of his great victories at Oudenarde. Louis would now have been ready for a peace on reasonable terms, but the Whigs in England had set their hearts on " no peace without Spain." On that point Louis would not yield. The war went on. France was defeated by Marlborough for the fourth time at Malplaquet (1709), but at even more frightful cost of life to victors than vanquished. The Tories became the predominant party in England ; they had already become a peace party. There was no more serious fighting after Malplaquet ; and in

1713 the Tory government in England, behind the backs of the allies, negotiated the Treaty of Utrecht, in which Holland and Austria had to acquiesce.

In the reign of Queen Anne, the last ruler of the Stuart dynasty, an event of the first importance to our national history was the union of England and Scotland as a single kingdom. The two states had been somewhat uneasily yoked together under one crown for a century, and in something like chronic hostility for five centuries before that period. At any time a union by consent would have been of mutual benefit to both countries, but was never available, the smaller and poorer being always, with very good reason, in dread that its own interests and rights would be subordinated to those of the larger and wealthier. Scotland's antagonism to a legislative union had not been diminished by experience under the union of crowns ; the Presbyterian Church would be endangered by intolerance in England, and Scottish commercial interests throttled, as those of Ireland were, for fear of injuring those of the English commercial community, which would make no concessions to any rival, Scottish, Irish or colonial. The colonial system was based on the theory that the interests of the colonies must be subordinated to English interests. Friction overseas resulted ; Ireland was particularly hurt by the English policy. English corn, by the aid of bounties, could be sold cheaper in Ireland than Irish corn could be cultivated. Irish cattle and wool production was discouraged in the interests of English farmers ; nothing was done to help on industry of any kind. Scotland, on the other hand, seized the opportunity in 1706-7 to make a good bargain and prospered.

England's Union with Scotland. It was palpable to the shrewder statesmen in Scotland that the necessary condition of true prosperity was a union, but only under adequate commercial and national guarantees. Now the unionists found an effective lever. Scotland, like England, had settled the succession in 1688-9, so far as concerned William, Mary and Anne. In 1701, on the death of the last of Anne's children, England chose as her future successor the Electress Sophia of Hanover, granddaughter of James I ; Scotland did not. William died ; the war began ; Anne might die. It was still open to Scotland, where Jacobite sentiment was strong, to recall the Stuarts. This procedure would certainly revive the old-time alliance of Scotland with France, for whom Jacobites were even now fighting; this England could not afford to risk. Scotland, moreover, would sever the already existing union of the crowns if England refused a more substantial union, by the removal of fiscal barriers and the guaranteed integrity of Scottish national institutions and, above all, of the Presbyterian Church. Therefore, in 1706, by dint of much skilful piloting, the Treaty of Union was negotiated and passed by both kingdoms. In 1707 the first united Parliament of Great Britain met at Westminster, though the permanence of the union was not finally assured till Jacobitism, as a political force, received its death-blow at Culloden forty years later.

Anne's reign and the war began with a united Parliament and a national ministry, but Whigs and Tories were soon at odds about the conduct of the war. Marlborough in the field and the Treasurer, Godolphin, at home were identified with the Whigs, while the queen was very largely under the influence of Sarah, Marlborough's duchess. A new Parliament in 1705, after Blenheim, was predominantly Whig, and Tories disappeared from the ministry by degrees. In 1709 Marlborough's position was weakened by the losses at Malplaquet. Tories and Whigs were hotly opposed at home on ecclesiastical policy, the queen herself holding strongly with the High Church and Tory hostility to the dissenters, who, though unpopular in the country as Puritans, were favoured by the Whigs. A Tory lady-in-waiting ousted the duchess in the queen's good graces; in 1710 the Whig ministers gave place to Tories and the Whig majority to a Tory majority in the Commons.

Party Government. Next year Marlborough was recalled and disgraced, and it was a Tory government that negotiated the Treaty of Utrecht (1713). It is to be noted, that while the practice of forming ministries from one party—in other words, party government—was actually initiated under William III, it was under Anne that it became customary. though the queen still appointed and dismissed ministers as she chose without waiting for the verdict of a general election, the ensuing election regularly endorsed her action. It had not yet become a constitutional principle that the ministers should be chosen from the party predominating in the Commons.

The Tory party, however, was not united. Officially it was as completely committed to the Hanoverian succession as the Whigs, but it included a strong Jacobite element. Its most brilliant member, Henry St. John, Viscount Bolingbroke, was bent on snatching its leadership from its official chief, Robert Harley, Earl of Oxford. In the country, though Jacobitism excited little enthusiasm outside of Scotland, the Electress Sophia and her son George excited none at all ; their succession was merely an irritating necessity, to keep the stubbornly Roman Catholic Stuarts out. Sentiment was on one side, material security on the other. There were plenty of Whigs who were at pains secretly to stand well with the exiled house of Stuart : but open advocacy would be treason. In 1714, when it was obvious that Anne had not long to live, Bolingbroke succeeded in ousting his Tory rival Harley. But it was already too late. It was not Bolingbroke and the Tories, but the Whigs that effected the *coup d'état*. On the second day after Harley's dismissal they had captured control ; on the fourth Queen Anne was dead and George I—son of Sophia, who had died a few weeks previously—was proclaimed.

That was the end of the Tory party for fifty years. Bolingbroke fled to France. To be a Tory was to be suspected of Jacobitism. For fifty years all the Parliaments were Whig ; changes of goverment meant that one set of Whigs took the place of another set. The hereditary elector of Hanover, a prince of the empire, was king of Great Britain, and his possibly divergent interests in those two capacities had to be somehow harmonized ; in England he was a king on sufferance, who would lose his throne unregretted if he annoyed his subjects. The year after his accession there was an abortive Jacobite rising, known in Scotland as " the Fifteen," but Jacobite plots without effective armed support were of no avail ; such support was not forthcoming, because for twenty years the French government's interests required friendly relations with the British government. Still, the risk of a Jacobite movement developing could never be wholly ignored.

Sir Robert Walpole. Since George knew practically nothing of the country of which he was king, he had no choice but to put himself in the hands of the experienced politicians to whom he owed his throne. Government by Parliament with an acquiescent king was the only possible course. A great financial crisis, resulting from a mania for speculation which was not confined to England, brought Sir Robert Walpole to the head of the ministry in 1721 ; in that capacity he became, in effect, dictator, and his dictatorship continued even more markedly through the first twelve years of the reign of George II (1727–60). The development of the national wealth by commerce, the avoidance of all measures, however just or profitable in themselves, which might excite heated controversy at home, the removal of trade restrictions or a calculated laxity in enforcing them, the preservation of friendly relations with the European powers (especially France), the evasion of all complications which could drag England into participation in any wars which might arise between other powers, and the elaboration of a system of bribery and corruption which assured him of Parliamentary majorities and enabled him to exclude from the government any ministers who attempted to oppose him—these were the features of his eighteen years' domination of British policy. During those years Britain piled up material wealth, and remained at peace.

But in 1739 Walpole's domination was brought to an end, though he retained office for a time. War fever broke out in the country with a violence which the minister dared not defy, in spite of its unreason. The source of the trouble was the secular quarrel with Spain over trade with Spanish America—smuggling and buccaneering on one side, illegal official high-handedness on the other. In both countries, agitation and popular clamour overrode common sense, forced the hand of the governments, and drove them into a declaration of war ; and next year both the belligerents found themselves involved in the quite separate complications of the European imbroglio called " the War of the Austrian Succession " or " of the Pragmatic Sanction " (*see* Lesson 15 in Modern History, volume 3, page 536).

LESSON 17

Early Days of British Rule in America and India

(See plate 25)

IN the preceding Lesson we were concerned mainly with the constitutional developments during the reign of Queen Anne, the last ruler of the Stuart dynasty, and with the accession to the English throne of the house of Hanover. We must now revert to antecedent developments in east and west, since the outbreak of the war with Spain (1739) was the opening event of a war-period which resolved itself into a duel between France and Great Britain for supremacy in America and India.

During the reign of James I English adventurers had planted the first continuous English colony, Virginia, on the North American coast-line, in the region of the Chesapeake. In the same reign the first group of Puritans, the " Pilgrim Fathers," had made a small settlement farther north at New Plymouth. In the first ten years of Charles I, large bodies of emigrating Puritans established the rest of the group of colonies known collectively as New England, the largest being Massachusetts, with its government centre at Boston. Another Chesapeake colony, mainly for Roman Catholics, was planted in Maryland. Between the New England and the southern groups the Dutch planted a colony on the Hudson River. English colonists also partly occupied Newfoundland on the north and some West India islands (to all of which Spain asserted a claim) to the south. On the other hand, both French and Dutch were in occupation of West India islands, though the semi-piratical traders of all three tended to make common cause against the Spaniards. From the days of Elizabeth the Spanish colonists were anxious to prevent the English merchants' acquisition of wealth by trading with the Spanish-American dominions. Finally, the French had taken possession of Canada, the north bank of the St. Lawrence, up to the Great Lakes, while the occupation of the territory between the St. Lawrence and the New England colonies—called Acadie by the French and Nova Scotia by the British—was claimed by both.

During the Commonwealth the English seized Jamaica from the Spaniards ; and during the reign of Charles II they annexed the Dutch colony on the Hudson (New York), planted the Quaker colony of Pennsylvania west of it, which received its name from its founder, William Penn, and started the Carolinas between Virginia and Spanish Florida. But before Charles's death a French expedition from Canada explored the Ohio, which flows from near the Great Lakes to the Mississippi, and the Mississippi to its delta on the gulf of Mexico ; if the French had occupied that river-basin the English colonies would have been entirely cut off from expansion westward. Sooner or later a battle for its possession was bound to come. The treaty of Utrecht ignored this as yet unrealized problem, though it definitely yielded Acadie to Great Britain ; and it also conceded to Britain very limited trading rights, hitherto refused, with the South Seas—

in other words, with the Spanish-American ports. It was the divergent interpretation of these rights that produced the explosion which plunged Great Britain and Spain into war in 1739.

Menace of Piracy. Throughout all these years buccaneering had not stopped, but the position of buccaneers had ceased to be anomalous owing to the vigorous action of the government in the late 17th century. During the Anglo-French war, in 1689, English buccaneers in West Indian waters had aided their own countrymen, while French pirates—by courtesy, privateers—had received from France high positions afloat. After 1697 there was fresh prohibition of privateering. Bereft of West Indian bases, where they could land and riot, the buccaneers robbed ships of all nations. A prominent English pirate was Edward Teach, who even after the Treaty of Utrecht had been signed and an international effort made to clear the seas of freebooters and filibusters, continued to loot. He was killed in 1718, but not before the coasts of the West Indies, Carolina and Virginia were reduced to a state of terror. Piracy, however, continued throughout the long-drawn-out wars of the 18th century.

East India Company. From the west we turn to the east. There the English had not attempted to colonize, or such tentative efforts as they made were frustrated by the Dutch, who, with all the resources of the Dutch government at their backs, monopolized the rich Spice Islands or Eastern Archipelago. The English government, on the other hand, gave only a very limited and fluctuating support to the East India (trading) Company, which had to protect its own interests out of its own resources. It had, in consequence, learnt practically to limit its operations to India, where colonization in the proper sense was out of the question. The Mogul emperors, their viceroys, and some dependent, if rebellious, potentates were lords of the whole peninsula with great armies at their disposal. The Company had no army with which to challenge them, though its fleets controlled the sea. At the end of the 17th century the only land it held in free possession was the island of Bombay, a gift to king Charles from Portugal in 1661. Elsewhere it had been permitted to establish trading depots and offices called factories, and even to fortify them, at Madras and Fort William (Calcutta), for security against raiding. The Dutch had never established a firm footing, but the French had very recently entered the field as commercial competitors, and during the first twenty years of the 18th century established themselves on much the same footing as the English Company.

A different change of the greatest importance was, however, taking place. The aggressive policy of Aurangzib (1658–1707) extended the Mogul empire, but made it very unwieldy, and at the same time revived the historic hostility between Mahomedan and Hindu which had been modified under Akbar and his son and grandson. Under Aurangzib's successors the central authority of the Mogul at Delhi weakened ; India was, in fact, ruled by rival viceroys of the great provinces, who paid only lip-service to the sovereignty of the " Padishah," which in 1739 met a shattering blow at the hands of a Persian invader, Nadir Shah, whose army sacked Delhi.

We return now to Europe. The War of the Austrian Succession, which began in 1740, has been dealt with in Lesson 15 in our Modern History Course (volume 3, page 536), and we need not refer to it further except to mention the bloodily spectacular battles of Dettingen (1743) and Fontenoy (1745), in which the British defeated and were defeated by the French respectively.

The Forty-Five. During the course of the struggle, " Bonnie Prince Charlie " made his daring and romantic attempt to recover the crown for his father in 1745–6. Most of the Highland clans rallied to him, and with his small force he routed the government troops and advanced into England. The English Jacobites were slow to rise, however, and at Derby the Prince's advisers practically compelled him to turn back. From that moment the doom of the whole adventure was assured. Before six months were past the clans were crushed at Culloden, and steps were taken by the government to destroy the hereditary jurisdiction of the Highland chiefs and to make the union of England and Scotland more solid.

The War of the Austrian Succession came to an end in 1748 with the Peace of Aix-la-Chapelle. Britain gained neither territory nor prestige, for Louisburg on the St. Lawrence, captured by the British during the war, was given back to France at the peace in exchange for the French conquest of Madras. In the next fifteen years, however, the struggle between France and Britian was renewed and fought to a decisive finish.

LESSON 18

Peace and War Under George II

(See plate 26)

THE rival French and British companies in India had carefully avoided hostilities before 1744, when war was declared between France and England; the Companies'
servants had been merely traders residing under the protection
of the native imperial government of India. The British East
India Company held three posts—Madras, Bombay and Calcutta
—their whole territory consisting only of a few square miles,
for which rent was paid to native governments. The British
had no intention of departing from precedent, but in 1746 the
French commander Labourdonnais (governor of Mauritius), in
spite of opposition from the British fleet, landed in India, assembled an army and compelled the ungarrisoned Madras to capitu-
late, but made honourable terms of ransom for his prisoners.
Dupleix, the French governor of Pondicherry—a man of imagination and unscrupulous ambition, who had already formulated the
project of a European empire in India—jealous of Labourdonnais'
interference, hampered his movements and drove him to return
to France. In 1748 Dupleix repulsed the English, now supported
by the arrival of a fleet, in their attack on Pondicherry, but in the
same year the peace of Aix-la-Chapelle obliged him to surrender Madras. He did not, however, abandon his ambitious
schemes. Two native vice-regal thrones became vacant; two
rival Indian candidates claimed each; the French offered their
aid to one allied pair, the British to the other pair.

Clive and His Sepoys. The French had devised and by now the
British had copied the plan of training native regiments, "Sepoys,"
under European officers. Both had a few white soldiers supplemented by volunteers from the civilian servants of the Company.
One of these ex-civilians, Robert Clive, proved himself a born
leader and a soldier of genius. While the main armies were
fighting round Trichinopoly and the French candidates seemed on
the verge of certain victory, Clive, with a force of volunteers and
sepoys, five hundred all told, made a dash from Madras on Arcot,
the capital of the Carnatic (within which lay both Madras and
Pondicherry), and captured it. A vast force of the native

allies of France was detached from Trichinopoly to recover Arcot. Clive's little band held it for seven weeks, then the enemy determined to storm the fort, and advanced, driving before them elephants whose foreheads were armed with iron plates to serve as battering-rams against the gates. A stampede of these huge beasts occurred when the garrison opened fire, and many of the enemy were trampled to death. Subsequently, after three desperate attempts, and heavy loss of life, the besieging forces retired. The British had made a poor show hitherto ; now their prestige rose with Clive's above that of the French and Dupleix. The struggle ended temporarily in a draw. The French secured the throne of the Nizam of Hyderabad for their candidate, the British that of the Nawab of Arcot for theirs. The French, having no wish to go on fighting, recalled Dupleix.

During this period, in America, also, the French pursued an aggressive policy and evoked reprisals from the British ; the former planted forts on the Ohio, and in an attempt to expel them a British company of regular troops was cut to pieces, though technically France and Great Britain were not at war.

William Pitt. In Europe, however, war was brewing—the Seven Years' War (1756)—deliberate, aggressive and vindictive. Austrian policy was directed to the formation of an overwhelming coalition, including France, for the crushing of Prussia and Frederick the Great. England was drifting under a ministry, headed by Newcastle, which was incapable of framing a strong policy. Newcastle, realizing his incompetence to deal with the difficult war situation, resigned in 1756, and as Secretary of State, William Pitt (1708–78), subsequently Earl of Chatham, became practically Prime Minister. He at once took vigorous action for the prosecution of the war and, being a man of outstanding ability and character, inspired the country with confidence. He was, however, dismissed by George II the following year, owing to his support of Admiral Byng, who, having failed to save the island of Minorca from the French in 1756, had been falsely accused of cowardice at his trial and condemned to be shot. The public, though they had howled with indignation against Byng, were appeased by his sacrifice, and Pitt's popularity was undiminished. Now that the country was in danger the " Great Commoner," as he was termed, was loudly called for because he was known to be above bribery. Though styling himself a Whig, Pitt was utterly opposed to the Whig system, in which patronage was distributed to those bringing most votes to the government. With power derived from popular confidence and support, he opposed power based on Parliamentary connexion and influence, and was thus paving the way for the new Toryism of his son, William Pitt, the younger, who later smashed the combined power of the great Whig families. Pitt was soon recalled to take office in combination with Newcastle, and became virtual dictator. At the same time, though the news did not reach England till the next year, Clive in India won the battle of Plassey (1757), which in effect made Bengal a British province within the Mogul empire.

Meanwhile the Seven Years' War raged on the Continent. France, allied with the Austrian combination against Frederick, concentrated on the war in Europe instead of on the next conflict with Great Britain. These events have been summarized in Lesson 16 in Modern History (volume 3, page 540), together with the tragic episode of the Black Hole of Calcutta and the campaign under Clive leading up to the battle of Wandewash in 1760, where Colonel Eyre Coote gained a victory, Pondicherry surrendering to him in 1761. The peace of 1763 left the French without a military foothold and the British without a European rival in India.

The struggle in America (also dealt with in Lesson 16 in Modern History) followed a different course, but with a like result. The position of the French on the St. Lawrence was strategically strong, but in 1759 Wolfe, with the skilful cooperation of a squadron on the river, captured Quebec after scaling the Heights of Abraham undetected. He himself fell in the battle. Though not immediately conclusive, the fall of Quebec was actually decisive, and with the Peace of Paris Canada became a part of the British Empire.

In the same year, 1759, the British naval predominance was turned into an unqualified supremacy by Hawke's brilliant victory at Quiberon Bay, after which no substantial French squadron was again able to take the seas. In 1760, however, George II, who latterly had reposed entire confidence in Pitt, was succeeded by his grandson, George III. This young man of twenty-two meant to free himself from the personal domination of Pitt and also from the Parliamentary domination of the great Whig families. Pitt, when he found that he no longer had a free hand, resigned ; and it was under his successor at the head of the ministry, Lord Bute, who had been the young king's tutor, that the Peace of Paris was negotiated in 1763.

Revival of Religion. During the reign of George II, although, in general, intellect and common sense were more highly thought of than morality or religious aspiration, there was a revival of these last, mainly owing to the writings of Bishop Butler (author of the " Analogy," an argument in favour of Christianity against the deists) and to the powerful preaching of Wesley and White-field, with their strong appeal to the masses. Whitefield, a born orator, attracted enormous crowds ; his friend, John Wesley, organized Methodism. After being forbidden to preach in London churches (against his will he had left the Anglican community), Wesley followed Whitefield's example and proclaimed the truth, as fervently believed by him, to vast congregations in the open air at Bristol, Newcastle and other centres. Wesley had great social and political influence. This is clearly brought out by Maldwyn Edwards in " John Wesley and the Eighteenth Century," together with an exposition on " it is almost true to say that Wesley discovered the poor."

The poor were indeed with us in his day. There is a sad reverse of any ideas we may formulate of a jolly and gallant life in the mid-eighteenth century ; Hogarth painted it often, and particularly in his terrible " Gin Lane." In every town below the strata of wealthy society, prosperous merchants and respectable citizens, the poorer classes were sunk in degradation. At this time, also, smuggling was widely practised in England, and the coasts of Hampshire, Kent and Sussex were terrorized by the activities of gangs of contrabandists, well armed and utterly reckless.

In 1751 an Act of Parliament adjusted the calendar, which was previously to that date eleven days wrong. Many people thought they had been cheated of eleven days when these were dropped out of the almanac to make the reckoning agree with the Gregorian Calendar, already adopted throughout Europe. In 1755 the second Eddystone lighthouse was destroyed by fire (the first, erected in 1696–1700, had been washed away by a great storm), and the third, constructed in 1757–59, remained until 1879. It was noted for its strength and the engineering skill displayed in building it of blocks of oolite encased in granite, dovetailed into the solid rock, and each block fitted into the next one.

Our Course in British History is continued in Volume 6.

CHEMISTRY

Atomic Types and Structure

WHEN the elements are arranged in order of increasing atomic numbers and in periods which represent the periodicity of chemical properties, it is found that each period ends with an inert gas. (*See* table, Lesson 4, volume 1, page 160.) The peculiar chemical and physical stability of the atoms of these elements leads us to believe that the outer shell of electrons in them has a very stable structure. Thus, for example, it requires an electrical force of 25 volts to remove one electron, that is, to ionize helium ; while only 5 volts are necessary to ionize lithium. This view is supported by the fact that elements which immediately precede or follow the inert gases tend to attain their structures wherever possible. For example, sodium, which has one electron more than neon, readily loses it to form a stable sodium ion, Na^+ ; while chlorine, which lacks one electron to complete the argon structure, readily gains one to form the stable chloride ion, Cl^-. It appears, therefore, that the inert gases mark important transition-points in building up atomic structures.

From the table in volume 1, page 160, and from that in volume 4, page 224, it will be seen that the development of the second quantum group from lithium to neon takes place quite regularly, and is repeated in the development of the third quantum group from sodium to argon ; hence the marked chemical resemblances between analogous elements in these two short periods. The first two long periods, which come next, each contain 18 elements ; in addition to the building up of an outer electronic group of 8, the outer but one group in each case expands from 8 to 18, and it is a matter of some importance to determine where this expansion takes place. In both groups it has been shown to begin with the third element ; thus potassium has the structure (2) (8) (8) (1) and calcium (2) (8) (8) (2), while scandium is (2) (8) (9) (2). The building up of the third quantum group to 18 then continues more or less smoothly to copper (2) (8) (18) (1), after which the outer (fourth) group is progressively completed. These elements, shown in the periodic table (volume 1, page 160) enclosed in an oblong frame, are called transition elements, and show remarkable chemical and physical properties. They all possess variable valency, catalytic properties, and form coloured ions—that is, solutions of their salts are coloured pink, yellow, green, blue, etc. Also they all possess paramagnetic properties.

Each one of these chemical properties can be readily explained as arising from the expansion of the inner quantum group. It is known that the energy difference between an orbit in the first sub-group of the fourth quantum group and the last sub-group of the third quantum group is relatively small. A transition from one of these orbits to the other is therefore not very difficult to bring about, which accounts for the phenomenon of variable valency. Moreover, as we have seen, the absorption of a quantum of visible light does not entail a very considerable energy change, so that the colours of the ions of these elements, which arise from the absorption of visible light, are also doubtless due to the same cause. Paramagnetism arises from a slightly different cause ; it is due to the fact that in these variable structures the magnetic fields caused by the rotation of the electronic charges are not exactly balanced, as they are in the more stable structures, and the atoms tend to orient themselves in a certain way in the presence of a magnetic field.

After the second long period in the table comes a period containing 32 elements. Here two expansions of inner quantum groups take place, the fourth from 18 to 32, and the fifth from 8 to 18. As in the previous two periods, therefore, we again find a group of transition elements, this time 22, 13 of which—called the rare earths—are so alike in chemical properties as to be almost indistinguishable. All of these elements possess to a very marked degree the characteristic properties of transition elements.

The last period is incomplete, the elements after lead (82) showing progressive instability of the nucleus.

Types of Atoms. To sum up, we can say that the Bohr theory leads to the recognition of four types of atoms :

(1) Those with complete electronic groups, such as the inert gases, which are very stable and do not form chemical compounds.

(2) Those in which all but the highest quantum group are complete, as, for example, the elements of the first two short periods : these elements have a fixed number of valency electrons and form colourless ions.

(3) Those having the two outermost electronic groups incom-

plete ; these are the transition elements, possessing coloured ions, and exhibiting variable valency and paramagnetism.

(4) Those in which three outer groups are imperfect, show properties and characteristics of class (3) to an even more marked extent, and are very similar chemically.

The next question is: to what extent can the formation of chemical compounds be interpreted in terms of the electronic theory ?

Valency has been defined as the power which the atoms possess of combining with one other. We have seen in Lesson 3, volume 1 (page 152), that when atoms come together under the right conditions they form a valency link, rather as though they have been attached to each other by hooks. A brief glance at some of the commoner compounds reveals at once the great variety of ways in which this power of forming links can take effect. For example, in common salt—NaCl—we have a stable, crystalline compound which dissolves readily in water to give sodium and chlorine ions ; sugar, on the other hand, though stable, crystalline and soluble in water, does not ionize ; methane, CH_4, is a very stable gas, which is insoluble in water ; while ammonia, NH_3, which in many respects is like methane, reacts with hydrogen chloride to give a salt-like solid, ammonium chloride, which is ionized in water. In addition, there is another type of compound, discovered by the German chemist Werner and called a co-ordination compound, in which two apparently stable molecules unite to form a third, for example, $PtCl_4(NH_3)_6$.

In general it may be said that chemical evidence points to three types of hooks or linkage between atoms : ionizable links, sometimes called polar links, as in NaCl ; non-ionizable or non-polar links, as in most organic compounds ; and coordination links of Werner, which unite apparently saturated molecules. The first definite hypotheses to account for these various types of linkage in terms of the accepted electronic theory were put forward independently in 1916 by the German physicist Kossel and the American chemist, G. N. Lewis. Kossel investigated polar or ionizable linkage, and found that atoms which possessed most strongly the property of forming ions were, in general, one or two places removed from an inert gas. As has been mentioned, this is undoubtedly due to the tendency of these elements to attain to the inert gas structure, and when an electro-positive and an electro-negative element of this type come together, this can be mutually achieved by an actual transference of electrons from one to the other. Thus, in the case of sodium and chlorine, we have the structures

Na, (2) (8) (1) and Cl, (2) (8) (7) ;

the sodium gives its spare electron to the chlorine to form one polar or electrovalent link. If the element has two electrons too many, e.g. Ca, it forms a divalent link, that is, it hooks itself to another atom in two places, and so on. Kossel's theory explained very well the nature of the link between atoms which were essentially dissimilar in character. It could not, however, be applied to molecules formed by the union of two similar atoms, as, for example, in the diatomic elementary gases like oxygen, hydrogen, nitrogen, and compounds composed of two electronegative elements such as sulphur dioxide, carbon monoxide, and so on. The explanation of these types of valency was due to Lewis.

Lewis also assumed that in forming compounds in this way the atoms strive to attain a stable electronic configuration ; but whereas in the Kossel linkage one electron is considered to be transferred from one atom to the other, in the Lewis linkage two electrons are shared equally by both atoms, one coming from each. The formation of a chlorine molecule from two atoms may then be represented thus ; only the outer shell of 7 electrons is given, the electrons in each atom being written differently for convenience.

$$ {}^{\circ\circ}_{\circ\circ}\mathrm{Cl}^{\circ} + {}_{\times}\mathrm{Cl}{}^{\times}_{\times\times} \longrightarrow {}^{\circ\circ}_{\circ\circ}\mathrm{Cl}{}^{\circ}_{\times} \mathrm{Cl}{}^{\times}_{\times\times} $$

This type of linkage is known as the normal covalent link ; it is formed between similar atoms, each single link or valency being due to the sharing of two electrons, one from each atom. A dicovalent link results when four electrons are shared in this way. It must be remembered that this method of representing the electronic structures of atoms is purely diagrammatic, since no significance is given to the motion of the electrons.

It has been mentioned that only the electrons in the outer incomplete groups function as valency electrons. In general, therefore, since 8 electrons constitute a stable outer group, we should expect that the re-distribution of electrons in chemical combination would lead to the production of a valency group of 8. This is the basis of the old " octet " theory of valency, and, with some conspicuous exceptions, is obeyed by most atoms.

Coordinate Covalency. Yet another type of linkage can exist, called coordinate covalency, in which both shared electrons come from one atom. For example, hypochlorous acid (HClO) may be written in the electronic sense thus : H $\overset{\circ}{\times}$ $\overset{\circ\circ}{\underset{\circ\circ}{O}}$ $\overset{\bullet\bullet}{\underset{\bullet\bullet}{Cl}}$: The chlorine now has three pairs of unshared electrons which can function as coordinate covalencies with three oxygen atoms, each of which lacks two electrons from its complete octet : thus

$$\overset{\circ\circ}{\underset{\circ\circ}{O}} : \overset{\circ\circ}{\underset{\bullet\bullet}{Cl}} : \overset{\circ\circ}{\underset{\circ\circ}{O}}\overset{\circ}{\times}H$$

In coordinate covalent linkages the essentials are that one atom (the " donor ") has a lone pair of unshared electrons, and that the other (the " acceptor ") has room for two in its octet. Coordinate compounds are less stable than normal covalent ones, though they are quite common in organic chemistry.

The question as to how the electrons are shared is of some importance, and has, in fact, only recently been satisfactorily explained. It now appears that the combining power of atoms depends on the electrical forces set up by the electronic charges spinning on their own axes. If one electron spin is, as it were, left unneutralized in one atom, it tends to pair off with another unpaired electron in another atom. Both spins are then neutralized by the formation of a chemical linkage.

LESSON 36

Methods of Inorganic Analysis

So far in these Lessons we have been concerned mainly with the means by which substances are produced, the chemical properties of those substances, and the nature of the changes which occur when they react to form entirely new compounds. These questions all refer to what has been described as " chemical change " ; their solution enabled chemists to understand clearly many of the processes which are continually taking place in every-day life, and in some cases to improve or prevent them. For example, the enormous increase in the production of synthetic chemicals, such as sulphuric acid, nitrate fertilizers, and so on, is the direct result of the systematic study of the phenomenon of catalysis ; the investigations of oxidation and explosion reactions have led indirectly to rapid improvements in the internal combustion engine, while a chemical study of the rusting of iron has resulted not only in the development of methods of preventing rust, e.g. by galvanizing the metal with zinc, but also in the production of many new non-corrodible alloys, such as the rustless steels.

These aspects of chemistry are of extreme importance ; but there is another task to which the chemist must apply himself, which is of even greater fundamental importance, namely, the task of finding out what things are made of. This aspect—called Analytical Chemistry—enables him not only to replenish the stores of natural products which are rapidly disappearing, e.g. Chilean nitrate fertilizers, but also to build up or synthesize— once the simple bricks or radicals have been found—new substances with new properties.

Process of Chemical Analysis. Expressed briefly, the objects of chemical analysis are to identify the substances present in a mixture or compound and to determine the amounts in which they are present. For example, in the analysis of a silver coin, we might be required to identify the metals of which the coin is composed—in this case silver, with small quantities of copper— and also to estimate the amounts of silver and copper present. Chemical analysis may thus be divided into two branches— qualitative and quantitative.

In what follows, the student will be given an outline of the more important methods used. There is not sufficient space in these Lessons to describe the various pieces of apparatus which the analytical chemist is continually using, or the commoner operations, such as filtration, evaporation, distillation, crystallization, etc., which he performs more or less unconsciously in the course of his work. For full details of modern methods of analysis, the student should consult " Systematic Qualitative Analysis," by R. M. Caven, or " Analytical Chemistry " (2 vols.) by Treadwell and Hall.

Hints for Practical Work. In analytical work in the laboratory only small quantities need be used, both of the substance to be tested and also of the reagent, that is, the substance which is expected on addition to give the required characteristic test. In general, if the substance is in the liquid state, half an inch in a test-tube is enough. Moreover, in order that impurities may not be introduced, it is essential that test-tubes, beakers and other apparatus should be kept scrupulously clean, and that solutions should always be made up with distilled water. Where a precipitate is formed, careful notes should be made of the manner in which it appears, whether finely-divided, gelatinous, curdy and so on, and also of its colour, which is often a good guide to its composition. Where precipitates have to be filtered, it is essential that the last traces of soluble matter should be removed by repeated washing of the residue on the filter-paper with distilled water. Various other precautions which are necessary will be referred to at the points at which they occur.

The substances identified by inorganic analysis consist almost entirely of acids, bases and salts, and elements and compounds which yield these, when dissolved in water, acids or the alkalis. The methods of analysis, therefore, depend on the systematic detection of the bases and the acid radicals. In general, the substance or mixture for analysis will be in the solid state ; the method of treatment may then be divided into two sections : first, a preliminary examination by what are called " dry reactions," and, second, a systematic examination for the basic—or metallic—and the acidic radicals.

Examination by Dry Reactions. Note the colour and general appearance of the substance ; many salts, such as sodium chloride, copper sulphate, etc., are definitely crystalline, others, like calcium carbonate, appear to be without crystalline form ; oxides of the metals are also generally amorphous. Many metals have coloured ions and form characteristically coloured salts ; for example, copper (blue and green), nickel (green), cobalt (blue and pink), ferrous iron (green), ferric iron (red to brown), chromium (yellow to red), manganese (pink or buff-coloured). These metals all belong to the class called transition elements ; the compounds formed from most of the others, such as aluminium, barium, calcium, and so on, are generally white, though mercury, lead and a few other metals give some coloured compounds.

Having observed the colour, the next step is to heat a little of the solid in a dry tube, preferably a narrow, hard-glass ignition tube, and note what happens. The following conclusions may be drawn :

(1) *If it changes colour ;* to black (carbonization), organic matter ; to brown, cadmium carbonate or bismuthous oxide (Bi_2O_3) ; to yellow (while hot), zinc oxide or carbonate ; to yellowish-brown, stannic oxide (SnO_2).

(2) *If it sublimes ;* note colour and appearance of the sublimate, that is, the substance which condenses from the fumes. The sublimate may be white ammonium, mercury, antimony or arsenic salts ; metallic mirror or globules, mercury, arsenic ; yellow or reddish-golden globules of sulphur, sulphur or sulphide.

(3) *If it gives off a gas*, these conclusions may be drawn : water (excluding water of crystallization), oxy-acids, such as H_3BO_3, H_2SiO_3, H_3PO_4, etc., and basic hydroxides, with the exception of those of the alkali metals and barium ; oxygen, recognized by causing a glowing splint to inflame, chlorates, chromates, nitrates, peroxides and some oxides such as HgO and Pb_3O_4 ; carbon monoxide, colourless gas burning at the mouth of the tube with a hot, blue flame, oxalates ; carbon dioxide, turning lime-water milky, carbonates and bicarbonates ; nitrogen perox- ide, recognized by reddish-brown colour, nitrites and nitrates ; ammonia, forming white fumes with hydrochloric acid vapour, ammonium salts ; sulphur dioxide, recognized by smell and by the decolorization of potassium permanganate solution, sulphites and thiosulphates ; sulphuretted hydrogen, smell of rotten eggs and turns lead acetate paper black, sulphides ; chlorine, recognized by smell, yellowish-green colour, bleaches litmus paper and turns starch-potassium iodide paper bluish-black, hypochlorites and chlorides of some of the heavier metals, e.g. platinum, copper, manganese.

By carefully testing the gases evolved in the manner described, it is possible to obtain some information about the composition of the substance.

Flame Colorations. A number of metallic salts impart to a colourless Bunsen flame a characteristic colour by means of which the substance can be identified. It is necessary that the salts should be volatile, and since the chlorides are, in general, the most volatile compounds, the reaction is usually carried out by moistening a little of the solid with hydrochloric acid on a watch glass, dipping a platinum wire into it and holding the wire in the flame. The platinum wire must first be thoroughly cleansed by repeatedly dipping into pure hydrochloric acid and holding it in the flame until it no longer shows a reaction. The following is a list of the more characteristic flame colours : barium, light green ; boron, bright green ; calcium, red ; copper, blue or greenish blue . potassium, lilac ; sodium, golden-yellow ; strontium, crimson . tin, lead and arsenic, grey or bluish-grey.

Mere traces of these substances may be detected by means of that exceedingly ingenious instrument the spectrometer, which resolves the light into a number of characteristically coloured bands or lines. If several metals occur together, their flame colours may mask one another ; the vivid yellow of sodium in particular completely obscures the colours due to potassium and other metals. A simple method of eliminating the sodium colour, and so making the others apparent, is to view the flame through blue glass or a glass prism filled with indigo solution ; potassium then appears to be crimson and calcium light green.

Some other dry tests may be applied if time permits, as, for example, the colours of borax and phosphate beads, and the reduction of the substance on charcoal ; but, in general, they do not add much to the information already gained from the effect of heat and the flame coloration. The next step is to apply systematic tests for the basic and acidic radicals.

LESSON 37

Analysis by Acid and Alkali

SOME information having been gained from the dry reactions, the next step is to treat the dry substance with acids and alkalis and attempt to identify the volatile products, if any. In general, volatile acids or decomposition products of unstable acids are driven off by the addition to their salts of less volatile or more stable acids. The following reactions, therefore, apply mainly to the detection of acid radicals ; in fact, the only base which can be identified in this way is ammonium. The order of procedure is as follows :

(1) Addition of *dilute hydrochloric or dilute sulphuric acid*, poured gently on to the powdered substance in a test-tube : if no gases are evolved the tube should be gently warmed. Gases may be identified by the characteristic reactions that have been described ; the following inferences may then be made, if oxygen is evolved, peroxides or permanganates ; carbon dioxide,

carbonates or bi-carbonates; hydrogen sulphide, sulphides; hydrogen sulphide with precipitation of white sulphur, polysulphides; chlorine, hydrochlorites; sulphur dioxide, sulphites; sulphur dioxide with precipitation of finely divided yellow sulphur, thiosulphates; nitrogen peroxide, nitrites.

(2) Addition of a small amount of *concentrated sulphuric acid* and gentle warming : hydrogen chloride, colourless, acid, fuming gas, turning silver nitrate solution curdy, chlorides ; confirmed by the addition of manganese dioxide, chlorine being evolved ; hydrogen bromide, colourless fuming gas, together with bromine, reddish-brown vapour, bromides ; hydrogen iodide, together with iodine, violet vapour condensing to a black solid, iodides ; nitric acid vapour, coloured brown with nitrogen peroxide, nitrates ; confirmed by the addition of copper turnings, nitric oxide being evolved, which turns brown in the air ; carbon monoxide and dioxide without charring, oxalates ; with charring and traces of sulphur dioxide, tartrates and citrates ; acetic acid vapour, characteristic smell of vinegar, acetates ; confirmed by a fruity smell after the addition of alcohol.

(3) The addition of *caustic soda solution* and gentle warming : ammonia gas is freely evolved from ammonium salts.

Reactions in Solutions. The tests so far considered belong to the class of dry reactions. The final stage of the analysis depends on "wet reactions," that is, reactions made with solutions both of the reagent and the substance to be tested. Water is the solvent employed wherever possible, but if the substance is insoluble in water other solvents must be tried. Dilute hydrochloric acid, concentrated hydrochloric acid, nitric acid or aqua regia ($3HCl$ to $1HNO_3$), will usually dissolve solids which are insoluble in water, and should be tried in that order. Sometimes complications occur, as, for example, when hydrochloric acid is added to salts of the metals of group 1, or when a phosphate or oxalate is dissolved in hydrochloric acid, it is immediately reprecipitated on addition of ammonia. Special precautions, given later, are taken to obviate these difficulties.

If the substance does not dissolve in any of these solvents, it must be decomposed by fusion, either with a finely powdered mixture of about 6 times its weight of sodium and potassium carbonates (alkali fusion) or by simply boiling the solid with strong sodium carbonate solution. In both cases double decomposition takes place, the acid radical forming a sodium or potassium salt which is soluble in water and can be readily removed by filtration, and the metal forming a carbonate, which is insoluble in water, but which can be dissolved in most cases in dilute hydrochloric acid. In this way it is possible to separate the basic and acidic radicals in different solutions.

When the substance has finally been obtained in solution by one of the methods described, the systematic analysis for basic and acidic radicals is carried out by the addition of special reagents—called " group reagents "—which cause the precipitation of insoluble compounds. As a rule, the examination for the bases is done first ; if oxalates, tartrates or phosphates are present, however, they must be tested for before the metals, since many of the salts of these acids are immediately precipitated on addition of ammonia at group 3. Oxalates and tartrates may be destroyed by ignition before the substance is taken into solution ; the phosphate separation is more difficult, and will be described after the separation for group 3. By means of the group reagents it is possible to separate the metals into different groups and successively eliminate them in the form of precipitates. Each of these precipitates may then be examined in detail for the metals of that particular group. In the following summary the various groups are given, together with what are called the " confirmatory tests," which must be applied to establish the identity of the metal in each case. It is now assumed that the student is conversant with the characteristic reactions of the various compounds.

It is important to remember that, in spite of certain resemblances, the analytical groups are not intended to coincide with the groups of the periodic table.

Group 1. The metals are conveniently divided into five groups : silver, lead, and mercurous mercury form group 1 ; group reagent, dilute hydrochloric acid, which on addition to a solution of the salts of these metals gives a white precipitate in each case. (It is obvious, therefore, that salts of these metals, if insoluble in water, must be dissolved in nitric acid.) The precipitate is filtered and washed, the filtrate being reserved for analysis for the later groups. The separation and detection of the three metals, which may be present in the precipitate, are carried out by first boiling the precipitate with water and filtering while hot. Lead chloride is fairly soluble in hot water, and may be detected in the filtrate by the addition of potassium chromate solution, which gives a heavy yellow precipitate of lead chromate. The residue—containing silver and mercury—is mixed with ammonia, warmed and filtered. Silver chloride dissolves in ammonia, and may be confirmed by acidifying the filtrate with dilute nitric acid, when the white curdy precipitate of silver chloride re-forms. A black residue left after the addition of ammonia indicates mercury; as a confirmatory test this may be dissolved in boiling hydrochloric acid to which a crystal of potassium chlorate has been added, the solution diluted with water and stannous chloride solution added ; a white silky precipitate of mercurous chloride at once forms.

Group 2. Where no precipitate is formed on adding dilute hydrochloric acid, or the precipitate, if formed, has been filtered off, the next step is to test for group 2 by passing sulphuretted hydrogen through the clear solution. The following metals are precipitated as sulphides (notice the characteristic colours which are given in brackets) : mercuric mercury, HgS (reddish-brown, or more usually black) ; lead, PbS (black) ; bismuth, Bi_2S_3 (shiny black) ; copper, CuS (black) ; cadmium, CdS (bright yellow) ; arsenic, As_2S_3 (yellow) ; antimony, Sb_2S_3 (orange) ; stannous tin, SnS (dark brown) ; stannic tin, SnS_2 (yellow). The sulphides of the last three metals differ from the preceding ones in being soluble in alkaline ammonium sulphide solution ; group 2 can, therefore, be conveniently divided into two sub-groups, of which the B sub-group contains arsenic, antimony and tin.

It is important at this point to make sure that all the group 2 metals have been precipitated, since if any remain in solution they will cause confusion in the later groups. The best method of ensuring complete precipitation is to filter repeatedly a small amount of the solution and test the filtrate with sulphuretted hydrogen until no trace of precipitate forms.

The precipitated sulphides are then filtered and washed, and the filtrate reserved for group 3. In order to separate group 2B from 2A, the washed precipitate is heated with a little caustic soda and yellow ammonium sulphide solution ; it is then filtered and the filtrate reserved for analysis for the metals of group 2B.

The residue, which may contain mercuric mercury, lead, copper, bismuth and cadmium, is boiled with dilute nitric acid and a few drops of dilute sulphuric acid, and filtered. Mercuric sulphide and lead sulphate are insoluble and remain on the filter paper ;

they may be tested for by the methods described in group 1. The sulphides of the other metals (Bi, Cu, Cd) dissolve to form nitrates ; they may be identified in the filtrate by their reactions with ammonia. Bismuth is completely precipitated in the form of a white, flocculent hydroxide ; copper and cadmium hydroxides both dissolve in excess of ammonia to form stable complex compounds ; the copper-ammonia complex is a vivid blue colour, the cadmium one is colourless. The procedure then is to add ammonia to slight excess ; a white precipitate indicates bismuth ; filter ; if the filtrate is bright blue in colour, copper is present ; potassium cyanide is added until the blue colour is destroyed, and sulphuretted hydrogen passed into the solution. If cadmium is present, a yellow precipitate of cadmium sulphide is formed.

The filtrate containing the metals of group 2B is analysed in the following manner : dilute hydrochloric acid is first added to reprecipitate the sulphides, then a little concentrated acid, and the liquid boiled and filtered. Arsenic sulphide is insoluble and remains behind as a yellow residue, which, however, dissolves on warming with water to which a little solid ammonium carbonate has been added. Antimony and tin may be detected in the filtrate from the concentrated acid by the addition of a piece of iron wire. The hydrogen which is evolved reduces the antimony chloride to metallic antimony, which deposits in spongy black masses ; the tin is reduced to stannous chloride. If a few drops of mercuric chloride solution are now added, a silky white precipitate of mercurous chloride slowly forms.

LESSON 38

Analysis of the Iron Group

IRON, aluminium and chromium constitute group 3 in the analytical classification begun in the preceding Lesson. The filtrate from group 2 is boiled in order to drive off any dissolved hydrogen sulphide ; a little dilute nitric acid is added to oxidize any ferrous iron to the ferric state and then excess of ammonium chloride, followed by ammonia. The addition of ammonium chloride is of great importance, since, without this, zinc and magnesium, which it is desirable to keep back until the later groups, are precipitated as hydroxides.

Group 3. Group 3 metals are precipitated as gelatinous hydroxides, ferric hydroxide, $Fe(OH)_3$, being brick-red, aluminium, $Al(OH)_3$, colourless, and chromium, $Cr(OH)_3$, dark green. The precipitate is filtered and thoroughly washed with water, the filtrate being reserved for group 4. The residue is suspended in water to which a little solid sodium peroxide is added, and gently boiled until oxygen ceases to be evolved. Ferric hydroxide is not dissolved by the sodium hydroxide produced by the per-oxide, but remains behind as a reddish-brown residue. As a confirmatory test it may be filtered off, dissolved in warm hydrochloric acid ; the addition of potassium ferrocyanide to this solution gives a dark blue precipitate of Prussian Blue.

Both chromium and aluminium hydroxides dissolve in excess of sodium hydroxide, and may be identified by dividing the filtrate into two and applying the following tests : chromium, add excess of acetic acid and lead acetate solution, a yellow precipitate of lead chromate is formed ; aluminium, acidify the other portion with hydrochloric acid and add ammonia just to excess, when a white gelatinous precipitate of aluminium hydroxide forms.

Phosphates of many metals other than those of group 3 are insoluble in alkaline solution and are immediately precipitated when ammonia is added to the filtrate from group 2 ; if, therefore, a phosphate has been found in the solution prepared for the precipitation of group 3, it must be removed before a separation of these metals can be carried out. This is done by making use of the fact that, while the phosphates of the later groups are soluble in acetic acid, those of group 3 are not. If a phosphate is present, the precipitate formed by the addition of ammonia is just re-dissolved in very dilute hydrochloric acid ; the solution, which should now be as nearly neutral as possible, is diluted to about 30 c.c., a few drops of acetic acid and 1 to 2 c.c. of saturated ammonium acetate solution are added, followed drop by drop by a solution of ferric chloride previously made neutral by the addition of dilute hydrochloric acid or ammonia. At first a pale pink precipitate of ferric phosphate forms, but when all the phosphate has been precipitated, the next drop of ferric chloride turns the solution red (ferric acetate). The liquid is then boiled for about a minute and filtered ; the filtrate, which should be free from phosphate and iron, may now be examined for groups 4, 5 and 6 in the ordinary way. The residue should be examined for aluminium and chromium as before ; iron must be tested for in the original substance.

Group 4. To the filtrate from group 3 is added a fairly considerable excess of ammonium chloride followed by ammonia ; sulphuretted hydrogen is then passed through the solution until precipitation is complete. The following metals are thrown down as sulphides : nickel and cobalt (black), manganese (pink), zinc (dirty white). Wash thoroughly and filter, reserving the filtrate for group 5. Digest the residue with cold dilute hydrochloric acid and filter ; nickel and cobalt remain behind as a black residue, which may be dissolved by heating with concentrated hydrochloric acid and a crystal of potassium chlorate. Dilute this solution fairly considerably, add saturated sodium bicarbonate solution and a few drops of bromine water and warm ; cobalt forms a clear apple-green solution, which on warming merely deepens in colour ; if nickel is present the white precipitate formed with the bicarbonate does not dissolve, and on warming it rapidly darkens, finally turning black. To the filtrate from HCl add sodium hydroxide to moderate excess and boil ; a precipitate, slowly turning brown, indicates manganese. Filter and pass hydrogen sulphide through the filtrate ; a dirty white precipitate indicates zinc.

Group 5. The filtrate from group 4 is first boiled until free from hydrogen sulphide ; ammonium chloride is added to excess, then ammonia and ammonium carbonate. Calcium, strontium and barium are all precipitated as white, finely divided carbonates. The precipitate is filtered and washed and dissolved in a little warm, dilute acetic acid. Potassium chromate solution is then added, barium being precipitated as pale yellow barium chromate. This is filtered off and the filtrate divided into two portions : (1) calcium sulphate solution is added and the liquid boiled ; a small white precipitate indicates the presence of strontium ; (2) if strontium has been found present, the solution is boiled with dilute sulphuric acid, filtered, and ammonia in excess and ammonium oxalate added to the filtrate ; a white crystalline precipitate indicates calcium. The presence of the metals of this group may also be confirmed by the flame tests given in page 148.

Group 6. To the filtrate from group 4, add ammonium chloride, ammonia and ammonium phosphate ; a fine white precipitate indicates magnesium. Filter, evaporate the filtrate to dryness, dissolve the residue in water and divide into two : (1) add sodium hydrogen tartrate or tartaric acid and allow to stand for five minutes ; fine white precipitate appearing slowly indicates potassium ; (2) add potassium pyroantimonate solution, shake and allow to stand ; a white crystalline precipitate indicates sodium. Both of these metals may be further confirmed by applying the flame tests already referred to in page 148.

Examination for the Acid Radicals. The simplest method of obtaining information with respect to the acid radicals is that already described in the last Lesson, namely, to observe the gases liberated by the addition of dilute hydrochloric and concentrated sulphuric acids. The salts of some acids, however, are not decomposed in this way, e.g. borates, sulphates, phosphates and arsenates, and must be tested for in solution. Moreover, it is advisable, even where the gases evolved by acids leave little doubt as to the nature of the acid radical, to apply at least one confirmatory test in solution.

Two reagents will be found very useful in the detection of the acid radicals in solution, namely, silver nitrate and barium chloride. In the first case, the solution of the substance to be tested is acidified with dilute nitric acid and silver nitrate added to slight excess. If a white, curdy precipitate forms, the solution may contain a chloride, bromide, iodide, cyanide, oxalate or a salt of a few less important acids. Of these, the chloride, bromide and iodide only are insoluble in hot, concentrated nitric acid, while all but the iodide are soluble in ammonia, the bromide being only sparingly soluble. If no precipitate forms, the nitric acid present is neutralized with dilute ammonia added drop by drop. The following silver salts may be precipitated : phosphate and arsenite (yellow), arsenate (brown), chromate (brick-red).

To test for the acids with barium chloride, the solution is first acidified with dilute hydrochloric acid and barium chloride added. A white precipitate, insoluble in all acids, indicates the presence of a sulphate If no precipitate forms, ammonia is added until the solution is just alkaline ; the following barium salts may be precipitated and tested for : phosphate, arsenite, arsenate and borate, all of which are soluble in acetic acid ; oxalate and tartrate, soluble in excess of acetic acid, but the addition of calcium chloride precipitates the appropriate calcium salt.

Wherever possible, independent confirmatory tests should also be applied, as, for example, the brown ring test for nitrates (*see* Lesson 17, volume 2, page 135), the ammonium molybdate test for phosphates—a canary-yellow precipitate in nitric acid solution—and the copper sulphate test for arsenites and arsenates; the former gives a grass-green, the latter a pale-blue precipitate.

Quantitative Analysis. This portion of the subject is concerned with the determination of the amounts of the various components of a compound or mixture of compounds. It is divided into two sections—analysis by weight or *gravimetric analysis*, and analysis by volume or *volumetric analysis;* the latter always refers to volumes of solutions and not to the analysis of gaseous volumes, which is usually referred to as *gas analysis.*

Gravimetric analysis is carried out by converting the known constituents of the substance for analysis into insoluble forms or combinations which may be weighed exactly and of which the chemical composition is accurately known. The process will be illustrated by describing the method of estimation of sulphate or barium by means of the precipitation of barium sulphate.

About one gram of the substance for analysis (say, crude copper sulphate) is placed either on a watch-glass or in a weighing bottle and accurately weighed on a chemical balance. It is then dissolved in distilled water, boiled, a little ammonium chloride solution added to make the barium sulphate precipitate granular, and a boiling solution of barium chloride is added until precipitation is complete. The precipitate is then allowed to settle, is filtered, thoroughly washed until free from barium chloride (test with $AgNO_3$), and dried. When dry it is ignited on the filter-paper in a platinum or porcelain crucible, allowed to cool in a desiccator, that is, out of contact with atmospheric moisture, and weighed; this process of heating, cooling and weighing is repeated until the weight is constant. From the weight $BaSO_4$ it is possible to calculate the weight of SO_4, and hence the percentage composition of the original substance. The same method is used for the estimation of barium, in which case the solution of a pure sulphate is added to the barium salt for analysis.

This procedure can be applied wherever an insoluble stable compound can be produced. For example, silver and chloride can be estimated as silver chloride, phosphate as magnesium phosphate, many of the metals, such as Cu, Zn, Fe, Al, Cr, Ca, etc., as oxides after precipitation as hydroxides (by addition of ammonia) or as carbonates (by addition of sodium carbonate). For descriptions of the methods employed in each case, the student is referred to "Practical Chemistry," by Bruce and Harper.

LESSON 39

Methods of Volumetric Analysis

GRAVIMETRIC analysis depends on the weighing of the product of some particular reaction ; the methods are tedious and liable to various sources of error, such as loss of precipitate in drying, and so on. Volumetric operations, on the other hand, can be performed rapidly and accurately, and are to be preferred whenever they are available. In volumetric analysis the substance for estimation is dissolved in water, and a solution containing a known weight of the reagent, which causes the desired reaction, is added. The volume of the second solution is measured out carefully from an accurately graduated burette, the end-point of the reaction being made apparent by the addition of a sensitive indicator, such as litmus, methyl orange, etc., which undergoes a sharp change in colour with the merest trace of excess of the reagent. This process of adding a solution from a burette is known as " titration " ; the solution of the substance for analysis is usually placed in a conical flask, and can be shaken during titration without loss by splashing.

In comparing the masses of substances which react chemically, use is made of the principle of equivalent weights, described in Lesson 6 (volume 1, page 165). In the case of a compound, the equivalent weight is that weight which contains, will combine with or will displace one gram of hydrogen or the equivalent weight of another element or compound. It is obvious, therefore, that compounds will react in amounts which are proportional to their equivalent weights, since these weights are each equivalent to 1 gram of hydrogen. For example, in the neutralization of sodium carbonate by hydrochloric acid, the reaction for which is written :

$$Na_2CO_3 + 2HCl \rightarrow 2NaCl + H_2O + CO_2$$

106 parts by weight of carbonate are neutralized by 2×36.5 parts of HCl, or 53 parts by 36.5 parts of HCl. But 36.5 is the equivalent weight of HCl, since that amount contains 1 gram of replaceable hydrogen, and, similarly, 53 is the equivalent weight of Na_2CO_3, since in 106 grams 2 grams of hydrogen have been displaced by 2 sodium atoms.

VOLUMETRIC ANALYSIS

It is important to notice that the equivalent weight of a compound is not always obtained by reference to the number of hydrogen atoms which have been displaced in its formation ; as will be seen in the section on Oxidation Reactions, the value may vary according to the nature of the reaction considered.

Normal Solutions. In volumetric analysis solutions of known strength are used ; in the neutralization reaction mentioned above, 20 c.c. of a solution containing 53 grams of sodium carbonate per litre will be exactly neutralized by 20 c.c. of a solution containing 36·5 grams of hydrochloric acid per litre. Solutions like these, containing known amounts of a substance, are called standard solutions, and in order to simplify calculations as much as possible, the unit used in the preparation of standard solutions is the equivalent weight. A standard solution of this kind, containing the equivalent weight in grams per litre, is called a *normal solution*, written N ; if it contains $\frac{1}{2}$ of the equivalent weight, a *semi-normal solution* (N/2) ; if $\frac{1}{10}$, a *decinormal* (N/10).

The reactions made use of in volumetric analysis may be divided into three classes : (1) neutralization reactions, the study of which is called acidimetry and alkalimetry, (2) oxidation reactions, and (3) reactions involving the use of silver nitrate.

Acidimetry and Alkalimetry. These methods apply to all cases of the neutralization of an acid by an alkali and vice versa. We have seen that a normal solution of a monobasic acid, such as HCl or HNO_3, contains the molecular weight of the acid in grams per litre, a normal solution of a dibasic acid, such as H_2SO_4, $\frac{1}{2}$ of the molecular weight, and so on. Moreover, a normal solution of an alkali is equivolumetric with a normal solution of an acid ; in other words, 1 c.c. of a normal solution of any acid is equivalent to 1 c.c. of a normal solution of any alkali.

In preparing standard solutions of this kind it is sometimes possible to obtain substances in a sufficiently pure state to weigh out the exact amount required. In the majority of cases, however —as, for example, the inorganic acids—this cannot be done, and the solution is prepared by measuring out roughly the quantity of concentrated acid needed to give a solution of approximately the desired strength, and titrating this solution against some standard solution prepared by accurate weighing. Standard solutions of the acids are usually prepared by titration against an accurately made up solution of sodium carbonate. Pure anhydrous sodium bicarbonate is repeatedly heated in a platinum dish, cooled in a desiccator and weighed until its weight becomes constant. Exactly 26·5 grams of this pure carbonate are then dissolved in distilled water, and the solution made up to 500 c.c. in a graduated flask ; this gives a normal solution.

Indicators. The indicators usually employed in neutralization reactions are litmus, phenolphthalein and methyl orange ; the colours of these in different solutions are :

	acid	*alkali*
Litmus	red	blue
Phenolphthalein	colourless	pink
Methyl orange	pink	yellow

Only a few drops are necessary in each case. Both litmus and phenolphthalein are sensitive to carbon dioxide, which in solution reacts as a weak acid ; in titrating a substance which gives carbon dioxide, therefore—as, for example, a carbonate—methyl orange must be used, or, alternatively, if litmus is used, the solution must be boiled from time to time in order to drive off the carbon dioxide.

Standardization of Sulphuric Acid. 28 c.c. of concentrated acid (density 1·81 and therefore weight approximately 50 grams) are dissolved in water, added to a litre flask and the solution made up to the mark ; this gives an approximately normal solution. It is then poured into a burette which has previously been washed with water and rinsed with a few c.c. of the acid. 25 c.c. of N sodium carbonate are withdrawn by means of a pipette into a 250 c.c. conical flask, a few drops of methyl orange added, and the acid carefully run into the flask, which is shaken continually until the colour just changes to pink. When the end-point is approached it is advisable to add the carbonate solution drop by drop. Three independent titrations are carried out in this way, and the average value taken. If 20 c.c. of acid are required for 25 c.c. of N carbonate, the strength of the acid is 25/20 N, since 1 c.c. of N acid is equivalent to 1 c.c. of N carbonate.

Oxidation Reactions. Two classes of oxidizing agents are used in volumetric analysis, potassium permanganate and potassium dichromate, which under certain conditions liberate free oxygen, which is then available for oxidation purposes, and iodine, which oxidizes indirectly. In the case of permanganate, the following reaction takes place in acid solution :

$$2KMnO_4 + 3H_2SO_4 \rightarrow$$
$$[2 \times 158] \quad 2MnSO_4 + K_2SO_4 + 3H_2O + 5O \ [5 \times 16]$$

WHITE MOULDS. Growth of Mucor, a mould forest that appears on the surface of jam or cheese in a few hours when conditions are favourable.   BOTANY 30

Photomicrograph, John J. Ward

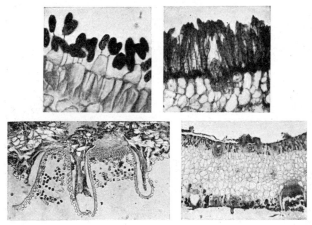

FUNGAL STRUCTURE.   Left to right : top, Basidium from mushroom gill, bearing stalked basidiospores ; Puccinia graminis or black rust, showing teleutospores. Bottom : Puccinia graminis, showing aecidiospores in cluster cups ; section of barberry leaf with pycnospore and aecidiospore clusters caused by rust.   Magnification 435, 103, 46 and 69 respectively.
BOTANY 31

Photomicrographs. H S Cheavin

BRACKET FUNGUS on bole of a tree, showing gills on undersurface of the fruit body. BOTANY 31

H. S. Cheavin

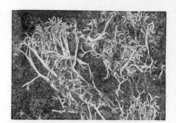

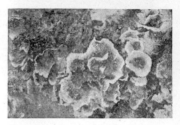

LICHENS. Two specimens of the compound plants known as lichens are seen here : Dog lichen (Peltigera canina) and (above) Reindeer moss (Cladonia rangiferina). BOTANY 32

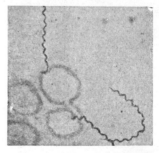

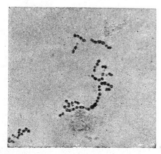

THREE KINDS OF BACTERIA. Top left, bacillus of anthrax, a rod-shaped organism ; the transparent points seen on the bacillus are spores ; × 1,000. Bottom left, streptococci, or rounded bacteria occurring in chains ; × 1,500. Above, spirochaete, a spiral-shaped micro-organism ; the round objects are red blood cells ; × 1,500 approx. BOTANY 32

Plate 18.

Volume V

CROMWELL IN DEATH. This vigorous death mask of the great Protector, first exhibited in 1928, has been handed down from the family of Cromwell's granddaughter.
BRITISH HISTORY 13

Courtesy of Messrs. Spink & Son

'BE GONE, YOU ROGUES!' Cromwell became virtual dictator after the coup d'état of 1653, when, backed by the army, he summarily dissolved the Long Parliament which had been sitting since 1640, and was, he declared, polluted by self-interest. In this satirical Dutch print of the time an inscription on the wall states that "This Hovse is to Lett." In the foreground the Protector points with his cane the way out to retiring members, and in the background Lenthall, the Speaker, is being forcibly removed from the chair. BRITISH HISTORY 13

British Museum

CHARLES II. Though popularly known as the "Merry Monarch" on account of his partiality for mistresses, Charles II (1630–85) was a consummate politician and for some years before his death enjoyed autocratic power. His sardonic features are cleverly reproduced in this bust by Honoré Pellé, dated 1684.
BRITISH HISTORY 14

Victoria & Albert Museum

RESTORATION OF CHARLES II. This animated print corroborates Samuel Pepys' well-known account of the enthusiastic scenes at Dover when, on May 26, 1660, King Charles II set foot on English soil after his long exile. "Infinite the crowd of people and the horsemen, citizens, and noblemen of all sorts. . . . He talked awhile with General Monk and others, and so into a stately coach there set for him. . . . The shouting and joy expressed by all is past imagination." BRITISH HISTORY 14

British Museum

Plate 20

Volume V

that is, 316 grams of permanganate liberate 80 grams of oxygen or 31·6 grams liberate 8 grams of oxygen. Since 8 grams of oxygen are equivalent to 1 gram of hydrogen, a normal solution of permanganate contains 31·6 grams per litre. Similarly, the equivalent weight of a substance standardized by means of an oxidizing reaction of this kind is the weight oxidized by 8 grams of oxygen. For example, in the oxidation of a ferrous salt,

$$2FeO + O \rightarrow Fe_2O_3$$

56 grams of ferrous iron are oxidized by 8 grams of oxygen, so that a normal solution of a ferrous salt, as determined by this reaction, contains 56 grams of ferrous iron. If the reaction had been a neutralization reaction, on the other hand, a normal solution would have contained $\frac{1}{2}$ of 56, i.e. 28 grams, since ferrous iron is divalent.

In permanganate titrations no indicator is necessary, the end-point being given by the change from the purple of the permanganate to the colourless manganous salt.

Reactions with Iodine Solution. The use of iodine depends on the reaction :

$$I_2 + 2Na_2S_2O_3 \rightarrow 2NaI + Na_2S_4O_6$$

so that the amount of free iodine present in a solution can be readily determined by titration against a standard solution of sodium thiosulphate. Since 2 gram molecules of thiosulphate react with 2 gram equivalents of iodine, a normal solution of thiosulphate will contain 1 gram molecule of the salt. The oxidizing action of iodine may be represented by the equation $I_2 + H_2O \rightarrow 2HI + O$, or, in other words, 127 grams of iodine liberate 8 grams of oxygen.

Titrations with thiosulphate may be used in any reactions which liberate or remove iodine. For example, if potassium iodide is added to a solution of bleaching powder or a hypochlorite, iodine is set free and may be estimated in this way. The method thus gives the amount of available chlorine in bleaching powder. In iodine titrations a few drops of starch paste are used as an indicator ; this gives an intense blue coloration with a trace of iodine.

Silver Nitrate Titrations. When silver nitrate is added to a chloride, a white curdy precipitate of silver chloride is formed. If a few drops of potassium chromate are present, when all the chloride has been precipitated, the next drop of silver nitrate forms a red precipitate of silver chromate. The latter is slightly more soluble than silver chloride, which is therefore precipitated first. Silver nitrate may be conveniently used to estimate the strengths of solutions of chlorides, bromides or iodides, potassium chromate being used as indicator in each case. Silver chromate, however, is soluble in acid solution, so that, if an acid such as HCl is present, the solution must first be neutralized with calcium carbonate.

In the case of sodium chloride, the reaction is

$$NaCl + AgNO_3 \rightarrow NaNO_3 + AgCl$$

Both sodium chloride and silver nitrate are salts of monobasic acids; their equivalent weights are therefore the same as their molecular weights. A normal solution of silver nitrate contains 170 grams per litre.

LESSON 40

Chemistry of the Organic Compounds

IT is mentioned in Lesson 20 (volume 2, page 151) that the old distinction between organic and inorganic chemistry had its origin in the belief that many of the carbon compounds found associated with living things could be produced only by the agency of vital organisms; these animal and vegetable products were, therefore, known as organic compounds, and for a long time it was thought impossible to prepare them artificially in the laboratory. This distinction between organic and inorganic compounds existed until 1828, when the great German chemist, Friedrich Wöhler, succeeded in preparing urea (an excretion of certain animal organisms) by synthesis from an inorganic salt called ammonium thiocyanate.

This rather startling discovery was soon followed by others of a similar kind, chiefly at the hands of the French chemist, Marcelin Berthelot, who is sometimes known as " the founder of synthetic chemistry." In about the middle of the 19th century Berthelot prepared synthetic acetylene by the direct combination of carbon and hydrogen, and then made alcohol, formic acid, fats and sugars, as well as many derivatives of each of these compounds. Within recent times great progress has been made in synthetic chemistry; in fact, it may now be said that not only can practically all vital products be made artificially, but also that the synthetic chemist is able to prepare a constantly increasing host of bodies, as, for example, valuable drugs, inducing sleep, relieving pain or destructive to micro-organisms, etc., which are closely allied to vital products, but which are entirely unknown in living or lifeless Nature. The name "organic chemistry," therefore, has no longer any real significance, and is now more or less loosely applied to the chemistry of the carbon compounds.

Composition of Organic Compounds. Compounds containing carbon occur in extraordinary abundance—in fact, more than three million are known. Moreover, in spite of their great number, they are closely related to one another, and show general properties which are quite different from those of compounds containing other elements. Many of these compounds are made up of two elements only—carbon and hydrogen—and are called hydrocarbons; some, such as the carbohydrates, sugar, starch, etc., contain oxygen also; others contain nitrogen as well as the other three elements, and others, again, contain sulphur, phosphorus, the halogens and a few other elements.

Because of the chemical resemblances which exist between organic compounds, their separation from a mixture, purification and analysis differ considerably from the methods used in the case of inorganic compounds. Separation from a mixture or from an inorganic substance may be effected either by dissolving the constituent compounds in a suitable solvent, such as alcohol, ether, chloroform or benzene, which does not generally dissolve inorganic salts, or by the process of fractional distillation. In the first case a separating funnel is used (Fig. 1) with solvents which do not mix, and the solutions divide in layers and can be run out separately; the second process, applicable to mixtures of liquids, depends on the fact that many mixtures containing two liquids of different boiling points boil at some intermediate temperature, the value of which depends on the amount of each substance present. The method is simply to distil the mixture and collect the distillate in fractions at intervals of 5° or 10°. Each of these portions is then re-fractionated, and in this way it is possible to separate the components in what is a practically pure condition, boiling at constant temperatures.

Fig. 1

Tests of the purity of organic compounds are usually made by observing the melting point (in the case of a solid) or the boiling point (in the case of a liquid). Pure substances have very definite melting and boiling points, and the presence of impurities not only makes the values indefinite, but also lowers the melting point and often raises the boiling point. Melting point determinations are carried out in the apparatus shown in Fig. 2.

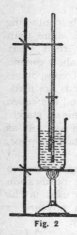

Fig. 2

A minute amount of the substance is placed in a capillary tube sealed at the bottom and attached to a thermometer. It is then immersed in a small beaker containing some high boiling liquid, such as concentrated sulphuric acid, which is vigorously stirred during the heating. The acid is heated very gently and the temperature at which the substance just melts observed.

Quantitative Analysis. Tests for purity are supplemented by an estimation of the quantities in which the various elements are present in the compound. Practically all organic compounds, when passed through red-hot copper oxide, are completely decomposed, the carbon being oxidized to carbon dioxide and the hydrogen to water. The method of estimating carbon and hydrogen, therefore, consists in oxidizing a known weight of the substance in this way, and collecting and weighing the products, which are carried through the furnace by means of a stream of pure, dry air or nitrogen. A typical furnace is shown (diagrammatically) in Fig. 3 ; water is absorbed in weighed calcium chloride tubes and carbon dioxide in potash bulbs.

If nitrogen is present it is estimated by the method of Dumas

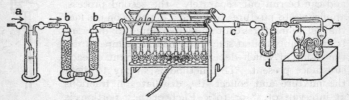

COMBUSTION OF ORGANIC COMPOUND BY MEANS OF CuO Fig. 3. a, wash-bottle containing caustic potash for removal of carbon dioxide ; **b,** drying towers containing pumice saturated with sulphuric acid ; **c,** hard-glass combustion tube in furnace ; **d,** weighed tube containing calcium chloride to collect water . **e,** weighed potash bulbs (or bulbs containing potash) to absorb carbon dioxide.

or of Kjeldahl. In the former the nitrogenous substance is ignited with copper oxide as before. The combined nitrogen is set free as nitrogen gas, and after absorption of the carbon dioxide in potash, its volume is measured in a specially graduated tube called a nitrometer. Kjeldahl's method, used very widely in agricultural laboratories, depends on the fact that when compounds containing nitrogen are completely decomposed by hot concentrated sulphuric acid, the nitrogen is converted into ammonium sulphate. An estimation of the ammonia present gives indirectly the amount of nitrogen present in the compound.

Chlorine, bromide and iodine are generally estimated by the method of Carius, in which the compound is oxidized by means of concentrated nitric acid in the presence of silver nitrate. The decomposition is carried out in a strong glass tube, about 40 cm. long, which is sealed up and heated to about 180° C. for some hours. When quite cold the silver halide is removed, and the amount of halogen present estimated.

Other elements, such as the metals, may be estimated by the methods used in inorganic determinations. From the quantitative estimation of the various elements present—that is, the percentage composition of the substance considered—it is possible to determine the simplest expression of the ratio of the atoms in a molecule ; this is termed the empirical formula of the compound. Its true molecular formula is then obtained by reference to its molecular weight, which is determined by one of the methods described in Lessons 7 and 9 (volume 1, pp. 169 and 177)—if the substance is a liquid, by measurement of the vapour density ; if a solid, by measurement of the lowering of freezing point or elevation of boiling point of some suitable solvent.

Structure of Organic Compounds. After the molecular formula of an organic compound has been established, there still remains the difficult task of determining the arrangement of the atoms within the molecule, i.e. the graphic or structural formula of the compound. Many cases exist where two or more entirely different organic compounds have the same molecular formula, as, for example, methyl formate and acetic acid ($C_2H_4O_2$), referred to in Lesson 4 (volume 1, page 156). Similarly, there are two compounds having the formula C_4H_{10}, three of the formula C_5H_{12}, at least six of the formula $C_3H_6O_2$, and so on. It is essential, therefore, that the arrangements of the atoms within the molecule should be determined, and this can be done indirectly from a consideration of the valencies of the elements in the compound, and also its chemical and physical properties. No compound is known containing one atom of carbon combined with more or less than four univalent elements or their valency equivalent; carbon, therefore, is always quadrivalent (see Lesson 4, volume 1, page 156), and the possible arrangements of its four valency bonds may be written graphically thus:

$$-C\equiv \quad , \quad =C= \quad , \quad =C\Big\langle \quad , \quad -\overset{|}{\underset{|}{C}}-$$

according as to whether it is attached to trivalent, divalent or univalent atoms. This may be illustrated by such compounds as

$$H-C\equiv N \quad ,$$

$$O=C=O \quad , \quad O=C\Big\langle \begin{matrix} Cl \\ \\ Cl \end{matrix} \quad , \quad H-\overset{\overset{\displaystyle H}{|}}{\underset{\underset{\displaystyle H}{|}}{C}}-H$$

Each of these forms of linkage reacts chemically in a particular manner, so that, from a consideration of the chemical reactions of the substance, it is possible to decide on the nature of the linkage. Similarly, divalent oxygen may be $=O$ or $-O-$,

trivalent nitrogen $\equiv N$ or $\rangle N-$, and so on.

As an example of the application of these principles to the determination of the structure of a compound, the cases of ethyl alcohol and dimethyl ether may be cited. Both of these compounds have the molecular formula C_2H_6O and, therefore, the possible structures

$$H-\overset{\overset{\displaystyle H}{|}}{\underset{\underset{\displaystyle H}{|}}{C}}-\overset{\overset{\displaystyle H}{|}}{\underset{\underset{\displaystyle H}{|}}{C}}-OH \quad \text{or} \quad H-\overset{\overset{\displaystyle H}{|}}{\underset{\underset{\displaystyle H}{|}}{C}}-O-\overset{\overset{\displaystyle H}{|}}{\underset{\underset{\displaystyle H}{|}}{C}}-H$$

$$(1) \qquad\qquad\qquad\qquad (2)$$

It is found that sodium metal reacts readily with ethyl alcohol to form a compound of the formula $NaOC_2H_5$, and that once one H atom has been replaced by sodium, the other five cannot be displaced, however much sodium is added. It must be concluded, therefore, that one H atom is attached differently from the other five, and since the property of displacement of hydrogen by sodium is common to the OH grouping, it is obvious that this group occurs in ethyl alcohol. These and other considerations led to the adoption of formula (1) for this substance. In dimethyl ether, on the other hand, all the six hydrogen atoms are equally difficult to remove, and from its chemical properties it was possible to decide that its molecule is graphically represented by formula (2).

Graphic or structural formulae are, therefore, of great importance in organic chemistry. It must be remembered, however, that these formulae are not true pictures of the arrangements of the atoms in the molecule ; they are merely projections in one plane, that is, two-dimensional diagrams. As the student will see later in this Course, there is every reason to believe that the atoms in a molecule are arranged in a space of three dimensions.

LESSON 41

Compounds of Carbon and Hydrogen

WE have seen in the preceding Lesson that in all its organic compounds carbon is quadrivalent, a fact which might have been anticipated from a knowledge of its electronic structure (*see* Lesson 35, page 141). The atomic number of carbon is 6 and therefore its electronic configuration is (2) (4) ; it thus has four valency electrons, which it can share with other atoms, forming four covalent links. One unique property of the carbon atom is that it is able to combine with other carbon atoms to an almost unlimited extent, and it is this tendency to combine with itself that leads to the formation of the almost endless number of carbon compounds. Many of these compounds are composed of carbon and hydrogen only ; they are called hydrocarbons and must not be confused with the carbohydrates, which, as will be seen later, contain oxygen as well. Hydrocarbons may be divided into three classes (1) the paraffins (2) the olefines and (3) the acetylenes, according as the molecule contains only single-bonded, one or more double-bonded or triple-bonded carbon atoms. The first class is usually known as the saturated, and the second and third classes as the unsaturated, hydrocarbons. There is still another group of hydrocarbons, the aromatic or benzene hydrocarbons, but these are structurally different and are classed in a separate category. In order to distinguish them from the aromatic hydrocarbons, the above mentioned three types are referred to collectively as the aliphatic or straight-chained hydrocarbons.

Saturated Hydrocarbons or Paraffins. The simplest compound of this class is methane or marsh gas, CH_4, which, as the name suggests, is frequently found bubbling out of the ground in marshes and other places where organic matter is decomposing under water. Methane is also found in coal-mines, and it is to mixtures of this gas—called fire-damp—and air that explosions in mines are due. Ordinary coal-gas contains about 40 per cent of methane. The gas can be prepared from the elements only with great difficulty—a temperature of at least 1200°C. is necessary—but it can be readily obtained in the laboratory by heating in a hard glass retort a mixture of anhydrous sodium or potassium acetate and caustic soda or soda-lime. The equation for this is written

$$CH_3COONa + NaOH \xrightarrow{} CH_4 + Na_2CO_3$$

Methane is a colourless, odourless gas which is practically insoluble in water and burns in air with a pale blue, non-luminous flame. It is very stable and can be passed through bromine or nitric or sulphuric acid without undergoing any change. When mixed with chlorine gas and exposed to direct sunlight, it explodes, carbon being deposited and hydrogen chloride formed. In diffused light the reaction is much less violent and a mixture of four compounds is produced, one atom of chlorine successively replacing each of the atoms of hydrogen. The names of these compounds are : CH_3Cl, methyl chloride ; CH_2Cl_2, methylene dichloride ; $CHCl_3$, chloroform ; CCl_4, carbon tetrachloride, and the amounts of each formed depend on the relative amounts of chlorine and methane present. Owing to the nature of their formation they are called " substitution products " of methane, mono-, di-, tri-, etc., according to the number of hydrogen atoms replaced by chlorine. This process of substitution brings out an important aspect of the structure of hydrocarbons of this type. Since this is the only way in which methane can react with another atom, it must be assumed that the carbon atom already has all its valency bonds satisfied with hydrogen atoms. This agrees with the formula, CH_4, written graphically

$$
\begin{array}{c}
H \\
| \\
H-C-H \\
| \\
H
\end{array}
$$

Such compounds, in which the maximum valencies of the carbon atoms are satisfied by single links, are said to be " saturated " ; their exceptional stability depends upon this fact.

The next simplest hydrocarbon of this type is ethane, C_2H_6, which also occurs in the gas which issues from the earth in the neighbourhood of petroleum deposits. It is prepared in the laboratory by the reduction of ethyl iodide with nascent hydrogen, produced by means of a zinc-copper couple and water. Ethane is a colourless, odourless gas which closely resembles methane and burns in air to produce carbon dioxide and water. Like methane it is a saturated compound and forms various substitution products with chlorine. Its formula is written

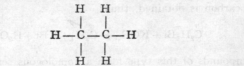

or shortly CH_3—CH_3, so that it really consists of two methyl radicals.

Methane and ethane are the first members of a long series of compounds which are very similar in constitution and therefore in chemical properties. The first four members are colourless gases, subsequent members are colourless liquids, whilst the highest members are white, wax-like solids. The first five members are :

Methane CH_4	Butane C_4H_{10}
Ethane C_2H_6	Pentane C_5H_{12}
Propane C_3H_8	

Each member differs from its predecessor by CH_2, while the general formula for the nth member is C_nH_{2n+2}. Such a series, in which the members are similar in constitution and therefore in chemical properties, is called a homologous series.

Petroleum and the Paraffins. It has been mentioned that methane and ethane occur in the regions of petroleum deposits. Petroleum consists almost entirely of hydrocarbons, undoubtedly

(169)

produced by the destructive distillation far below the earth's surface of the fatty remains of animals and of vegetable products. In many parts of the world, for example in Pennsylvania (U.S.A.) and south-east Russia, the natural gas which escapes from the oilfields is used as an industrial fuel. Petroleum oil is roughly separated into its constituent hydrocarbons by fractional distillation (*see* Lesson 40) ; the first fractions obtained in this way are colourless, mobile liquids, having boiling-points from 40° to 70° and 70° to 90° C. ; they are used in petrol engines and as solvents. The second fractions, boiling-points from 120° to 150° C., are used for cleansing purposes ; the third fraction, 150° to 300° C., called kerosene, is used as an illuminant, and the fractions boiling above 300° C. are used as lubricating oils and as vaseline. Paraffin wax is generally obtained by the destructive distillation of shale.

Olefine Series of Hydrocarbons. When the halogen mono-substitution products of the paraffins, such as ethyl bromide, are heated with an alcoholic solution of potash another type of hydrocarbon is obtained, thus :

$$C_2H_5Br + KOH \rightarrow C_2H_4\uparrow + KBr + H_2O$$

Compounds of this type form a homologous series, analogous to that of the paraffins but having the general formula C_nH_{2n} ; they are called the " olefines " (olefiant, oil-making ; Lat. *oleum*, oil) because the lightest members react with chlorine to form oily liquids. The simplest member of this series is ethylene, C_2H_4, which occurs to the extent of about 6 per cent in coal-gas. Besides the method given above for its preparation, ethylene can be readily prepared in the laboratory by the dehydration of ethyl alcohol by means of sulphuric or phosphoric acid. The equation may be written

$$C_2H_5OH \rightarrow C_2H_4\uparrow + H_2O$$

Ethylene is a colourless gas, with a sweet smell ; it burns with a luminous flame and forms a highly explosive mixture with air or oxygen. Unlike the paraffins, it combines directly with many elements and compounds, such as H_2, Cl_2, HBr, etc., to form saturated addition compounds. For example, when passed into bromine, it is rapidly absorbed, giving ethylene dibromide, $C_2H_4Br_2$, which is a colourless oil. As a result of its readiness to form addition compounds of this type (contrast the substitution

COMPOUNDS OF CARBON AND HYDROGEN

products of the paraffins) ethylene has been shown to have the constitution

$$\begin{array}{cc} H & H \\ \diagdown & \diagup \\ C = C \\ \diagup & \diagdown \\ H & H \end{array}$$

in which the two carbon atoms are linked by a double bond. The presence of the double bond enables the molecule to combine directly with univalent atoms or radicals ; it is therefore said to be unsaturated. When combination takes place, the double bond is broken and the atoms in the resulting saturated compound are then attached to one another by single valency links.

Acetylene Series. The third homologous series of hydrocarbons, having the general formula $C_nH_{2n} - _2$, contains a triple-bonded carbon atom. The simplest member, acetylene, C_2H_2, occurs in very small quantities in coal-gas and is prepared quantitatively by the action of water on calcium carbide, according to the equation

$$CaC_2 + 2H_2O \rightarrow C_2H_2 + Ca(OH)_2$$

Acetylene can also be prepared by causing an electric arc to pass between two carbon poles in an atmosphere of hydrogen. This method is important, since acetylene can be readily reduced to ethylene, which can be converted into ethyl alcohol. As ethyl alcohol forms the basis of the preparation of many organic substances, all of these may therefore be said to be produced synthetically from the elements carbon and hydrogen.

Acetylene is a colourless gas with a garlic-like smell ; it is highly inflammable and burns with a hot, smoky flame, due to the large percentage of carbon which it contains. With suitably constructed burners, however, its flame becomes dazzlingly white and it has had a wide use as an illuminant for this reason. When passed into an ammoniacal solution of cuprous chloride or silver nitrate, acetylene produces insoluble compounds called copper and silver acetylides, Cu_2C_2 (red), and Ag_2C_2 (white), which are violently explosive and detonate when rubbed or touched. Explosions in the pipes leading from acetylene generators have been attributed to the formation of the copper compound. Acetylene combines readily with hydrogen in the presence of finely divided nickel, giving first ethylene and finally ethane. Similarly it forms addition compounds with the halogens, sometimes with explosive violence, for example

$$C_2H_2 + 2Cl_2 \longrightarrow C_2H_2Cl_4$$
tetrachlorethane

From a consideration of these and other chemical properties, it has been proved that acetylene has the constitution H—C≡C—H, in which the carbon atoms are attached to each other by a triple bond. All the compounds of the acetylene series have a linkage of this kind and their chemical properties are therefore very similar.

LESSON 42

The Alcohols and their Derivatives

WHEN methyl chloride is prepared as described in the last Lesson by the reaction of a large excess of methane with chlorine, and is heated in a closed vessel with a dilute aqueous solution of potassium hydroxide, a colourless, mobile liquid, possessing a wine-like odour and a burning taste, is produced. This is called methyl alcohol, CH_3OH, the equation for its formation being written

$$CH_3Cl + KOH \longrightarrow KCl + CH_3OH$$

Methyl alcohol is the first member of an homologous series of hydroxide-like compounds, each of which can be prepared from the corresponding member of the analogous paraffin series in this way.

Methyl alcohol is prepared on a large scale by heating wood in iron retorts out of contact with the air ; water, methyl alcohol, acetic acid, tar and some volatile hydrocarbons condense in the receivers and are separated first by the addition of lime, which removes the acetic acid, and then by filtration through charcoal and fractional distillation. This partially purified methyl alcohol is usually known as wood spirit. Methyl alcohol burns with a pale blue non-luminous flame, producing carbon dioxide and water ; it dissolves many solid organic compounds and for this reason has an important commercial use as a solvent for dyes, gums, resins, varnishes, and so on. It is also used to render ethyl alcohol, employed for commercial purposes, unfit for drinking ; " methylated spirit " contains about 90 per cent of aqueous ethyl alcohol and about 10 per cent of partially purified wood spirit.

The chemical properties of methyl alcohol, and, in fact, of all the members of the alcohol series, are to some extent character-istic of the properties of the OH radical. Like water, it reacts vigorously with sodium or potassium metal, forming unstable, salt-like compounds called methoxides or methylates, thus :

$$2CH_3OH + 2Na \rightarrow 2CH_3ONa + H_2 \nearrow$$

Also, though neutral to litmus, in the presence of strong acids such as HCl, alcohols behave like weak bases, giving a class of compounds analogous to inorganic salts and called esters. Thus, with HCl, methyl chloride is formed

$$CH_3OH + HCl \rightarrow CH_3Cl + H_2O.$$

It has been mentioned that when vigorously oxidized by being burnt in air, methyl alcohol is completely decomposed into carbon dioxide and water. Less vigorous oxidation, as, for example, with nitric or chromic acid or potassium permanganate, results in the production of new products without the disruption of the molecule. If one atom of oxygen is added—that is, if two atoms of hydrogen are removed—the resulting product is formaldehyde, CH_2O ; if another oxygen atom is added, formic acid, CH_2O_2, is produced.

From a consideration of the valencies of the atoms in the molecule and also the chemical properties of methyl alcohol, it has been proved that its structure may be represented

by the formula

$$H-\overset{\displaystyle H}{\underset{\displaystyle H}{\overset{\displaystyle |}{\underset{\displaystyle |}{C}}}}-OH \; ;$$

this type of structure, in which one OH radical is attached to a carbon atom to which are also attached either hydrogen atoms or univalent radicals such as the methyl radical, CH_3, is common to all the alcohols of this series ; they are called the monohydric alcohols. If the C atom, to which the OH group is attached, has two H atoms, the alcohol is called a primary alcohol; if the C atom has only one H atom and 2 univalent radicals, the alcohol is called a secondary alcohol, and so on.

Ethyl Alcohol and Fermentation. The next member of the monohydric series is ethyl alcohol, C_2H_5OH, usually known merely as alcohol. Because of its method of preparation by fermentation, alcohol is sometimes called " spirits of wine." When grape-juice is kept for a short time under fairly warm conditions, the sugars, glucose and fructose, which it contains are decomposed into alcohol and carbon dioxide.

$$C_6H_{12}O_6 \rightarrow 2C_2H_6O + 2CO_2$$
$$\text{glucose} \qquad \text{alcohol}$$

This process is called alcoholic fermentation. It is brought about or " catalysed " (see Lesson 15, volume 2, page 127) by living vegetable organisms, present in the grapes, called ferments : the particular ferment active in this case is yeast or saccharomyces. It is not the yeast itself which causes the decomposition of the sugar, but substances called enzymes— zymase, maltase and invertase—which are present in it. During the process of fermentation, the yeast multiplies rapidly by growing buds on its rounded cells (gemmation) and forms a scum on the surface of the fermenting liquid. Enzymes are very complex nitrogenous substances, and since their catalytic properties appear to cease after they have been raised to higher temperatures, fermentation must be carried out between 5° and 30° C.

Beer. Spirits and Wine The chief source of beer is barley malt ; when the grain is moistened with water and exposed to the air it begins to germinate, producing during the process an enzyme called diastase. The grain in this state is called malt and consists mainly of starch, which is another carbohydrate having the same general formula as sugar. The germination is then stopped by raising the temperature to between 50° and 100° C., and the malt is stirred up with water and kept at about 60° C., when, as a result of the catalytic action of the diastase, the starch is converted into sugars resembling glucose. Hops, the flowers of the hop plant, are then added to give flavour, and yeast to start the alcoholic fermentation. Beer usually contains about 3–6 per cent of alcohol, small quantities of starch, sugars and colouring matter, as well as carbon dioxide produced during fermentation, to which it owes its refreshing qualities.

ALCOHOLS AND THEIR DERIVATIVES

Spirits are produced by the distillation of alcoholic liquors; whisky is obtained from barley-malt liquors, brandy from grape-juice, rum from fermented molasses. The amounts of alcohol (per cent by weight) present in these and other alcoholic beverages are given in the following table.

Brandy	..	60%	Port	20%	Claret	7%
Rum	60%	Sherry ..	16%	Burton ale ..	6%
Whisky ..	50%	Hock	9%	Beer	5%
Gin	40%	Bordeaux ..	8%	Lager	4%

Alcohol for industrial purposes is prepared on a large scale by the fermentation of potatoes, grain and other substances rich in starch or sugar. The diastatic fermentation is allowed to proceed as described above, and the liquor subjected to fractional distillation; the distillate containing 80 to 90 per cent of alcohol is called raw spirit and can be concentrated by further fractionation. The strength of a sample is usually estimated by measurement of specific gravity or density and reference to standard tables. The standard of reference for the strength of spirits is called " proof spirit," and contains 49·3 per cent by weight or 57·1 per cent by volume of alcohol; liquors containing more or less than this amount are said to be " over proof " or " under proof " respectively. Thus, 20 per cent under proof means that 100 volumes of this particular sample contains as much alcohol as 80 volumes of proof spirit.

Aldehydes. It has been mentioned that when methyl alcohol is gently oxidized a compound called formaldehyde, having the formula CH_2O, is first produced. This substance is usually prepared by passing a stream of air, saturated with alcohol vapour, through a tube containing a copper spiral or platinized asbestos heated to redness. The pungent-smelling liquid which collects in the receiver contains 30 per cent of formaldehyde with methyl alcohol and water. Formaldehyde is a gas at ordinary temperatures, but it polymerises slowly to form ultimately a white solid called paraformaldehyde. Aqueous solutions are strong-smelling and neutral to litmus. Owing to the readiness with which formaldehyde undergoes oxidation to formic acid, it is a strong reducing agent; if added to an ammoniacal solution of a silver salt, for example, it reduces the salt to metallic silver, which is deposited in the form of a shiny mirror.

Formaldehyde is a strong antiseptic; and as formalin, a solution of about 40% in water, it is widely used for this purpose.

One extremely interesting aspect of formaldehyde is that it has the same empirical formula, CH_2O, as the carbohydrates, namely, the sugars and the starches. It seems probable, therefore, that this substance, which is found in those plant cells which contain the green colouring matter called chlorophyll, is an intermediate compound in the synthesis of the carbohydrates from the carbon dioxide which the plant absorbs from the air.

Acetaldehyde, C_2H_4O, usually known merely as aldehyde, is the next member of the aldehyde series. It is prepared in a similar manner to formaldehyde by the oxidation of ethyl alcohol by means of a platinum catalyst or potassium dichromate and sulphuric acid. It is a colourless, volatile liquid of boiling point about 22° C. with a characteristic penetrating smell. Like formaldehyde it polymerises to form paraldehyde, is a strong reducing agent and is readily oxidized to acetic acid. It combines directly with sodium bisulphite to form a colourless, crystalline compound, and also with ammonia to form solid aldehyde ammonia.

Aldehydes are formed by the oxidation of the appropriate primary alcohol, two atoms of hydrogen being removed in each case, thus

$$C_2H_5OH - H_2 \rightarrow C_2H_4O$$

From a consideration of the properties of these compounds it was shown that one of the hydrogen atoms comes from the OH group; the constitution of acetaldehyde is therefore represented graphically thus, $H_3C-C\diagdown_{O}^{H}$ and it is to the univalent aldehyde-group—$C\diagdown_{O}^{H}$, which is common to all aldehydes, that the characteristic chemical properties of this class of compounds are due.

Acetone. When a secondary alcohol, such as iso-propyl alcohol, $CH_3 CH(OH) CH_3$, is oxidized, a substance called a ketone is formed. This reaction is analogous to that which takes place in the formation of aldehydes, and because of their structural similarity aldehydes and ketones have somewhat similar properties. Acetone is the most important ketone; it is prepared by the oxidation of iso-propyl alcohol with potassium dichromate and sulphuric acid, and has the formula

CH_3-C-CH_3. The divalent group $>C=O$
$\underset{O}{\overset{\|}{}}$

is common to all ketones. Like aldehyde, acetone combines with sodium bisulphite ; but it does not polymerise nor does it reduce silver solutions of silver salts to metallic silver. Moreover, it is oxidized only with difficulty, and when oxidized it decomposes into carbon dioxide and water. Acetone is prepared commercially by the dry distillation of calcium or barium acetate, thus

$$(CH_3COO)_2Ca \rightarrow CH_3COCH_3 + CaCO_3$$

It is a colourless, mobile liquid which, like alcohol, dissolves many organic compounds and is used in industry as a solvent for gums, varnishes, resins, etc. It is very inflammable and is used as a source of heat and light.

LESSON 43

Ether and the Fatty Acids

WE have seen that in some respects the alcohols resemble the hydroxides of the metals, for example, in reacting with an acid to form esters which are analogous to inorganic salts, thus :

$$CH_3OH + HCl \rightarrow CH_3Cl + H_2O$$

Univalent groups or radicals such as CH_3, C_2H_5, and so on, may therefore be looked upon as being somewhat analogous to the metals, and are referred to as " alkyl " groups. If these alkyl groups are so like metals as to form hydroxides, they might also be expected to form oxides. This is indeed the case, the term " ether " being the generic name used to refer to such organic oxides. The simplest of the ethers is methyl ether, sometimes called di-methyl ether, which is written $CH_3 \cdot O \cdot CH_3$, and is obtained when one molecule of water is removed from two molecules of methyl alcohol (CH_3OH). Similarly, ethyl ether

(177)

has the formula $C_2H_5 \cdot O \cdot C_2H_5$; methyl ethyl ether, $CH_3 \cdot O \cdot C_2H_5$, and so on ; the general formula of this type of compound being $R \cdot O \cdot R_1$, where R and R_1 may be the same or different alkyl groups.

Ethyl ether, usually called simply ether, or sometimes sulphuric ether because of its method of manufacture, is prepared by heating ethyl alcohol with concentrated sulphuric acid at about 140° C. In order to keep up a continuous stream of ether, which distils over and condenses in the receiver, alcohol is added to the distilling flask by means of a dropping funnel at about the same rate as the ether distils. The reaction proceeds in two stages, the first being the conversion of some of the alcohol into the ester, ethyl hydrogen sulphate, according to the equation

$$C_2H_5OH + H_2SO_4 \rightarrow C_2H_5HSO_4 + H_2O$$

This compound then reacts with excess of alcohol thus :

$$C_2H_5HSO_4 + C_2H_5OH \rightarrow C_2H_5 \cdot O \cdot C_2H_5 + H_2SO_4$$

Theoretically, therefore, a small amount of sulphuric acid should convert an unlimited quantity of alcohol into ether ; this is, however, not realized in practice, since the acid is constantly being diluted by the water formed in the first stage. This process of manufacturing ether by the dehydration of the corresponding alcohol by means of sulphuric acid can be applied quite generally ; it is known as the continuous etherification process. Ether may also be prepared by warming a mixture of sodium ethylate and ethyl iodide. The reaction, written

$$C_2H_5 \cdot O \cdot Na + I \cdot C_2H_5 \rightarrow NaI + C_2H_5 \cdot O \cdot C_2H_5$$

is of considerable theoretical importance, as it enabled the constitution of ether to be decided upon.

Properties of Ether. Like most of this series of compounds, ether is a colourless, mobile liquid which boils at about 35° C. The vapour which it gives off at this very low temperature is, like the liquid itself, extremely inflammable, so that there is considerable danger in handling ether near an unshielded flame. When inhaled, ether produces insensibility, and is used in large quantities as an anaesthetic in surgery. It dissolves resins, fats, oils, etc., and is employed very largely as a solvent in industrial chemistry. Unlike alcohol, it is comparatively unreactive ; it is not acted upon by sodium or potassium metals, and is quite stable to acids when cold.

The Fatty Acids. It has been mentioned that the complete oxidation (without decomposition) of methyl and ethyl alcohols leads to the formation of formic and acetic acids respectively. The relation of these two compounds to the paraffins, the alcohols and the aldehydes is shown in the following table :

Paraffins	Alcohols	Aldehydes	Acids
$H \cdot CH_3$	$H \cdot CH_2 \cdot OH$	$H \cdot CHO$	$H \cdot CO \cdot OH$
$CH_3 \cdot CH_3$	$CH_3 \cdot CH_2 \cdot OH$	$CH_3 \cdot CHO$	$CH_3 \cdot CO \cdot OH$

Formic and acetic acids are the first members of a homologous series of acids known as the fatty acids, because many of the higher members occur in the combined state in natural fats. Just as the grouping — CHO is common to the aldehydes, so the univalent group is common to all acids of this series and, in fact, is responsible for their characteristic properties ; it is called the carboxylic group.

Formic acid occurs in Nature in ants (*formicae*), from which it derives its name, and in nettles ; the irritation caused by the sting of the nettle is partly due to this acid. It can be obtained as a weak aqueous solution by macerating ants or nettles with water, and distilling the resulting mixture. Its preparation by the oxidation of methyl alcohol or formaldehyde under the catalytic influence of platinum black has been mentioned. Formic acid is a colourless, mobile liquid with a pungent smell like that of sulphur dioxide ; it behaves like a weak monobasic mineral acid, turning litmus red, and reacting with alkalis to form salts called formates, e.g. sodium formate, $H \cdot CO \cdot ONa$. Only one hydrogen atom, namely, that in the carboxylic group, is replaceable by the metal. When mixed with concentrated sulphuric acid, formic acid is rapidly decomposed into carbon monoxide and water, according to the equation $H \cdot CO \cdot OH \longrightarrow CO + H_2O$; the reaction, therefore, consists merely in the removal of the elements of water by the sulphuric acid.

Acetic acid ($CH_3 \cdot CO \cdot OH$) occurs in Nature combined with alcohols in the essences or volatile oils of many plants. It is obtained in large quantities as a by-product in the extraction of wood spirit (*see* Lesson 42, p. 172), by the destructive distillation of wood, and also by the oxidation of ethyl alcohol or acetaldehyde. When a weakly alcoholic liquor, such as wine or beer, is left exposed to the air for any length of time, it rapidly becomes sour owing to the formation of acetic acid. The reaction, which is written $C_2H_5OH + O_2 \rightarrow CH_3COOH + H_2O$, is really brought about by a ferment called *Mycoderma aceti*. As the ferment is killed by strong alcohol, the process takes place only in weakly alcoholic liquors ; the fermented solution, containing about 6 to 10 per cent of acetic acid, is called vinegar. Pure anhydrous acetic acid is obtained by distilling anhydrous sodium acetate with concentrated sulphuric acid ; it condenses into a colourless, crystalline solid, which is usually called glacial acetic acid to distinguish it from the hydrated liquid form. It has an acrid, penetrating smell and readily dissolves most organic compounds, and many inorganic substances, such as sulphur, iodine, etc. Like formic acid, it behaves as a monobasic acid, and reacts with hydroxides and carbonates to form stable, crystalline salts called acetates. These are soluble in water and are decomposed by mineral acids, with liberation of acetic acid. The presence of acetic acid, or an acetate, is readily shown by warming the substance for analysis with a few drops of alcohol and a little concentrated sulphuric acid. If an acetate is present, ethyl acetate, a volatile fruity-smelling ester, is evolved.

Higher Homologues of Acetic Acid. All the acids of this series resemble formic and acetic acids in methods of preparation, chemical properties, etc. They are all monobasic, the hydrogen atom of the carboxylic group being the only one replaceable by a univalent metal. Of the higher acids, three are of considerable importance because of the part they play in the composition of certain familiar natural products. They are butyric acid, which, in combination with glycerol, is an important component of butter, and palmitic and stearic acids, which, with a closely allied body, oleic acid, form part of all natural oils and fats.

Butyric acid, C_3H_7COOH, may be obtained from butyl alcohol, but it is most commonly known as a characteristic product of the fermentation of lactic acid with bad or fermented cheese. When, for example, milk is left exposed to the air, fermentation sets in, and the lactose, or milk sugar, is converted into lactic acid, which gives the milk its sour taste. If now a little bad cheese is added, and the liquid kept neutral by the addition of calcium carbonate, butyric fermentation starts. The mechanism of these processes was studied by the great French chemist, Louis Pasteur, who showed that each of the changes is due to a special ferment —in the first place, the lactic ferment and in the second, the butyric ferment. Pasteur also showed that the microbes causing the butyric fermentation multiply indefinitely without requiring the least amount of air. In fact, in the presence of the oxygen of the air they are immediately killed. This, briefly stated, is the historic discovery of the anaerobic microbes—those which cannot grow in the presence of free oxygen. It is interesting to note that when lactic acid is converted into butyric acid in this way, hydrogen is also produced, and occasionally, when butyric fermentation occurs in the stomach, the hydrogen can be lit on emerging from the mouth.

Palmitic ($C_{15}H_{31}COOH$) and stearic ($C_{17}H_{35}COOH$) acids occur in combination with glycerol in all vegetable and animal oils and fats, such as palm oil, and beef and mutton fats ; they are prepared on a large scale from these sources chiefly for the manufacture of stearin candles and of soaps.

Manufacture of Soap. When a fat or oil, which consists of the glycerin ester of a fatty acid, is decomposed by means of superheated steam, a process takes place which is called saponification and which is analogous to the hydrolysis of certain inorganic salts. Just as hydrolysis leads to the formation of a base and an acid, so saponification of a fat leads to the formation of glycerin and the fatty acid. This reaction proceeds much more rapidly if caustic soda be added, as the fatty acid is then converted into the sodium salt and removed as fast as it is formed. Such a sodium (or potassium) salt of these higher fatty acids is called a soap. In the manufacture of soaps the fats are boiled with caustic soda, and the soap floats to the surface and is allowed to set in moulds ; the very valuable glycerin may be recovered from the residue. If caustic potash is used, soft soap is obtained. As a rule, commercial soap contains a small amount of free alkali, which greatly adds to the cleansing properties. A certain amount of free sodium hydroxide is also formed by the process of hydrolysis which takes place to some extent when the soap is added to water. If the water is hard, that is, if it contains dissolved calcium and magnesium salts, the addition of soap causes the formation of insoluble calcium and magnesium salts of the fatty acid present in the soap, and these are precipitated as a curdy scum on the surface of the water. That is why it is difficult to produce a lather in hard water, a considerable amount of soap being wasted in the precipitation of the dissolved salts.

Our Course in Chemistry is continued in Volume 6.

Drawing Circles and Tangents

THE definitions of a circle, diameter, radius, tangent, etc., have been given in the " Terminology of Geometrical Drawing " (Lesson 22, vol. 4, page 229), but the following facts should also be known :

1. The circumference of a circle is nearly 3⅐ or, more accurately, 3·14159 times its diameter. Archimedes discovered that the ratio lies between 2²⁄₇ and 2²²⁄₇₁.

2. A straight line which bisects a chord of a circle at right angles passes through the centre of the circle.

3. The straight line which is drawn at right angles to the diameter of a circle, from its extremity, is a tangent.

4. The angle in a semicircle is a right angle.

1. To describe a circle passing through three given points, A, B, and C. Join AB and BC. Bisect each by the perpendiculars intersecting at D. With D as centre, and DA or DB or DC as radius, describe the circle required.

This problem shows how the centre of a circle may be found by assuming any three points in its circumference, how to describe a circle about a given triangle, and how to describe an arc equal to a given arc with the same radius.

2. To draw a tangent to a circle through a given point A in its circumference. Find the centre B and draw the radius BA,

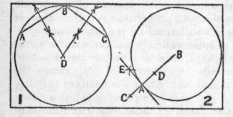

and produce it to C. Make AC equal to AD (any convenient distance). With centres C and D, and any radius, describe arcs intersecting at E. Draw AE, the required tangent.

3. To draw a tangent to a circle through a given point A without it. Find the centre B of the circle, draw BA, and bisect it in C. With C as centre, and CA as radius, describe

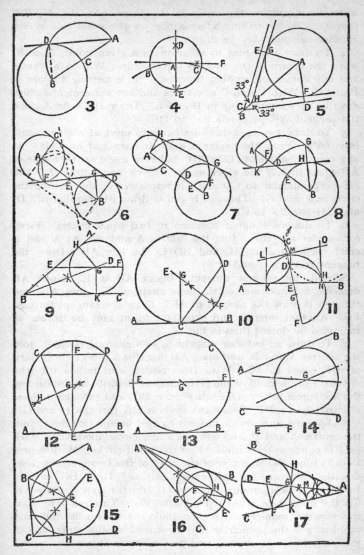

a semicircle, cutting the circle in D. Draw AD, the required tangent. By describing a semicircle on the other side of AB, another tangent may be drawn.

4. To draw a tangent to an arc from a given point, A, in it, when the centre of the circle is inaccessible. With A as centre and any convenient radius, describe a circle cutting the arc in B and C. With B and C as centres and any convenient radius, describe arcs intersecting in D and E. Draw DE. At A draw the tangent AF perpendicular to DE.

5. To draw two tangents to a circle to meet at a given angle (say, 66°). From the centre A draw any straight line AB. At any convenient point, C in AB, make an angle on each side of AB equal to *half* the given angle, 66°. From A draw AD and AE perpendicular to CD and CE respectively, and cutting the circle in F and G. Through F and G draw FH parallel to CD, and GH parallel to CE.

6. To draw a tangent common to two equal circles. First, for *exterior* tangent. Join the centres A and B. At A and B erect perpendiculars AC and BD to the line AB. Draw the tangent through C and D.

Second, for *interior* tangent. Bisect AB in E. Upon AE describe a semicircle, cutting one circle in F. Join AF, and through B draw BG parallel to AF. Draw the tangent through FG. Another interior and exterior tangent may be drawn, as indicated by dotted lines in Fig. 6.

7. To draw an exterior tangent to two unequal circles. Join the centres A and B, and upon AB describe a semicircle. Mark off DE equal to AC. With B as centre, and radius BE (the *difference* of the radii of the given circles), describe an arc cutting the semicircle in F. Through F draw BG, and through A draw AH parallel to BG. Draw the tangent HG through H and G.

8. To draw an interior tangent to two unequal circles. Join the centres A and B, and describe a semicircle upon AB. Mark off ED equal to the radius AF of the small circle. With centre B and radius BD (the *sum* of the radii of the two given circles), describe an arc to cut the semicircle in G. Draw BG, cutting the large circle's circumference in H, and through A draw AK (on the other side of AB) parallel to BG. Through HK draw the tangent required. Another could be drawn in this and problem 7 if the semicircle were described on the other side of the line joining the centres, and proceeding as above.

CIRCLES AND TANGENTS

9. To inscribe in a given angle, ABC, a circle of given radius (say, ·4 in.). Bisect the angle ABC by the line BD, and draw EF parallel to BC and ·4 in. from it, intersecting BD in G. With G as centre and radius ·4 in., describe the circle touching the sides of the angle in H and K. The points of contact are found by drawing from G, GK and GH perpendicular to BC and BA.

10. To describe a circle passing through a fixed point D, and touching a given straight line AB in a fixed point C. Join CD and bisect it by the perpendicular EF. Through C draw CG perpendicular to AB, and cutting EF in G. With G as centre, and radius GC, describe the required circle.

11. To describe a circle tangent to a given straight line AB and passing through two fixed points C and D without the line. Join CD, and produce the line to cut AB in E, and make EF equal to EC. Bisect DF in G, and draw a semicircle on DF with radius GF. At E erect a perpendicular to DF cutting the semicircle in H. Mark off EK from E on EA equal to EH. At K erect a perpendicular KL, and bisect CD in M by the perpendicular LM, which also cuts KL in L. With L as centre and radius LK draw the required circle. When AB is not parallel to CD, *two circles* can be drawn as shown.

12. To describe a circle tangent to a given straight line AB, and passing through two fixed points C and D, which are equidistant from the given line. Join CD and bisect the line in F by FE cutting AB in E. Join CE or DE, and bisect it by GH, cutting EF in G. With G as centre and radius GC describe the circle.

13. To draw a circle passing through a given point C, touching a given straight line AB, and having a given radius (say, ¾ in.). Draw a line EF parallel to AB and ¾ in. from it. With centre C and radius of ¾ in. intersect EF in G. With centre G and radius GC describe the circle.

14. To describe a circle of a given radius EF, to touch two converging lines AB and CD. At a distance equal to EF draw parallels to AB and CD intersecting at G, the centre required.

15. To describe a circle touching three given straight lines, AB, BC and CD, which make angles with each other. Bisect the angle DCB by the line CE, and the angle CBA by the line BF, intersecting CE in G. From G draw perpendiculars to the three given lines ; then either perpendicular is the radius of the required circle.

(185)

16. To describe a circle which shall touch two given converging lines AB and AC, and pass through a fixed point D between them. Bisect the angle BAC by the line AE. Join D with A. From any point F in AE draw FG perpendicular to AC, and describe a circle touching AB and AC, and cutting AD in H. Join FH, and through D draw DK parallel to HF, cutting AE in K, which is the centre of the required circle.

17. To describe two or more circles touching each other and two converging lines AB and AC. Bisect the angle BAC by the line AD. From any point E in AD draw a perpendicular to AC. With E as centre and EF as radius describe the circle touching AB and AC. Draw HK tangential to the circle. Make KL equal to KF, and at L erect a perpendicular to AC, cutting AD in M, the centre of the next circle.

LESSON 28

Hexagonal and Octagonal Prisms

THE hexagonal prism has a regular hexagon for each of its ends, and oblong for each of its other surfaces, but both shapes will, of course, vary infinitely *in appearance* according to the point of view from which they are seen. In Fig. 1 (which is the appearance of the prism when the student is directly opposite the end, but the object below the eye level), a system of construction lines (dotted) will be noticed—viz. AD, which is parallel to BC and EF; also BF and CE, *vertical* lines through B, F and C, E, respectively. If GH is bisected in K, it will be seen that there are *four equal parts* along AD—viz. AG, GK, KH, and HD. These, of course, will not appear equal when the object is placed in such positions as represented in Figs. 2–8.

A view, as shown in Fig. 2, is a good one from which to learn the method of drawing this object. Begin by determining the position of the corner C with relation to surrounding objects, then the direction of apparent slant of the edges BC and Cc and their respective apparent lengths. From B, C, and c draw vertical lines BF, CE, and ce, and determine the relative height of CE. Through E draw Ee converging with Cc, and EF with CB. Bisect CE in H, and BF in G. Through G and H draw AD converging with both CB and EF. Fix the position of K by drawing the diagonal BE. Make HD slightly—very slightly—longer than KH, and AG very slightly shorter than GK. The student should consider carefully why these are apparently different lengths.

Join AB, CD, DE, and FA, which will complete the apparent shape of the nearer end of the prism. Through D, E, and F draw lines converging with Cc. The line Ee intersecting with ce determines the height of ce. Through c draw dc converging *downwards* with DC, and through e draw de converging *upwards* with DE, and ef converging with EF, thus completing the drawing. The dotted lines at the farther end are put in to show the

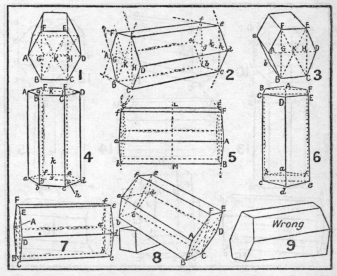

full construction, and that again we have an instance of the farther end being *apparently* slightly wider from a to d than from A to D at nearer end, but, of course (owing to the convergence of Ee with Cc), the length of ce is shorter than CE.

In Fig. 2 it should be observed that there are *four* directions of convergence: first, Cc, Dd, Ee, and Ff, converging to the right; second, CB, DA, EF, and ef, to the left; third, DC, FA, and dc, downwards to the left; and fourth, DE, BA, and de, upwards to the left. Compare Fig. 2 with 9, which is an incorrect drawing of the same view, showing the many usual errors made by beginners.

In Figs. 4 and 6 notice how BA, DE, and ab converge with one another ; also AF with DC and cd ; and CB with EF and cb. Fig. 5 shows the representation when the observer is directly opposite the dotted line LM and the object below the eye level. Notice the *three* sets of converging lines, and that AB is apparently smaller than AF, and FE much smaller still. In Fig. 3 observe the peculiar apparent shape of the face ABba. A view like that shown in Fig. 7 often gives considerable difficulty to beginners, owing to very great foreshortening of the visible end, but it is constructed just like Fig. 2. Fig. 8 is also rather difficult, because of the tilting

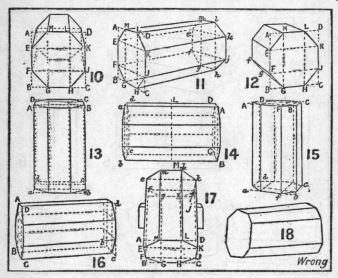

of the object. Notice that the corners E and F are not *vertically* above B and C respectively, and that the construction lines FB, EC, fb, and ec, converge *downwards*. There are also, as in Fig. 2, *four* directions of convergence.

The Octagonal Prism. This model has a regular octagon at each end, but oblongs for each of its other surfaces, and both shapes may have an infinite number of appearances from different points of view. Fig. 10 is an end view, and shows how the regular octagon may be enclosed in a square ABCD. Then, if the relative sizes of BG and GH are determined, the construction is easily made, for AE, AM, BF, BG, CH, CJ, DK, and DL are all equal in this view. Draw the construction lines as indicated.

Fig. 11 gives the usual system of guide lines. First, determine the position and distance apart of the vertical lines AB and CD, and obtain the apparent height of CD. Draw CB and DA converging at the correct angle towards the left, thus completing the *apparent shape* of the skeleton square ABCD. Then, by careful comparison, fix the positions of the points G, H, J, and K, and through each draw the respective construction lines, which at certain intersections give the positions of the corners of the octagon's *apparent shape*. Join these corners by the lines as shown. Fig. 11 should be compared with the *incorrect* drawing shown in Fig. 18, which contains many common errors.

There is no need to give detailed explanations of the other representations of the octagonal prism as shown in Figs. 12–17, as the drawings, with the dotted construction lines, speak for themselves as regards the method to be used in obtaining the various apparent shapes. The student must place the prism as indicated and draw *from the object*. Fig. 13 is the appearance when the student is opposite the front face, but the object below the eye level. Fig. 14 gives the representation when viewed from a point opposite the line LM. Fig. 15 shows how the drawing should be made when seen from a point practically opposite the edge Ff. Fig. 16 shows the drawing of the difficult view when the near end is much foreshortened, while in Fig. 17 the object is tilted upwards directly away from the observer.

LESSON 29

On the Drawing of Circular Objects

I N this Lesson we are concerned with the representation of circles or rings. First it should be clearly understood that although the rim of an object, e.g. of a cup, vase or wheel, may be the same thinness all round, it will not necessarily appear so to the observer.

Horizontal Positions. Figs. 1 and 2 indicate the construction when the ring is lying in a horizontal plane. The first difficulty is with regard to the *direction* of the major axis, and when determining this the student should not be misled by the apparent direction of the edges of surrounding objects, such as the edges of, say, a board, box, table, etc. Whatever the apparent direction of the latter may be, the major axis of the ring or wheel will always appear horizontal when the ring is lying in a horizontal plane. This may be verified by placing the ring on a flat table or board, so that the edges of the latter are receding in various directions, as in Figs. 7 and 8. Therefore, begin the construction by drawing a horizontal line AB for the major axis of the top outer ellipse, carefully observing how high or how low it should be with regard to neighbouring objects.

When the length of AB has been fixed, bisect the axis at C, and through C draw the minor axis DE at right angles to AB. Then determine the apparent length of this minor axis compared with AB, and through the four points, A, B, D, and E draw the curve of the ellipse, which represents the outer top edge of the ring. Now we come to the most important principle to be observed concerning this and similar objects—although the top inner edge is really parallel with the outer edge, it does not appear so. By careful observation of the model it will be seen that the ring appears considerably wider at AF and JB towards the ends of the major axis than it does at EG and DH, the ends of the minor axis.

It should be noted that the major axis of the inner ellipse does not quite coincide with that of the outer ellipse, but is very slightly above. The further top thickness, DH, is also apparently slightly less than the nearer top thickness EG. Then draw the inner ellipse through the four points F, G, J, and H. Now determine the apparent upright thickness EK, which is practically about the same as AF or JB, but theoretically a little larger, because EK is slightly nearer than AF or JB; the difference, however, is scarcely appreciable, unless the ring is very large. The lower outside edge, it must be remembered, is part of another ellipse vertically under the top outer one, which was drawn first. In Figs. 1 and 2 the construction shows the invisible portion by dotted lines. There is yet another curve, also part of an ellipse, the lower and inner edge, which is but little seen in Fig. 1, but better in Fig. 2.

Oblique Positions. Figs. 3 and 5 are representations of the ring in a leaning or slanting position. If the pencil is held so that it apparently passes through the two points C and D—the apparent intersections of the upper and lower inner edges—

the major axis appears to be in the same *direction*, but not exactly in the same *position*, for the major axis is practically midway between the point E on the farther side, and F on the nearer part of the outer edge. *This holds good when the ring is in any position whatever* (*see* Figs. 1 to 5). After the direction, position and length of the major axis are determined, the construction is the same in method as in Figs. 1 and 2. The major and minor axes are always at right angles to each other.

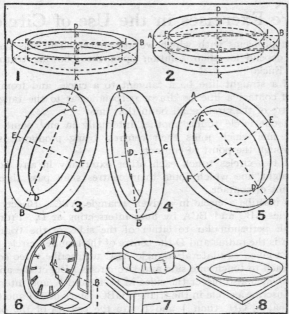

Vertical Position. Fig. 4 supposes the ring to be below the eye level, and standing in a vertical plane, as the wheels of a cart or carriage might be. It may be thought that the major axis must be upright since the ring is upright, but it is not necessarily so ; in fact, the axis can only appear vertical when the centre of the ring is exactly on a level with the eye of the observer.

The foregoing is applied in the drawing of the clock in Fig. 6, where an imaginary line through I and VII for the major axis of the dial is at right angles to AB, the axis of the clock, although the face is really in a vertical plane. The clock, for the purposes of this drawing, is assumed to be above the eye level. Particular attention should be given to the width of the rim of the front of the clock, Fig. 6, the hat brim in Fig. 7, and the rim of the plate in Fig. 8.

LESSON 30

More Exercises in the Use of Circles

THE problems with which we are concerned in this Lesson depend for their solution upon the following truths in Euclid :

(1) If a straight line be a tangent to a circle, and from the point of contact a line be drawn perpendicular to the tangent, the centre of the circle shall be in that line.

(2) If one circle touch another internally in any point, the straight line which joins their centres, being produced, shall pass through the point of contact.

(3) If two circles touch each other externally in any point, the straight line which joins their centres shall pass through that point of contact.

1. To inscribe a circle in a given triangle ABC. Bisect any two angles ABC and BCA by lines intersecting at D. From D draw DE perpendicular to either of the sides of the triangle, then DE is the radius and D the centre of the required circle.

2. In a given equilateral triangle ABC to inscribe three equal circles, each to touch one side and two circles. Bisect the angles by lines which also bisect the sides in D, E, and F, and intersect at G. Inscribe a circle in the triangle GBC. Mark off GJ and GK, each equal to GH, then J and K are the centres of the other circles.

3. In a given square ABCD to inscribe four equal circles, each to touch one side and two circles. Draw the diagonals and the diameters intersecting at E. Inscribe a circle in the triangle EBC. With centre E and radius EF mark off EG, EH, EJ, each equal to EF, then G, H, and J are the centres of the other circles.

4. In any given regular polygon (say, ABCDEF) to inscribe as many equal circles as the figure has sides, each circle touching

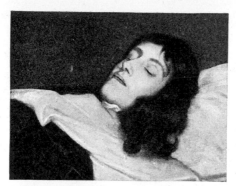

UNHAPPY MONMOUTH. This painting by Sir G. Kneller shows James Scott, duke of Monmouth (1649–85), after he had died on the scaffold for his ill-fated essay in rebellion. Monmouth was believed to have been the natural son of Charles II by Lucy Walters, and was regarded by a powerful faction as the champion of Protestantism. BRITISH HISTORY 15

National Portrait Gallery

JAMES II's FLIGHT TO FRANCE. This engraving by Romeyn de Hooghe depicts James II making his second, and successful, attempt to leave his kingdom to seek an asylum with Louis XIV BRITISH HISTORY 15

WILLIAM III AND MARY II. William III (1650–1702) had been Prince of Orange and Stadtholder of Holland for a number of years when in 1688 he was invited by the dissentients in Britain to deliver them from the misgovernment of his father-in-law, James II. Accepting the invitation, he landed at Brixham in Tor Bay, on November 5, 1688, as shown in the upper painting in Hampton Court Palace, and ruled as William III from 1689 to his death. On the right is his wife Mary (1662-94), daughter of James II and Anne Hyde, who became joint sovereign with her husband. BRITISH HISTORY 15

After Wissing, National Portrait Gallery; upper illustration, by permission of the Lord Chamberlain

ENGLAND'S FIRST 'PRIME MINISTER.' Thanks largely to the German origin and ways of the monarchs he served, Sir Robert Walpole (1676–1745) enjoyed an unprecedented degree of power as first minister of the Crown from 1721 to 1742. This picture of him conversing with Speaker Onslow in the House of Commons was painted by Hogarth and Sir James Thornhill. BRITISH HISTORY 16

QUEEN ANNE (1665–1714). Younger daughter of James II by his first wife, Anne Hyde, she succeeded her brother-in-law, William III, in 1702. Of her 17 children, William, duke of Gloucester seen in this portrait, by Michael Duhl, alone survived infancy.
BRITISH HISTORY 16
National Portrait Gallery

GEORGE I (1660–1727). Great-grandson of James I, he was proclaimed king on the death of Anne in 1714, as the nearest Protestant member of the royal house. He married a cousin, Sophia Dorothea, whom he divorced in 1694. Ignorant of English, he perforce became a "constitutional" sovereign.
BRITISH HISTORY 16
After Kneller, Guildhall, London

Plate 24

Volume V

one side and two circles. Divide the figure into equal triangles, and inscribe a circle in each, as shown.

5. To inscribe a circle in a given square ABCD. Draw the

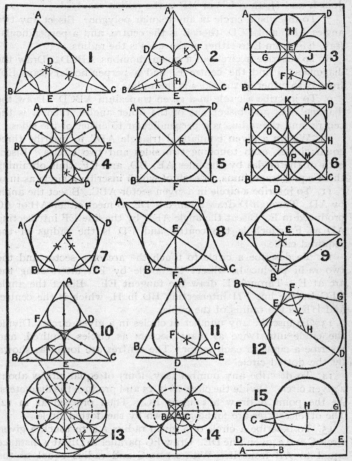

diagonals and diameters to find the centre E, and with radius EF describe the circle.

6. Within a given square ABCD to inscribe four equal circles,

each touching two sides and two circles. Draw diagonals and diameters as before. Join F, G, H, and K. The intersections L, M, N, O, with the diagonals, are the centres of the circles. Join L and M, then LP or MP is the radius required.

7. To inscribe a circle in any regular polygon. Bisect any two angles ABC and BCD, then E is the centre, and a perpendicular (say, EF) from E to either of the sides is the radius.

8. To inscribe a circle in a given rhombus ABCD. Draw the diagonals to find the centre E, and a perpendicular (say, EF) from E to either of the sides is the radius.

9. To inscribe a circle in a given trapezium ABCD. Draw the diagonal AC, and bisect one of the other angles, then E is the centre, and the radius is a perpendicular to either of the sides.

10. Within a given equilateral triangle ABC to inscribe three equal circles, each touching two sides and two circles. Bisect each of the angles by the lines AE, BD, and CF, thus obtaining three equal trapeziums, in each of which inscribe a circle as in 9.

11. To inscribe a circle in a given sector ABC. Bisect the angle by AD. Through D draw a tangent DE to meet either AB or AC produced in E. Bisect the angle AED by the line EF intersecting AD at F, which is the centre, and FD is the radius of the required circle.

12. To describe a circle to touch the arc of a sector and the two radii produced. Bisect the angle by BD intersecting the arc at E. Through E draw the tangent EF. Bisect the angle EFG by the line FH intersecting BD in H, which is the centre, and HE is the radius of the circle.

13. To inscribe any number of circles in a given circle. Divide the circle into twice as many sectors as circles required, and inscribe a circle in each sector. The centres are found as shown by the dotted circle.

14. To describe any number (say, four) of equal circles about a given circle. Divide the circle as in 13 and produce the diameters. At the point A draw a tangent BC. Then proceed as in 12. The other centres are found as shown by the dotted circle.

15. To describe a circle of a given radius AB to touch a given circle C and a given line DE. Draw FG parallel to DE at a distance equal to AB from it. With centre C and radius equal to the sum of the radius of circle C plus AB describe an arc cutting FG in H, which is the centre required.

This Lesson concludes our Course in Drawing and Design.

LESSON 13

Alcohol, Potatoes and Tobacco

BEER and wine are typically European commodities. Until dairying reached a reasonable organization, both in the number of milch cows and in the preparation and distribution of the liquid which they yielded, the poorer qualities of beer and wine were the alternatives to water as a drink; the prevalence of tea, coffee and cocoa as modern substitutes for beer and wine is in part due to the improvements in milk production. Potatoes and tobacco came to Europe from America, potatoes from the south and tobacco from the centre.

Beer is a manufacture, brewed from barley and hops; it provides the main reason for the growth of these crops. Barley was, probably, the chief cereal bread-plant of ancient times; it yields more prolifically than wheat, and can be grown in areas which are either too cold or too wet for wheat, or too dry for maize. Out of favour with the baker, barley is now grown to provide the brewer with malt; this is barley-grain that has been set to sprout, and commenced plant growth, which has then been stopped. The chief areas of production are the grass-lands in the U.S.A. and Canada on the middle-west prairies and the Russian steppes; yet Germany, Hungary, Rumania and Spain, and India and Japan, grow considerable quantities.

Hops are the female flowers of a climbing plant. The crop rapidly exhausts the soil, and cultivation tends to be confined to localities in which the soil is specially suitable and fertilizers can be obtained and used with success. The world's production is shared almost equally between three countries: Greater Germany, Britain, and the U.S.A. Within these countries the crop is localized, chiefly in Kent and Hereford, in Britain; and in Franconia, Bavaria, and Bohemia (now a protectorate) in Germany. It is a curious fact that the statistics show, if anything, an increase in the production of hops in the U.S.A. during the last decade, while the production of beer, formerly the largest in the world—even in excess of that of Germany—and the recorded consumption of beer have almost disappeared.

Beer and Wine in Commerce.   Ignoring the U.S.A., Germany produces most beer ; Britain three-quarters as much as Germany ; while the production in France and in Belgium is about a quarter and a half respectively that of Britain.   Consumption of beer is almost, in total quantity, in the same proportions as production ; but, per head of the population, consumption is different.   In Britain the peak years of consumption were about 1900 ; since then it has declined, and is now just about half as much per head.   In Germany a similar change has occurred, for throughout the period the German has, per head, consumed but 80 per cent of the Briton's consumption.   The greatest beer drinkers are the Belgians ; they consume twice as much as the

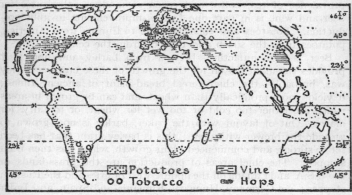

Germans.   In Denmark and Sweden present-day consumption is on the German level, and in France it is even less.   In Britain the decline in the consumption of beer has been accompanied by a 50 per cent increase in the per capita consumption of tea. In the U.S.A. per capita consumption of coffee has been doubled, cocoa has come into favour, and tea has declined.   The place names associated with beer are Dublin, Burton, Munich, Pilsen.

Wine as a commodity has two values : its local value for immediate use and its stored value as an article of commerce, a value which depends upon its vintage year.   Local wine is a common beverage in the countries of production.   In Britain wine is not a free commodity ; its importation has been affected by political considerations, for it is a source of revenue, and the British taste in wine has been formed at the dictates of national policy.

ALCOHOL, POTATOES AND TOBACCO

The statistical records aver that the consumption annually per head of the population in France is in the neighbourhood of 140 gallons; in Italy it is about 120 gallons; in Spain, Portugal and Switzerland, about 70 gallons; and in Austria and Hungary, about 20 gallons. Nowhere else is wine consumed in quantities of commercial magnitude. In these countries the consumption accounts for the bulk of the wine produced, except in Hungary, where a surplus is exported, and in Switzerland, where a deficit is made good by imports. On this commercial scale Empire wines from South Australia and South Africa are of little moment.

The production of wine depends upon the grape vine. The fruits require a long summer; the roots can penetrate deep into the soil, so that aridity during the summer is not of too serious import. High quality wine is a manufactured product which requires considerable skill and valuable machinery on the one hand, and suitable soil and climatic conditions on the other; hence it is highly localized, and its varieties—port, claret, champagne, etc.—indicate this localization.

Production of Tobacco. Tobacco is produced mainly in the tobacco belt of the eastern U.S.A. If the production there be taken as 100, that of India—of a very different quality—is 85; Russia comes next, 33; then Brazil 12. In Central America, Cuba has 4; Mexico, Guatemala, San Domingo, and Puerto Rico have less; in Mediterranean lands, Greece, 10, Italy and Turkey, 7, Bulgaria and Rumania 4; in the East, Japan, 9, Korea, 3, the Philippines, 6, Java, 4, are minor producers. The total production in British Africa roughly equals that of Java.

Commercial tobacco, manufactured into cigarettes, pipe tobacco, and cigars, is based upon the cured leaves of the Nicotiana group of plants, which can be grown almost everywhere provided the summer is warm enough. Its use is due to its stimulating and narcotic qualities. In Britain tobacco is a source of revenue; its cultivation was formerly forbidden in the interests of Virginia. The plant is susceptible to white frosts and dislikes standing water about its roots; these facts govern its commercial cultivation. The chief importers of tobacco are Germany and Britain; the chief consumers per capita are Belgium, Germany, and the U.S.A.

Potato Growing. The potato is a prolific food crop; its multiplication occurs below the ground, and it is thus suitable for growth in the cool, humid climates where the ground preserves its heat later than the atmosphere. It can be grown within the Arctic Circle, although there the tubers are small in size. Historically, it is probably an error to assert that the potato was introduced into England by Raleigh from Virginia.

The chief potato growers are Germany and European Russia, in almost equal quantities; each produces 12 times as much as Britain. Next comes Poland, with ten times as much as Britain. Then come France and the U.S.A., 50 to 75 per cent more than Britain. Eire produces about a third of the British crop. Holland, Belgium and Spain each produce about half as much as Britain, and Japan rather more than either. Sweden, Austria, Hungary, Rumania and Canada each produce rather less than the quantity grown in Ireland.

In the following countries production roughly equals consumption: Germany, Russia, France, the U.S.A., Belgium, Spain, Sweden, Austria, Hungary, Rumania and Canada. Britain alone, apparently, buys abroad in any quantity, and the consumption almost equals production. This rough analysis, based on the tabulated statistics, indicates that potatoes do not enter largely into the foreign trade of any country. The Channel Islands crop of early potatoes is included in that of Britain.

LESSON 14

The Three Chief Textiles

THE museum of history preserves the story of the early production of textiles from animal fibres. The story runs, in the broad way, by three stages : first, the development of the habit of preferring wool or the fibres of the sheep to all others for general purposes ; second, the growth of large-scale pastoral farming for sheep ; third, a growing distaste for wool as a fibre of commercial importance. In this story woollens came to represent wealth in the England of Edward III, and thus also the West Riding and the Australia of the last century were great because of wool.

The passing pageant of geography, momentarily stopped for inspection on the map in page 199, depicts the beginnings of decay. Sheep require vast open spaces with a climate of a suitable range ; these spaces are relatively poor, for they lack people and also machines ; transport of raw wool from the sheep to the loom is the fundamental cost ; wool must be cleaned, for it is greasy ; its quality cannot be controlled, for Man governs neither breeds nor weather ; as populations increase wool tends to become an expensive luxury. Wool is produced, out of a total of seven parts, one part in Europe as a whole, one part in the U.S.A., one part in Argentina and Uruguay, one part in the Union of South Africa, and three in Australia and New Zealand.

The production of wool on a commercial scale depends also for its success upon the salable qualities of the mutton from the

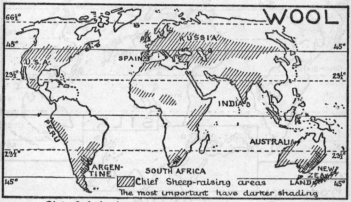

Chief Wool-producing Countries

sheep. Woollens are produced near the coalfields of Europe and North America. The signs of the decadence of the woollen industry are the facts that production depends upon refrigeration of meat for its profits, surpluses of raw wool accumulate, the modern desire for change and variety which disdains the durability of woollens, the newer knowledge that comfort in clothes does not depend on the fibre used but upon the " weave " and the style and number of the skin-coverings.

Wool comes from the temperate grass-lands ; the vegetable fibre, cotton, is produced on the sub-tropical grass-lands, where the white man controls cheap coloured labour. In history the cotton-belt of the U.S.A. stand out as the chief producer, and the story is enwrapt in politics, for the emancipation of the slaves and the problem of the coloured man in the U.S.A., British activities in Egypt and India, and the growth of the British Empire ultimately hang on the demand for raw cotton from the plantations in these lands. Cotton can be produced in other areas of similar character—minor areas are Brazil, China, Asiatic Russia, and the Sudan—and vigorous efforts have been made to

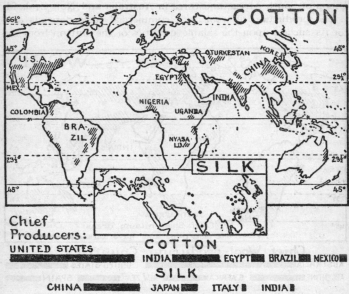

Chief Producers:

COTTON

UNITED STATES ████████ INDIA ████████ EGYPT ███ BRAZIL ██ MEXICO █

SILK

CHINA ████████ JAPAN ███ ITALY █ INDIA █

break the U.S.A. monopoly of production; but the efforts tend to be futile, for expansion of production avails little on a dwindling market.

Cotton. The production of cotton is controlled by transport charges; it is subject to the accidents of weather and to attacks of parasitic plant diseases, and moreover, is influenced by the selling power of the manufactured product. South-east Lancashire has dominated cotton commercially and politically; it used to be claimed that the peculiar climate and the hereditary skill of the workers were the factors which sent Lancashire cottons into all the markets of the world. These are matters of history; the present geographical facts suggest, however, that

Lancashire enjoyed a monopoly which the mere passage of time and the mere accretions to human numbers were bound to destroy. The dominant factor at the moment appears to be the skill of the producer to make cottons which he can sell in sufficient quantity. Cotton mills in the U.S.A., in Germany, in India and in Japan compete in an attempt to satisfy a demand for cotton goods which are suitable to their immediate ends, and the durability of the fabric is one of the least important of these ends. Standards of quality are changing ; clothes are not intended to remain in use when they show signs of wear ; their expectation of life is much shorter.

The production of cottons is associated with the chemical industry, for bleaching and calico-printing and the use of synthetic dyes are all related to the salability of the goods. It is also associated with the production of machinery and the power to run the looms. Cottons must be cheap ; the wages of cotton operatives tend to be low, and will only reach a high level when the number of operatives is reduced (or their weekly hours of labour are curtailed), because the yield per hour per human unit has been greatly increased. The consumption of cotton is shared between the U.S.A., six parts ; Britain and Japan, two parts each ; and France, Germany and Italy, roughly, one part each.

Silk. Coming now to silk, so long as the silk fibre was the product of the silkworm the production of raw silk was localized in the Mediterranean and monsoon lands, where mulberries flourished. China, India, Italy, France, and Switzerland were areas of production and consumption ; some fibres were gathered in China from areas where the fibres were produced naturally and not under cultivation. Two-thirds of the natural silk comes from Japan, about 10 per cent from China and almost 10 per cent from Italy.

The rayon or artificial silk industry represents modern conditions with the manufacturer attempting to escape the limitations which Nature imposes. Rayon is a synthetic product dependent largely upon the vegetable matter of the soft-wood trees. The product, silk fibre, is to some degree under control, and human inventiveness will but increase this control. The product is obviously more easily standardized, and can be made to fit the machines. Weather conditions, the conditions referred to above with regard to the grass-lands and the winter-rain mulberry lands, tend to be unimportant. At the moment the threatened shortage in the world's supply of soft-woods appears to be serious, but the chemist will probably discover other sources for cellulose.

We live in a changing world, and probably the changes are of supreme importance, especially to Britain, in reference to the textile industries. We were content in older days to pay for natural qualities in the fibres from which materials were woven ; now, we tend to buy appearances and surface qualities, and leave to the manufacturer the job of supplying those wants from the materials which he can acquire. The West Riding and south-east Lancashire will continue to weigh in the world's scale of values only so long as they continue the advance in textile design and production already made, and leave behind the crudities of the woollen and cotton industries of the nineteenth century.

LESSON 15

Rubber's Place in the Modern Economy

THIRTY years ago most of the rubber produced in the world was wild rubber. This basis of an industry was primitive and crude, typical of the period, when the more remote parts of the world were being combed for raw materials which might be of industrial use. The stage of development was akin to that of the early Newfoundland cod-fishers of three centuries ago ; rubber collectors, like the earlier cod-collectors, frequented an area where Nature supplied the article they valued and where they might chance upon a good harvest. Wild rubber was, and still is, limited to the tropical forests, the hot wet forests of equatorial regions ; the forests of the Amazon gave half the yield and allowed Brazil to produce half the rubber used by British manufacturers. The corresponding African forests of the Congo sent to the world and to Britain a tenth of their respective supplies. The remainder came mainly from Malaya and the East Indies. At that time rubber was used by the United States to the extent of about half the supplies, and the rest was almost equally divided between Germany and Britain.

The trees are tapped for their sap, which coagulates after treatment. The amount of sap depends on the age of the tree. The quantity is negligible until after the seventh year of growth ; it then increases, and old trees may yield as much as 10 lb.

annually. The collector found his trees, gashed the bark and collected the outflow. Obviously, the collector had to be a native, because he was cheap, and because he alone could endure the climatic hardships. Equally obviously, his methods were nothing but surface skimming of those trees he found by chance, a method of pure exploitation. Over-bleeding was inevitable, and collection became more arduous. In the early years of the century the problem of future supplies was not regarded with disquietude, for it was expected that over-tapped trees would recover, that further exploration would discover other areas of

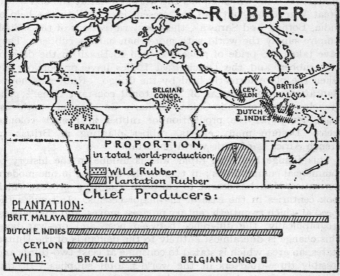

wild rubber trees, and that plantations, then largely experimental, would merely add to supplies.

Supply and Consumption. Consumption depended upon the provision of waterproof sheetings, where rubber tended to displace leather and other surfaced oiled fabrics ; and the provision of air-tight sheeting which was plastic and mouldable was to some degree a novelty. The world, however, steadily increased its demands, and plantations were opened in Ceylon, Malaya, and East Africa, and extended in the East Indies. Brazil yielded increased supplies for a decade, but the maximum was then reached, and a steady decline in production has reduced the present supply to but two-thirds of the yield of 1903. Supplies from the Congo declined at once, and are now a fifth of what they were. In recent years nine-tenths of the rubber is produced on plantations; in three decades Man has assumed control of this crop. Plantation supplies became important about 1914, and in fifteen years from that date the world's supply has increased fivefold. Ceylon now produces twice as much as Brazil produced in its best years. Malaya, i.e. the Straits Settlements, the Federated and Unfederated Malay States, produces a total which equals the world's total at the end of the Great War and is but half the present crop. With the help of India, Borneo, and Sarawak, these eastern sections of the British Empire supply the world with more than half its rubber. They have taken the pride of place accorded to Brazil in the days of wild rubber, and the Dutch East Indies have proportionately taken the place formerly held by the Congo. Rubber is now a plantation crop on areas of "equatorial constant rains." The French colony of Indo-China, similarly an area in south-east Asia, dominates the production of rubber in French colonial areas. Despite many efforts, rubber planting in British or French Africa is of little world importance.

This change has been rapid, and is unique in the history of commercial commodities; it typifies the fact that in one modern generation Man has learnt to cultivate a crop, a process which took centuries in the case of the major cereals. It typifies the speed at which twentieth century progress moves, and emphasizes, geographically, the difference between post- and pre-war days. This change is due almost entirely to the demands of the United States, an area which is stated to consume at least two-thirds and possibly three-quarters of the world's total supplies. In this area the amount of rubber used is twenty times as great as it was thirty years ago. The corresponding increases in Britain and Germany are but eight and four times, respectively. Italy, Japan and Canada have each almost attained the rank of Germany, and France occupies a position midway between Britain and Germany. So stupendous a development obviously tended to over-production and, in common with other raw materials, a surplus of rubber is now produced, the situation being complicated by the inevitable improvements in the quality of the manufactured product; rubber goods last longer. There is possibly no better known example of this change than the increased lasting power of the motor tire. Punctures are almost unknown on new motor-cars freshly shod ; when they accidentally occur the fault does not lie in the quality or the craftsmanship.

The development of the rubber industry, which is unceasing in its search for new and novel uses of rubber, is largely in the hands of the chemists, who have still many fields to conquer, especially in connexion with the plastic substances, such as clays and rubber. Out of this new knowledge which slowly accumulates will come the remedy for surplus production. Rubber is unique as a container for both water and air, and its tensile or elastic qualities give it other uses. Floor coverings for bath-rooms may be rubber, and recently rubber wall coverings for bathrooms have been patented. Here, as in the case of motor tires, the backing is important, since rubber does not adhere to every type of substance, and the new wall-covering depends upon a paper backing which is made to adhere to the wall.

In some economic respects rubber resembles tea, since its modern service to Mankind is due to business organization and acumen, behind the mere attempt to make a natural resource of abundant utility. Rubber became cultivable because the scientists at Kew were skilful. It will be still more profitable when scientists in works laboratories complete their researches.

LESSON 16

Iron and Steel in the World of Today

COMMODITIES may be broadly grouped in three grades : those which are perishable either from the mere lapse of time or in use, such as foodstuffs and raw materials, the primary vegetable and animal produce of the world ; those which are not affected by the passing of time or by use, such as the bullion, the diamonds, the materials in which wealth is accumulated ; and, in between these two grades, those which are but slowly affected by the passage of time and are but slightly affected in use ; of this grade iron and steel are examples. The second grade, that of the bullion and diamonds, owes its value to mere consent ; if all men ceased to revere and worship these materials, their value would vanish. It happens, then, that the transient perishable wealth given to Man by the farmer, the planter, the forester, is accumulated as capital in commodities such as iron and steel goods, and one of the chief purposes of Man is to make his iron and steel less perishable. Hence the incomplete yet growing metallurgy of the iron and steel trades ; hence, also, the belief of the engineer that his products dominate the world, and that the creative engineer is more important to humanity than any other class of worker.

The steady lengthening in the life of iron and steel by the processes of galvanizing, tin-plating, and of reducing the inherent liability of steel to rust, and by the production of varieties of iron and steel more closely related to their purposes and, therefore, more durable, is of importance, for it means that a ton of iron ore put into human economy is more effective year by year. From another point of view it implies that the capitalization of wealth in the form of iron and steel things is on a compound interest scale, for the units annually added are of more worth as time passes.

Since 1870 the population of the world has not doubled ; the main change has been the transference of folk into the U.S.A., so that the States now contain three times as many inhabitants as they did 60 years ago. Since 1870 the world's production of iron ore per annum has been multiplied by six ; it was doubled by 1895, roughly in 25 years ; by 1912–13 it was doubled again, roughly in 17 years ; had this progress been maintained it should have certainly doubled again by 1930 ; but the Great War intervened, and the 1912–13 situation did not recur until 1925–26. Here is an illustration of the fact that the world's compound interest rate of accumulations of capital in the form of perishable or usable wealth has been slowed down, while the recorded accumulations in terms of coin and bullion have not been slowed down ; hence the discrepancy which is at present disturbing the bankers and the chancellors of the exchequer.

Centres of Production. During this period the iron ore mined in Britain—in Furness and Cleveland and on some of the coalfields—has remained roughly constant. On the Continent the chief iron sources are mainly surrounding Luxemburg ; at various times these have been under different political control, and this area has increased its ore production tenfold.

In the United States, production annually is now 25 times what it was. By 1890 it was 5 times as great, by 1902 it was 10 times as much as in 1870; by 1913 it was 20 times; between 1890 and 1913 production in the U.S.A. had annually slightly exceeded production in the European continental centre and had developed at the same speed; in 1890 production in Britain, on the Continent and in the U.S.A. was roughly equal, each at about a quarter of the world's total. Outside these three old centres there are two other groups of producers: first, Sweden, Spain, and Russia; second, on a smaller scale, Algeria, India, Newfoundland, Austria, and Bohemia-Moravia.

In general, the consumption of ore in manufacturing processes has followed the changes in the amount of ore mined; the less important mining areas such as Spain and Newfoundland

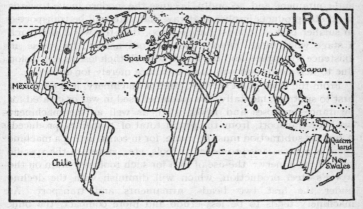

sell their ores or use their supplies locally, and are too small to matter on a world scale. Britain has maintained a steady production of ore, and by purchases of ore from Spain and Sweden has been able to consume and manufacture more iron; but the differences are immaterial in contrast with the developments in the other older iron centres on the Continent and in the U.S.A.

Principal Uses of Iron and Steel. The use of iron and steel has three main purposes: armaments, transport, machinery. Expenditure of capitalized iron and steel on armaments may be regarded, in peace time, as a means of insurance, and it would be of surprising interest to discover the premiums paid annually during the period 1890–1913, which were enormous. Shipbuilding yards on the Clyde, the Tyne, and the Oder; steel works at Barrow, Sheffield, Essen, Le Creusot, Birmingham, are in this sense gigantic insurance companies. When humanity decides that such insurance is a futile waste of capital, these industries must inevitably suffer from a declining market.

The use of iron for transport implies iron and steel ships, railway lines and bridges, marine engines and locomotives. From this point of view the iron industry of Middlesbrough, Newcastle, Pittsburgh and other centres thrives in accordance with requirements for more ships for overseas traffic, or more railways to supply or distribute cargoes ; permanent dock works are implied as accessories. Transport values are changing—first, because the use of the air instead of the sea requires different engines and containers, and, secondly, because the modern move towards synthetic products implies that raw materials will be transported in smaller bulk. It must happen, too, that the world will reach a stage when more railway lines are not needed, for those in existence will suffice, and the iron trade will then lose its expansion due to new needs and will have to suffice merely for upkeep.

From the third point of view, that of machinery, it is necessary first to subtract, mentally, the machines used in war or created for insurance purposes and never used, as well as the machinery used for transport, from the grand total of machines produced. A further subtraction must be made, for in constructing a machine there is a necessary provision of tools, etc., suited to the specific type of machinery ; the use of iron for such tools is a drain on the world's steel production, which will diminish with the decline under the first two heads, armaments and transport. As machinery tends to be less crude and more compact, the bulk of ore used will decline. Relative to output, modern farm machinery is more economical than the farm machinery of 1900, or it would not be used. Printing presses are more efficient in terms of the cwt. of ore used in their construction ; machines are more durable, motor-cars have a longer life.

On these counts it is obvious that the trade in iron and steel is not likely to continue to grow at the old speed, and it is less likely that it will pay to develop and exploit outlying iron ore deposits in the remote confines of the world, such as the iron sands on the sea shore at Taranaki, New Zealand. It is not surprising that iron deposits in Australia, as at Iron Knob, and iron and steel works in New South Wales are not a source of wealth to the Commonwealth. Retrenchment, contraction, seem inevitable.

LESSON 17

Geographical Distribution of Precious Metals

(See plate 27)

THE world has a surplus of the useful things, like wheat, wool, cotton and coffee, because these things occur in such quantities that it does not pay to transport part of them to market ; the world is like an orchard with apples and pears and plums rotting on the trees or on the ground.

Diamonds. The world has a surplus of diamonds, and the world sees manufacturers busy over the fashioning of cut glass for necklaces, and so wasting energy, when there are enough diamonds, so it is said, stored in vaults to provide necklaces as cheaply and more beautifully. Some of us may not buy bread or clothes as cheaply as we should because the world's finance is out of joint ; most of us are not allowed to buy diamonds as cheaply as is possible because the possession of diamonds is regarded as a privilege. Diamonds are a freak of Nature. They are useful for cutting and boring tools, as they are extremely hard. They occur in the Kimberley district in South Africa, in a clay formation which is found within cylindrical cavities on the earth's crust ; they occur elsewhere generally as alluvial outwashings from such clays as have reached the surface and been eroded. These pipes or cylinders are abnormal phenomena. Apart from its unusual manner of occurrence, the diamond is still a freak in its constitution, for it is merely one form of carbon—a variety of graphite or black lead and of coal—which does not behave like graphite, as a lubricant, or like coal, as a source of heat and power. It is neither consumed nor destroyed by mere use. It can be accumulated without deterioration. This means that diamonds are a handy means of storing wealth or capital, provided the value of a unit diamond can be kept constant.

Gold. The world has a surplus of gold ; this is a paradox in these days, when the business world complains of a shortage of gold and the price of unit gold has gone up $33\frac{1}{3}\%$. As a commodity, useful in itself to serve Man's purposes in daily life, there is a surplus ; few people make real use of gold, and they can easily use substitutes. The business world complains of a gold shortage because the march of events in the existing scheme of things has made it desirable to accumulate stocks of gold in fixed centres, and there is not enough gold to satisfy the desires of financiers that these piles of gold should attain dimensions x by y by z cubic yards or cubic miles. It is ordained that chunks of gold shall be moved hither and thither, to deplete one pile, to enlarge another.

Gold ore is a mineral which occurs in alluvial deposits in the beds of ancient or existing streams and in parent reefs among the rocks of the earth's crust. Except in occasional nuggets, the metal exists as a small percentage of the auriferous earth which is mined. The earth or ore is treated, usually chemically, to extract

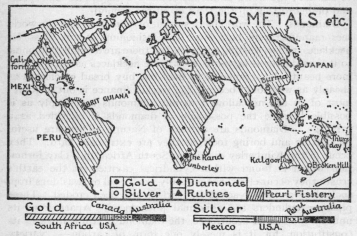

the metal, which becomes ingots or bar gold. The amount extracted has not kept pace with the demands of the financiers, for, relatively, the reserve of gold approaches exhaustion, and there seems little chance of lucky strikes in the future. In round figures, the world production of fine gold in 1880 was 150 tons, in 1900, 400 tons, in 1920, 500 tons and in 1930, 600 tons ; the peak period, 700 tons annually, was in 1912–15. The U.S.A. provided 33%, 30%, 15%, 11% at the dates specified, and 20% during the peak period ; Australasia, 20%, 30%, 6% and 3% at corresponding dates, with 10% towards the peak.

South Africa came into production later, and by 1900 produced 25%, which has grown to 50% since, with 40% at the peak. Gold from Canada has recently reached the production of the U.S.A.

PRECIOUS METALS

Gold from Russia is increasing in quantity; it now amounts to about 15% of the grand total. The rest of the world's gold comes from tiny sources widely scattered. South Africa dominates gold, as it dominates diamonds. The chief gold-producing localities—Kalgoorlie, Klondyke, the Rand, and California—are shown on the map.

It is estimated that the value of the gold accumulated between 1500 and 1840 was £600,000,000 on a pre-War scale of values. By 1880 this had been trebled, an amount which was doubled in the next 20 years. The present value on this scale is estimated at £5,000,000,000—about £3 per head of the world's population. From 25% to 30% of the annual production was absorbed for industrial purposes and the rest became coin or bullion at the disposal of the financier; recent events will have reduced the stocks of industrial gold to swell the financier's or banker's or nation's piles. In pre-War days the total annual trade of Britain and the other countries of western Europe and of the U.S.A. amounted to a value greater than the accumulated financial gold of the world. If gold had been perishable, the total stock would not have sufficed for a year's trading; obviously, trade was conducted not with gold but with equivalents, which were held to be gold-equivalents by common consent. Gold is useless as a medium of exchange.

Silver. The story of silver points this moral conclusively. By 1840 the world's stock of silver was £1,400,000,000; it is now £4,000,000,000. The value of the quantity mined has grown from 50 to 70 millions annually since 1890, and most of the metal has been absorbed into coins since that date, usually into a coinage which has but a nominal value; the quantity is inadequate for the small change of the world. Since 1890 some 60% of the mined silver has come from the U.S.A. and Mexico; during the period Mexico has advanced production relatively from just under half this total to about two-thirds. Recently Canada and Peru have each mined about half as much as the total from the U.S.A., and Australia has mined about half the Canadian total.

Precious Stones. Apart from diamonds, the values of precious stones are negligible. The following summary indicates their chief characteristics :

Aquamarine and cat's eyes come from Ceylon.

Varieties of corundum are the following gems (chiefly from Ceylon)—sapphires, blue stones, rubies (of which the pigeon's blood stones are mainly found in Upper Burma), and oriental topazes or amethysts.

Emeralds are chiefly found in Colombia and the valley of the Orinoco ; the trade in emeralds exceeds in value that in rubies. Jet, unlike the other gewgaws, is a vegetable product, being a hard kind of lignite ; it is found at Whitby, and in Aude (France), Germany and Hungary.

Opals are found in Hungary, Mexico and New South Wales.

Pearls are chiefly obtained in the warm waters of the East and West Indies, Western Australia, the Dutch East Indies and Ceylon. Pearl shell and mother-of-pearl are by-products. Thursday Island is a centre for the pearl fishery.

Turquoises are exported mainly from Iran

Most of the minor precious stones are associated with Asia and the East, and are related to the fragments of the ancient continent of Gondwanaland, which split into the major portions of the three southern continents. The alluvium and the young folded mountains of Europe lack both precious stones and precious metals.

LESSON 18

Economics of the Baser Metals

THE occurrence in Nature of the metalliferous ores is accidental. While we can investigate the climate of an area, study the typical natural vegetation, and so forth, and can determine the ecological character of a region and so control human energy that the area will produce the necessary crops, etc., it is not similarly possible to prognosticate that any area will yield payable quantities of any ore. Even when we can determine the character of the geological horizons we can do little more than indicate the possibility that sufficiently rich and continuous veins or seams or deposits of ore will make mining worth while. The different baser metals are as a rule associated with limited industries—copper is used electrically, tin for plating, zinc for galvanizing, lead for plumbing and for type metal, and so on—yet the minor uses, either separately or as components of alloys or amalgams, are important.

Copper. Copper comes first. In 1900 the world produced nine times as much copper as in 1850. The United States produced half of this copper. In 1850, 30 per cent of the world's copper was produced in Britain : since 1890 Britain has not produced more than a minute quantity of copper. In 1900 Germany, Japan, Mexico, Chile and Australia were each producing about 5 per cent of the world's supplies, while Spain produced 15 per cent. In the next decade the output was almost doubled, to be nearly doubled again by 1930; and production in the U.S.A. has remained constant at a third of the grand total Production in Germany and Spain has been steady ; in Japan, Mexico and Australia the amounts produced have fluctuated : new sources have arisen in Canada, Peru, the Belgian Congo ; and so great a relative development has occurred in Chile that production has increased tenfold, and Chile now produces a sixth of the grand total, a quantity nearly twice as great as the yield of N. Rhodesia or Canada, the competitors next on the list. Britain, as one of the three most important users of copper, is forced to buy abroad practically all the metal that is required.

Lead. The changes in the production of lead since 1850 have been similar in total to those which occurred in the case of copper · growth has been steadier and not quite so rapid. Since 1880 the United States have produced 40 per cent of the world's lead. In the period 1850–70 Britain produced about a third of the production at that time ; since then the relative quantity produced has declined to negligible proportions. At the present time Mexico produces 15 per cent of the present total, for during recent years the output of Mexico has been doubled, and Mexico is now the second important producer. Australia comes next with 11 per cent, and Canada next with 10 per cent ; the quantity produced in Canada has been trebled within the last decade. Lead mining on a largish scale in Europe is confined to Spain and Germany, which together produce about as much as Canada. Silver and lead are frequently associated in the ore, and some silver is obtained during the metallurgical processes for the extraction of lead. Britain has to buy much lead ore and sheet lead abroad.

Zinc. The United States are, and have been for long, responsible for more than a third of the world's zinc. Belgium and Germany vie for the second place, with each about a third of the U.S. total. Production in Mexico has been quadrupled since 1925, while production in Australia is now at the same level as it was before the Great War, when it exceeded half the then total of the U.S.A. Canada has come forward since the Great War, now equalling double the Australian totals. These are the principal producers in the world today, where the fifth producer is Poland, now mining zinc which would have been

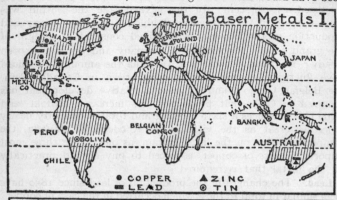

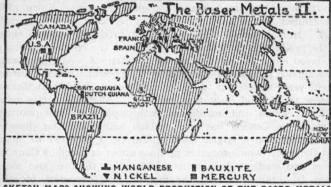

SKETCH MAPS SHOWING WORLD PRODUCTION OF THE BASER METALS

counted as German but for political changes. The total production of zinc in Germany-Poland was steady, except during wartime, and slightly greater than the production of Australia; then Germany lost rather more than half the yield. Italy and Spain are both minor producers. In 1880 Britain produced half as much zinc as the United States; now Britain's yield is smaller than that of Greece. The amount of ore mined in Belgium is small, although the zinc mines of the neighbourhood across the frontier (Moresnet, Aachen, etc.) are important; yet Belgium has the chief zinc works in Europe, and comes second in this respect to the United States. The zinc district of Upper Silesia really takes the second place in the production of spelter, but the political changes of 1919 left Poland third and Germany fourth in the world order. Britain is a buyer of zinc ore and spelter.

Tin. Tin is the one important metal of which the United States lack supplies. The world's production of tin has doubled since 1900, and during that period Malaya has been responsible

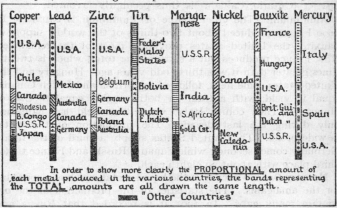

In order to show more clearly the **PROPORTIONAL** amount of each metal produced in the various countries, the bands representing the **TOTAL** amounts are all drawn the same length.
▬▬ "Other Countries"

BASER METALS. Chart showing the relative total productions in different countries of the world.

for half the world's total. Before 1870 most of the world's tin was mined in Britain; the present output in Britain is meagre.

The Dutch East Indies have been, especially of late, relatively more productive than Malaya; they yield about an eighth of the present world's total. They occupy now the third place, since the quantity they produce has been exceeded by the yield from Bolivia during the last decade. The chief tin works are in Britain, although since the Great War there has been a great development in the United States in tin works which deal with the refashioning of used or "second-hand" tin.

Manganese, commonly known as a constituent of permanganate of potash, and used in the manufacture of steel and some pigments, is chiefly mined in India, Russia and Brazil ; in the United States a considerable quantity of manganese-iron ore is mined. Production was much interfered with during the War, most of the producers having only recently recovered ; recovery in Brazil has been slow, with the result that the Gold Coast, which has come into prominence as a supplier during the last decade, now yields more than Brazil.

Canada has almost a world's monopoly in the mining of nickel ore and in the production of the metal itself therefrom. The only serious rival, and that only to an extent of one-tenth of the supply, is New Caledonia, from which French colony in the Pacific France obtains ores for her nickel works. The Sudbury district (Ontario, Canada) is thus peculiarly favoured.

Aluminium. The chief source of aluminium is bauxite. In 1900 France produced about two-thirds of the world's supply of bauxite, the United States providing most of the remainder. Now France produces but a sixth of the total, which is twenty times greater than it was thirty odd years ago. Hungary and the United States come next, followed by British and Dutch Guiana, equal in yield, with a total for both roughly equal to that of Hungary. Then comes Italy, where the yield has happened only during the last decade. The production of the metal is widespread. The United States supply a third of the total ; Germany comes second ; while Canada, Russia and France tie for third place with about an eighth each.

Mercury Ore. Mercury is the liquid metal which is responsible for the amalgams. The statistics of the production of the ore contain many gaps. In 1901 it is recorded that Russia and Austria were almost equal sources of the world's supplies. In 1911 Italy and Austria shared similarly the total yield of almost the same quantity. In 1918 the United States stood alone with a production never before, or since, equalled. Recently Italy has monopolized the production, which has fallen to the former level. Throughout the period Spain alone has yielded persistent supplies of a relatively smaller tonnage. It is recorded throughout the period that the production of the metal itself has been steady at about 4,000 tons annually. Of these totals, Spain and the United States have supplied the major portion. Production has practically ceased in Austria and Russia, has declined in the United States, but risen in Italy.

Our Course in Economic Geography is continued in Volume 6.

ECONOMICS

LESSON 37

Results of Increased Saving

IN a normal year since the War the inhabitants of Great Britain have been in the habit of saving annually some £500,000,000. This means that year by year we are increasing our stock of factories and plant, of electricity generating stations and the means of distributing the current, of ships and the means for building ships, as well as of the necessary raw material for utilization by these increased instruments of production. In a word, the £500,000,000 saved annually have become embodied in fixed and circulating capital. In the last Lesson we saw how the people who save make their savings available for investment either by accumulating money in the banks or by purchasing shares. This, however, is merely the financial side of saving and investment. What is the actual effect on the economic system when a business man invests money in new plant and machinery ?

Crusoe's Alternatives.　In order to avoid the complications of the industrial system, let us take the simplest possible case, by observing how Robinson Crusoe saved and invested. When Crusoe landed on his island, he at first maintained a hand-to-mouth existence by gathering nuts and fruit. To improve his position it was necessary for him to adopt some sort of civilized production—the cultivation of the soil, fishing, and so forth. But how was he to set about it ? In order that he might fish, he had first to provide himself with a canoe and a net ; and the construction of these things will take time. He must save. This he can achieve in any one of three ways. We will suppose that he can build the canoe in 240 hours, and that he is in the habit of working ten hours a day and six days a week, thus requiring a working month to complete his canoe. The first alternative open to him is to go on gathering nuts and fruit for ten hours a day, but to put aside a portion each day until he has accumulated a sufficient store to maintain himself for a month while he is building the canoe. The second alternative is for him to lengthen his working day. In this case he can maintain his consumption at the former level ; the sacrifice he will have to make will take the form of a diminution in leisure. The third alternative is for him to restrict the number of hours which he spends each day on gathering nuts and fruit to, say, eight, and to devote the remaining two hours to constructing his canoe.

Saving by a Modern Community. If we assume the length of the working day to be fixed—and it is more or less fixed both by trade unions and State regulation, as well as by custom—the process of saving in a modern community obviously corresponds to the third alternative. When a community decides to increase its savings, it does not continue to produce the same amount of consumable goods as before, until it has accumulated a store of them to live on while it increases its capital equipment. If an additional £1,000,000 is saved in any year, then £1,000,000 less is spent on consumable goods. On the other hand, £1,000,000 more is spent on capital goods (i.e. material equipment) by business men to whom the additional savings have been transferred by the banks and the " issuing houses." The industries producing capital goods will be able to meet this extra demand, because less capital and labour will now be required in the industries producing consumers' goods. This transfer of capital will be effected by the price mechanism. The increased demand for capital equipment will cause capital equipment to rise in price, while the reduced demand for consumers' goods will cause the price of these goods to fall. It will, therefore, be profitable to transfer capital and labour from the light to the heavy industries, i.e. from the industries producing consumable goods to the industries producing capital goods.

Thus, the first effect of an increase of saving is to reduce the output of consumable goods. The second effect is to increase the output of capital goods—an increase made possible by the liberation of capital and labour from industries producing consumable goods. The third and final effect is an increase in the output of consumable goods as a result of the new machines and other aids to production in which the new savings are embodied.

Our analysis of the changes which take place in the economic system as a result of an increase of saving enables us to arrive at an important conclusion. The higher the proportion of the national income which is saved, the more roundabout the processes of production become. For, as we have seen, savings become embodied in durable instruments of production, and the raw materials which are necessary to enable these instruments to function. And, the more machines and other durable equipment are used in production, the greater will be the proportion of the workers producing these machines, and the smaller will be the production of the workers producing things for direct consumption. But this smaller proportion of workers in the light industries, i.e. those producing for consumption, will be more effective than the former larger proportion owing to the more elaborate machines which cooperate with them.

From the point of view of the community, the advantage of an increased volume of savings consists in the larger supply of commodities made available thereby. In the eyes of many people, however, this greater abundance of commodities is a curse rather than a blessing. For, it is asserted, as there is not a corresponding increase in the amount of purchasing power available, the markets will be glutted with commodities that cannot be sold, with the inevitable consequence of unemployment. This view, however, overlooks the fact that an increase in the volume of savings enables production to be carried on more cheaply than hitherto. For, as we have seen, savings become embodied in equipment of various kinds, the *raison d'être* of which is to increase the effectiveness of the workers of the community. Every pound spent by business men in possessing the more efficient equipment will yield them a greater quantity of output. Hence, they are able to lower their prices without trenching on their profits ; and this fall in prices enables consumers to purchase the increased supply of commodities, despite the fact that their money incomes have not increased.

LESSON 38

The Time Factor in Production

IN the preceding Lesson we were concerned with the effects of an increase of saving on the economic organization. We saw that such an increase resulted in a shift of productive power (i.e. capital and labour) from the light industries, which produce consumers' goods, to the heavy industries, which produce material equipment. Thus the higher the proportion of the national income that is saved, the higher will be the proportion of the capital and labour of the community that is engaged in the heavy industries. That is to say, processes of production will become more roundabout.

In the final analysis, then, an increase in savings enables a community to adopt methods of production which are more roundabout. But why, it may be asked, should we wish to adopt these methods ? The answer is, of course, that experience shows that a greater result is obtained by producing goods in roundabout ways than by producing them more directly. It is a more round-about method, for example, of transferring coal from one place to another to build a railway, and to construct locomotives and trucks in which to transport it, than to put it on the back of pack horses, as was done in 17th and 18th century England. Thus a community can always increase its productivity by adopting more roundabout methods.

Roundabout Production. Let us illustrate this point by a simple example. Robinson Crusoe, let us suppose, requires drinking water. Now there are various methods by which he can supply this want. In the first place, he can go to the spring each time he is thirsty and drink out of the hollow of his hand. This is the most direct way ; but it is highly inconvenient, because he must not only go to the well as often as he is thirsty, but also go without water for other purposes. A second method that he can adopt is to take a log of wood and hollow it into a pail, which is a roundabout method involving a considerable expenditure of time and energy. A third method is for him to fell a number of trees, to split and hollow them, and to make a runnel, which is a yet more roundabout method, but is much more efficient. This illustration enables us to see that a community can always increase its productivity in proportion as it is prepared to adopt methods which are more roundabout.

The use of roundabout methods, however, involves a dis-advantage which tends to offset their greater productivity—the sacrifice of time. It is this sacrifice which restricts their use ; otherwise there would be no conceivable limit to the capital equipment constructed. For, the greater the extent to which roundabout methods are adopted, the greater is the average period of time involved in the production of commodities. And this sacrifice of time means that we must be prepared to be less well off in the present in order that we may be better off in the future. We cannot, in fact, devote a greater proportion of our resources of capital and labour to increasing the capital equipment of the community without withdrawing them from the industries producing consumers' goods and without, therefore, restricting the supply of commodities available for immediate consumption.

Russian Five Years' Plan. Thus every community has to decide how far it is worth while sacrificing present income in order to increase future income. As the significance of this problem is usually veiled from us by the complex financial transactions which it involves, we cannot do better than consider it as it presents itself in Russia. The Russian government was anxious to effect the industrialization of Russia as quickly as possible, and to that end drew up the Five Years' Plan. The main feature of this plan was its provision for a phenomenal expansion of the heavy industries, such as iron and steel, engineering, electricity, and coal. In order to expand these industries, the government had substantially to increase the amount of capital and labour employed in them. Thus it was compelled to inflict on the peasants, who form the bulk of the population, a great sacrifice in the matter of consumption while the plan was being completed. It was for this reason that the government sought to prevent the peasant from selling his produce in a free market. By compelling him to exchange his produce at rates fixed by itself the government was able to obtain the food which the town population required at a smaller cost in terms of manufactured goods than it could otherwise have done. In a word, the peasant had to exchange his produce for manufactured goods at a low rate arbitrarily fixed by the government. By this means the release of the capital and labour from the industries engaged in producing consumers' goods was effected—a release necessary for the expansion of the heavy industries. Thus in forming a judgement on the wisdom of the Five Years' Plan, it is necessary to decide whether the loss of welfare in the present is or is not more than counterbalanced by the increase of welfare in the future.

Influence of Interest Rates. How will a community decide whether a particular roundabout method of production is worth the sacrifice of time involved ? It is in determining the answer to this question that the rate of interest plays its fundamental rôle, namely, that of limiting the demand for capital (i.e. waiting) to the available supply. Given the general circumstances of the community, the supply of capital will determine the price of it, i.e. the rate of interest paid for the loan of it. The rate of interest will in its turn determine whether a particular roundabout method shall be adopted. The business man who is contemplating its adoption will estimate whether the yield which he will obtain from it will cover the rate of interest he has to pay for the capital he has to borrow to embark on it.

Having ascertained the effect of an increase in saving on the structure of industry, we have finally to consider very briefly its effects on the distribution. Clearly, an increase in saving will tend to increase the proportion of the national income which goes to the owners of capital, for it will mean that the number of units of capital on which interest is paid is larger than before. As there is a tendency in the modern world for the rate of saving to increase, the proportion of the national income received by the owners of capital also tends to increase. This does not imply, however, that the accumulation of capital is inimical to the wage-earning and salaried classes. On the contrary, it has been one of the main factors responsible for the rise in the general standard of living which has taken place in modern times, since the more roundabout methods which the accumulation of capital has enabled us to adopt have vastly increased the productive power of labour. While, therefore, an increase in the supply of savings tends to raise the proportion of the national income which goes to the capitalist class, it tends at the same time to raise the absolute amount which goes to the salaried and wage-earning classes : and it is this latter effect which really matters.

LESSON 39

Factors Affecting the Wage Level

IN the previous eight Lessons of this Course we have discussed the problems which arise in connexion with two of the factors of production, land and capital. We now turn our attention to the remaining factor of production, labour. Our discussion will turn on three main questions, which are of special interest and importance. These three questions are : (1) What determines the general or average level of wages ? (2) What determines particular wages ? Why, for example, is a bricklayer paid more than an agricultural labourer ? (3) How can the State or the trade unions act so as to raise wages ?

The first question we must endeavour to answer, then, is : What factors determine the general or average level of wages ? Why, for example, is the general level of wages today four times as high as it was a century ago ? Now we have already gone far to answer this question in our discussion of distribution. We saw that economists are mostly agreed that the income of the community is distributed among the factors of production in proportion to their respective marginal productivities. We also saw that the central figure in this process by which the distribution of the national income takes place in conformity with this Marginal Productivity Theory, is the entrepreneur. The entrepreneur, it will be remembered, stands in the same relation to the factors of production as the consumer stands to the various consumable commodities that are produced. The consumer endeavours to distribute his income among the various commodities in such a way that he will derive the maximum satisfaction from his expenditure. He purchases, therefore, just so much of each commodity as will bring its marginal utility to him into conformity with its price. But how will he know whether he has succeeded in doing this ? The answer is that, if he finds that he cannot transfer with advantage any part of his expenditure from any one commodity, say cigarettes, to another commodity, say beer, then he will know that the marginal utility of each commodity he purchases is equal to its price and that he is, therefore, deriving the maximum satisfaction from his income.

Productivity Theory of Wages. Similarly, the entrepreneur has a certain amount of capital to expend on the various factors of production, and he naturally desires, like the consumer, to obtain the maximum return from his expenditure. He, too, will know that he has succeeded in doing this, if he finds that he cannot transfer with advantage any part of his expenditure from one factor, say labour, to either of the other factors. That is to say, he will derive the maximum return on his capital if the marginal productivity of each factor is equal to its price. The price of a factor of production, therefore—and, in particular, the price of labour—tends to equal the marginal productivity of that factor, just as the price of a commodity tends to equal its marginal utility to consumers. That is to say, the general level of wages tends to equal the marginal productivity of labour.

We have thus ascertained one of the main factors determining the general level of wages. Wages tend to be high or low according

to the high or low productivity of the worker. Any factor, therefore, which raises the efficiency of the worker, such as better
training, better health, greater intelligence, will raise also the
general level of wages. It is important, however, to realize the
limitations of the productivity theory of wages. It is merely a
static law ; that is to say, it is a law which tells us what it is that
determines wages, if we leave out of account all the factors
which are at work in the economic environment except the
efficiency and the supply of labour. The productivity theory of
wages tells us that, if we take as fixed the natural resources,
the capital equipment, the efficiency of employers and of the
economic organization, then the general level of wages is determined by the productivity of labour.

Effects of Environment. The worker's wages, however, do
not depend entirely on his own efficiency. They depend also on
the environment of the worker ; environment includes such
factors as the amount of capital cooperating with his labour, the
efficiency of his employer, and, of course, the efficiency of the
economic organization in general. Anything which improves the
economic environment in which he works will tend to increase his
wages, for it will tend to raise his marginal productivity. An
increase in the amount of capital, for instance, would mean that
there would be more machines and more equipment generally
to cooperate with the worker. Similarly, an improvement in the
organization, as, for example, the rationalization of an industry,
or a rise in the general level of the efficiency of the employers,
would render the efforts of the worker more productive.

Any improvement, therefore, in the economic system of the
community tends to raise the general level of wages, because it
increases the income of the community. And the social income
is the source from which the demand for labour is derived.
Different kinds of improvement, however, affect wages differently ; that is to say, some improvements tend to raise wages
more than others. Thus an increase in the national income by
10 per cent due to an increase in the efficiency of the workers
would raise wages more than a similar increase of the national
income caused by an increase in the amount of capital. In the
first case the demand for labour would increase to a greater
extent than in the second, so that a larger share of the 10 per cent
increase of the social income would go to labour than would be
the case if the rise had been due to an increase of capital.

THE 'YOUNG PRETENDER.' Charles Edward (1720–88), son of the "Old Pretender" and known to legitimists as King Charles III. His desperate invasion of Britain in 1745 ended in disaster at Culloden Moor (1746), and it was only after many adventures that the prince managed to escape to France. BRITISH HISTORY 17

From a painting by Le Tocque

GEORGE II (1683-1760). Son of George I, he married in 1705 Caroline of Anspach, and in 1727 became king. Guided by Walpole, he acted the part of a constitutional monarch, though more interested in Hanover than in Britain. BRITISH HISTORY 17

After T. Hudson, National Portrait Gallery

JOHN WESLEY (1703–91). Born at Epworth, he took holy orders, and at Oxford, in conjunction with his brother Charles, formed a little society of earnest evangelicals, called Methodists on account of their methodical lives. In 1739 he began to preach in the open air and during the next 50 years travelled many thousands of miles and preached more than 40,000 sermons.
BRITISH HISTORY 18

Wesley Museum

WILLIAM PITT, EARL OF CHATHAM (1708–78). Entering Parliament in 1735, he became paymaster-general in 1746, and from 1756 to 1761 was first minister in fact if not in name. In 1766 he became premier, but wrecked his influence by accepting an earldom, and resigned in 1767. He opposed the war with the American colonists. BRITISH HISTORY 18

National Portrait Gallery

Plate 26

Volume V

MAN'S GREATEST EXCAVATION. Since diamonds were discovered there in the eighteen-seventies, they have occupied a large place in South Africa's economic life. The chief centre is Kimberley, but the largest of all mines of its kind is the Premier, situated twenty-five miles east of Pretoria. This mine is about 500 feet deep, and the photograph shows the huge gash effected by the removal of the diamond earth. The world's largest white diamond, known as the Cullinan, was found in the Premier in 1905.

ECONOMIC GEOGRAPHY 17

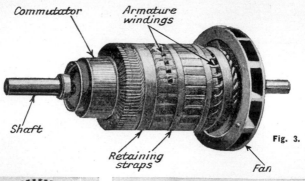

Commutator

Armature windings

Shaft

Retaining straps

Fan

Fig. 3.

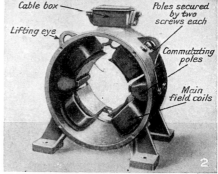

Cable box

Lifting eye

Poles secured by two screws each

Commutating poles

Main field coils

2

ARMATURE DESIGN. Fig. 2 (above). Typical armature core disk. **Fig. 3** (top of page). Armature for small machine. ENGINEERING 30

General Electric Co., Ltd.

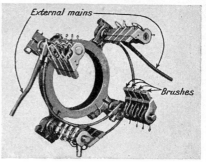

External mains

Brushes

DIRECT CURRENT GENERATORS. Fig. 2 (above, right). Typical frame for a four-pole machine. **Fig. 4** (below). Left, commutator ready for fixing; right, four sets of brushes mounted in a frame. Each brush can be lifted and adjusted independently of the others. ENGINEERING 31

Courtesy of British Thomson-Houston Co., Ltd., and General Electric Co.

Plate 28

Volume V

Effect of Introduction of Machines. It is often thought that an increase in the supply of machines and other forms of material equipment is detrimental to the worker. As machines are introduced in order to save labour, how, it is asked, can they benefit labour ? Is it not the multiplication of machines that is responsible for a considerable part of the world's unemployment ? It is, of course, true that the introduction of machines is not infrequently inimical to the interest of particular groups of labourers. Readers of Charlotte Brontë's " Shirley " will remember the resentment of the shearmen in the woollen industry when they found that the introduction of the new machine by which the shears can be worked by mechanical power had rendered their skill, which hitherto had commanded a high wage, superfluous. Again, in our own day the introduction of more efficient machines which economize in fuel has been partly responsible for the heavy unemployment and the depressed wages which have prevailed in the coal industry since 1925.

But the introduction of new machines in the modern world causes far less injury to the workers affected by it than it did in the early phase of Industrialism. This is due to the fact that the skill required by the modern worker is far less specialized than was formerly the case. The skill of the shearmen consisted in the efficient manipulation of a particular tool, whereas the skill of the modern worker consists in the skill and intelligence required to control elaborate machines. The introduction of a new machine, therefore, usually requires little more than a small adaptation on the part of the worker who controlled the old machine.

LESSON 40

Why Do Barristers Earn More Than Bricklayers?

HAVING discussed the first of the main questions which arise in connexion with labour, namely, the factors which determine the *general* level of wages, we now proceed to discuss the second question, the question of why there are inequalities in the earnings derived from work. What are the factors which counteract the general tendency of the earnings

H5

of each unit of any particular factor of production to become equal ? The earnings of capital in the various industries, for example, constantly tend to equality. If, after allowing for differences in risk, the return to capital in one industry exceeds the return to capital in another industry, then new capital will be diverted from the less profitable to the more profitable industries, until equality is restored. This process of adjustment may extend over a considerable period, as some capital takes a long time to wear out. The existence of different rates of return, therefore, at particular times, does not invalidate our assertion of a general tendency to equality. It is merely evidence that all economic adjustments encounter friction of various kinds.

Similarly, the earnings derived from work in the various occupations tend to equality. If the wages in one occupation rise relatively to wages in other occupations, labour will be attracted towards the higher-paid occupation, thus tending to reduce the discrepancy. Nevertheless, in spite of this tendency for the remuneration in the various occupations to become equal, there are permanent inequalities in the income derived from work. It is these permanent inequalities which constitute the problem of particular wages as distinct from general wages. Why, for example, do professional men earn more than manual workers ? Why does a miner earn more than an agricultural labourer ? To put the question in another way, why do not the relatively high earnings in some occupations attract people away from relatively low-paid occupations ?

Differentiating Factors. There are three main factors which explain the permanent differences in pay of the various occupations. First, there is the relative attractiveness of the work ; secondly, the cost of the necessary training ; thirdly, the skill or natural endowment required. Let us take the first point first. It is obvious that, even if the cost of training and the skill required for the various occupations were equal, there would nevertheless be differences of pay. Some occupations are more pleasant, more healthy or less irksome than others. If the pay of agricultural workers and miners were the same, most miners would prefer to take up farm work, and the mines would be more or less deserted. The competition among the coal-owners, however, for the diminishing number of miners would then force up their rate of pay. On the other hand, the competition among the increasing number of workers seeking farm work would force down the pay of agricultural workers. The shift from mining to agriculture would continue until the lower rate of pay in farming was just sufficient to offset the superior attractiveness of farm work.

Secondly, it costs more to fit oneself for some occupations than others. A doctor, for example, must undergo a long and expensive university and hospital training before he is qualified to practise. In order to induce him or his parents to undergo this expense, the pay offered in the medical profession is higher than that in an occupation requiring little training. It may be noted that the difference in pay may be either more or less than is sufficient to compensate for the cost of training. On the one hand, the number of people who can afford the expense of training may be so few as to create a scarcity of professional men. Thus, in a country like England, where incomes are very unequal, where the cost of a university education is relatively high, professional men will tend to be more scarce, relatively to the demand for their services, than in a country like Germany or Switzerland, where incomes are more equal and where education is much less expensive. On the other hand, the social prestige which a professional man acquires, or the greater attractiveness of work in the professions, may attract a relative abundance of men who are willing to undergo the necessary training.

The third factor tending to produce inequality of remuneration is the fact that some occupations require unusual skill or natural endowment. It is no use attempting to become a barrister, for example, unless one has exceptional natural endowments of a particular kind ; another case in point is afforded by the high salaries earned by film stars. The explanation, then, of the relatively high pay of barristers and film stars lies partly only in the cost of training. It also lies in the scarcity of the skill or natural endowment required.

There are, then, permanent inequalities in the incomes derived from work—differences due to three factors—the relative attractiveness of the work, the cost of training, and the scarcity of the necessary skill or natural endowment. These factors will probably never be eradicated so long as freedom to choose one's occupation exists. There is, however, another factor making for inequality of incomes, namely, the artificial barriers hindering the mobility of labour. The most important of these artificial barriers is the hierarchy of classes into which society is divided.

Now the class organization of society promotes inequality by creating artificial scarcities of certain kinds of labour. A good example of this kind of artificial scarcity is to be seen in certain kinds of clerical work. The banks, for example, select their staff from the middle class, and often from a small section of that class, namely, from persons who have been to a public school. By insisting on these two qualifications, the banks have to pay higher salaries to their clerical staff, for the number of people who belong to the middle class and who have been to a public school is relatively small. If the banks were willing to employ any-one who had the necessary capacity for the work, the competition for the available jobs in the banks would be keener, thus lowering the rate of pay for bank clerks and raising the pay in other occupations. Similarly, the barriers of class tend to raise the rate of pay in the professional occupations. To become a professional man, it is almost invariably necessary to possess the tone of a particular class. The professions, therefore, are in the main a preserve of the middle classes, and even in some cases of the upper middle classes.

Influence of Trade Unions. There is another artificial barrier to the mobility of labour, second only in importance to the barriers of class. Trade unions, like the organizations of professional men, endeavour to maintain a certain standard of conditions and pay in their respective industries. In order to achieve this objective it is often necessary to prevent free entry into a trade. There are two main methods by which a trade union can achieve this objective. In the first place, a trade union can endeavour to impose certain qualifications which will restrict the number of new recruits to the industry. Thus, in certain sections of the building trade, a long period of apprenticeship is imposed by the unions. To become a bricklayer, it is necessary to work for a number of years for little or no pay—an important consideration to a working boy choosing his occupation.

The second method by which a trade union can curtail the supply of labour in its trade is by fixing a minimum rate of pay above the competitive level and prohibiting the employment of labour below this rate. As the demand for labour varies inversely with the rate of pay demanded, a trade union can restrict the supply of labour in its industry almost to any extent desired by fixing the union rate at a sufficiently high level.

LESSON 41

Trade Unions and the Wages Level

IN the preceding Lesson we were concerned with the causes of the inequalities of income paid to workers. In Lesson 39 we ascertained the causes which determine the general level of wages under conditions of free competition. It now remains for us to inquire whether it is possible to raise the general level of wages above the competitive level.

Let us inquire, in the first place, what power the Trade Unions possess to raise the general level of wages. We have already seen that a Trade Union, if it is strongly organized, has the power to raise wages *in its particular trade*. This, however, does not necessarily mean that Trade Unions have the power to raise the *general* level of wages. If, for example, the National Union of Railwaymen is successful in raising the wages of railwaymen, we cannot say offhand that the general level of wages has been raised, for the rise in the wages of the railwaymen may have been at the expense of the workers in other industries. So long as the efficiency of the economic organization remains unchanged, the general level of wages remains rigidly determined, which means that a rise in wages in any one industry can only take place at the expense of other industries. We have only to inquire into the method which a Trade Union adopts to raise wages in order to see that this must be so. As we saw in Lesson 40, a Trade Union, in order to raise the wages of its members, must restrict entry into its particular trade. It is, in fact, by curtailing the supply of labour that a Trade Union raises wages. But, clearly, if the entry into a particular industry is restricted, the excluded labour will be compelled to seek employment elsewhere. In other industries, therefore, the competition for employment will be more intense, with the inevitable result that, outside the favoured industry, wages will fall.

It has been maintained, however, that the raising of wages by Trade Union action will actually result in an increase in the productivity of industry. Thus J. W. Rowe, in his " Wages in Theory and Practice," maintains that, while the immediate effect of a high-wage policy is to create unemployment and to increase the competition for employment in other industries, the ultimate effect is different. The high-wage policy of the Trade Unions, he argues, will stimulate employers to organize industry on more efficient lines. This they will be impelled to do, because they will be unable to obtain their labour as cheaply as hitherto. In order, therefore, to earn their former rate of profit, they will have to plan better and think out more efficient methods for running their businesses. As a result, industry will become more productive, the national income will expand, and the means for meeting the higher wages bill will be provided.

Effect of Rationalization. As we shall see later, there are special circumstances in which the raising of wages has stimulated employers to become more efficient. It is, for example, generally recognized that the interference of the State to raise wages in certain sweated industries has had this effect. But to generalize from these special circumstances scarcely seems justified. We must not overlook the principle of substitution. The normal reaction of an employer to a rise in the price of his labour is to dispense with a part of his labour force by substituting more labour-saving machinery. It is highly probable, indeed, that in recent years this process has actually been taking place in this country. Certain of the world's leading economists have expressed the view that much of what has been taking place under the name of rationalization is simply the reaction of employers to the restrictive policy of certain of the Trade Unions. If this view is correct, then we shall expect this process of rationalization to produce a large volume of unemployment. For the introduction of more elaborate machines and other forms of equipment in response to a fixation of wages above the competitive level results in a permanent displacement of labour.

But even though, so long as the economic situation remains unchanged, a Trade Union is powerless to raise wages except at the expense of the workers in other industries, it does not follow that Trade Unions ought to be abolished, for they perform highly important services both to their members and to the community. They enable the worker to obtain the full value of his contribution to industry, they raise his wages when the productivity of industry is increasing sooner than he would be able to do by his own unaided bargaining power, besides protecting him from tyrannical and irresponsible conduct on the part of his employer.

The State and Wages. The State, like the Trade Unions, has the power to raise wages in particular industries. It can prohibit, as indeed it has done under the Trade Boards Acts, the employment of labour, in certain industries, below a certain minimum wage. Clearly, however, the power of the State to raise the general level of wages suffers from the same limitations as that of the Trade Unions.

Are we, then, forced to the conclusion that State interference in the sphere of wages is pernicious or, at the best, futile ? Many economists hold that, in the generality of cases, the answer is in the affirmative. There are, however, important exceptions. In certain occupations the standard of living may be abnormally low. This may be due to one of two reasons. In the first place, the workers may be so dispersed, or ignorant, that the employers are able to exploit them. By exploitation is meant the payment of wages below the value of the contribution of the worker to the product of that particular industry. Secondly, the workers in a particular occupation may have been so degraded by a low standard of living as to render them inefficient. In both these cases the State can intervene with advantage. It was recognition of this fact that led to the Trade Boards Act of 1909. By this and subsequent amending Acts in 1913 and 1918 the Board of Trade, and subsequently the Ministry of Labour, is empowered to set up special machinery for the fixation of wages in " sweated " industries. The rates thus determined become the legal minimum in the trades to which they apply.

LESSON 42

Why and Wherefore of Foreign Trade

THE theory of international trade deals with two main problems. Primarily, it is concerned to explain the course of international trade ; it inquires, that is to say, why the production of commodities is specialized in the various countries ; why, for example, Britain imports bacon and eggs from Denmark, and why Denmark imports manufactured goods from Britain. Secondly, it is concerned to describe and to explain the advantages which the various countries derive from this international specialization ; it tells us, that is to say, why countries derive greater benefit from importing the commodities they do import than they would if they produced these commodities for themselves.

But why, it may be asked, do we need a special theory of international trade ? In what way does international trade differ from the internal trade of a country ? The internal trade of a country is, of course, based on regional specialization. Lancashire, for instance, produces $\frac{9}{10}$ of the cotton goods manufactured in Britain, for the simple reason that no other district possesses the three essential factors, climate, proximity to coal, and proximity to a great port, in such an eminent degree. But the foreign trade of a country is also based in exactly the same way on regional specialization.

Immobility of Labour. It is quite true, as these questions indicate, that the principles on which the internal trade of a country is based are not dissimilar from the principles of international trade. In trade between countries, however, a new complication arises. Whereas labour is comparatively mobile within the borders of any country, it moves from one country to another only with great difficulty. It is this immobility of labour *as between* countries that necessitates a special theory of international trade. Let us take an illustration. An Italian, we will suppose, contemplates emigrating to America in order to take advantage of the higher wages obtaining in that country. What difficulties and drawbacks will he have to contend with ? In the first place, he will have to sever all his social connexions and to transplant himself to an alien environment—a very serious consideration to most men. Secondly, he will have to consider the expense of transporting himself, and perhaps his family. Thirdly, he will encounter the difficulty of language. A further factor hindering the international mobility of labour is the widespread ignorance of the conditions and opportunities for employment in other countries. In addition to these natural hindrances to the mobility of labour there are also the barriers erected against immigration by the different governments.

Mobility of Capital. Nor is labour the only factor of production which cannot move freely from country to country. Land, with the concomitant factor of climate, is, of course, absolutely immobile. Capital is the most mobile of all the factors of production. If, for example, English capitalists find they can earn a higher return in a foreign country, they will invest their capital in that country, a fact to which the £4,000,000,000 of foreign investments owned by British subjects testifies. Yet capital itself, although the easiest of all the factors to transfer from one country to another, is not perfectly mobile. Owners of capital have a certain prejudice in favour of investing in their own country, where the conditions are better known and where they feel they have more control over their investments.

Now, as Professor Ohlin, the Swedish economist, has pointed out, international trade may be regarded as a substitute for the mobility of the factors of production. Some countries possess a relative abundance of certain factors of production—it may be a particular grade of land, such as the vineyards of France, or the wheatlands of Canada ; it may be a particular kind of skill or natural endowment of a country's industrial personnel, such as the skill and originality of English engineers, or the taste of French designers. Now the fact that a particular factor of production is relatively abundant in any country will mean that it commands a relatively low price in that country. Wheatland, for example, is more abundant in Canada than in most countries and commands, therefore, a lower price there ; while low-grade labour is abundant and consequently cheap in Calcutta.

Advantages of Specialization. How is the world to derive advantage from the fact that certain countries possess particular factors of production in relative abundance ? There are two methods by which it can do so. In the first place, the factors of production can redistribute themselves, so that they are equally abundant, or equally scarce, throughout the world. This method, however, as we have seen, is only practicable in certain cases. The great movement of labour from Europe to America and other new countries in the 19th and in the first decade of the 20th century is an example of this method, as also is the flow of capital in the same direction. The second method is for the various countries to specialize in those commodities the production of which requires the utilization in a higher degree of the factors which it possesses in relative abundance. Thus Canada, by specializing in the production of wheat and exporting it to England, is virtually transferring a part of her abundant wheatland to the latter country. Suppose it were possible for Canada to transfer part of her wheatland to England. What would be the effect ? The price of wheatland and, therefore, the price of wheat would fall in England, while in Canada the reverse would happen, the price of wheatland rising, as it became more scarce. But this is an exact description of what took place when the interior of Canada was opened up and the export of wheat began to develop.

Thus international trade, as we have already remarked, is a substitute for the mobility of the factors of production. Looking at it from this point of view, the two main problems with which the theory of international trade is concerned are much simplified. The first problem, it will be remembered, was to explain the course of international trade. Why do the various countries specialize in certain kinds of production ? At first sight, the answer to this question seems obvious enough. Do not countries specialize in those commodities for the production of which they are most fitted ? In a sense this answer is correct : but it is also misleading. A country may specialize in a commodity for the production of which it is less fitted than the country to which it exports that commodity Britain, for example, imports large quantities of bacon, eggs and butter in spite of the fact that it is quite as well fitted to produce these things as the countries which export them. This is due to the fact that Britain possesses a greater advantage in the production of those commodities which it exports as payment for these imports. The price of a country's imports are its exports, as we shall see in Lesson 43. As long, therefore, as a country is obtaining its imports at a lower real cost (i.e. in terms of labour, capital and land) than it could do by producing them for itself, it is deriving an economic advantage from the trade.

An employer may be able to do his own housework more efficiently than his servants, and the head of a big business the clerical work of his firm more efficiently than his clerks. Nevertheless, the employer would be a fool not to specialize in the work of directing his business. For the same reason a country will profit by specializing in those commodities in the production of which it has the greatest comparative advantage. But how, it may be asked, can a country know which commodities to specialize in ? The answer is that the price indicator will direct a country's resources into those industries from which it will derive most advantage. For in any particular country those branches of industry which use a high proportion of the factors of production which it possesses in relative abundance will be able to operate at lower costs.

LESSON 43

How International Debts are Settled

EXCLUDING the borrowing and lending transactions of a country and payment of interest on past loans, the value of a country's imports must equal the value of its exports. Over any considerable period—say, a year—the trade account between imports and exports must balance. But, the reader may remark, how can this statement be true in the face of the well-known fact that Britain imports much more than she exports? Every year the value of Britain's imports of merchandise exceeds the value of the merchandise she exports by many millions of pounds. This is perfectly true, but it does not contradict the statement that imports and exports balance, for the simple reason that other items besides merchandise appear in the balance sheet of a country. A country may import or export services of various kinds. Britain, for example, is the greatest exporter of services in the world. Every year she exports shipping services; that is to say, the British mercantile marine renders services to other countries to the value of £x millions a year. In addition, she exports banking, financial, and insurance services to the value of £y millions a year. These items in a country's balance sheet are called the invisible items. But the reader may insist that, even if we add the value of all these invisible items to the value of the export of merchandise, there will still be an excess of imports to the extent of several hundred millions. This statement is also correct. This excess of imports, however, represents the interest on the vast sums which we have invested in other countries. We are in the fortunate position, therefore, of receiving a substantial portion of our imports without having to export goods or services in return.

In view of the fact that the volume of a country's imports and exports is the result of the purchases and sales of individual importers and exporters, how does it come about that these purchases and sales exactly balance one another? In a country like Russia, where the Government has the monopoly of foreign trade, no problem arises. If the Russian Government finds that it is importing more than its exports will allow it to pay for, then it will cut down its foreign purchases. In a capitalist country, however merchants are free to purchase foreign commodities on any scale they please, while the volume of exports obviously depends on the willingness of other countries to purchase its products. In order to understand how, in these circumstances, the imports and exports of a country come to balance, it is necessary to acquaint ourselves with the mechanism by which payments between countries are effected.

Use of Bills of Exchange. Debts which arise in the course of trade between countries obviously cannot be settled in the same way as debts which arise in the course of internal trade. If an English merchant imports silks from France, he cannot pay the French exporter in English pound notes or by cheque. As we have seen in Lesson 7 (volume 1, page 227), payments between countries are affected by bills of exchange. The French exporter, having drawn a bill on his English customer, hands it over, together with the documents which give control over the goods, to his bank, which will credit his account with the value of the goods minus the appropriate discount. The French bank then sends the bill and the documents to its London branch, or to its London correspondent, who presents the bill for acceptance to the English importer, who then obtains the documents which will give him possession of the goods.

In some cases bills of exchange are payable at sight, but usually a bill is not payable until after the expiration of 60 days or some equivalent period. The bank, having obtained acceptance of the bill, either discounts it in the London market or holds it until it matures. Mr. Barrett Whale points out in " International Trade " :

" As a result of this chain of transactions, the exporter's bank has paid out money in France, but is credited with a balance with its London correspondent. But this same bank may have other customers who are importing from England, or who have for other reasons to make payments to that country. Let us suppose that some of these customers are importers who have arranged for bills drawn by their exporters to be accepted on their behalf by London Accepting Houses, and who will, therefore, have to remit money to London to cover these acceptances on maturity. By selling drafts on London to these, our French bank will be able to convert its balance in London into funds in France, thereby restoring its original position."

By this simple process of offsetting the debts which foreign importers have contracted with foreigners against the credits which French exporters are due to receive from foreigners, the banks obviate the necessity of transferring gold.

This simplified account of the process has the advantage of putting in the foreground the fundamental fact that the settlement of debts between countries does not normally involve the transfer of money or gold. It is effected by the far simpler and infinitely more economical process of offsetting described above.

But the reader will have remarked that it has been assumed that the imports and exports of any two countries are equal in value. This fact, however, does not prevent the process of settling international debts by offsetting; it merely makes it more complicated. Mr. Whale observes :

" While country A may owe on balance to country B, other countries, C and D, etc., may owe on balance to A ; and some of these may be owed on balance by B. This gives the possibility that A may meet her balance of indebtedness towards B by ceding her surplus claims on C or D, thereby enabling B to cancel in whole or in part her indebtedness to that country. If what each country has to pay to other countries collectively were always just equal to what these other countries together owed to it, if, that is to say, the total balance of payments of each country against the rest of the world were always square, it should be clear that all international indebtedness could be cancelled by this wider process of offsetting, however great the differences in the payments due between any two countries."

To put the matter more simply, let us suppose that there are only three countries, and that in the accompanying diagram the direction of the arrows indicates the direction of net indebtedness.

If A's debit balance with B is equal to B's credit balance with C, and C's debit balance with A, then it is possible through the mediation of the banks and the bill brokers for the total indebtedness between these countries to be settled by the method of offsetting.

LESSON 44

Corrective Action of the Foreign Exchanges

IN the previous Lesson we saw that international debts are not settled directly by the costly method of transmitting gold, but through the mediation of the banks and bill brokers, by a process of what is known as offsetting. Now this process of offsetting, it is clear, can be effected only so long as the debits and credits of a country balance one another.

Let us suppose that, for some reason or other, England has been importing goods in excess of the value of her claims on other countries. In the circumstances envisaged, the merchants of other countries will be drawing bills on England in excess of the value of the bills which English merchants will be drawing on foreigners. This will mean that foreign banks are accumulating balances in London and depleting their balances at home, for the customers of these foreign banks are selling more to England than they are buying from her. To rectify this position the foreign banks will lower the price of drafts on London to their customers at home, and will at the same time increase the number of bills which their London correspondents sell to the London bill brokers. Thus the sterling exchange will depreciate both in London and in foreign centres, for the value of the currency of any country in terms of other currencies is determined by the supply and demand for bills of exchange and drafts on that country. If, therefore, a country increases its imports without increasing its exports, the foreign exchanges will move against it.

It is this movement of the foreign exchanges which tends to correct the balance of trade, owing to the fact that the prices of a country's imports and exports in foreign currencies are determined by the rates of exchange. Let us take a simple illustration. An English coal merchant, we will suppose, is selling coal to Italy at the equivalent of £1 per ton, when the exchange is at lira 100=£1. If the rate of exchange falls to lira 90=£1, then the Italian importer will find that he is getting his coal at $\frac{9}{10}$ the former price, for he has to pay only lira 90 for every £1, instead of lira 100 as formerly. This will constitute an inducement to him to purchase more English coal. Thus a fall in the pound stimulates exports, since, for the time being, it lowers the prices of English commodities in terms of foreign currencies. On the other hand, it tends to contract imports. The English wine merchant, for example, when he finds that he has to pay a higher price for a draft on Paris, will reduce his purchases of French wine. A corresponding rise in the price of foreign commodities in terms of sterling will extend over the entire range of our imports. A fall, therefore, in the value of the pound in terms of foreign currencies makes England a better country to buy from and a worse country to sell in, and thus tends to rectify the balance of trade.

On the other hand, if in consequence of an exporting of goods by England in excess of the value of her imports the pound rises in value, imports will be stimulated and exports checked. By way of illustration, let us again suppose that the normal Italian exchange is lira 90=£1. What will be the effect on our exports if the £ rises to such an extent that lira 100=£1 ? Let us suppose that the British price for coal stands at £1 per ton. Then before the rise the Italian importer would be paying lira 90 for a ton of British coal. The appreciation of the pound, which raises the rate of exchange to lira 100=£1, will mean that the Italian merchant now has to pay lira 100 instead of lira 90 for every ton of British coal. The Italian demand for British coal, and likewise for other British products, will therefore decline with the rise in their prices in terms of Italian currency. The rise of the pound, however, will have precisely the opposite effect on British imports. The prices of foreign commodities in terms of the pound will fall, as British importers will be able to obtain more foreign currency for every pound. Thus movements of the exchanges are as effective in rectifying excess of exports as in rectifying excess of imports.

We are now in a position to see that international trade consists essentially in an exchange of exports for imports. The sole reason why a country sacrifices its capital and labour to produce goods which it does not consume but sends abroad is to obtain the products of other countries which its inhabitants desire to consume or to use as raw material for its industries.

International trade, however, was not always regarded in this light. Many of our 18th century statesmen, for example, regarded it in quite another way. These statesmen looked on exports as a means of obtaining not desirable foreign products, which would promote the well-being of the country, but the coveted precious metals—gold and silver. Nowadays, of course, we realize the true function of gold. We know that it is not an end in itself, but merely a means—a means to the stability of the economic structure of a country. No one today urges the Bank of England to hoard all the gold that it can get. We realize that any gold which the Bank possesses in excess of the amount necessary to provide an adequate base to the pyramid of credit is a positive loss. Hoarded gold is barren ; it earns no interest.

Now, the fact that imports are paid for by exports has important implications. It implies that any change in the volume of our imports is followed by a corresponding change in the volume of our exports, and vice versa. Hence, if the inhabitants of this country decide to purchase more foreign products, thus increasing the volume of imports, our exports (of goods or services) will be correspondingly stimulated. This stimulation of exports will be brought about by the movement of the exchanges, since the unfavourable balance of trade created by the increase of imports will result in a depreciation of the pound. But this depreciation of the pound will, as we have seen, make our products and our shipping, insurance, and other services cheaper in terms of foreign currencies.

On the other hand, a contraction of imports will tend to contract exports. If, for example, as a result of a reduction in demand or of the success of a " Buy British " campaign, we take less foreign products, or if, as the result of a tariff, foreign products are shut out from this country, then the exports of this country will tend to contract. For a contraction of imports has the initial effect of creating a favourable balance of trade, thereby raising the pound on the foreign exchanges. But an appreciation of the pound means that British products have become more expensive in foreign countries. The foreign demand, therefore, for British products will fall off and exports, whether of goods or services, will decline.

Our Course in Economics is continued in Volume 6.

Magnetism in Engineering

ELECTRICAL engineering covers such a very wide range that it would be impossible to deal with all its aspects in this brief Course. It has been decided, therefore, to confine the remaining Lessons to the consideration of the principles underlying the operation of electrical machines, and the methods used in practice for the generation, transmission and distribution of electricity. The fundamental principles of magnetism and electricity are dealt with in our Physics Course.

Magnetism. The peculiar property possessed by certain bodies whereby they attract or repel each other is called magnetism. Any magnetized body has two kinds of magnetism in it, concentrated at opposite ends. If the end of a compass needle be held near the opposite ends of a bar magnet in turn, it will be found that the needle is attracted by one end and repelled by the other end. The earth itself is a magnet ; and if a small magnet be suspended freely at its centre and allowed to take up its own position, it will be found that the ends will point north and south. The ends of the magnet are called " poles "— one the north-seeking pole (or north pole), and the other the south-seeking pole (or south pole).

If the north pole of a magnet be brought near to the north pole of another magnet freely suspended at its centre, it will be seen that the end of the suspended magnet will be repelled and will swing away. If, however, the south pole of one be held towards the north pole of the other, the two will be attracted, and the end of the suspended magnet will swing towards the other magnet. We thus have the rule that unlike poles attract each other, and like poles repel each other.

The magnetizing properties of a magnet extend into the space surrounding the poles, so that a second body may be magnetized without making contact with the first magnet. This point may be well illustrated by sprinkling iron filings over a flat sheet of glass or cardboard and holding a magnet underneath. If the glass or cardboard be given a few light taps, the filings will arrange themselves end to end, and take up definite directions, as shown in Fig. 1. These lines along which the filings arrange themselves give the direction of the lines of force radiating from the poles of the magnet. The lines pass through the metal from one pole to the other, radiate outwards from

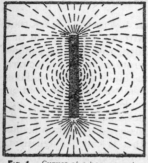

this pole, and then arch around in curves and re-enter the magnet at the first pole. If a piece of iron or other metallic material be introduced into the field of the magnet, i.e. into a region containing these lines of magnetism, the lines will be diverted towards the piece of iron and will pass through it in preference to the air. It is the passage of these magnetic lines through the iron that causes it to act as a magnet. The greater the number of lines passing through

Fig. 1. Curves of a bar magnet.

the magnet the greater is its force of attraction or repulsion. The number of lines of magnetism per unit of area of cross-section is called the " flux density," and represents the degree to which the body has been magnetized.

Soft iron presents an easy path for magnetic lines, or, in other words, it is easily magnetized. It is only a temporary magnet, however, because when the source of the magnetism is removed, the piece of iron loses all its magnetic properties. A piece of hard steel, on the other hand, is not easily magnetized, but when it does become magnetic it will retain this property for some considerable time, that is, it becomes a permanent magnet. Permanent magnets are almost always made of hard steel, and are magnetized by inserting them in a strong magnetic field.

Electro-Magnetism. It has been found that an electric current has magnetic properties. When a current flows along a conductor it is surrounded by a magnetic field ; if the electric circuit is broken and the current reduced to zero, this magnetism immediately disappears. If the conductor is a straight wire, as shown in Fig. 2, the lines of magnetic force are circular and concentric with the wire ; they extend right along the length of the wire, are most dense close to the wire, and decrease in intensity as the distance from the wire increases. If the wire be bent into a circular loop (Fig. 3), the lines of force will all be in one direction inside the loop, and all in the opposite direction on the outside of the loop. The directions of these lines of force are shown for the sections of the wire at the top and bottom of the loop ; at all points on the conductor the lines of magnetic force produced by the current are in the same direction, tending to produce a strong magnetic field inside the loop.

The intensity of the magnetic field inside the loop of wire is directly proportional to the strength of the current flowing in the wire, and depends also upon the substance through which the lines of force have to pass. Just as some substances are better conductors of electric currents than others, so also some substances offer an easier path to lines of magnetism. The easier the path the more permeable is the substance said to be. The permeability of soft iron is about 3,000 times that of air, so that if a piece of iron be introduced into the interior of the loop of wire considered in Fig. 3, the magnetic field will be

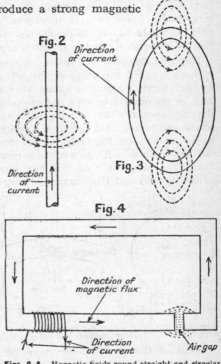

Figs. 2-4. Magnetic fields round straight and circular conductors, and a magnetic circuit.

greatly increased. It will be seen also that if, instead of having a single loop of wire, a coil be formed of a number of continuous loops, the strength of the field will be increased in proportion to the number of turns in the coil.

A coil of wire used to produce a magnetic field in this way is called a solenoid. It is made by winding the necessary number of turns of insulated wire on a former. If the solenoid is to have an air core, the wire is wound on a tube of some insulating material, such as ebonite, or cardboard coated with shellac. If the solenoid is to have an iron core, the insulated wire is wound directly on the surface of the iron core. Magnets for all purposes are formed in this way, varying in size from that used to ring an electric bell to the huge magnets used to lift scrap iron and steel in large quantities. In all cases the magnetic field is produced by switching on the electric current, and disappears again when the circuit is broken.

Magnetic Circuit. The path followed by the magnetic lines of force is called the magnetic circuit, just as the path followed by an electric current is called an electric circuit. The total flux, or the number of lines of force passing through a substance, depends upon the magnetizing force and upon the permeability of the substance. Fig. 4 shows a piece of iron bent round with an air gap between the ends. A coil wound upon a portion of the bar, and supplied with an electric current, generates the magnetic flux. The magnitude of this flux increases with the strength of the current and the number of turns of wire in the coil, but decreases as the re-sistance to its passage around the circuit increases. The per-meability of iron is so high compared with that of air, that a very small air gap will often be the de-termining factor in the total flux generated in a magnetic circuit.

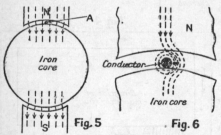

Figs. 5-6. Diagrams illustrating the principle of the electric motor.

Some of the above points may be further illustrated with reference to the principle underlying the action of the electric motor and the dynamo. Both consist essentially of a number of electro-magnets, of which two are shown in Fig. 6, and an iron core between the magnets to provide an easy path for the magnetic flux. The lines of force pass from the north pole N across the air gap to the core, through the core and across the air gap to the south pole, S, and thence back to the north pole through the outer casing to which N and S are connected. A number of electrical conductors are arranged to lie axially along the surface of the core ; the end of one of these conductors is shown at A just under the north pole of the magnet. When no current is flowing in the conductor the lines of force pass directly across from the north pole to the core, as shown by the dotted lines in Fig. 5. When a current flows in the conductor a new magnetic field is generated around the conductor, the direction of the lines of force depending upon the direction in which the current is flowing. In Fig. 6 this direction is clockwise, and its effect upon the original field is to distort the lines of force so that a larger number pass to the right-hand side of the conductor than to the left. The result is that the more dense magnetic field on one side of the conductor exerts a force upon it and causes it to move to the left. The conductor is fixed to the surface of the core, which, therefore, revolves about its axis. Thus the electrical energy supplied in the current is converted to mechanical energy in rotation of the motor shaft.

The principle underlying the action of the dynamo is similar to that of the motor, so far as the magnetic circuit is concerned. In this case, however, the conductors lying upon the face of the core are moved by mechanical means across the path of the magnetic field, and a current is thereby caused to flow in them. Thus in the dynamo the action is simply the reverse of that in the motor ; mechanical energy is supplied in causing the rotation of the conductors through the magnetic field, and this appears as electrical energy in the current generated in the conductors.

LESSON 29

Electric Current and Its Measurement

A N electric current will only flow in a closed circuit, and it is forced around the circuit by a difference in the pressure, or potential, of the electricity at two points in the circuit. In order that the current may continue to flow it is necessary, therefore, that every circuit should include some means whereby the pressure is raised from its lowest to its highest value. This potential difference may be generated by an electric cell or by a dynamo, according to the quantity of electricity required. The magnitude of the current, or the rate of flow, depends upon

the potential difference causing the flow, and upon the resistance
to flow offered by the materials of which the circuit is composed.

It will often be found very helpful to compare the processes in
an electric circuit with those in a circuit in which some material
substance, water or air, for example, is flowing. Imagine a
circuit in which air flows continuously, receiving energy at one
point in the circuit and giving out energy during the remainder
of the circuit. The energy is supplied by an air compressor,
driven by some external source of energy, such as a petrol engine
or an electric motor. The energy is expended in overcoming the
frictional resistance of the pipes conveying the air to and from the
machine operated by the compressed air, and in doing useful work
in the machine. The air leaves the compressor at a high pressure,
there is a slight fall in pressure in the pipe leading to the machine,
most of the fall takes place in the machine, and there is a further
slight fall in returning to the low pressure side of the compressor.
The greater the pressure difference on the two sides of the compressor, the greater the amount of work done by a given quantity
of air flowing through the machine, that is, the greater the resistance that may be overcome.

The electric circuit corresponding to a compressed-air circuit
is shown in Fig. 1. The difference in potential, or pressure, is

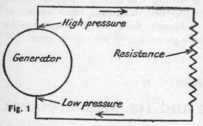

Fig. 1

supplied by the dynamo;
most of the difference in
potential is used in forcing
the current through the
resistance, and the re-
mainder in overcoming the
resistance of the conduc-
tors. The resistance in
which the useful work is
done may be any appliance
for the conversion of electrical energy to some other form, for
example, a heater or a lamp or a motor driving a machine. Just
as in the compressed-air circuit, the pressure difference, the current
flowing, and the resistance of the circuit are bound together in a
definite way. For a given current flowing in the circuit, the
greater the resistance the greater the potential difference required
to cause the current. For a given potential difference, the greater
the resistance the smaller will be the current forced through that
resistance. This relationship between potential difference,

current, and resistance may be expressed in a numerical form called Ohm's Law, which is $\dfrac{\text{Potential difference}}{\text{Current}} = \text{Resistance}$.

Electrical Units. One of the greatest difficulties to be mastered by the student of electrical engineering is the meaning of the various units employed, because these do not in themselves give any indication of the fundamental dimensions involved. In mechanical engineering the units are simpler to understand ; e.g. pressures may be expressed in lb./sq. in., rates of flow in feet per sec., gallons per min., etc., energy in ft.lb., and so on. In electrical engineering the units have been given names derived usually from the names of the pioneers in the science of electricity, and while these units have definite meanings, they do not in themselves suggest the quantities they represent. For example, the practical unit of potential difference, or pressure, is the volt, named after Volta ; the unit of current is the ampère, after the scientist of that name ; the unit of resistance is the ohm, and so on for other quantities.

It is now possible to express Ohm's Law in another form, viz., $\dfrac{\text{Volts}}{\text{Ampères}} = \text{Ohms}$. Thus, if a current of 10 ampères flows in a circuit under a potential difference of 200 volts, the resistance of the circuit must be $\dfrac{200}{10} = 20$ ohms. Alternatively, if the resistance of a circuit is 20 ohms, and it is desired to obtain a current of 10 ampères in the circuit, the potential difference required will be $20 \times 10 = 200$ volts.

The unit of power is the watt, and is the amount of energy used in each second in a circuit in which a potential difference of one volt produces a current of one ampère. In any circuit in which the potential difference is E volts and the current is C ampères, the power is $C \times E$ watts. For many engineering purposes the watt is an inconveniently small unit, and the kilowatt (1,000 watts) is a better practical unit. Then the power required to supply a current of C ampères at E volts is given by $\dfrac{C \times E}{1000}$ kilowatts. The power of an electric generator is always given in kilowatts, and the power of the engine driving the generator is always given in horse power. It is convenient to connect these two methods of expressing power. This factor is 1 kilowatt = $1\frac{1}{3}$ horse power.

The kilowatt-hour is the legal unit of electrical energy, and is the energy expended in one hour in a circuit in which the power is one kilowatt, that is, a circuit in which the product of volts and ampères is 1,000. The kilowatt-hour is the unit fixed by the Board of Trade as a basis for public supply purposes, and is usually known as the Board of Trade Unit. It is on this unit that the charge for electrical energy is based, and it is interesting to convert from electrical to heat units of energy, and to compare the heating effect of an electrical current with that of coal. One Board of Trade Unit is equivalent to 3,412 British Thermal Units of heat, that is, it will supply enough heat to raise the temperature of 3,412 lb. water through 1 degree Fahrenheit. Now 1 lb. of good coal will produce about 15,000 British Thermal Units of heat, and, taking the price of coal as 50 shillings a ton, one unit of electricity will give as much heat as about one sixteenth of a pennyworth of coal.

Resistance of Conductors. Different materials differ widely in the resistance they offer to the passage of an electric current, and for any given material the resistance depends upon the area of cross-section and the total length. The greater the area of cross-section the smaller the resistance, and the greater the length the greater the resistance. Copper is the best conductor among the metallic substances, with the exception of silver, which is ruled out of use in practice on account of its cost. Conductors in electrical machines and in underground cables are almost universally made of copper ; for overhead cables aluminium is being used to an increasing extent. Aluminium offers nearly twice as much resistance as copper, so that a conductor required for a given current would have to be twice as large in cross-section as a copper conductor ; for aerial conductors, however, one of the deciding factors in the size of the wire is the weight of the wire to be carried between the supports. Aluminium has an advantage here, as its density is less than one third that of copper.

When an electric current flows in a conductor, the resistance offered by the conductor represents a loss of electrical energy. This energy is converted to heat and the temperature of the conductor rises. The resistance must, therefore, be kept sufficiently low to prevent excessive heating, and this may be done by the provision of a sufficiently large cross-sectional area in the conductor. A safe rule for copper is to allow one square inch of cross-section for every 1,000 ampères flowing. Thus if the maximum current to be carried in a circuit is 100 ampères, the wire should be one-tenth of a square inch in cross-section.

Insulators. Non-conducting materials are called insulators, and are used to confine the flow of an electrical current to its specified path. Many different substances are used for this purpose, depending upon the particular conditions involved. Overhead transmission lines are insulated from their supports by porcelain cups, often two or three cups being used in series to offer increased resistance to leakage across the insulator. Various forms of rubber are used as a covering for underground cables, the rubber being protected from injury by an outer covering of some metallic substance ; lead coverings are usual for small cables and steel wire for larger ones.

Resistance of Systems of Conductors. A number of conductors may be arranged in " series," that is, the total current passes through each resistance in turn, or they may be in parallel, when only a part of the current passes through each conductor. An example may be given : Fig. 2 shows three resistances, of 10, 15 and 20 ohms respectively, connected in series between mains which have a potential difference of 200 volts. The resistances may be composed of suitable lengths of wire, usually

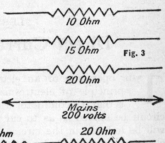

ELECTRIC CURRENT. Fig. 2. Theoretical diagram showing resistances connected in series between the mains. **Fig. 3** (above). Same resistances arranged in parallel.

wound in coils to keep the size within convenient limits. With the resistance in series, as in this case, the 200 volts potential difference has to force the current through each resistance in turn, and the combined effect is that of a single resistance of 10 + 15 + 20 = 45 ohms. The current flowing through the resistance is, therefore, $\dfrac{200}{45}$ = 4·45 ampères.

The same resistances arranged in parallel are shown in Fig. 3.

The full potential difference of 200 volts acts on each resistance separately, and the current through each may be calculated.

Current through 10 ohm resistance $= \dfrac{200}{10} = 20$ ampères.

Current through 15 ohm resistance $= \dfrac{200}{15} = 13\cdot33$ ampères.

Current through 20 ohm resistance $= \dfrac{200}{20} = 10$ ampères.

Hence total current in combined resistance $= 20 + 13\cdot33 + 10 = 43\cdot33$ ampères. The single resistance which would have the same effect as the three resistances in parallel $= \dfrac{200}{43\cdot33} = 4\cdot62$ ohms. It will be seen that by arranging a number of resistances in series or in parallel, or in a combination of both, a wide range may be covered in the effective resistance of the arrangement.

LESSON 30

Direct Current Generators

(See plate 28)

THE operation of an electric generator depends upon the principle of electro-magnetic induction. This principle is that if a conductor which forms part of a closed electrical circuit be moved so as to cut magnetic lines of force, a current will be induced in the circuit. The voltage, or pressure, of the electricity generated depends only upon the rate at which the magnetic lines of force are cut, so that the voltage may be increased by increasing the flux density of the magnetic field, or by increasing the speed at which the conductor is moved across the field. The magnitude of the current induced in the circuit will depend only upon the voltage and resistance of the circuit; if the resistance is high the current will be low and vice versa.

The direct current generator is so called because the current flows continuously in the same direction. The alternating current generator, in which the direction of the current changes rapidly, will be dealt with later. It might be mentioned here, however, that the name " dynamo " is usually confined to direct current generators, while alternating current generators are called alternators. The word dynamo is a contraction for

DIRECT CURRENT GENERATORS

dynamo-electric machine, the name given by Faraday to any machine in which an electric current is generated by the movement of a conductor across a magnetic field, and is thus really applicable to both direct and alternating current generators.

The action of a dynamo is illustrated in a diagrammatic manner in Fig. 1. A conductor is formed into a loop, A, two sides being parallel to the pole faces of two electro-magnets, N and S. The magnetic flux passes from the north pole N to the south pole S,

and lines of force are cut by the two sides of the loop as the loop is revolved about its axis. If the direction of rotation of the loop is as indicated in the figure, the direction of the current in each side of the loop will be as shown by the arrows. The directions are opposite in the two sides, because the two parts of the

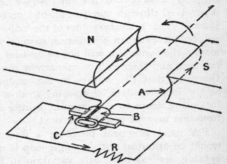

DIRECT CURRENT GENERATORS. Fig. 1. Diagram showing the action of a dynamo. Explanatory reference to the lettering will be found in the text.

conductor are cutting the lines of force in opposite directions. By joining the farther ends of the two conductors and forming a single loop, as shown, the direction of the current is continuous throughout the conductor, and the voltage is doubled by cutting twice as many lines of force as would be cut by a single conductor. The free ends of the loop are connected to opposite sections of the commutator, B. In the elementary case considered, the commutator consists of a ring formed by two pieces of copper separated by strips of insulating material, so that the ends of the conductor A are not in electrical contact. Two commutator brushes, C, made of strips of copper or pieces of carbon, are pressed against the surface of the commutator, and are connected to the external resistance, R. This external resistance represents the purpose for which the electricity is required, such as lighting, heating, or driving a motor, or for any combination of these.

With the above arrangement one brush is always in contact with the conductor passing the north pole, and the other brush is always in contact with the conductor passing the south pole.

Although the direction of flow in each conductor changes as it passes from one magnet pole to the other, the corresponding part of the commutator passes from one brush to the other at the instant when the direction of the current changes, and thus the direction of the current in the external circuit is continuous.

The magnitude of the voltage generated varies with the position of the loop as it revolves. As stated above, the voltage of the induced current depends upon the rate at which the magnetic lines of force are cut. Now when the conductor loop, A, is revolved through one quarter of a revolution from the position shown in Fig. 1, the two sides of the loop will be vertical, and they will be travelling in a direction parallel to the magnetic lines of force ; the conductor will not be cutting any lines of force in this position, and there will be no current generated. It will be seen, therefore, that the voltage in the conductor varies continuously as the loop revolves, decreasing from a maximum to zero and increasing again to a maximum, during the time taken to move from one magnet pole to the next.

For most practical purposes a fluctuating voltage such as would be obtained with a single loop is undesirable. In electric lighting, for example, any variation in the voltage results in a variation in the intensity of the light, and a periodic fluctuation gives a flickering light, which is unsuitable for reading or similar purposes. These fluctuations are eliminated by using a large number of conductors at different points in the revolution, connected in series with one another. All the conductors will be cutting lines of magnetic force at different rates, depending upon their positions relative to the magnetic poles, and the voltage induced in each conductor will be different in consequence. The direction of the current will be the same in any group of conductors which are moving in the same direction across the magnetic field, and if all these conductors are connected in series, the total voltage in the group of conductors will be equal to the sum of the instantaneous voltages in the individual conductors. Although the instantaneous voltage is different in the different conductors, their sum will be approximately constant if the number of conductors is large. The connexion of one conductor loop with another is made at a segment of the commutator, so that the number of segments in the commutator depends upon the number of conductors. The conductors are supported in slots on a revolving drum, the armature.

DIRECT CURRENT GENERATORS

In Fig. 1 only two field magnets are shown, but four is a more usual number, and in many cases this is further increased. By increasing the number of field magnets surrounding the revolving armature, the rate at which the lines of magnetic flux are cut by each conductor is correspondingly increased, and thus, for a given speed, the external voltage is increased. In order to generate a given voltage, therefore, with a given density of magnetic field, two alternatives are available, namely, a low number of field magnets with a high speed of revolution of the armature, or a large number of field magnets and a slower speed of revolution. The arrangement to be adopted in any particular case would depend upon the conditions imposed by the type of power plant used to drive the dynamo. A steam turbine, for example, would run best at a high speed, but large oil engines and large water turbines would have to be operated at a comparatively low speed.

In the case considered above, and shown in Fig. 1, the conductor loop was supposed to be revolving in the air-space between the two magnets. In Lesson 28 (page 241), dealing with electromagnets, it was shown that an air-gap in a magnetic circuit reduces the density of the magnetic field, and the longer the air-gap to be traversed by the lines of magnetic force, the less dense the field. In the dynamo the length of this air-gap is reduced by introducing an iron core and fixing the conductors in grooves along the surface of this cylindrical core. This is the armature, and the clearance between the outside of the finished armature and the inner surface of the field magnets is made as small as possible. The conductors must, of course, be insulated from the iron core, otherwise all the conductors would be in electrical contact with one another. While the covering of the conductors with insulation prevents the passage of an electric current from the conductors to the iron core, it does not affect the strength of the magnetic field between the poles of the magnets, and hence it has no effect upon the generation of electricity by the conductors cutting these lines of magnetic force.

If the armature core were made from a single piece of iron, it would act as a conductor revolving in a magnetic field, and currents would flow in a longitudinal direction, that is, parallel to the axis of rotation. In heavy-duty machines these eddy-currents, as they are called, would reach a high magnitude, and would result in a serious loss of energy, and in undesirable heating of the core of the armature. The generation of eddy-currents is prevented by building up the armature core from thin sheets of iron, insulated from each other, and clamped together by end-plates. A typical armature lamination is shown in Fig. 2 (Plate 28). The hole in the centre fits on the dynamo shaft, and the slots receive the insulated conductor windings.

A complete armature for a small machine is shown in Fig. 3. The illustration shows clearly the insulated conductors fitted in the slots along the surface of the armature core. The ends of the conductors are connected to the proper segments of the commutator. When the armature revolves there is a tendency for the conductors to move outwards owing to the centrifugal forces set up in them. On account of the small clearance between the armature and the field magnets, this movement must be prevented, or kept within small limits. On large machines wooden wedges are fitted along the tops of the slots above the conductors, while on small machines the ends of the core are wound with wire or provided with steel straps.

When an electric current flows through a conductor there is a certain heating effect, the amount of heat generated representing the energy required to force the current through the conductor. For a given current, the smaller the cross-sectional area of the conductor the more intense is the current, and the greater the heating effect. In the dynamo heat is generated both in the armature windings and in the field coils, and this heat is carried away by a draught of air provided by a fan.

LESSON 31

More About Direct Current Generators

(See plate 28)

IN the preceding Lesson the action of a direct current generator was explained, and the construction of the armature was described. The other important parts still to be dealt with are the field magnets, the commutator, and the brush gear. The arrangement of the magnetic field in a four-pole machine is shown in Fig. 1. The outer circular frame is generally divided in two pieces, so that the upper half may be lifted away. The pole pieces project inwards from the frame, to which they are

MORE ABOUT D.C. GENERATORS

usually secured by bolts. Insulated copper wire is wound around each pole piece, as indicated by the cross-shaded portion. When electric current is passed through these coils, a magnetic field is set up, as explained in Lesson 28 (page 241). The direction of the magnetic field depends upon the direction in which the current flows around the coil, and these directions are arranged to be opposite in alternate coils. The path followed by the magnetic lines of force is then as indicated by the arrows on the dotted lines in the illustration. The lines of magnetic force due to coil A, for example, pass inwards from the frame to the pole-tip, and then across the air-gap to the armature. Here the field divides, half going to

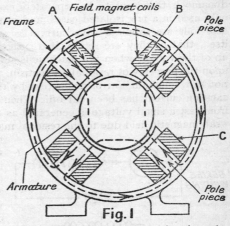

Fig. 1. Magnetic field arrangement in a four-pole generator.

coil B, and half to C. The lines of magnetism cross the air-gap again to reach the pole-tips of coils B and C, and return through the frame to A. Thus the magnetic circuit is complete. When the armature revolves, carrying conductors arranged along its surface, these conductors cut across the magnetic field between the pole-piece and the armature, and an electric current is generated in the conductors.

A typical frame for a four-pole machine is illustrated in Fig. 2 (Plate 28), the armature having been removed. The four field magnets are clearly shown, and in one case it is possible to see the two screws by which each pole is secured to the outer frame. The field-coils are covered with insulation and rendered moisture-proof. The two small poles seen on the horizontal centre-line are fitted for a special purpose, which it is not necessary to explain here. Suffice it to say that they are necessary to ensure proper commutation, that is, to prevent sparking at the commutator as the brushes pass from one segment to another.

Methods of Excitation. Excitation is the name given to the building up of the magnetic field, and this may be done in different ways, depending upon the purpose for which the power is required. For example, the necessary current for the excitation of the field-coils may be supplied from external sources; the dynamo is then said to be separately excited. This method is only used in a few isolated cases, and in nearly all dynamos the field-coils are supplied with current generated by the dynamo itself, that is, they are self-excited. In such cases the building up of the voltage when the machine is started from rest depends upon the property of residual magnetism, which means the retention of a small amount of magnetism by the pole-pieces after the exciting current has been cut off. When the dynamo is started from rest a small voltage is generated as the conductors cut the weak magnetic field due to the residual magnetism. This voltage drives a small current through the field-coils, increasing the strength of the magnetic field, and thus increasing the voltage, and this process goes on until the operating voltage has been reached.

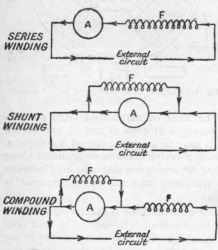

Fig. 3. Methods of current excitation.

Three possible methods of taking the exciting current from the main circuit are shown in Fig. 3. In each case A represents the armature and F the field-coils. In the first arrangement the field-coils are in series with the external circuit, that is, the whole of the current generated passes through the field-coils. In the second arrangement the field-coils are connected across the terminals of the armature, that is, they are in parallel with the external circuit. In this case the exciting current does not depend upon the current in the external circuit, but only upon

CONDUCTORS. Fig. 3. Stator end windings for a large 6,000 k.v.a. turbo-alternator, 3,000 r.p.m. ENGINEERING 33

Courtesy of the General Electric Co., Ltd.

ROTOR CONSTRUCTION. Fig. 2. Showing how the windings for the poles are embedded in slots in the surface of the rotor. The rotor shown here is for a large turbo-alternator in course of construction. ENGINEERING 33

Courtesy of the General Electric Co., Ltd.

LADY MARY WORTLEY MONTAGU (1689–1762). One of the most accomplished women of her time, a satirical wit and friend of wits, a great linguist and vivacious leader of society; her literary reputation rests on her "Letters," written from the Levant, 1716–18, but not published until 1763. She introduced inoculation for smallpox into England.

ENGLISH LITERATURE 33

Permission of the Earl of Wharncliffe

LORD CHESTERFIELD. Philip Dormer Stanhope, 4th Earl of Chesterfield (1694–1773), held various state posts, but is chiefly remembered for the letters he wrote to his natural son Philip Stanhope, and for the stinging rebuke administered to him by Dr. Johnson in connexion with the "Dictionary."

ENGLISH LITERATURE 33

MARY WOLLSTONECRAFT (1759–97). After keeping a school, she took to writing, and in 1792 issued her "Vindication of the Rights of Woman." She married William Godwin, the anarchist philosopher, in 1797, but died soon after giving birth to a daughter, Mary, who became the second wife of Shelley.

ENGLISH LITERATURE 33

After S. Opie

Plate 30

Volume V

THOMAS CARLYLE (1795–1881). Born at Ecclefechan, Dumfriesshire, he became a schoolmaster, but soon turned to a literary life. In 1826 he married Jane Welsh, and in 1834 moved to Chelsea. " Sartor Resartus " (1833), " The French Revolution " (1837), " Heroes and Hero Worship " (1840), " Past and Present " (1843), and " Cromwell " (1845) were his greatest works.

ENGLISH LITERATURE 34

From the painting by Whistler in the Glasgow Art Gallery

JOHN RUSKIN (1819–1900). Son of a wine merchant, he devoted himself to the study and exposition of art, as in " Modern Painters " and " Seven Lamps of Architecture." In other works he attacked the evils of industrialism.

ENGLISH LITERATURE 34

Photo, Elliott & Fry

LORD MACAULAY (1800–59). Thomas Babington Macaulay entered Parliament in 1830, and in 1857 was raised to the peerage. His essays were equalled in popularity by his " Lays of Ancient Rome " and " History of England."

ENGLISH LITERATURE 34

After Sir Francis Grant

CHARLES LAMB (1775–1834). For more than thirty years a clerk in the London office of the East India Company, in his leisure hours he was poet and essayist. The famous " Tales from Shakespeare " (1807) were written in conjunction with his sister Mary.

ENGLISH LITERATURE 35

ROBERT SOUTHEY (1774–1843). One of the most prolific authors of his age, he wrote poetry and drama, history and biography. Almost his only enduring work is his " Lite of Nelson," published in 1813—the year in which he was appointed poet laureate.

ENGLISH LITERATURE 35

Plate 32

Volume V

the voltage generated in the armature and the resistance of the field-coils. It is therefore possible to obtain a much steadier voltage with the shunt winding than with the series winding, because with the latter the strength of the magnetic field, and therefore the voltage generated, varies with the current flowing in the external circuit.

The third arrangement shows a compound winding, in which each pole has two distinct windings, one in parallel with the external circuit and one in series with it. This arrangement is useful when it is required to regulate the voltage according to the load, and it will be seen that a change in the current flowing in the external circuit may either increase or decrease the voltage, according to whether the series and shunt windings on each pole are in the same or in opposite directions. If, for example, the two coils are wound in opposite directions on the pole, the strength of the magnetic field will be less than with a shunt winding alone. A reduction of the external current will mean a corresponding reduction of the current flowing in the series part of the winding, and thus a decrease in the effect of this winding in reducing the field due to the shunt winding. The resultant magnetic field will be strengthened, and the voltage will increase to a corresponding extent. If, on the other hand, the two coils are wound in the same direction, the resultant magnetic field is the sum of the fields due to each winding alone. A reduction of the external current would reduce the magnetic field due to the series winding, and hence reduce the resultant field, and the voltage would be correspondingly reduced.

Commutator Brush Gear. A photograph of a commutator ready for fixing to the end of the armature will be found in Fig. 4 (Plate 28); it consists of a number of copper segments, insulated from each other and from the supporting ring to which they are attached. The inner ends of the segments, that is the ends towards the armature, are fitted with connecting pieces extending radially outwards; to the ends of these the corresponding conductors are attached. The brushes are mounted on a frame bolted to the casing, as shown in Fig. 4. This illustration shows a gear in which there are four sets of brushes, this number corresponding to the number of conductors in which the voltage reaches its maximum value at the same instant. The number of sets of brushes required in any case depends upon the number of field magnets and upon the arrangement of the armature windings, but a detailed consideration of the various arrangements used in practice is not possible here.

The brushes themselves are of carbon, and are pressed on the surface of the commutator by light springs. Each brush is connected by a copper wire to one of the mains leading to the external circuit, and opposite sets of brushes are connected together. The external mains are then connected to two adjacent sets of brushes, as shown in Fig. 4.

LESSON 32

Direct Current Motors

THE principle underlying the action of an electric motor is just the reverse of that which applies to the dynamo, and may be stated thus : If an electric current flows through a conductor which is situated in a magnetic field, the conductor tends to move across that field. As was explained in Lesson 28 (page 241) on electro-magnetism, the passage of the current along the conductor sets up a magnetic field around the conductor, and it is the interaction of this field with the fixed magnetic field which results in the movement of the conductor. In the dynamo, conductors are moved by mechanical means across a magnetic field, and an electric current is induced in each conductor, whereas in the motor the procedure is just the opposite. Electrical energy is supplied to conductors lying in a magnetic field, and mechanical energy is produced in the resulting movement of the conductors. The same machine may be used either as a dynamo or as a motor ; if the conversion of energy is from mechanical to electrical, the machine is a dynamo ; if the conversion is from electrical to mechanical, the machine is a motor.

This property of reversibility of function is made use of in some of the most up-to-date engine-testing plants, especially for small high-speed engines such as are suitable for road vehicles. The engine is coupled to a dynamo which absorbs the power generated, at the same time offering a ready and accurate method of measuring the power output of the engine. The same machine, supplied with power from the electric mains, is also used as a motor to give the engine its initial run-in before it starts running on load.

DIRECT CURRENT MOTORS

When the armature of a motor revolves, the cutting of the magnetic field by the conductors sets up a voltage in the armature circuit. This induced voltage is opposite in direction to the applied current, so that the actual current flowing in the armature is proportional to the difference between the applied voltage and the induced voltage. The magnitude of the current is given by Ohm's Law :

$$\text{Current in amperes} = \frac{\text{Voltage}}{\text{Resistance in ohms}}$$

If E = voltage applied, and
e = induced voltage due to rotation of the armature,

then effective voltage = $E - e$, and current flowing in armature = $\frac{E-e}{R}$, where R = resistance of the armature.

Now the current flowing in the armature determines the size of the cross-section of the armature conductors, in order to prevent overheating, and it is usual to design the conductors to suit running conditions at full load. But the conditions when starting from rest are not the same as when running at normal speed. It must be remembered that the opposing voltage induced in the armature conductors is proportional to the rate at which the magnetic field is cut—that is, it depends upon the speed, and when the speed is zero the opposing voltage is zero. Thus, when the motor is starting from rest, the current flowing through the armature would be given by :

$$\text{Current} = \frac{E}{R}, \text{ since } e = 0.$$

This current might well be many times as great as the normal full load current, and precautions must be taken to prevent such an excessive rush of current through the armature. The usual method is to provide a variable resistance in the armature circuit. This resistance is all in at starting ; then, as the speed rises, and the induced voltage increases, the resistance is gradually cut out, until at full speed the resistance is all out.

As with the dynamo, the performance of a motor depends upon the type of field winding, whether series, shunt, or compound. Any of these arrangements may be used, depending upon the conditions under which the motor is required to work. The arrangement of the winding is the same as that illustrated in page 256, for the dynamo.

Series-Wound Motors. The field-coils are in series with the external circuit, so that the whole of the armature current flows through the windings. The strength of the magnetic field is therefore proportional to the strength of the current flowing in the armature. Now the torque or twisting moment exerted by the armature is proportional to the product of the armature current and the strength of the magnetic field. When the motor is being started from rest, the opposing voltage induced in the conductors is small, so that, as explained above, the armature current would be excessive if suitable precautions were not taken. The increased armature current produces, in the series-wound machine, an increased strength of magnetic field, and hence an increase in the torque exerted by the motor. This increased torque at starting is very useful for some purposes, especially traction motors for tramways and railways, as it gives a higher acceleration than a constant-torque machine, and such motors are generally series-wound.

Shunt-Wound Motors. In this case the field winding is shunted across the mains—that is, it is in parallel with the armature current, and not in series with it. The current flowing through the field-coils then depends only upon the mains voltage and upon the resistance of the coils themselves. If the mains voltage remains constant the strength of the magnetic field will also remain constant, and will be independent of the armature current. Shunt-wound motors are generally fitted where it is not required to start under full load, and where approximately constant speed is required. They are suitable for machine tools, textile machinery, lines of shafting, etc.

Compound-Wound Motors. As with the dynamo, the compound winding consists of two separate coils on each pole of the field magnet ; one coil is in series with the armature current and the other is in parallel with it. The winding is a combination of shunt and series, and the performance of the motor will depend upon the relative strengths of the two separate windings.

Speed Control of Motors. The speed of a motor depends upon the strength of the magnetic field and upon the voltage applied to the armature. In a series-wound machine an increase in the load means a reduction in the speed, for the reasons outlined above, but it is possible to vary the speed of shunt- and compound-wound machines by altering the strength of the current flowing through the field-coils. This alteration is usually effected by inserting a variable resistance in series with the field windings. Then the current flowing through the coils, and hence the strength of the magnetic field, depend upon the amount of the resistance in circuit. If the resistance be increased the current will be reduced, and the corresponding weakening of the magnetic field causes a reduction in the opposing voltage induced in the armature conductors. This increases the effective voltage applied to the machine, and the speed rises until the induced voltage increases to its original value. This induced voltage, it will be remembered, is proportional to the rate at which lines of magnetic force are cut, that is, to both the strength of the magnetic field and also to the speed at which this field is cut by the conductors.

The speed may also be varied by altering the voltage applied to the armature, but the arrangements are more complicated than for the more usual method described above.

LESSON 33

Construction of A.C. Generators
(See plate 29)

THE principle underlying the generation of an electric current in a moving conductor is explained in Lesson 30 (page 250). Fig. 1 of that Lesson is reproduced in Fig. 1 here, with one alteration. The commutator attached to the armature of the direct current machine is replaced by two continuous rings, to which the ends of the conductor loop are attached and upon which the current collecting brushes press. If the conductor loop be revolved in the direction shown, the cutting of the magnetic field between the north and south poles causes currents to flow in the two sides of the loop in the directions indicated by the arrows. The magnitude of the voltage generated depends upon the rate at which the magnetic lines of force are cut, and the direction in which the current flows depends upon the direction in which the conductor is moved across the magnetic field.

If the conductor moves at a uniform rate in its circular path, the rate at which magnetic lines of force are cut is greatest when the conductor is beneath the centre of the field magnet, and the rate decreases to zero at the point where the conductor is moving parallel to the lines of force. Hence the voltage generated in the conductor loop is a maximum in the position shown in Fig. 1, and it decreases to zero after one quarter of a revolution, that is, when the loop is in a vertical position. As the loop continues its movement past this position and approaches the horizontal again, each side of the loop begins to cut lines of magnetism again, but in a different direction this time, so that the voltage begins to increase again but the current is reversed in direction. The voltage, as well as the strength of the current, reaches its maximum again after half a revolution from the first position, falls to zero after three-quarters of a revolution, after which point it again reverses in direction and increases to its original value and direction as the revolution is completed. The same sequence of events takes place in the conductor loop of a direct current machine, but the collecting brushes are so arranged on the commutator that one end of the external circuit is always in contact with that side of the loop in which the current

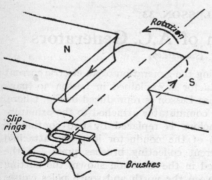

is flowing in one definite direction, and, when the direction of flow reverses, the loop is put in contact with the other brush. The function of the commutator on the direct current machine is to ensure a continuous current in the external circuit.

When the collecting brushes are placed in contact with two separate rings to which the ends of the conductor loop are attached, as shown in Fig. 1, the current in the external circuit will exactly follow the changes in the conductor loop as it revolves. It will rise and fall in magnitude and reverse in direction as described above, as it passes through each cycle of events. The time taken for one cycle is the time required for the conductor loop to move from one north pole to the next north pole, or from one south pole to the next south pole, depending upon

ALTERNATING CURRENT GENERATOR. Fig. 1.
Diagram illustrating the action of the generator. This illustration should be compared with the diagram in page 251.

the starting point chosen. The north and south poles are, as described in Lesson 31 (page 254), placed alternately, so that, for any machine, no matter how many field magnets it may have, the time for one cycle is the time to pass two poles. For example, a machine having four poles, and revolving at 1,500 revolutions per minute, would give 3,000 cycles per minute, or 50 cycles per second. The number of cycles per second is called the frequency of the current, and the above figure of 50 is the one used for the commercial distribution of power.

In the simplified case here dealt with, only one conductor loop and one pair of poles were considered. The conductor loop may, of course, consist of several turns of wire, all in series and placed close together, the extreme ends being connected to the slip rings, as shown for the single coil in Fig. 1. The voltage would then be increased in proportion to the number of turns of wire in the loop. In a machine having more than two poles, a separate loop may be placed opposite each pair of poles ; then the variations of voltage and current will take place simultaneously in the different groups, and they may be joined up in series with one another, and the voltage will be increased accordingly. Such a machine, in which the current rises and falls at the same time in all the conductors, is known as a single-phase alternator.

If, in the arrangement shown in Fig. 1, another conductor loop were introduced in a position at right angles to the first, and its ends attached to a second pair of slip rings, it would generate an alternating current as it revolves, but its current would be *out of phase* with that generated in the first loop, that is, the variations in magnitude and changes of direction do not take place simultaneously. The current in the second loop would be zero when that in the first loop is at its maximum, and vice versa. The phase difference would correspond in this case to one quarter of a cycle, and the machine gives *two-phase* alternating current. A more usual arrangement in practice is to have three separate conductor loops to each pair of poles, giving *three-phase* current. In a machine having more than two poles, each loop is connected to the corresponding loop two poles ahead, so that there are three distinct circuits in the winding. The current variations take place simultaneously in the various conductors of any one circuit, but the three circuits have different phase timings.

For economical transmission of power the use of a high voltage is essential. The power delivered is given by the product of voltage and strength of current (volts × ampères), so that, for a given power, the current flowing in the transmission line may be reduced by increasing the voltage, and hence the size of wire required for the conductor may be correspondingly reduced. With the high voltages usual in practice, the arrangements for the insulation of the conductors are simplified by reversing the arrangement shown in Fig. 1 ; the conductor loops are stationary while the field magnets revolve. The field magnet windings are built up on a revolving shaft and are supplied with current from a direct current supply by means of two slip rings attached to the shaft. As in the direct current generator, alternate field-coils are wound in opposite directions, so that north and south poles come alternately. The exciting current for the field-coils is usually supplied by a small direct current generator, the armature of which is fixed to an extension of the alternator shaft.

For slow speed machines the required number of magnetic poles to give the desired frequency are mounted separately on the periphery of the revolving wheel, and the construction of each coil is similar to that already described when dealing with direct current machines. At high speeds, however, such as are usual with steam turbines, the size of all revolving parts must be reduced to the minimum, on account of the centrifugal forces set up. In order to give the same frequency as the slow speed machine, the number of poles may be reduced in inverse proportion to the speed ; a rotor revolving at 3,000 revolutions per minute, for example, requires only one pair of poles to give a frequency of 50 cycles per second. The windings for the poles are embedded in slots in the surface of the rotor, as shown in Fig. 2 (Plate 29).

The groups of conductors in which the alternating currents are generated are fixed in slots in a stationary frame, called the stator, and the ends of the separate circuits are connected directly to the external mains. Fig. 3 shows the end of the stator for a large turbo-alternator, the rotor having been removed in order to show the stator windings.

Our Course in Engineering is continued in Volume 6.

LESSON 21

Prepositions, Conjunctions and Interjections

A PREPOSITION is a word which shows how things, or their actions or attributes, are related to other things : e.g. " Coming *through* the rye " (*through* showing the relation of the action *coming* to the thing *rye*) ; " London is full *of* people " (*of* showing the relation of the attribute *full* to the thing *people*). The noun or pronoun following a preposition is in the objective case, " governed by " the preposition. Prepositions may be classified as *Simple* and *Compound*. The simple prepositions are *at, by, for, from, in, of* or *off, on, through, till, to, up, with.*

The most important compound prepositions are :

aboard	astride	but (by-out)
about	athwart	down, adown
above	before	except
across	behind	inside
against	below	outside
along	beneath	since
amid(st)	beside(s)	toward(s)
among(st)	between	underneath
(a)round	betwixt	after ⎫ formed by the
aslant	beyond	over ⎬ comparative
		under ⎭ suffix *-er*

Beside is used of *place*, to denote either nearness to, or remoteness from : thus, " They wandered beside the stream " (meaning *by the side of*) ; " She was almost *beside* herself with grief " (meaning *out of her mind*). When, however, the sense of *over and above* is intended, *besides* is generally used, as " *Besides* Latin, he is also learning Greek."

But is a preposition when it means *except*. It should then be followed by the objective case, as " No one was saved but *me*."

Sans and *Maugre* are found in Shakespeare, Milton, and other early writers. *Sans* is the French preposition, meaning *without* : e.g. " a confidence *sans* bound " (" Tempest "). Maugre is the French *malgré*, in spite of : e.g. " *Maugre* the Roman " (" Paradise Regained ").

Certain participles, such as *considering, concerning, respecting, pending, during, notwithstanding, saving, save*, are often used as prepositions, though they are not really such. Thus, in " *Notwithstanding* your cruelty, I forgive you," the true construction is, " Your cruelty *notwithstanding*, I forgive you," the first three words being in the nominative absolute, and *notwithstanding* filling its proper part as a participle.

Many prepositions are also adverbs, but it is easy to distinguish the two uses. If the word in question governs a noun or some substitute for a noun, it is a preposition ; if not, it is probably an adverb. We say " probably," because it might be a conjunction, or even occasionally some other part of speech.

Examples : " He walked *along* the river " (preposition); " He walked *along* very fast " (adverb). " *Since* his death, I have lived here " (preposition) ; " He died long *since* " (adverb) ; " *Since* he is dead, we must not speak evil of him " (conjunction).

In " but me no buts," *but* is used first as a verb, secondly as a noun.

When *to* is used as an adverb, it is spelt *too* (" It is too cold for you to go out today ").

A preposition should, if possible, immediately precede the word which it governs. Even in relative and interrogative sentences this order should be observed. It is better to say " Of whom are you speaking ? " than " Whom are you speaking of ? " When, however, in a relative sentence, the relative pronoun is omitted, the preposition is usually placed at the end of the sentence, as : " he is not a man I am fond of " (i.e. " of whom I am fond ").

Conjunctions. Conjunctions are words which join sentences together—as : " I will wait *till* you come." Here *till* joins together the two sentences, " I will wait " and " you come." Not every word, however, that connects two sentences is a conjunction, for we have seen that relative pronouns (*who, which*, etc.) and relative adverbs (*when, where*, etc.) often connect one sentence with another. With these two exceptions, all words which join sentences together are conjunctions.

The conjunction *and* is peculiar, because, in addition to joining two sentences, it can also join two words, provided they are both of the same kind and stand in the same relation to some other word in the sentence : e.g. " two *and* two are four," " egg *and* milk are a good mixture." But in a sentence like " my parents and my cousins are here," *and* joins two *sentences* (" my parents are here " and " my cousins are here "), not two *words*. *And* is the only conjunction that can join words, though it is sometimes said that *but, or,* and *nor* join words. We shall find, however, that in every case these conjunctions really join sentences : e.g. " Neither this nor that is right " stands for " this is not right, that is not right." Such sentences are contracted compound sentences.

Co-ordinative Conjunctions. Conjunctions are divided into co-ordinative and subordinative. Those in the former class join co-ordinate sentences, that is, sentences of the same rank (Latin *ordo* = rank), neither of which is dependent on the other. The co-ordinative conjunctions are *and, both, but, either, or, neither, nor* (and, according to some grammarians, *because, for, as,* and *whether*).

Either is the distributive pronoun, and *whether* the relative pronoun, used as conjunctions : e.g. " *Either* of the two suits me " (pronoun) ; " *Either* you or I shall perish " (conjunction).

But was originally a preposition, meaning *without, except*. In phrases like " I cannot but think," " There is no-one but knows," it is a conjunction ; also in all cases where it joins two sentences, as " strike, but hear me," " he loved not fatherland, but himself."

Subordinative Conjunctions. The conjunctions in this second class join subordinate clauses to a main clause, that is, they unite sentences one of which is dependent on the other : e.g. " He'll kill himself yet, *though* he has been lucky so far." Here, the second clause depends on the first, or is subordinate to it, therefore the conjunction uniting them is subordinative. Such a sentence as the above is called a *complex* sentence, as opposed to a compound sentence, which consists of two or more co-ordinate clauses united by a co-ordinative conjunction. In a complex sentence, one clause is called the principal clause, and all the other clauses are called subordinate. These subordinate clauses play the part of adverbs, adjectives, or substantives, and are called accordingly, *Adverbial, Adjectival,* or *Substantival Clauses.*

The most important subordinative conjunctions are :

1. *That*, introducing substantival clauses : e.g. " he said that he was cold."

2. *If, unless, except,* etc. (conditional).

3. *Though, although, albeit* (concessive).

4. *That*, meaning " so that " (consecutive) as : " It was so cold that the water froze."

5. *That*, meaning " in order that," *lest* (final) as : " He went out that he might get warm."

6. *After, before, till, until, ere, since, now, while, as* (temporal).

7. *Because, since, for, as* (casual).

8. *Than* (comparative).

Than is now regarded as a conjunction, though it is strictly a relative adverb, meaning *when, at which time*. The noun or pronoun following *than* may be in the nominative case or in the objective, according to the predicate to be supplied, thus : " he hates me more *than* you " may mean " he hates me more than he hates you " (*you* being objective), or " he hates me more than you hate me" (*you* being nominative). A relative pronoun following *than* is always put in the objective case, even when it is strictly nominative, as : " Caesar is dead, than *whom* no greater Roman ever lived." *Whom* ought to be in the nominative, as the sentence stands for " Caesar is dead, and no greater Roman ever lived than *he*."

Interjections. These are words interjected or " thrown in " to express some emotion. They do not stand in any grammatical relation to other words, and are independent of the construction of the sentence.

Examples : *Hurrah ! Alas ! Oh ! Ah ! Pshaw ! Ha, ha ! Good-bye !* (God be with you), *Hullo ! Whoa ! Welcome ! Hail !*

LESSON 22

Simple Schemes in Parsing and Analysis

WE have in our Course in the English Language now gone through all the parts of speech in detail, and have been " parsing " words, perhaps unconsciously, throughout the process. For to " parse " a word is simply to say to what part of speech it belongs, and how it is related to other words in the same sentence. The following is a parsing scheme :

1. NOUN. Give (1) general class—i.e. proper, common, abstract, collective ; (2) gender ; (3) number ; (4) case ; (5) reason for the case.

2. ADJECTIVE. Give (1) class, whether of quality, quantity or relation ; (2) degree, whether positive, comparative or superlative ; (3) its qualification of the substantive. If the adjective in

question is pronominal—i.e. also used as a pronoun—state this in parsing it.

3. PRONOUN. Give (1) class ; (2) gender (if possible) ; (3) number ; (4) case, with reasons for the number and the case.

4. VERB. If a finite verb, give (1) voice ; (2) mood ; (3) tense ; (4) number ; (5) person, and the subject with which it agrees ; (6) principal parts—i.e. present indicative, past indicative, and past participle.

If an infinitive or gerund, give (1) voice ; (2) tense ; (3) case, with a reason for the case.

If a participle, give (1) voice ; (2) tense ; (3) number ; (4) case, and the substantive with which it agrees.

In *all* moods, say whether the verb is transitive or intransitive, whether of weak conjugation or of strong, and give the principal parts of the verb.

5. ADVERB. Give (1) class ; (2) degree ; (3) what it qualifies.

6. PREPOSITION. State what it governs.

7. CONJUNCTION. Give its class, and say what sentences or words it connects.

EXAMPLE OF PARSING.

" But then the mind much sufferance doth o'erskip,
When grief hath mates, and bearing fellowship." (" King Lear.")

But. Co-ordinative conjunction, connecting this sentence with what has gone before.

Then. Adverb of time, modifying " doth o'erskip."

The. Demonstrative adjective (sometimes called definite article), pointing out " mind."

Mind. Abstract noun, neuter, singular, nominative because subject of " doth o'erskip."

Much. Adjective of quantity, positive, qualifying " sufferance."

Sufferance. Abstract noun, neuter, singular objective, governed by " doth o'erskip."

Doth o'erskip. Verb, transitive, weak conjugation, active, indicative, present, singular, third person, agreeing with its subject " mind," from *o'erskip, o'erskipped, o'erskipped.*

When. Relative adverb (or conjunctive adverb) of time, modifying " hath."

Grief. Abstract noun, neuter, singular, nominative because subject to " hath."

(269)

Hath. Verb, notional (not auxiliary here), transitive, weak, active, indicative, present, singular, third person, agreeing with its subject " grief," from *have, had, had.*

Mates. Common noun, common gender, plural, objective after " hath."

And. Co-ordinative conjunction, joining the two sentences " grief hath mates," and " bearing (hath) fellowship."

Bearing. Abstract noun, neuter, singular, nominative, subject to " hath " understood.

Fellowship. Abstract noun, neuter, singular, objective after " hath " understood.

NOTE. Parse compound tenses of a verb : e.g. *have been, shall be leaving,* all as one word. We could, of course, parse the words separately, but there is no need to do this.

Analysis. In Lesson 15 (volume 3, page 317) we dealt with the analysis of a simple sentence. Now we come to the dissection of a sentence containing a principal clause and one or more subordinate clauses, i.e. a complex sentence. To analyse this we first pick out the principal clause, and insert the subordinate clauses as parts of the sentence. Then, omitting the connecting words, we can analyse the different subordinate clauses in turn. The student should familiarize himself with the various kinds of clauses.

There are three kinds of subordinate clauses :

(1) SUBSTANTIVAL. Clauses that play the part of a substantive in relation to some part of the sentence. Examples : " We know *that you are wrong* " (this clause is the object of " know ") ; " *When the election will come* is uncertain " (this clause is the subject of " is ").

(2) ADJECTIVAL. Clauses that play the part of an adjective in relation to some part of the sentence. Examples : " Give me the portion of goods *that falleth to me* " (qualifies " portion ") ; " That is the spot *where Nelson fell* " (qualifies " spot "). Care must be taken, however, to distinguish such clauses from clauses involving an indirect question—as : " Tell me *where Nelson fell*," " I asked *where I was*," " I know *why you have come*." In these sentences the dependent clauses are substantival, representing substantives ; there is no antecedent to which they can relate.

(3) ADVERBIAL. Clauses that play the part of an adverb in relation to some part of the sentence. Examples : " I like her,

because she is cheerful (modifying " like "), " Do *as I tell you* " (modifying " do ").

The formal analysis below shows the structure of the sentences :

(1) " There is some soul of goodness in things evil
    Would men observingly distil it out."

The principal clause is " There is some soul of goodness in things evil," and the subordinate clause " (If) men would observingly distil it out."

Subject	Limitation of Subject	Verb	Limitation of Verb	Object	Limitation of Object
(1) soul	(a) some (b) of goodness	is	(a) in things evil (b) would men observingly distil it out	—	—
men	—	would distil	(a) observingly (b) out	it	—
(2) (you)	—	give	(a) him (b) if you catch him when you reach home	message	(a) the (b) which I will give you now

(a) If you catch him when you reach home					
you	—	catch	when you reach home	him	—
(b) When you reach home					
you	—	reach	home	—	—
(c) Which I will give you now					
I	—	will give	(a) you (b) now	which	—

(2) " If you catch him when you reach home, give him the message which I will give you now."

The principal clause is " give him the message "; the other three clauses are subordinate.

Notes on English Punctuation

PUNCTUATION is the right method of inserting stops (Latin *puncta*, points). Stops are written marks to represent oral pauses. If we speak to anyone for a few minutes, and notice carefully the manner of our speech, we shall find that we make pauses of greater or less duration, mainly—though not entirely— for the sake of clearness. If our remarks were then written down, these different pauses would be represented by different stops. Where we completed a sentence, a *period*, or *full stop*, would be used (.). Where we made a decided pause, but not so decided as in the first case, a *colon* (:) or *semi-colon* (;) would be used. Where only a slight pause was made, a *comma* (,) would be used.

The meaning of a sentence ought to be plain without the aid of any stops whatever. Stops are a comparatively modern invention ; they do not appear on ancient manuscripts, and at one time they were not allowed in our Acts of Parliament. At the present day, too, in legal documents stops are usually conspicuous by their absence

Very often the entire meaning of a sentence can be altered by a slight alteration of punctuation—a fact of which full advantage is taken in many riddles that are propounded, and in many traps that are set for the unwary. Thus, in the well-known statement, " King Charles walked and talked half an hour after his head was cut off," nonsense becomes sense by the insertion of a colon after " talked."

Full Stop. This is used to mark the completion of a whole sentence, whether simple or complex. It is also used after abbreviations : i.e., R.S.V.P., Rev., D.D., M.P., Dr., Mr.

Colon. The *colon* originally marked off the parts of a compound sentence. It is now used after a sentence which, though grammatically complete, is followed by another closely connected in sense : here a full stop would mark too great a break. A colon is also used to introduce a quotation. For example :

Cowards die many times before their deaths :
The valiant never taste of death but once.

PUNCTUATION

Semi-colon. This is a modern form of the colon. It is impossible to lay down rules for their respective use, but, roughly speaking, the semi-colon marks a less complete pause than the colon. The semi-colon is usually placed between the co-ordinate members of a compound sentence *when the connexion is marked by a conjunction,* as : " You do not understand the lessons you have learnt ; but this is only because you are inattentive." If the sentences are short, and closely connected in meaning, commas are used instead of semi-colons, as :

> We carved not a line, and we raised not a stone,
> But we left him alone in his glory.

Comma. The *comma* is not used as frequently as formerly. A sentence should not be overloaded with commas ; they should be used only where it is absolutely necessary for the sake of clearness. Common sense must be the guiding element in their usage. But a few points may be mentioned :

1. A comma should be used to mark the end of a substantive clause forming the *subject* of a verb, as : " That the days are longer in summer than in winter, admits of no dispute." But if the clause either follows the verb, or is the object of the verb, no comma is used, as : " He said that he was cold."

2. In a list of words of the same nature—nouns, adjectives, adverbs, etc.—brought together in the same connexion, a comma is inserted after each word except the penultimate when it is followed by " and," as : " The fence was painted in stripes of green, brown, black and white."

3. The comma is used after an adverbial clause that comes before the verb which it modifies, as : " When he comes, tell me." But if the adverbial clause *follows* the verb, the comma is not needed, as : " Tell me when he comes."

4. There is no need of a comma between the antecedent and the relative pronoun if the relative introduces a limiting, or restricting, clause ; but if the relative is continuative or ampliative a comma must be introduced.

Restrictive. " He broke the pen which I lent him."

Continuative. " His eldest son, whom he had lost many years before, had always been his favourite."

5. A comma is used to separate a noun in the vocative (or nominative of address) from the rest of the sentence, as : " Mother, may I go out to play ? "

Other Stops. The *note of interrogation* (?) is placed at the end of all direct questions, as : " Who is there ? " It is not used after an indirect or reported question, as : " He asked who was there."

The *note of exclamation* (!), used after interjections and exclamations, e.g. " Alas ! " is also sometimes used after the vocative case, as : " All hail, great master ! "

Curved and square brackets ( ), [ ], are used to separate certain words from the rest of the sentence, to add an explanation of a difficult word, etc.

Inverted commas, double "—", or single '—', are used to mark quotations. When a quotation occurs within a quotation, the inner quotation is generally marked by single inverted commas, as :

> " Breathes there the man with soul so dead,
> Who never to himself hath said,
> ' This is my own, my native land ' ? "

LESSON 24

On the Writing of Good English

THE main object of our study of the English language is that we may be able to express ourselves clearly in it, whether in writing or in speech. We must aim not only at meaning exactly what we say, but also—and this is all-important—at saying exactly what we mean.

Absolute clearness of style is the result of long and careful discipline, but it is a result that will well repay the labour. It can be cultivated better in writing than in speech, because we can revise what we have written, whereas the spoken word is usually forgotten as soon as uttered. We should, therefore, make it a practice at first to read and re-read everything that we write, looking carefully for any ambiguity or any loophole for misunderstanding. We may be certain that if a thing is not quite clear to the writer of it, the chances are that it will be far from clear to anyone else.

Perhaps in no matter is this more important than in one where it is as a rule most neglected—viz. that of writing business letters.

ON WRITING GOOD ENGLISH

The necessity for a clear style is a very practical matter indeed, as thousands of people have discovered. It is impossible to mention all the errors of style that can be committed, but the following are the most common.

(1) Words are often left without any relation whatever. Examples : " Your guilt is as great or greater than his," where *as* has nothing to which to relate.

" He is not only acquainted, but well versed in English literature," where *acquainted* should be followed by *with*, to bring it into relation with the rest of the sentence.

" Having crossed the stream the banks on either side fell in," where *having crossed* has no relation to any other word of the sentence. As it stands, it agrees with *banks ;* but the banks did not cross the stream.

" Alarmed at the appearance of the sky, a terrific peal of thunder shook the house, so that he ran out," where *alarmed* is not related to any other word. Grammatically, it agrees with *peal of thunder*, but it was not the peal of thunder that was alarmed. The subject of the main sentence should, of course, be *he*.

(2) Many errors arise from a wrong or misleading *order* of words. As a rule, a sentence should run in its natural order : subject (and its limitations), predicate, object (and its limitations), adverbial limitations of the predicate—as : " The dying hero spoke words of consolation and of cheer in the midst of his mortal agony." For the sake of emphasis, e.g., " Great is Diana of the Ephesians," or for certain other reasons, the order may be altered. But whatever be the order, the important point is that the meaning shall be clear.

Great care is needed in dealing with relative pronouns, lest they seem to refer to a substantive which is not intended to be their antecedent. For example : " Much energy was displayed by Mr. Smith in running down the street after his silk hat, which he felt might have been devoted to a better purpose." The only way of avoiding this pitfall is to place the antecedent *immediately* before the relative—thus : " Mr. Smith, in running down the street after his silk hat, displayed an amount of energy," etc.

Equal care is necessary in dealing with adverbs or adverbial phrases, as these have an awkward knack of appearing to qualify words which they are not intended to qualify. Examples :

" The Moor seizing a bolster full of rage and jealousy smothers her."

" Erected to the memory of John Phillip accidentally shot as a mark of affection by his brother."

" The young man coloured with pleasure and promised to return in quite a gratified tone of voice."

(3) Further errors of style are : the use of unnecessary phraseology for simple words, e.g. " the nasal organ " (for nose), " the lower extremities " (for legs), " the tender passion " (for love) ; the use of stereotyped expressions (clichés), hackneyed allusions and quotations, e.g. " fit as a fiddle," " the Swan of Avon," " the cup that cheers but not inebriates " ; and the use of needlessly involved sentences.

As a mental training the art of reading the English classics aloud is worth cultivating. Clearness depends on grasping the author's meaning, and then conveying that meaning adequately to others. Correct emphasis is essential, and monotony must be avoided by proper inflection of the voice.

While it is highly important in the formation of style to read the great masters of English literature, it should be remembered that each person has a natural style of his or her own. The study of the great stylists should therefore be with the aim of perfecting the reader's particular style rather than with the idea of slavish imitation. The student will find the Authorised Version of the English Bible hard to beat in clearness and simplicity ; he will naturally not copy its archaic phrases. His first requirement is to write good, direct English, not to be led away by false gods of style ; to be able to read Carlyle without falling into his habits, to pass unscathed through the labyrinth of Lytton Strachey's winding sentences and withstand Oscar Wilde's worst mannerisms.

This Lesson concludes our Course in the English Language.

Scholarly Writers of the Eighteenth Century

(See plate 30)

ENOUGH has now been said to make it evident that the study of English prose must be pursued on lines different from those on which English poetry is to be studied. Whereas poetry is universally the voice of inspiration, prose in its development departs from the sphere of literature proper. Sometimes retaining but frequently losing its claim as literature, it becomes in turn the servant of theology, the handmaid of history, the medium of science, the channel of philosophy—essential alike to religious and atheistical propaganda, to practical and to theoretical ends.

At the beginning of the 18th century the student stands at a parting of the ways. He has to distinguish between what is prose literature and what is not. To a certain extent the answer will depend upon his own bent or humour, but he still has to ascertain why and when and by whom particular books were written. He must learn not only the history of those books, but become acquainted with their relationships—their position in regard to the treatment by others of the subjects with which they deal—before he is able to satisfy himself as to their value.

It is proper at this point to urge the advisability of some study of the political and social developments of which particular books were either a cause or an outcome. The extent of this study will depend largely upon the reader's desire to confine himself to, or to range beyond, the scope of belles-lettres. By belles-lettres is meant literature that is distinguished by the charm of its style or form, apart from its claim as a vehicle of instruction. It has to be borne in mind in this connexion that in the last result prose lives because of its power, not for its prettiness.

Charm and distinction of style are peculiarly characteristic of our 18th century prose. The century " found English prose antiquated, amorphous, without a standard of form ; it left it a finished thing, the completed body for which," as Sir Edmund

Gosse says, " subsequent ages could do no more than weave successive robes of ornament and fashion." The wider our knowledge of the literature of this period grows, the more clearly shall we see the injustice of the common indictment of the age as one of shams and sentiment. Apart from Johnson, the age of Berkeley, Wesley and Whitefield cannot be described as devoid of enthusiasm.

It was the age of our great historians. It was adorned by some of our greatest philosophers and keenest critics. English writers of the time influenced Continental thought more, perhaps, than did the writers of any other period of our history. Eighteenth century England, as we have already seen, discovered Shakespeare before the Germans. It standardized the essay, sowed the seeds of modern Nature study and modern chemistry, gave birth to our first great novel, laid the foundations of our periodical literature, stood sponsor to the beginnings of daily journalism, and crushed the system of literary patronage. It was the age, also, of political economy and of public eloquence.

Famous Letter Writers. The 18th century is also rich in its letters. The correspondence of Horace Walpole has been already referred to. Philip Dormer Stanhope, fourth earl of Chesterfield (1694–1773), was a statesman and wit who is remembered today chiefly for his " Letters to His Son." Given to the world in 1774 by the son's widow, these letters were described by Johnson as displaying the morals of a courtesan and the manners of a dancing-master. They argue, nevertheless, despite their worldliness, a sincere solicitude for the welfare of the son to whom they were addressed. They furnish also an example of writing that is at once clear, simple, forcible and polished. The aim of the writer is apparent throughout. The means he adopts to further that aim are direct. He describes things that are desirable, and against them sets the means by which they are to be attained. If the chance that ambition may not be sufficiently stimulated is sometimes provided for by an appeal to fear—the fear of ridicule—the fact is not to be counted for affectation on the writer's part. To him the most important thing in life was to shine in the fashionable society of his period.

Among other letter-writers of the 18th century must be named the poets Cowper and Gray. The letters of Cowper afford, perhaps, the best argument against the effectiveness of ornamental diction when it is confronted with a style that is simple and sincere. Cowper's delightful letters describe in the most natural and most charming of language the surroundings and incidents of the poet's life at Olney and Weston. Gray's letters possess the qualities of the bookman and the scholar, and represent a man who seems never to have permitted himself to appear in " dressing gown and slippers." The " Letters " of Lady Mary Wortley Montagu (1689–1762) describe, in the simple and elegant style of an accomplished if worldly woman, her experiences of travel in Europe and the Near East between 1716 and 1718.

The " Natural History of Selborne," by Gilbert White (1720–93), marks the beginning of popular Nature studies. Probably no book on natural history has been more widely read or more loved. With just sufficient formality to give it 18th century charm, it is composed of letters to the writer's friends, written, it is believed, at the suggestion of the Hon. Daines Barrington (1727–1800), who was an antiquary and a naturalist as well as a lawyer. Thomas Pennant (1726–98) was another famous naturalist and a friend of Gilbert White ; his " British Zoology " and " History of Quadrupeds " were for a long time classics.

Among the divines whose work continues to be read are William Law (1686–1761), whose " Serious Call to a Devout and Holy Life " stands by the side of Jeremy Taylor's " Rule and Exercises of Holy Living " as one of the most impressive devotional treatises in the language ; William Warburton, bishop of Gloucester (1698–1779), author of a voluminous work entitled " The Divine Legation of Moses Demonstrated " ; and William Paley (1743–1805), who wrote lucidly on the subject of Christian evidence. His " Treatise on Natural Theology " and " View of the Evidences of Christianity " are still read, as is also his " Horae Paulinae," a defence of the genuineness of St. Paul's Epistles, perhaps his most important work.

Conyers Middleton (1683–1750) wrote a remarkably rationalistic " Free Inquiry " into the miraculous powers which were supposed to have existed in the Christian Church. His vigorous, direct style has many admirers. The " History of Civil Society," by Dr. Adam Ferguson (1723–1816), has been ranked as a companion to Adam Smith's " Wealth of Nations." Thomas Reid (1710–96), who wrote " An Inquiry into the Human Mind on the Principles of Common Sense," had a distinguished follower in the " common-sense " philosophy in Dugald Stewart (1753–1828).

Following David Hartley (1705–57) and Abraham Tucker (1705–74) in adopting the theory of the association of ideas came

Joseph Priestley (1733-1804), a Unitarian divine and ardent Radical, who is best remembered as the father of modern chemistry, the author of a " History of Electricity," and as the man who discovered oxygen.

Thomas Paine (1737-1809) wrote an influential book on " The Rights of Man " (1790), in answer to Burke, and " The Age of Reason," the Bible of rationalistic deism, in 1793, when a prisoner in Paris under the " Terror." A second part appeared in 1795.

The Greek scholarship of Richard Porson and that of Elizabeth Carter, the translator of Epictetus ; the translation of Demosthenes by Dr. Thomas Leland ; the still unapproached translation of the Koran by George Sale ; the version of Plutarch's " Lives " by J. and W. Langhorne ; the standard translation of Josephus's " History of the Jews " by William Whiston ; the still popular version of " Gil Blas " by Tobias Smollett, whose " History of England " must also be noted ; the translation of the " Satires " of Horace by Christopher Smart—all these testify to the fact that the 18th century was an age of scholarship.

And even this list, long as it is, and irrespective of the facts that fiction is reserved for separate consideration, while poetry and drama have already been dealt with in this Course, is far from comprehensive. There yet remain to be noted for the student's due attention, Sir William Jones's translations from the Sanskrit, the scholarly " Discourses " of Sir Joshua Reynolds, John Horne Tooke's valuable " Diversions of Purley," the histories and biographies of John Strype, the " History of the Puritans Down to 1689 " of Daniel Neal, Sir William Blackstone's authoritative " Commentaries on the Laws of England," the " Anecdotes " of Joseph Spence, Mrs. Thrale's " Anecdotes of Samuel Johnson," the " Travels " of Mungo Park, the admirable Shakespearean studies of Farmer, Steevens and Dennis, and Mary Wollstonecraft's " Rights of Woman," published in 1792, the forerunner of the literature which helped to win the suffrage for women.

Eighteenth Century Journalism. In the domain of journalism it is of interest to remember that *The Times,* first started as *The Daily Universal Register* in 1785, came out with its present title on January 1st, 1788 ; that the " Gentleman's Magazine " was originated in 1731 ; and that there was a " London Magazine " in 1732, a " Monthly Review " in 1749, a " Literary Magazine " and a " Critical Review " in 1756 ; while, in addition to other encyclopedias, the " Encyclopædia Britannica " appeared for the first time in 1771, in three volumes.

At this point the great distinction has to be noted between the 18th century and our own time : that the term " a man of letters " formerly stood—even into the middle of the Victorian Age—for one who had ranged at will in all those fields of study represented in this review of 18th century prose-writers—philosophy, travel, history, fiction, science, religion and so on. Unhappily, but perhaps inevitably, the 19th century saw a great change in the direction of " specializing," not only by writers, but also by readers. In the 18th century it was accounted no discredit to a writer that he expended his energies in many different fields of thought, that he wrote histories, biographies, poems, criticisms, philosophies, stories. In our day such versatility is regarded with suspicion, and authors, encouraged by their publishers, find it profitable to limit themselves to one branch of literature only. That is the author's excuse, and it is perhaps a valid one ; but the reader who confines himself to only one class of reading has no excuse. The man who to-day would be well read should go for example or precedent to the " men of letters " of the 18th century, who regarded the whole field of literature as their hunting-ground.

LESSON 34

Short Review of 19th Century Prose

(See plates 31 and 32)

NINETEENTH century prose, infinite in its variety of style, is distinguished by its rich complexity of matter and its widely contrasted points of view. Goethe's remark that there are many echoes but few voices is largely true of all literary periods ; but the voices of the nineteenth century will compare advantageously with those of any preceding period. Where prose is concerned they are heard at their best, perhaps, in the novel. But they are hardly less resonant in the essay, the biography, the history, the book of theology, the narrative of travel, the scientific treatise, the studies of philosophy, art, education and economics. While a certain complacency, or easy optimism, was characteristic of some eminent writers, there was a greater number of eminent writers loudly protesting against self and national satisfaction, opposing such thought with a spirit of inquiry and unrest, with a passionate denunciation of social and human ills and injustices.

If the twentieth century opened for us with a wider mental outlook it is due largely to the work accomplished in the preceding century in the domain of English letters, when our great writers took to heart the aphorism of an eighteenth-century poet. They saw with Pope that " the proper study of mankind is man."

The literature of knowledge and the literature of power belonging to this period are alike marked by a dominating but informed interrogative ; for it was not only in imaginative writing that the last century witnessed what Watts-Dunton called " the Renascence of Wonder," but in all fields of literature—in criticism and science, not less than in poetry and romance—this re-birth of " wonder " took place. The originator of the phrase thus explains it : " The Renascence of Wonder merely indicates that there are two great impulses governing man, and probably not man only, but the entire world of conscious life : the impulse of acceptance —the impulse to take unchallenged and for granted all the phenomena of the outer world as they are—and the impulse to confront these phenomena with eyes of inquiry and wonder."

Before studying the effects, let us glance at the causes of this change in the nation's literary life. The French Revolution shattered the scholastic formalism of English letters. Jean Jacques Rousseau stirred up a feeling for humanity such as England had never before acquired from French or Italian writers, much as she had been influenced previously by Continental models. The effects of the French Terror threw the thoughtful back for a time into the slough of despond. We have seen how Wordsworth, for example, was bowed down in this way. Then a Scottish teacher read Mme. de Staël's " De l'Allemagne," set himself to master the German language, put Jean Paul Richter in the place of Jean Jacques Rousseau, and by the exercise, on the one hand, of the extraordinary knowledge he acquired of German philosophy and German individualism, and his painstaking elucidation of the Cromwellian epoch, on the other, set aloft an ideal of manhood and patriotic duty which influenced materially the popular view of history, and the outlook on Nature and Life.

There were others, besides Carlyle, who drank deeply at the Teutonic spring. Wordsworth was one, Coleridge another, Byron a third ; Scott and De Quincey were of the company. Each was affected differently, but at the same time profoundly.

Had there been no " Renascence of Wonder " we had seen few, if any, of the marvellous inventions which rubricate the nineteenth in the calendar of centuries. Thus romance was reborn ; metaphysics acquired a new meaning ; humour was reincarnated. Men longed to look at things as they were—to see them " whole." Carlyle entered as an iconoclast into the temple of " the Gigmanities," and of all the master-minds of the century Carlyle is the one who, both directly and indirectly, stirred most deeply the heart of the vast reading public called into being by the mechanical inventions of " the Wonderful Century."

The history of the essay, both critical and constructive, in the century we are considering, is bound up with the history of the periodical. Something of the same kind may be said of both poetry and the novel. The various periodicals having a political bias, if not basis ; literature developed more or less under the aegis of politics. The writers made the reviews, and the reviews helped to make the writers.

Today much of the vital force which animated the work of earlier writers has been scattered, much of their " thunder " has been stolen, the knowledge in the light of which they wrote has been found to be misleading. But the saving salt of an individual style preserves many an old and obsolete book from the blight of oblivion.

Among the influences on later prose must be remembered the prose of the poets—the prefaces of Wordsworth, the miscellanies of Scott, the critical essays of Coleridge, the letters of Byron, Shelley and Keats. But the student has a wonderful variety of object lessons in style before him, apart from these great names. There are the Puritan fervour, the irony, and grim humour of Carlyle, the gentle intimacy of Charles Lamb, the graceful confidences of Leigh Hunt, the aerial cadence of De Quincey, the emphatic, unmistakable vigour of Cobbett, the brilliant antitheses of the sometimes prejudiced, sometimes complacent, but always vitally interesting Macaulay, the incisive phrases of Hazlitt, the wit of Sydney Smith, the beautiful imagery and deeply penetrative criticism of Ruskin, the flowing sea-music of Swinburne, the classic beauty of Landor's dialogues, the perfect serenity and harmony of Newman, the scholarly prose of Matthew Arnold, the undecorated diction of Hallam and Freeman, the

(283)

picturesque pages of Froude, the jewelled sentences of Walter Pater, the sparkle of Stevenson, and the austerely great prose of Charles Doughty, whose " Travels in Arabia Deserta " was for long so little known. In the main the prose writer who aspires to style must be an artist just as the poet is an artist, but the secret of style is, ultimately, the harmony between the subject and its treatment.

For general purposes style has been considerably influenced by the usage of journalism. The Press is responsible for a marked lessening of the distinction between written and spoken language. There must always be some distinction between the two. The skilled writer must of necessity possess a close acquaintance with the meaning of words ; and it is, perhaps a defective knowledge of the meaning of words that lies at the root of most failures in composition.

The speaker, by means of accent, emphasis, look, gesture, personality, can lend significance to a comparatively poor speech. The writer must find literary equivalents for the methods and circumstances of platform and pulpit. But the aim of the writer who addresses himself to a wide public should be directed to the perfection of a style that shall be distinctive—a copied style is but a mask—clear and colloquial, yet avoiding baldness and vulgarity, and in which foreign words are used sparingly.

While the essayists have done much to increase our knowledge of bygone literature, as well as to popularize various branches of scientific learning, the biographers have given to the prose of the period some of its greatest intellectual assets. Southey's " Nelson," Lockhart's " Scott," Carlyle's " Cromwell," and " Sterling," Lewes's " Goethe," Froude's " Carlyle," Masson's " Milton," Spedding's " Bacon," Stanley's " Arnold," are classics.

The influence of English historical methods has been world-wide. The nineteenth century historians—Hallam, Buckle, Macaulay, Lecky, Green and others—are worthy successors of Gibbon. They have determined the unity of history, and made it fascinating.

Theology and science, philosophy, politics, economics, art, education and travel will be discussed later. Meantime, two facts of especial interest must be noted. One is the high literary value of much of the scientific literature of the time, as disclosed, for example, in the writings of Huxley ; the other is the distinction attained by women writers.

LESSON 35

Some 19th Century Critics and Essayists

(See plates 32–34)

DUE attention has already been given to the poetical productions of Samuel Taylor Coleridge (1772–1834) and Robert Southey (1774–1843). With regard to their prose writings it has to be said that no serious student of English criticism can afford to neglect those of Coleridge. His " Lectures and Notes on Shakespeare " are especially valuable both on account of their great intrinsic worth and of the effects they had on later estimates of the national poet. As for Southey, few men whose names are remembered in literature ever wrote more that has been forgotten than did he. His fertility of production was as amazing as its variety. He was a scholar, and, considered as a stylist alone, claims a high place among his contemporaries. And yet, " of what is called style," he said, " not a thought enters my head at any time. I only endeavour to write plain English, and put my thoughts in language which everyone can understand." Herein lies the secret of his style, however. To think that academic prose need be great prose is to conjure up the fallacy that style can exist apart from matter. His greatest prose work is the classic " Life of Nelson."

Sir Walter Scott (1771–1832) wrote almost as incessantly and as variously as Southey, but with greater success, independently of his greatest work as a novelist. His essays on chivalry, romance and the drama, and his letters on demonology and witchcraft, are still eminently readable ; and he was a painstaking as well as a capable editor, especially of Swift.

John Wilson (1785–1854), the " Christopher North " of " Blackwood's Magazine," is chiefly remembered as the literary parent of De Quincey, as part author of that brilliant series of dialogues " Noctes Ambrosianæ," and as author of a work entitled " Lights and Shadows of Scottish Life."

John Gibson Lockhart (1794–1854), Scott's son-in-law, and Wilson's friend and colleague on " Blackwood," who succeeded Gifford as editor of the " Quarterly," gave to journalism much that by right should have been devoted to literature. His masterpiece is the " Life " of Scott.

One of the greatest, as he is one of the least pretentious, of English prose writers is Charles Lamb (1775–1834). Master of as many styles as he possessed moods, he is full of elusive echoes of the old writers whom he loved. His is the art that conceals art, for seemingly he is as frank and as communicative as Montaigne. His character is written in his " Essays " ; his autobiography in his Letters. But Lamb was not only an essayist of unique charm ; he was also a critic of rare insight and surprising accuracy. Nothing that he wrote, or that others wrote of him, should the student neglect. He dared to be original in criticism and forestalled George Bernard Shaw in the use of paradox. " The paradoxes of a critic as great as Lamb are aflame with the insight of genius, and he brought readers to see that conventional judgements may prove even wilder and more fallacious than the new and surprising point of view " (" English Literature in the Nineteenth Century," Laurie Magnus).

William Hazlitt (1778–1830) was indebted to Lamb, and acknowledged the indebtedness ; but with a critical faculty as keen as that of Lamb he possessed not a scintilla of " Elia's " human sympathy ; hence, whereas the one is loved the other is given the meed of almost frigid praise. Yet Hazlitt's is a name of first importance. He is the master of the apt and illuminating phrase. The student of Shakespeare owes much to Coleridge's " Lectures," he owes much also to Lamb's " Critical Essays," but he must also study, and study with attention, Hazlitt's " Characters of Shakespeare's Plays " —a work dedicated to Lamb—and the " Lectures on the Dramatic Literature of the Reign of Elizabeth." Of equal note are the " Lectures on the English Comic Writers " and " Lectures on the English Poets." There is, however, more venom than justice in the personal sketches he called " The Spirit of the Age."

Thomas De Quincey (1785–1859) stands sponsor to the school of " prose poets," of which Swinburne is the great exemplar. He has much to attract, but is dangerous to follow. He lacks a certain dignity, is normally without what we understand by the word " reverence," and is at times terribly discursive ; but we must remember that the bulk of his work was anonymous journalism, and that the writer kept up a weak physique by the use of opium. The " Confessions," the historical essays, and the " Autobiographic Sketches " should be closely studied. De Quincey has been styled the " Boswell of Essayism," so intimate are his revelations of both himself and his associates. He possessed to an almost amazing degree an instinct for dramatic expression. Whatever some of whom he wrote may have thought of his character drawing, he was well liked personally. This great essayist was a rhapsodist, but he was, too, an inquirer, and his valuable influence was against cast-iron formality in prose.

William Cobbett (1762–1835) started life by scaring crows, but left a name which should be remembered. He may be said to personify the whole art of self-education. By self-denial and perseverance he acquired a vast sum of varied knowledge, and wielded immense influence as a politician and journalist.

Despite extraordinary difficulties, he learnt English and French so well as to be able to write grammars in both languages, and developed a literary style as natural as Defoe's, as vigorous as Swift's, brightened by humour and telling invective, and perhaps as characteristically Saxon as any that could be named.

Cobbett's " English Grammar " and " French Grammar " are written in the form of letters to his son, and are unsurpassed in the lucidity of their arrangement and their quality of genuine liveliness. The " English Grammar " may be commended as vastly entertaining as well as instructive. His " Weekly Political Register," started in 1802, was continued apart from one small break, until his death. In 1803 he began the " Parliamentary Debates," whence developed our present " Hansard." He wrote a " History of the Reformation," which is still read, though chiefly by Roman Catholics. His " Advice to Young Men " is full of practical common sense for men and women. Its vigour and frankness are as refreshing as the breath of the sea.

His best work is to be found in the picturesque accounts of his political tours on horseback, " Cobbett's Rural Rides." Cobbett is not a great literary character; but his style is the best of models for all who aspire to write clearly and correctly.

Walter Savage Landor (1775–1864) has already been dealt with as a poet. His prose masterpiece is his " Imaginary Conversations," 125 in number, published between 1824 and 1853. Full of fine thought expressed in a highly finished, eloquent style, felicitous in imagery and diction, and bearing a clear impress of genius and cultivated taste, they range over a vast area of topics, discussing questions of statesmanship, philosophy, poetry, literature, life and manners, and reveal strong dramatic qualities which have caused many to wonder why their author failed to write a great play. Among the dialogues specially admired for their dramatic intensity are those between Peter the Great and Alexis, and Henry VIII and Anne Boleyn. By one studying Shakespeare's life, Landor's " Citation of William Shakespeare " may be read as a charming piece of imaginative prose

Isaac D'Israeli (1766–1848), the father of Lord Beaconsfield, wrote a number of anecdotal works which, though somewhat slipshod, offer evidence of much culture and wide reading, being chiefly notable for the entertainment they afford and the stimulus they give to further inquiry in the by-paths of literary history. " The Curiosities of Literature" is the best of these ; its companions are " Calamities and Quarrels of Authors," " Amenities of Literature " and " The Literary Character."

William Hone (1780–1842) was a sort of minor Cobbett, with something of D'Israeli's feeling for letters. His " Every-Day Book," " Table-Book," and " Year-Book " bear tribute to his industrious study of old manners and customs, but are chiefly valuable as works of reference to the literary man.

The " Papers " of John Wilson Croker (1780–1857) and Thomas Creevey (1768–1838) supply much intimate detail of the Court, literary, and political life of their time, the one from a Tory, and the other from a Whig point of view. Croker was a frequent contributor to the " Quarterly Review." His chief work was an edition of Boswell which drew forth a remarkably bitter criticism from Macaulay.

Another essayist of considerable charm and versatility is James Leigh Hunt (1784–1859), whose friendships secure for him a greater need of recognition than his writings, though these are not unimportant. He introduced Shelley and Keats to one another and brought these poets before the public in " The Examiner," of which he was editor and part proprietor. The student of English literature will find much profit in his " Imagination and Fancy," " Wit and Humour " and " Men, Women and Books." His " Dante's Divine Comedy : The Book and its Story " is also of value, while his " Autobiography " contains enough to secure for it the permanent interest of all bookmen. London and " The Cockney School " found in him an energetic champion, and his gossipy volume on " The Town : Its Remarkable Characters and Events " retains a certain measure of popularity.

Three other minor writers of the period call for mention here. Nassau William Senior (1790–1864) was an acute literary critic

QUARTETTE OF ESSAYISTS. Upper row : left, William Hazlitt (1778–1830), who, after studying art, turned to literature and won his way into the first rank of English literary critics ; right, Thomas De Quincey (1785–1859), who, after youthful wanderings immortalized in his " Confessions of an English Opium Eater," became a prolific contributor to the literary magazines. Bottom row : left, Walter Savage Landor (1775–1864)—Carlyle's " unsubduable old Roman "—was an aristocratic republican who in the course of a chequered career wrote much excellent verse and prose ; right, James Henry Leigh Hunt (1784–1859), editor of " The Examiner," friend of Moore, Byron and Shelley, and the wielder of the delightfully humorous and fanciful style.

ENGLISH LITERATURE 35

WILLIAM COBBETT (1762–1835). Born at Farnham, Surrey, a farmer's son, he started in 1802 his " Weekly Political Register " and became one of the foremost Radical journalists. He wrote some forty books.
ENGLISH LITERATURE 35

JANE WELSH CARLYLE (1801–66). Born at Haddington, daughter of Dr. John Welsh, she married Thomas Carlyle in 1826, and remained his inspirer until her death from heart failure when driving in Hyde Park. A woman of brilliant gifts, she is famed as a letter writer.
ENGLISH LITERATURE 36

MID-VICTORIAN MEN OF LETTERS. Left to right : Edward Fitzgerald (1809–83), best remembered for his poetical translation of " The Rubaiyat of Omar Khayyam," first published in 1859 ; John Brown (1810–82), a Scottish physician who penned a number of humorous essays on a variety of topics ; George Henry Lewes (1817–78), after studying medicine, drifted into journalism, made several solid contributions to the literature of science and philosophy, and became the intimate friend of Marian Evans (George Eliot) ; John Forster (1812–76) edited the " Daily News " for a short time and wrote lives of Oliver Goldsmith and Charles Dickens.
ENGLISH LITERATURE 36

Plate 34   *Volume V*

19TH CENTURY MEN OF LETTERS. Left to right: top row: Walter Bagehot (1826–77), a banker who wrote excellently on the English constitution, the money market, sociology and literature; Sir Leslie Stephen (1832–1904), editor of the Dictionary of National Biography and author of many "lives" Walter Theodore Watts-Dunton (1832–1914), intimate friend of Borrow, Swinburne and Morris, and a highly esteemed literary critic. Below: John (Lord) Morley (1838–1923), a Liberal politician who held high office and wrote much in biography; Walter Horatio Pater (1839–94), exponent of the Renaissance; John Addington Symonds (1840–93), poet, essayist and translator, who revelled in things Greek and Italian.
ENGLISH LITERATURE 37

LATE VICTORIAN PROSEMEN. Left to right, above: Henry Austin Dobson (1840–1921), a civil servant who wrote verse and a number of studies in 18th century life and literature; Andrew Lang (1844–1912), a Scotsman, who produced a vast and varied quantity of literary journalism; Sir Edmund Gosse (1849–1928), one of the leading critics of his time. Below: Archibald Philip Primrose, 5th earl of Rosebery (1847–1929) Liberal premier 1894–5, and an eminent man of letters; John Richard Jefferies (1848–87) and William Henry Hudson (1841–1922), gifted writers with a remarkable insight into Nature. ENGLISH LITERATURE 38

CRITICS AND ESSAYISTS. Left, George Saintsbury (1845–1933), who was for twenty years professor of rhetoric and English literature at Edinburgh and came to be widely regarded as the leading authority on English and French literature ; right, Mrs. Alice Meynell (1850–1922) won fame as a poetess and as the writer of choice essays.
ENGLISH LITERATURE 39

'THE CHESTERBELLOC.' Gilbert Keith Chesterton (1874–1936) was born in London and studied art before he turned to poetry, the essay, criticism and fantastic fiction. A convert to Roman Catholicism and an ardent admirer of medieval ways and thought, in his political faith he was a " distributist," seeking the widest possible distribution of property and the strengthening of the " small man " in business and agriculture. Hilaire Belloc (right) was born at St. Cloud in 1870, and served for a time in the French artillery. Naturalized British in 1902, he was a Liberal M.P. 1906-10, when he retired disillusioned by politics and devoted himself to literature. For long he worked in close conjunction with " G.K.C." —Chesterton, e.g., illustrated several of Belloc's books—and hence the two were often referred to as " The Chesterbelloc." ENGLISH LITERATURE 39

Plate 36

Volume V

as well as a political economist. His " Essays on Fiction," contributed to the " Quarterly," " Edinburgh," and other reviews, were published in collected form in 1864. William Maginn (1793–1842), scholar, critic, humorist, was once a great force in the magazine world. He was one of " Blackwood's " most brilliant contributors, and as the conductor of " Fraser's Magazine," he gathered round him some of the most distinguished of contemporary writers. Finally, Anna Brownell Jameson (1794–1860) wrote on art and " The Characteristics of Shakespeare's Women."

LESSON 36

Carlyle, Macaulay and Froude

(See plates 31, 32 and 34)

THOMAS CARLYLE (1795–1881) began his literary career as a writer in " The Edinburgh Encyclopædia," for which, between 1820 and 1823, he wrote articles on Lady Mary Wortley Montagu, Montaigne, Montesquieu, Dr. John Moore, Sir John Moore, Necker, Nelson, Mungo Park, Lord Chatham, William Pitt, and several papers of a topographical character. Only one of these—the paper on Sir John Moore—can be described as inadequate.

From the first Carlyle seldom spared himself. In 1824 he published two translations—one from the French (Legendre's " Geometry ") and one from the German (Goethe's " Wilhelm Meister "). The latter work, praised by " Blackwood's " and the " Edinburgh," was attacked by De Quincey in " The London Magazine," to which Carlyle had been contributing his " Life of Schiller," the last chapters of which actually appeared simultaneously with the unjustifiable attack. Whatever pain may have been caused by De Quincey was more than assuaged by the commendation by Goethe, who wrote a eulogistic introduction to a translation of the Schiller volume which was published at Frankfort in 1830, three years after Carlyle's period of apprenticeship may be said to have been brought to a close with his studies of German Romance. Meanwhile, Carlyle had met Jeffrey and become a contributor to " The Edinburgh Review."

One of the real curiosities of literature is the distinction between the form of Carlyle's early writings and that known as

"Carlylese," the undoubtedly powerful, but electrical, explosive, ejaculatory style whose beginning may be noted in his "Sartor Resartus," a work of autobiographical as well as of philosophical interest, which, originally published in "Frazer's Magazine," first won adequate recognition in America.

The reader who would study Carlyle aright should begin by digesting Professor Nichol's masterly monograph in the "English Men of Letters" series; Froude's contentious pages may be left for a later stage.

Carlyle's greatest works are those in history, sociology and politics. But there is a great deal in his miscellaneous essays—those on Burns, Johnson, Scott, Voltaire, Diderot and Mirabeau, for example—that must not be overlooked by any reader who desires to understand the man himself. Carlyle has been greatly misunderstood; but his influence has been almost incalculable in Germany as well as in England. He was "human, like ourselves"; more, perhaps, of an iconoclast and a prophet than a constructive power; but he looked to the "foundations of society," he had a genuine love of truth, and his striving after truth has left to posterity a standard of thought which must remain a permanent social as well as literary force.

Appreciations—and depreciations—of his labours there are in abundance, but perhaps Walt Whitman touched the reality:

"As a representative author, a literary figure, no man else will bequeath to the future more significant hints of our stormy era, its fierce paradoxes, its din, and its struggling periods than Carlyle. He belongs to our own branch of the stock, too; neither Latin nor Greek, but altogether Gothic. Rugged, mountainous, volcanic, he was himself more a French Revolution than any of his volumes. . . . As launching into the self-complacent atmosphere of our days a rasping, questioning, dislocating agitation and shock, is Carlyle's final value."

Carlyle began life, in a sense, by teaching mathematics in a Fifeshire school; he remained a teacher to the end of the chapter. As a stylist he is the greatest "free lance" in the language; but the reader should beware lest he impute to the leader the sins of his would-be followers, as many a one has sought to thunder in Carlylean strain with the most unhappy results. Where Carlyle's style is concerned we must not judge him by the standard of any other writer; he claims by right to be judged by the vivid (and vivifying) result. Of no great writer could it be said with more cogency that " the style is the man."

It is impossible in a few words to formulate any plan for the especial study of Carlyle. From the wide range of his writings the general reader will take to such works as his fancy prompts, the student to those his studies suggest, and both may be left safely to come under the all-compelling influence of this virile and original thinker. Of Carlyle's works the general reader should at least be acquainted with " The French Revolution," " Sartor Resartus," " Heroes and Hero Worship " and " The Life of John Sterling." If one begins with " Heroes and Hero Worship," the appetite is more likely to be whetted than by entering the Carlyle treasure-house through the gate of " The French Revolution."

Wellnigh as interesting as anything Carlyle wrote was the story of his own married life, which, indeed, has been fruitful of more controversy than any of his boldest assertions in the domain of philosophy. Jane Welsh Carlyle (1801–66) was almost as notable a personality as her husband, for her " Letters and Memorials " prove her to have been one of the most accomplished women of her time, a shrewd critic, and fit to rank with the great letter-writers who have contributed no inconsiderable proportion of what we call our national literature. Mrs. Alexander Ireland wrote an excellent Life of Mrs. Carlyle.

Macaulay. Carlyle's greatest contemporary as an essayist and historian was Thomas Babington Macaulay (1800–59). Unlike Carlyle, Macaulay did not confine his labours to the desk. He was a public official and a member of Parliament as well as a man of letters. After a careful education he became famous at the age of twenty-five as the writer of an essay on Milton in " The Edinburgh Review." In this Review all his best-known essays appeared, if we except the biographies of Atterbury, Bunyan, Goldsmith, Johnson and Pitt, which were contributed to " The Encyclopædia Britannica." The Essays are rich in applied knowledge, drawn from the exceptionally retentive memory of an omnivorous reader. The judgements they contain, where these are not affected by the author's Whig sympathies, are usually sound. For a parallel to their diversity of subject matter we must go to Landor's " Conversations."

Macaulay was essentially a popular writer, one whose purpose was to think for his reader and to leave nothing to chance. Whole generations may be said to have been nurtured on his writings. His influence will always be considerable both as a stylist and- as a historian, though he needs careful editing.

His great quality is clearness of diction, which he shares with Cobbett, his great art that of detail-decorated abbreviation ; but his use of a succession of short sentences, while agreeable to the eye, is not invariably acceptable to the ear. His use of antithesis is responsible for much deplorably ineffective imitation. He remains, withal, a brilliant writer ; but, being brilliant, is hard. What he gains in glitter he misses in emotion ; he does not delve very deeply into the heart of things ; but without his aid many men and women of average insight and ability would never have been able to see so far or so well as they have seen. In this connexion the educative value of Macaulay's writings cannot easily be exaggerated ; it may be more easily satirized. In the realm of prose his relation to Carlyle is that of Tennyson to Browning in the realm of poetry, although Macaulay in his clear brilliance may better be compared with Pope. It is curious to note that, in judging Scott, both Carlyle and Macaulay erred, if at all, on the side of severity ; but it is useful to remember that neither had the Journal before him.

Macaulay has been infinitely happier in his biographer than was Carlyle in Froude ; the fine tribute of his nephew, Sir George Otto Trevelyan, to his memory reveals to us a family affection undisclosed in the Essays.

Perhaps the greatest of Carlyle's contemporaries was John Stuart Mill (1806–73), the philosopher whose " System of Logic," " Principles of Political Economy," " On Liberty," and " Subjection of Women " will not be read for any literary graces if they do not attract the student in search of profitable mental exercise. It would be difficult to overestimate the influence of the " Saint of Rationalism " (Gladstone's apt phrase) on contemporary thought in politics, logic and ethics.

A vigorous freedom of criticism, a display of conscience in judgement, and a certain earnestness in matters of the mind remained a worthy characteristic of the Victorian age, though tending to ponderosity and eventually declining into mere dullness. Many are the names that might be mentioned in this relation, but four only shall be alluded to here : Edward Fitzgerald (1809–83), of Omar Khayyam fame, mainly for his wonderful letters—amongst others those to Fanny Kemble .

Dr. John Brown (1810–82), the essayist, almost comparable with Lamb in lucidity, for his exquisite " Rab and His Friends " ; John Forster (1812–76) for his excellent " Life of Dickens " and " The Life and Times of Oliver Goldsmith," one of the best biographies in English literature ; and George Eliot's friend, George Henry Lewes (1817–78), a most able encyclopedist with a great gift of popularizing the abstruse. His " History of Philosophy " and " Life of Goethe " are very competent works ; " On Actors and the Art of Acting " is another of his books that will repay study. Lewes founded " The Fortnightly Review " which still exists—as a monthly.

Froude. The name of James Anthony Froude (1818–94) has been the centre of a veritable whirlwind of controversy, which relates to literary history rather than to the study of literature. The friend of Carlyle, whose literary executor he was, Froude had much of Carlyle's sincerity and he was not less able as a writer. Indeed, he stands with the supreme prose masters of the century, his thought often soaring to heights of true eloquence. But he rivalled Macaulay in partisanship when he wrote history, which was the main concern of his literary life. Froude's contentious character colours all he wrote, yet his " Nemesis of Faith," in which he reveals with deep sincerity his religious doubts, and " Oceana "—a delightful account of a voyage to Australia—are fascinating books, and his " Short Studies on Great Subjects " constitute the most brilliant and engaging series of essays and papers that ever emanated from one hand.

LESSON 37

Sensitive Masters of the Art of Criticism

(See plates 32 and 35)

JOHN RUSKIN (1819–1900) proved a great social force, as well as a great critic. Among his paramount services to criticism were his early recognition of Turner's genius and his defence of the pre-Raphaelites. (*See* Lesson 19 in Art and Architecture, volume 4, page 60.) He was the most influential art-critic of the century ; but his authority like that of many eminent Victorians suffered diminution during the early years of this century. Today he is quoted by most writers on painting, sculpture and architecture, and his ideas are frequently in accordance with the deepest thought of our time. The centre of his artistic creed was belief in " Truth to Nature," but he upheld the structural artist who explained natural forms against the artist who gave a momentary impression of them. Thus he praised Holman Hunt and Turner and blamed Constable and Whistler.

He imparted an incalculable impetus to the raising of the standard of labour ; whatever nature of labour it may be, it can hardly be regarded without some respect by anyone who has come under the influence of Ruskin's teaching. Like Carlyle, and, in a lesser degree, like Froude, Ruskin gloried in the power of imparting and inspiring enthusiasm. He sought after the truth with all the ardour of Carlyle, and the student of his works will witness how, time after time, he was compelled by his own discoveries to relinquish positions he at one time thought to be unassailable. He was the scientific spirit of inquiry—even his drawings he regarded rather as of scientific than of artistic importance.

Ruskin was the embodiment of the spirit of reverence, and a high priest of the temple of beauty. He has opened our eyes to the infinite variety and charm of external Nature, and even the clouds have a different meaning to us since Ruskin wrote about them. His style glows with rich colour, and is full of musical sweetness. It is impregnated with the influence of Bible study, an influence which, however, can be realized only by those whose knowledge of the Bible corresponds in some measure to Ruskin's own intimate grasp of it. Everything he wrote is worth reading, from " The Seven Lamps of Architecture " to " Fors Clavigera." A modern analysis of his life and work is contained in " John Ruskin " by R. J. Wilenski ; the author, in summarizing, accepts Ruskin as a lawgiver, and acknowledges his vital contributions to the theories of sociology and aesthetics.

Matthew Arnold (1822–88), whose work as a poet has already been discussed, combined social with literary criticism. He foretold the fall of the aristocracy, and distrusted the middle classes, but much that has been written and said concerning his " contempt for unintellectual people " is unjustified, and caused him no small amount of disquiet, as his " Letters "—especially the epistle written to his mother in 1868—testify. As a writer, he had much in common with Sainte-Beuve, perhaps the greatest literary critic of the nineteenth century, his standpoint in regard to art and letters being in many respects more French than

English. First and foremost, he was a scholar and valued scholarship highly. His " Essays in Criticism," " Culture and Anarchy," " Literature and Dogma," and an earlier work " On Translating Homer " are his most widely read books.

Another critic born in the same year as Arnold was David Masson (1822–1907). A Scottish author and editor of erudition and broad sympathies, he wrote much for encyclopedias, reviews, and the periodical press, and his contributions to our knowledge of the English novelists, and of De Quincey, Chatterton, Carlyle, Drummond of Hawthornden and—especially—Ben Jonson, are of value. His greatest work is his " Life of John Milton, Narrated in Connection with the Political, Ecclesiastical and Literary History of his Time," a work which has been described as the most complete biography of any Englishman. Masson held chairs of English Literature in University College, London, and (1865–95) at Edinburgh.

Goldwin Smith (1823–1910) had the true Carlylean independence and intolerance in his outlook on society, and although most that he wrote has a professional dryness of style, he could be attractive on purely literary subjects, as witness his books on Cowper and Jane Austen, and also his essays. But he was essentially an exponent of history and a controversialist. Another of that generation of thinkers was Alfred Russel Wallace (1823–1913)—famous also for his independent working out of the theory of natural selection chiefly associated with Charles Darwin—who wrote a good fluent style, especially in " Travels on the Amazon " and " The Malay Archipelago," whilst Augustus Jessop (1824–1914) had an attractive manner in such books as " The Coming of the Friars " and " Trials of a Country Parson."

Periodical journalism was now at its literary best in the weeklies like " The Saturday Review," " The Examiner " and " The Spectator," and in the monthlies like " Blackwood's " and " The Cornhill," and, of course, in the quarterlies. Their peculiar use was to give encouragement to good writers and also to produce men like Holt Hutton of " The Spectator," William Minto of " The Examiner," Henry Morley, who also edited that journal in the course of his wonderful career as a popularizer of good literature, and Walter Bagehot (1826–77), editor of " The Economist," who wrote authoritative works on the English Constitution and " Lombard Street," and " Physics and Politics," an attempt to apply Darwinian ideas to political development.

Frederic Harrison (1831–1923) was a young man when Carlyle had his generation by the ears, and he profited accordingly. He was a true scholar, who found his chief delight in the study of history, on which he wrote much and wisely. His interest in the Byzantine period induced him to try his hand at historic romance with "Theophano," but he was essentially a biographer, a literary critic—his instructive volume "On the Choice of Books" should be noted—and a writer on positivism, philosophy and religion.

Sir Leslie Stephen (1832–1904), brother and biographer of Sir James Fitzjames Stephen of "The Saturday Review," edited "The Cornhill" and wrote much in biography. He was the original editor of "The Dictionary of National Biography," and in "An Agnostic's Apology" made one of the most valuable additions to the literature of rationalism. His clear, unadorned style, just a trifle icy, is entirely suited to his clear argument. His "Hours in a Library" should on no account be overlooked. Of the same year as Stephen was that brilliant Irishman Stopford A. Brooke (1832–1916), who won renown as a Unitarian preacher as well as a critic of literature. His "Primer of English Literature" has been of great service to generations of young students, and his study of Tennyson is still unexcelled.

A particularly sensitive critic of literature—especially poetry—and one of the most potent critical forces of the last century, was Theodore Watts-Dunton (1832–1914). His "Studies of Shakespeare" and "The Renascence of Wonder" are notable productions, but for some of his most remarkable work the student must turn to "The Encyclopædia Britannica" and the leading reviews. For some forty years he was the close friend and companion of Algernon Charles Swinburne (1837–1909), whose poetry has already received attention (Lesson 25, volume 3, page 337). As a critic Swinburne had the faults of over-statement and passionate praise, which anyone would expect who first met him as a poet. His prose was the fine, vibrant prose of a poet, and his biographical and critical studies, ranging from the Elizabethans to the Victorians, offer unusual opportunities for the awakening of enthusiasms. If the reader is careful not to place himself too completely at the critic's disposition he will have considerable increase of literary understanding. Philip Gilbert Hamerton (1834–94) wrote a series of letters on "The Intellectual Life," which literary aspirants should not neglect.

Carlyle had written everything of his that mattered by the time John Morley (1838–1923) was twenty-one, but although we know that Morley was the pupil of John Stuart Mill—whence the austerity of his literary style—there are few whose names occur in this Lesson that gave more evidence of having been influenced by the liberal ideas which the Sage of Chelsea set himself to implant in the mind of his generation. His " Life of Gladstone " is his magnum opus, but before it appeared in 1903, he had won a European reputation by his studies of Burke, Voltaire, Rousseau, Diderot, Cobden and Machiavelli.

Two other eminent men of affairs born in the same year as Lord Morley, and whose literary work also entitles them to rank among the prose masters of the century, are Sir George Trevelyan (1838–1928), whose " Life of Lord Macaulay " is one of the great biographies, and Lord Bryce (1838–1922), whose principal productions, " The Holy Roman Empire " and " The American Commonwealth," are established standard works.

Eminent among the other critics who lent distinction to English letters in the latter part of the nineteenth century was Walter Horatio Pater (1839–94), whose exclusiveness was akin to that which so long kept Matthew Arnold aloof from the average reader, and whose " Sketches in the History of the Renaissance," " Imaginary Portraits " and " Appreciations " are marked by an exotic beauty of style, refinement of taste, breadth of culture, and keenness of insight. Into the point of view of Walter Pater it is not here necessary to enter, but this must come into consideration where the permanent value of his literary work is under appraisement.

A similar remark is called for in regard to the writings of another hedonist, John Addington Symonds (1840–93), who also helped to bring the bright side of the Renaissance, as well as that of Elizabethan England, before English readers. The splendid selfishness of these writers, however, cannot compensate for all the problems they left untouched. To them, engrossed in their introspection, it mattered not that the times were out of joint—as the times of their aesthetic movement, culminating in the writings of Oscar Wilde, undoubtedly were.

LESSON 38

Versatile Prosemen of the Late 19th Century

(See plate 35)

IT has already been frankly admitted that mere chronological order in the survey of a long and rich literature is almost as arbitrary a method of treatment as alphabetical order, but for the purpose of these Lessons it has advantages that cannot be denied. In the present Lesson it has the further justification that, of the critics, essayists and prose writers who figured most prominently in the literary activities of the second half of the nineteenth century, and in their own individual ways represented the later Victorian stream of thought, at least a dozen were born in the decade 1840–50 and had established their reputations before the century ended, although most of them were alive and still industrious when the twentieth century was well under way.

First of these in point of time was Austin Dobson (1840-1921), not a great prose writer but still a moderately good one. While he was elegant and charming in verse, he was somewhat self-conscious in prose, for, avoiding the ornate, he tended at times towards the bald. His " Eighteenth Century Vignettes " are however, full of an old-world charm.

William John Courthope (1842–1917), sometime professor of English poetry at Oxford, published an exhaustive " History of English Poetry " in six volumes which ranks as his chief work, but his " Life of Pope," written for his standard edition of Pope's works, and his " Life of Addison " are of value.

Edward Dowden (1843–1913), the gifted Irish critic, was a student of French and English literature, and his works on Shelley and on Shakespeare in particular have become classic. Every student should own Dowden's concise " Introduction to Shakespeare."

In his own day Andrew Lang (1844-1912) was the recipient of a more generous measure of adulation than he is likely to receive from posterity. A ripe scholar and exceptionally versatile man, he produced some first-rate translations from the Greek, and was poet, critic, philosopher, biographer, essayist, novelist, historian. In truth, there was not much in a literary way that he did not try his hand at, with a temporary degree of success. He was the brightest literary journalist of his age, but his historical work abounds in error ; his literary judgements, always delivered in the most engaging phrases, are not free from asperity and prejudice ; and in matters where he was no sort of authority he spoke with a cocksureness that fortunately did not always persuade his readers. But the literary student will enjoy Andrew Lang's critical works, such as " Books and Bookmen," " Letters to Dead Authors," " Letters on Literature " and " Essays in Little."

John Churton Collins (1848–1908) was a skilled professional critic of literature. His knowledge of English literature prior to his own day was as profound and accurate as his knowledge of contemporary letters was slight and perfunctory. His most competent works, such as " Studies in Shakespeare," " Greek Influence on English Poetry " and " Voltaire, Montesquieu and Rousseau in England," should be read for their scholarship.

In Edmund Gosse (1849–1928) urbanity and literary scholarship were happily combined. Although he wrote much he seldom wrote hastily, his judgements are usually convincing, and his work is as assured of permanence as any modern criticism of letters can be. Either in critical biography or in pure criticism the student has a wide choice among the works of Sir Edmund Gosse—he was knighted in 1925. " Gossip in a Library," " French Profiles " and his " Life of Congreve " are representative works, and in " Father and Son " he gave a fine and dignified study in the intimacies of biography.

Lord Rosebery (1847–1929) must be declared a might-have-been in literature as he was in politics. But his literary achievement is the more lasting ; it is, indeed, so substantial that it is regrettable that he did not devote himself to the life of letters, where the highest success as a master of prose was easily within his attainment. Everything that he wrote is informed with the subtle charm of a winning personality and the magical contact of a true bookman. There is some excellent criticism of letters in his " Appreciations and Addresses," and also in his later work, " Miscellanies, Literary and Historical," while such studies in biography as " Pitt," " Napoleon : the Last Phase " and " Oliver Cromwell " prove that he could have stood with the best of his age.

William Hurrell Mallock (1849–1923), a nephew of Froude, was the master of a very brilliant and incisive prose style, which he used with great effect in his many philosophic and fictive writings. He was greatly concerned all his life with religious and political questions, but although " The New Republic " and " The New Paul and Virginia," which came about the beginning of his literary career, have both had a vogue and may still find readers, the stuff of immortality is not in his work.

Writers on Nature. Thirty-nine years, and three or four of them years of pain and hardship, were all that were measured out to Richard Jefferies (1848-87). He was thirty before he had made a real success with " The Gamekeeper at Home." Nine years later he was dead, yet a whole shelf-ful of memorable books forms his legacy to us : novels, descriptive essays, autobiography. The reader will not regret whatever time he gives to Jefferies, and he will find in him how his native tongue can be written with a joyous expressiveness which on analysis seems to be so simple that it might be thought to be entirely effortless, though writers know that the greatest pains have often been exerted where there is least evidence of any. Jefferies was a conscious artist in words, just as he was a conscious philosopher in his reading of earth's secrets. His acquaintance with the teeming life of the hedgerow was accurate, not sentimental, penetrative, not superficial. " The Story of My Heart " is one of the most engrossing books of confession in our language.

William Henry Hudson (1841-1922) must be placed with the best of the prose masters of his age and in the very forefront of writers about Nature. His style, which is so perfectly contrived for the forthright expression of his observations and opinions that it seems to make use of the only possible words, and those the simplest, has that rare and tenuous charm which pleases continuously without ever making us conscious of the art that is the source of our pleasure. He has no sort of resemblance to Stevenson, and yet in this matter of pure prose he is his peer. Everything of Hudson's will repay reading : no man in our time looked upon wild Nature with a more understanding eye or depicted it with a more friendly pen. " The Naturalist in La Plata " and " Far Away and Long Ago " may be singled out from his many books for particular commendation, and " The Purple Land " and " Green Mansions "—this last containing his wonderful creation Rima—are notable rather for their style than for their stories. Many of his writings are devoted to birds, though in " A Shepherd's Life," one of his finest Nature books, the descriptions of countryside characters, of sheep-dogs, foxes and rabbits and of the wide grasslands of Salisbury Plain, are all lovely things grouped round the central figure of an old Wiltshire shepherd from whom Hudson learnt many of the episodes related.

R.L.S. The name that rubricates the two closing decades of the nineteenth century is that of Robert Louis Stevenson (1850–94) ; and that because Stevenson was the true herald of a return to literary style in an age when slovenliness was common. Stevenson realised with Lowell that the true preservative of literature is style. He never wrote a careless or ill-considered phrase. Thus " Kidnapped " and " Treasure Island " were originally written for a boy's paper, in which disregard of literary grace might have been excused if due respect were paid to the laws of grammar. Yet they were written with all that sensitive feeling for the rhythm of prose, with all that savour of the right and just word, which marked his finest work at the height of his powers.

Stevenson has been described as " the happiest master of vagabond discourse in the whole of the nineteenth century." He began as an essayist, and his chief prose works, apart from fiction, are " An Inland Voyage," " Travels with a Donkey in the Cevennes," " Virginibus Puerisque," " Familiar Studies of Men and Books," " Memories and Portraits," and " Across the Plains." He won fame first as a writer of romance, and then in his intimate prose essays revealed to the public a most winning personality. Some of his best prose is to be found in his short stories, wherein he excelled all his contemporaries.

LESSON 39

Critics and Essayists at the Turn of the Century

(See plate 36)

I⊤ is when the end of a century looms near that the weakness of the system of " thinking in centuries " becomes manifest. There is then a tendency to indulge in a kind of intellectual stock-taking and in an assessment of values, heedless of the fact that, in respect of literature particularly, the perspective of time is all-important to the forming of a lasting estimate. The defects of this system are all the more manifest when the end of a century coincides so exactly with the end of an age as that of the nineteenth century did with the close of the Victorian age. Actually, of course, in matters of the mind change is no more abrupt between one century and another than between any one year and another, and the current of literature flows on in one unbroken stream. Thus many of the writers—Samuel Butler, Hardy and H. G. Wells, for instance—who were prominent in the latter part of the nineteenth century, were emerging from Victorian ideas of permanency and of belief in the perfection of present civilization, while many have done the more important part of their work in the lifetime of the present generation.

A leading critic for many years was Professor George Saintsbury (1845–1933), a veritable storehouse of literary knowledge, with a range wellnigh universal and a fine humanity in his interests. His works are numerous—" A History of Criticism " is especially valuable—and their scholarship is unassailable ; their critical content is distinguished by knowledge and acute perception, but is expressed in phrases oddly rugged and often unkempt.

Almost coeval with Professor Saintsbury is Augustine Birrell (1850–1933), widely known as the author of " Obiter Dicta," " Res Judicatae," " Men, Women and Books," and a collected edition of suave and charming " Essays " prefaced by a characteristically frank and revealing introduction. Pleasure and profit are to be gathered from everything he wrote. Birrell belonged to the amateurs of the pen, as literature was never more than a walking-stick to him ; the law and politics were his crutches. But it is a very elegant walking-stick.

Alice Meynell (1850–1922) wrote profoundly meditative and beautiful essays possessing exceptional grace of diction. Her literary criticism was penetrating and sympathetic, revealing her acquaintance with life. The student of lovely and living prose should on no account miss " The Collected Essays of Alice Meynell " (1914). Her touch is sure, and her severely disciplined emotions permitted clarity of vision.

Sir William Robertson Nicoll (1851–1923) played an almost unique part in the literary world of his time, exercising great influence through the medium of " The British Weekly." He was a critic of the utmost catholicity, nearly always right in his opinions, as his taste in letters was delicate and true. Though not to be classed among the prose masters, he had a style that was supple and pleasing ; at his best he seemed almost worthy of the succession of the great critics of literature, and failed of a high and permanent place only because he was too much of a journalist to take the excessive pains that literature demands.

Clement King Shorter (1857–1926) was another journalist who was also a distinguished man of letters. Both from a literary and a pictorial standpoint he introduced a new spirit into English illustrated journalism, and through his weekly Literary Letter in " The Sphere," which he founded in 1900, he acquired an influence hardly less than that of Sir William Robertson Nicoll. As a critic and biographer Shorter specialized in the Brontës, George Borrow and Napoleon, and his " Handbook of Victorian Literature " should be noted by the student.

Sir Walter Raleigh (1861–1922), professor of English literature at Glasgow during 1890–1904 and then at Oxford from 1904 until his death, gave us much important literary criticism in his monographs on " The English Novel " and on " Style," and in his studies of Milton, Wordsworth and Shakespeare.

Arthur Christopher Benson (1862–1925) was the eldest of the three sons of Archbishop Benson, all of whom achieved some distinction in the world of letters. His best critical work is contained in his monographs on Rossetti, Edward Fitzgerald and Walter Pater, but he is noteworthy also for having won for the essay a popularity rivalling that of the successful novel. Beginning with " The Upton Letters," published anonymously in 1905, he produced a number of volumes of essays, " From a College Window," " The Gate of Death," and others, weakened by his habit of playing for safety with the provision of alternatives, by a too easy fluency of language, indeed, but with a mellow surface of culture that greatly pleased the general public.

Sir Arthur Quiller-Couch (b. 1863) first made a reputation as a novelist, and in that capacity is the subject of further attention in a later Lesson, but has made a later and perhaps more enduring name as a critic of literature. " The Oxford Book of English Verse," which he edited in 1900, ranks with the very best anthologies, and equally scholarly discrimination is manifested in later anthologies of Ballads, Victorian Verse, and Prose. Appointed King Edward VII Professor of English Literature at Cambridge in 1912, he attracted large audiences to his lectures, which as " On the Art of Writing " and " On the Art of Reading " have since had very wide distribution in volume form. No student should fail to master both these works, or overlook Q's "Studies in Literature," "Charles Dickens and other Victorians," and "Shakespeare's Workmanship."

Three other men who may be mentioned briefly here are Arthur Machen (b. 1863), who in "The Hill of Dreams," "The House of Souls," "Far Off Things," and other rare and individual works, has shown himself almost too much of an artist in words, but still an adept at suggesting colour and atmosphere, a master of the short story and the essay ; Arthur Symons (b. 1865), a real prose master, author of numerous works in criticism, interpretative biography, description and the spirit of place ; and Richard Le Gallienne (b. 1866), who has written with distinction on many literary subjects since he produced his brilliant study of Meredith in 1890.

There yet remain two men born in this same decade who must be mentioned in this Lesson, although they, too, will receive fuller consideration in the Lessons dealing with English fiction. Arnold Bennett (1867–1931) is an outstanding example of a man who went into the writing business in the same spirit as others go into stockbroking, engineering, or the brewing trade. From the first he set out to write, and to make money by writing, fiction, both in what may be called the "grand manner" and also in the more popular style, critical essays, reviews, daily journalism, plays—almost everything in the domain of general literature save poetry. He was a noteworthy product of the changes in time by which the essay has become the article and the prose writer finds in the columns of the newspapers an opportunity of addressing audiences incalculably larger than he can ever hope to reach through the medium of the bound book. Arnold Bennett's weekly notes on books in an evening newspaper had an influence that was almost incredible and has been acquired by no other writer of the time. Into much of this ephemeral criticism he also put an amount of personality that presents him as a far more engaging figure than he appears in much of his fiction. His "Journals" will almost certainly rank as one of the most revealing self-portraits by any literary man.

The other notable figure is Herbert George Wells (b. 1866), the most astonishing figure in the English world of letters today. His intellectual vitality is inexhaustible, his range of interests immensely wide. Profoundly curious about life and its meaning, Wells is, indeed, more an intelligence than a personality. During the Great War no writer of established reputation so considerably extended his influence and usefulness as H. G. Wells, the direct discussion of old and new problems raised by the war taking the place of the fictional appeal, though of all his war-time writings it is his war novels that will endure.

Hilaire Belloc (b. 1870) is one of the most accomplished and versatile of English men of letters. An essayist of lightest touch, deft artist in descriptive narrative, an engaging novelist, brilliant biographer, a writer of verse, learned exponent of French history, authoritative critic of military affairs, a student of politics—he is one of the few who, in an age of narrow specialization, have maintained the larger tradition of the finest periods of literature by displaying a wide range of interest and confident power in many branches of the art. As a historian he identifies himself intimately with the period on which he happens to be writing. " A traveller in time," he returns in creative imagination to an age that is gone. But, first and last, he is an essayist with a notable gift of humour, at once urbane and hearty, which lights up most of his writing. " The Path to Rome " is one of his most characteristic works.

Gilbert Keith Chesterton (1874-1936) was pre-eminent among present-day critics and miscellaneous writers. No man ever ventilated his opinion on social and religious matters with more engaging frankness. Whether his use of paradox as a literary device did or did not sometimes lead him whither he had not intended to go is perhaps arguable ; but he was always interesting, and probably most interesting when the reader least agrees with his opinions. Assuredly the Chestertonian slogan was " To be Interesting is Everything." Nevertheless, you cannot read him in such works as his " Dickens," " George Bernard Shaw," or " The Victorian Age in Literature," without stimulation, and his numerous collections of essays, like " All Things Considered " and " Tremendous Trifles," are unfailing sources of entertainment. His literary style, though always nervous and bright, lacked that agreeable touch of courtliness which gives distinction to the prose of his friend and sometime collaborator, Hilaire Belloc. As historians of England, they both took the standpoint that the Reformation was a criminal blunder which destroyed the golden age of medieval faith ; both were engaged in controversies which centred round their advocacy of Roman Catholicism. G. K. C.'s Autobiography appeared in 1936.

LESSON 40

Some Notable Writers of Today

(See plate 37)

THE twentieth-century prosemen carry forward the literary tradition on lines somewhat different from those that were followed by the writers of even the later part of the previous century. We have seen how the newspaper and the magazine diverted the great eighteenth-century talent for letter-writing from private into public channels. What now becomes noticeable is how the changes in the newspapers and magazines themselves have modified the style and, to a considerable extent, the point of view of those whom we call the writers of today. In the main the essay has become the " article," and the article, as a rule, has a very definite character foreign to the essay proper. This is due in its turn to the progress of that popular movement inaugurated by the first Reform Act, and the rise of the newspaper press. The article is, in other words, the answer to the demand of the people for concise information on subjects which they have had no special opportunity to study.

With the widespread development of education the specialized power of the pen passed from the hands of an exclusive " literary " class ; the men of letters ceased to be a sort of priesthood. There is no literary " class " today, although vastly more men and women make their livelihood by the pen than in any previous age. There is no literary class, because so many are potentially literary who are content to remain readers. Then, again, those who write for a livelihood must address themselves to the interpretation and solution of what are called " questions of the day," because it is " journalistic interest " that rules. These " questions," it is true, are often literary in a sense, but every writer who now secures any considerable hold upon the public is compelled to recognize that life is greater than literature.

It was in journalism that George Bernard Shaw (b. 1856) began his career, as a dramatic critic and then, after joining the Fabian Society, as the champion of socialism, " not "—to quote the words of G. K. Chesterton—" as a matter of sentiment but as a matter of common sense. The realism that he applied to the industrial problem he proceeded to apply with mordant wit and infinite zest to many other things, including vegetarianism and anti-vaccination." Detailed reference has already been made to his distinctively individual genius in Lesson 17 (volume 2, page 277), dealing with his plays, and here it suffices to name two of his more recent prose works, " The Intelligent Woman's Guide to Socialism," etc., and " Adventures of a Black Girl in Search of God."

Robert Bontine Cunninghame Graham (1852-1936) was a romantic literary figure. Son of a Scottish laird, he became at various periods in his life a strike leader, an anarchist, a great traveller, a Member of Parliament, a Justice of the Peace, and a Deputy Lieutenant. From his " Mogreb-el-Acksa " (Morocco the Most Holy) Bernard Shaw took most of the local colour for " Captain Brassbound's Cônversion," acknowledging the theft in a vividly descriptive sketch of Cunninghame Graham appended to the play. Other vigorous and fascinating writings include " Progress," " His People " and " Scottish Stories."

One respect in which the twentieth century has witnessed a remarkable development of public taste in reading is the very great increase in the output and circulation of books other than fiction. Of late years a hundred books by essayists and descriptive writers have seemingly found readers where before the War not more than five would have tempted a publisher to incur the expense of their production. This is a healthy sign, and so, too, is the increasing interest in history, in critical and biographical studies and in personal reminiscences and autobiography.

That there is also a large public intelligently interested in scientific subjects lucidly presented is evidenced by the large sale enjoyed by such works as Sir James Jeans's " The Universe Around Us"; "An Outline of Modern Knowledge," edited by Dr. William Rose; and Professor Lancelot Hogben's "Mathematics for the Million" and "Science for the Citizen." Julian Huxley (b. 1887), a biologist of repute, is another writer whose scientific works, written alone or in collaboration with other such eminent men as Professor J. B. S. Haldane and H. G. Wells, have a very considerable circulation. Havelock Ellis (1859-1939) gathered a large audience for his psychological and philosophical studies ; and Bertrand (3rd earl) Russell (b. 1872) holds a foremost place among mathematicians and philosophers, and provokes wide interest by his keenly intellectual lucubrations on a variety of scientific, philosophic, ethical, economic and social problems.

Among the writers who have devoted themselves to history and biography a prominent place must be accorded to the Right Hon. Winston Churchill (b. 1874), who has crowded into his life a quite extraordinary number and variety of activities and adventures. His first book, " The Story of the Malakand Field Force " was published in 1898, when he was only twenty-four, and it was followed the next year by " The River War."

His Life of his father, Lord Randolph Churchill, published in 1906, is an addition to the small number of first-rate biographies in our literature, and the same tribute may be paid with even greater justice to his biography of his great ancestor, the first duke of Marlborough. His most important contribution to history in the grand manner is " The World Crisis," published in four volumes between 1923 and 1929 ; Mr. Churchill may be confidently expected to retain high place among historians.

Lytton Strachey (1880–1932) introduced a new style into biography of which the preface to his " Eminent Victorians " is the manifesto. He declined to treat his subjects as models for academy portraits or memorial statues, and presented them instead on the human level as men and women. Read without prejudice, he neither shocks nor depreciates. " Eminent Victorians," " Queen Victoria " and " Elizabeth and Essex " are the three books by which he will be deservedly remembered.

Other biographers who may be singled out for mention are Philip Guedella (b. 1889), who, with his " Palmerston," " Gladstone and Palmerstone " and other studies, shares the principles of writing created by Strachey ; Lord David Cecil, with " The Stricken Deer," a noteworthy life of Cowper ; Percy Lubbock, with his " Samuel Pepys " and, more importantly, his " Earlham," a charmingly fragrant Quaker family history ; Lascelles Abercrombie, with his " Thomas Hardy," though his critical works, " The Theory of Poetry " and " The Idea of Great Poetry," are more important to the student ; David Garnett, with his " Pocahontas " and other biographical studies ; Edith Sitwell, a writer of entirely delightful English prose, whose " Alexander Pope " is of first-rate quality, both as biography and as criticism ; with her must be named her brothers, Osbert Sitwell (b. 1892), author of, among many other books, " Before the Bombardment," and in a different genre " Winters of Content " ; and Sacheverell Sitwell (b. 1900), whose " Life of Mozart " is a really competent piece of work.

Writers of noteworthy books that fall into a slightly different category are H. M. Tomlinson, with his vivid travel books, " The Sea and the Jungle " and " London River " ; Francis Yeats-Brown (b. 1886), author of " Bengal Lancer " ; Siegfried Sassoon, author of " Memoirs of a Fox-hunting Man " and " Memoirs of an Infantry Officer " ; and Edmund Blunden (b. 1896), author of " Undertones of War."

Among writers of the literary kind as distinct from the journalistic article, John Middleton Murry (b. 1889) holds honourable rank. Rebecca West (b. 1892), journalist and novelist, has also produced " The Strange Necessity," a stimulating collection of essays. Violet Paget, better known as Vernon Lee, published a long succession of charming literary essays.

New books are issued from the press at the rate of something like 12,000 or 13,000 a year, and hence the writers named in this Lesson are only singled out for mention as representative types from the large host of men and women who are carrying the banner of our national literature forward today. It is often lamented that our literary standards are low and commercial, but the student cannot escape from the conclusion that the general level of English prose literature in the first third of the twentieth century is much higher than the mean of the nineteenth century.

LESSON 41

The English Novel and Its Creators

(See plate 38)

ONE could betray no greater ignorance of literature than to suggest that prose fiction was unworthy of serious study on the ground that " mere fiction " can be of no use to anyone. It may, indeed, be the very essence of truth ; in the hands of the master-writers it is truth. An historical novel may present a picture closer to life than a factual chronicle would be.

Cut out the romance, the novel, and the short story from English literature, and it would be small comfort to protest that there still remained to us the history, the essay, the poem, and the drama ; yes, even though these preserved a Carlyle, a Lamb, a Keats and a Shakespeare ! Our prose fiction must be accounted one of our greatest national treasures.

The great novel is, in a word, one of the indispensable means of modern culture. Jane Austen's description of the novel as it should be can hardly be improved upon. A novel, according to this peerless exponent of one phase of the art of fiction, is a work in which the greatest powers of the mind are displayed, in which the most thorough knowledge of human nature, the happiest delineation of its varieties, the liveliest varieties of wit and humour are conveyed to the world in the best chosen words.

It is too frequently forgotten that novels, as a form of art, must be regarded as critically as we regard dramas and poems. Drama is composed of two main divisions, comedy and tragedy, but each of these divisions has many subdivisions ; and the quality of a play is to be judged by its relation to the standard of its particular division. This is true of the poem and its relation to what we understand by the epic, the narrative, and the lyrical standards. What is true of the play and the poem is true of the novel ; with the further point that the novel is susceptible of more numerous gradations, a more intricate classification.

It was due to the first English translators of those Italian and Spanish works of genius—" The Decameron " by Boccaccio, " Lazarillo de Tormes " (that earliest known picaresque novel which was long ascribed to Hurtado de Mendoza, though now the attribution is commonly regarded as doubtful), " Don Quixote " by Cervantes and other foreign imaginative works, that the novel of adventure and gallantry, the pastoral romance, and the picaresque novel (or novel of roguery, of Spanish origin) had become naturalized in Britain by the beginning of the seventeenth century.

Meanwhile, England had produced a form of prose fiction which was indigenous. The outstanding examples were the Latin allegories of More (" Utopia," 1516), Barclay (" Argenis," 1621), and Bacon (" New Atlantis," 1627). In 1579–80 appeared " Euphues," the first original prose novel written in English. The author of this work was John Lyly (1553–1606), to whom as a dramatist attention has been given in Lesson 9 (volume 1, page 343). The story, though received in Elizabethan Court circles with much delight, is less interesting to the modern reader, but the style in which it was written suggested a new word, " euphuism," and promoted a form of popular " polite " dialogue the influence of which is traceable in Shakespeare (Adriano de Armado in " Love's Labour's Lost," and Malvolio in

" Twelfth Night "); Ben Jonson (Puntarvolo in " Every Man out of His Humour "), and Sir Walter Scott (Sir Piercy Shafton, in " The Monastery "). Lyly has been unduly despised and much misrepresented. His importance as one of the first writers of witty prose dialogue in English and his lyrical gift are the chief facts to bear in mind in regard to him.

Next to Lyly's " Euphues," the posthumous " Arcadia " (1590) of Sir Philip Sidney (1554–86) claims attention. Indebted as Sidney was to foreign influence, and particularly to the Italian Sannazaro and the Portuguese Montemayor, both disciples of Boccaccio, his pastoral romance enshrines true passion and has a ring of chivalrous sincerity that is absent from " Euphues." Sidney borrowed, but gave also. French and English writers felt his influence. Shakespeare is one of his debtors, and Sir Walter Raleigh points out that Richardson is the " direct inheritor " of the analytic and sentimental method in romance which Sidney developed. Sir Walter Raleigh says :

"The ' Arcadia ' is in some sort a half-way house between the older romances of chivalry and the long-winded ' heroic ' romances of the seventeenth century. Action and adventure are already giving way to the description of sentiment, or are remaining merely as a frame on which the diverse-coloured flowers of sentiment may be broidered."

" The Pilgrim's Progress," written by John Bunyan and published in 1678 (see Lesson 29, volume 4, page 334), is the first great popular allegorical narrative in the language. Twenty years after its appearance the novel of contemporary life may be said to have begun with " The Fair Jilt " and " Oroonoko," two works of that romantic literary figure Mrs. Aphra Behn (1640–89), spy, brilliant conversationalist scintillating amongst the Restoration wits, and first English professional authoress. She was also the first literary abolitionist, anticipating in " Oroonoko " the story of " the royal slave," and affecting the writings of Chateaubriand and J. J. Rousseau. In her day she enjoyed vast popularity as a dramatist.

Realism in fiction reached immediate perfection in the hands of Daniel Defoe, whose " Robinson Crusoe," published in 1719, remains unsurpassed in this respect. Its realism finds an imaginative contrast in that immortal and wonderful story book, the satire " Gulliver's Travels " of Jonathan Swift, which appeared in 1726. In neither work is any great appeal made to the emotions. The influence of both these writers on the development of English prose is considered in Lesson 31 (volume 4, page 342).

The " literature of the drawing-room," which Lyly began, was humanized by Samuel Richardson (1689–1761), who may be called the father of the domestic novel. As a lad he was the confidant of the young women in the neighbourhood of his home in Derbyshire. He read and wrote their love-letters for them, which accounts in some measure for his extraordinary success as a writer, chiefly for women, in his later years. At the age of two score and ten, when he was a printer in Salisbury Court, Fleet Street, he was induced by two bookseller friends to take up the task of writing a book of " Familiar Letters on the Useful Concerns in Common Life." He was doubtless engaged in this work when he became acquainted with the story which inspired his first novel, " Pamela ; or, Virtue Rewarded " (1740), although the latter was published several months before the " Familiar Letters." His masterpiece, " Clarissa Harlowe," followed in 1748, and " Sir Charles Grandison," in 1753. These three works form a kind of triology, dealing respectively with humble, middle-class and high life.

Richardson's adoption of the epistolary style was burlesqued and condemned by Fielding, but, though Fielding's protest was well grounded, the method had its advantages, and is still sometimes adopted. Even Fielding admired the penetration displayed by Richardson in his characterization of " Clarissa Harlowe," and the novel had a vogue in France. Perhaps the greatest obstacle in the way of a popular appreciation of Richardson today is his prolixity ; and other drawbacks are his passion for moralizing and stagnant sentimentality. For the student of eighteenth century life, however, the novels of Richardson contain much that is invaluable.

Two years after " Pamela " was issued there appeared " The History of the Adventures of Joseph Andrews and his Friend Mr. Abraham Adams, Written in Imitation of the Manner of Cervantes, Author of ' Don Quixote.' " In this work Henry Fielding (1707–54), barrister, journalist and playwright, essayed a satire and achieved a masterpiece just as Cervantes himself had done. The Parson Adams of the story takes rank in the gallery of the heroes of English fiction with Goldsmith's Dr. Primrose—just as Sophie Western sits with the daughter of the Vicar

of Wakefield. " The History of Tom Jones, a Foundling,";
appeared in 1749 ; " Amelia," in 1751. The " History of the
Late Mr. Jonathan Wild the Great " was published among his
" Miscellanies " in 1743.

Fielding's knowledge of the law marks all his writings. Full of
odd passages containing permanent beauties, " Amelia " shows
Fielding in his aspects of reformer and lawyer rather than of
novelist. It is on this account none the less interesting to the
modern reader. As a literary artist Fielding has a place above
Richardson, and Sir Walter Scott styled him the " Father of the
English Novel." He is a humorist, which Richardson is not.
His knowledge of life is wide, his sympathies are catholic, his
humour is of the rarest vintage, his style is like the vigour of a
spring morning, and his constructive faculty is classical ; his
novels are as charged with life today as when they first won the
admiration of his contemporaries. Dr. Johnson considered
" Tom Jones " vicious, though he was fascinated by " Amelia " ;
but if the former great novel is too indulgent to the frailties of
man, it is an open question whether it may not be so and yet
remain a work of sounder morality than Richardson's " Pamela,"
in which we are supposed to witness " virtue rewarded," but a
brand of " virtue " that will not bear analysis. Fielding is securely
a classic ; he has, moreover, created a crowded gallery of memorable
characters, and this is the true test of the novelist.

LESSON 42

Some 18th Century Humorists and Romantics

(See plate 39)

IN addition to Fielding, three other novelists, Sterne, Smollett
and Goldsmith, are included amongst Thackeray's representative humorists of the eighteenth century. In the case of
Laurence Sterne (1713–68), however, a distinction is made with
which most modern readers will agree. The distinction is that
Sterne is a great jester rather than a great humorist. " He is
always looking in my face, watching his effect, uncertain whether
I think him an impostor or not ; posture-making, coaxing, and
imploring me." The author of " The Life and Opinions of

Tristram Shandy, Gent." and " A Sentimental Journey through France and Italy " owed much, doubtless, to an acquaintance with the works of Rabelais and Cervantes and Burton's " Anatomy of Melancholy," but, as Augustine Birrell has said, " Sterne is our best example of the plagiarist whom none dare make ashamed." In Corporal Trim and " My Uncle Toby " he has created immortal types of character ; they would raise " Tristram Shandy " to a place among the classics of English prose fiction even without the spirit of inimitable drollery which rollicks through its pages.

Careless, usually, of his grammar, Sterne can on occasion find the " only word." He is ribald, but not salacious. His slipshod method cannot be held up to admiration, but at the same time it must be admitted that it adds to the care-free and exuberant expression of his jests.

The " Hogarth of English Letters " is a phrase applied to Tobias Smollett (1721–71). Masson includes " The Adventures of Roderick Random," " The Adventures of Peregrine Pickle " and " The Expedition of Humphrey Clinker " with " Joseph Andrews " and " Tom Jones " among the most amusing novels in the language. In them, he says, " for the first time British literature possessed compositions making any approach, in breadth, bustle and variety of interest, to that form of literature, always theoretically possible, and of which other countries had already had specimens in ' Don Quixote ' and ' Gil Blas '—the comic prose epic of contemporary life." In the novels of Fielding and Smollet is represented the kaleidoscope of life, whereas Richardson keeps the attention more intimate with the feelings of his chief characters.

Of Oliver Goldsmith (1728–74), to whose masterly and delightful achievements in other domains of literature attention has been drawn in earlier lessons, it has been said that *Virginibus puerisque* might have been his appropriate and uncontested motto. His one novel, " The Vicar of Wakefield," which appeared in 1766, written though it was with a moral motive akin to that which induced Richardson to write " Pamela," is a work that stands alone. " There are a hundred faults in the thing," says the author in his preface, but, as it has been wittily observed, a hundred things might plausibly be said to prove them beauties.

Some seven years earlier, the novel having come well to the fore in literature, Samuel Johnson (1709–84) essayed his " Rasselas," writing it during the evenings of a single week. It is a prose narrative embodying the views expressed in his poem, " The Vanity of Human Wishes," and has been compared with Voltaire's " Candide," with which it has something in common. Dr. Johnson's genius, however, lay in directions outside the realm of fiction (*see* Lesson 32, volume 4, page 346).

Although Fielding had set up a definite and adaptable form for the novel of character, and despite the sentimental romance of Richardson and the fresh naturalness of " The Vicar of Wakefield," the tendency was to tickle the palate of the common reader with tales of so-called " Gothic romance," a euphemism for fantastically conceived stories of adventures in remote and gloomy castles. Horace Walpole, in " The Castle of Otranto," produced in 1764 one of the best of the supernatural type. There was, however, many other fictions of merit and some that have endured in reputation at least until our own day : Henry Mackenzie's " The Man of Feeling," for example ; " The Monk," an excellent " thriller " by Matthew Gregory Lewis ; " Vathek," a powerfully imaginative conception by William Beckford ; and Charles Robert Maturin's " Melmoth the Wanderer."

The number of women writers who came forward in response to the demand for interesting and sensational novels is very noteworthy. Sarah Fielding, the sister of the author of " Tom Jones " ; Clara Reeve, highly popular with romantic fiction like " The Old English Baron " ; Mrs. Inchbald, who wrote " A Simple Story," which still finds readers ; Charlotte Smith, Mrs. Opie, Regina Marie Roche and that thrilling, ultra-romantic writer of the period, Mrs. Ann Radcliffe, who was an incomparable adept at the art of exciting narration ; but there were two other women novelists whose work excelled the standard of any of those yet mentioned.

Fanny Burney, Madame d'Arblay (1752–1840), is one of the most attractive literary figures of her day. When she was twenty-six she published " Evelina, or a Young Lady's Entrance into the World," which, according to Macaulay, " was the first tale written by a woman, and purporting to be a picture of life and manners, that lived or deserved to live. It took away reproach from the novel." Written in the epistolary manner, it was issued anonymously by a firm that did not know the name of the writer, and attained an immediate and immense success, which gave the author a foremost place in the literary world of her day.

Fanny Burney, who was the second daughter of Dr. Burney, had picked up an education at home, without any tuition whatever, but had the advantage of browsing in her father's large miscellaneous library, and observing his brilliant circle of friends. She knew something of the Johnson circle before she wrote " Evelina," and became the doctor's pet. Later, Fanny Burney wrote " Cecilia," longer and more complex than " Evelina," and for this she received two thousand guineas. " Camilla " brought her three thousand guineas.

The appearance of " Evelina " was a real event in the annals of fiction, for Fanny Burney had caught the secret of the quiet charm that may be disengaged from a narration of a series of entirely credible events imagined as taking place in the course of everyday domestic life. In this she was the precursor of a greater than herself—Jane Austen.

The second woman novelist of classic measure to arrive at this period was Maria Edgeworth (1767–1849), whose delightful character finds eloquent expression in her first novel, " Castle Rackrent," published anonymously in 1800. This is in many respects her best work. Later came " The Absentee," " Belinda," " Helen," " Tales of Fashionable Life " and " Moral Tales." Sir Walter Scott confessed that reading these stories of Irish peasant life made him feel " that something might be attempted for my own country of the same kind as that which Miss Edgeworth so fortunately achieved for Ireland " ; something that would procure for his own countrymen " sympathies for their virtues and indulgence for their foibles."

LESSON 43

Novels of Scott and Jane Austen

(See plate 40)

TWO figures of supreme importance in the history of the English novel dominate the earlier years of the nineteenth century—Jane Austen and Sir Walter Scott—and both remain unexcelled in their own spheres.

Jane Austen (1775–1817) wrote six novels : " Sense and Sensibility " (1811), " Pride and Prejudice " (1812), " Mansfield Park " (1814), " Emma " (1816), " Northanger Abbey " (1818), and " Persuasion " (1818)—all of which were written in her father's house, the Rectory at Steventon, near Basingstoke, or, after his death, in the house at Chawton where she lived with her mother and sister. Her close intimacy with the latter enabled her exquisitely to express sisterly relationships in her novels. Though slow to publish, Jane Austen began writing at a very early age. " Pride and Prejudice " she started in 1796 ; " Northanger Abbey," which, like " Persuasion," was published posthumously, was begun about 1798.

Macaulay suggested that Jane Austen among writers most nearly approached Shakespeare in the genius for character drawing which she displays in her novels ; also that there were in the world no compositions " which approach nearer to perfection." She wrote in direct opposition to the " Gothic " romances in vogue at the end of the eighteenth century. " Northanger Abbey," indeed, is in part a parody of Mrs. Radcliffe's " Mysteries of Udolpho " and other blood-curdling fiction, bestsellers of the day. A notable feature is the impersonal nature of her works. She tells us nothing about herself, and is oblivious of the happenings beyond her own circle. She is a satirist minus indignation ; hers is the quiet irony of the cultured mind. Her stories are development of character ; they are neither emotional nor sentimental. To study her books is to be given a series of lessons in the art of observation, to know what went on in English parsonage, villa, town and country house at the beginning of the nineteenth century.

Jane Austen's method was appreciated by Scott. After the third reading of " Pride and Prejudice " he wrote : " The big bow-wow strain I can do myself, like any now going, but the exquisite touch which renders ordinary commonplace things and characters interesting from the truth of the description and sentiment is denied me. What a pity such a gifted creature died so early ! " She has been compared to the miniature painter, but few if any miniature painters have possessed the cosmic touch of Jane Austen—a touch which enabled her to portray the scenes of quiet contemporary life with precision of detail and yet to maintain in the pattern of her novels a true relation with humanity at large.

Sir Walter Scott (1771–1832) is easily first of the great writers of English historical romance. His career illustrates the renewal and decision of the old battle between verse and prose for the prerogative possession of romantic themes. Scott "took the bread out of the mouths of the novelists" by his metrical romances, "The Lay of the Last Minstrel" (1805), "Marmion" (1808), "The Lady of the Lake" (1810); then, turning to prose, he proved that the historical and romantic interests need not be imperilled by the admixture of qualities that are known only to prose. In his works the novel proper and the romance, which had long been coquetting with each other, were at last wedded.

Scott's genius was stirred by several causes—among them being the French Revolution, the Napoleonic wars, Percy's "Reliques of Ancient English Poetry," the songs of Burns, the ballads of Bürger, and the early poems of Goethe. Nor must the example of Fielding be discounted. But the Irish novels of Maria Edgeworth first inspired in him the thought which found such eloquent expression in that vast treasure-house, the "Waverley" novels.

As a preliminary to their reading one should study the "General Preface," written by Scott in 1829, which will be found in the first volume of all good editions; and also the "Epistle Introductory to the Fortunes of Nigel," written in 1822. He explains, in the Epistle, that he was quite aware of the aims of Fielding, Smollett, Le Sage, and others, as writers of novels, but he goes on to remark that it was enough for him could he "write with sense and spirit a few scenes, unlaboured and loosely put together, but which had sufficient interest in them to amuse in one corner the pain of body; in another to relieve anxiety of mind; in a third place to unwrinkle a brow bent with the furrows of daily toil; in another to fill the place of bad thoughts, or to suggest better; in yet another to induce the idler to study the history of his country; in all, save where the perusal interrupted the discharge of serious duties, to furnish harmless amusement."

Others before Scott had attempted the historical novel, "but wholly without his knowledge of history and of the actual way of living and thinking in various periods of the past." He it was who first "made the dry bones of history live." The casual reader needs to be reminded of the stores of varied and accurate learning which were garnered in Scott's capacious mind. This man was a student from his youth upwards. It is important also to secure at the outset of a study of his romances a knowledge of his methods of dealing with history. Scott's plan was never to make a famous character of history the central personage of his tale. He never coped with the records of actual events. But he achieved effects which were altogether denied to some of the most painstaking and letter-faithful among historians proper. In all that he wrote we breathe the free mountain air.

Scott's novels, it must be remembered, do not finally depend for their popularity upon their plots. Taking time to arrange a story was a sore point with Scott. He confesses that " the regular mansion " he always strove to build " turned out a Gothic anomaly." But it is questionable whether we should have been so long held captive by the spell of the Wizard if he had achieved those trim-built mansions he set out to construct, instead of the crazy gargoyled edifices his rich and vigorous imagination reared for us. In their very irregularity of plot and style lie half their charm and all their vitality. It has to be remembered, also, that much which was new when Scott wrote has now become hackneyed, and as we do not base our claim for Scott on the excellence of his plots, haphazardly constructed, so we do not fall back upon his style, of which the best that can be said is that it is a free and easy medium wherewith he brings more valuable things than style alone before us. His merit is so gigantic that he can be made the subject of the severest criticism in details, concerning which he was often slovenly, without detracting from the mighty mass of his achievement.

By taking up the novels in the order in which they were published rather than as fancy or other reasons may dictate, the student will be able to discern the workings of the author's mind when dealing successively with special phases of character and particular situations in human life. The introductions and notes may be reserved for consideration till each story has been read. The following table gives the date of publication of the novels and an indication of the period of each.

A glance at the list in page 320 will serve to show that with few exceptions Scott, with all his love of the Gothic, preferred to deal in his novels with periods not far remote from his own time ; but he did for Scottish romance what Cervantes did for Spanish chivalry. Delightfully entertaining as are " Ivanhoe," " Quentin Durward " and "Anne of Geierstein," it is in the Scottish stories, which deal more directly with the realities of Scottish life, that he excels.

" Waverley " was published in 1814, and thenceforward, for sixteen years, says Herford in his " Age of Wordsworth," " the wonderful series of the ' Scotch novels,' as they were called, issued from the Ballantynes' press without a pause ; and for the last ten, at least, their appearance was watched for as eagerly

Date	Title	Period
1814	Waverley ; or 'Tis Sixty Years Since	1745
1815	Guy Mannering	1760
1816	The Antiquary	1798
1816	Old Mortality	1679
1816	The Black Dwarf *	1708
1817	Rob Roy	1715
1818	The Heart of Midlothian*	1736
1819	A Legend of Montrose	1644
1819	The Bride of Lammermoor*	1700
1819	Ivanhoe	1194
1820	The Monastery	1559
1820	The Abbot	1570
1821	Kenilworth	1575
1821	The Pirate	1700
1822	The Fortunes of Nigel	1620
1823	Quentin Durward	1470
1823	Peveril of the Peak	1660
1823	St. Ronan's Well	1804
1824	Redgauntlet	1770
1825	The Betrothed	1187
1825	The Talisman	1193
1826	Woodstock	1651
1827	The Surgeon's Daughter	1765
1827	The Two Drovers†	1765
1827	The Highland Widow†	1755
1828	My Aunt Margaret's Mirror†	1700
1828	The Tapestried Chamber†	1780
1828	The Laird's Jock†	1600
1828	The Fair Maid of Perth	1402
1829	Anne of Geierstein	1474
1827} 1830}	Tales of a Grandfather	{1707 {1788
1831	Count Robert of Paris*	1090
1831	Castle Dangerous	1307
	* Tales of My Landlord.	
	† Chronicles of the Canongate.	

in Paris and Weimar as in London. The poems had thrown the British world into a passing excitement ; the novels enlarged the intellectual horizon of all Europe, created in half a dozen nations the novel of national life, and opened a new epoch in the study of history."

Our Course in English Literature is continued in Volume 6.

WINSTON CHURCHILL (b. 1874). Son of Lord Randolph Churchill, he was a soldier before he entered politics. He has held many of the highest offices in the Cabinet, and is the supreme living example of the writer statesman.
ENGLISH LITERATURE 40

REVEALERS OF THE WAR. Both Siegfried Sassoon (left ; b. 1886) and Edmund Charles Blunden (right ; b. 1896) served as young officers in the Great War ; both experienced and gave literary expression to the sense of frustration and disillusion to which their early idealistic dreams soon gave place. For a time Blunden was lecturer in English literature at Tokyo University. His "Undertones of War" is a work of rare distinction. ENGLISH LITERATURE 40

MASTERS OF TRAVEL DESCRIPTION. R. B. Cunninghame Graham (1852-1936) went to Harrow, was M.P. for N. Lanarkshire 1886-92, and travelled long and far. Some of his most popular books describe his journeyings in Morocco and South America. Right, H. M. Tomlinson (b. 1873) served on "The Morning Leader" and the "Daily News," was war correspondent 1914-17, and literary editor of "The Nation" 1917-23. Before achieving fame as a novelist he wrote some vivid books of travel. ENGLISH LITERATURE 40

LYTTON STRACHEY (1880 – 1932). He was educated at Trinity, Cambridge, and published his first book in 1912. His "Queen Victoria" (1921) may be said to have set the fashion for a new style of historical writing.
ENGLISH LITERATURE 40

CREATORS OF THE ENGLISH NOVEL. Top, Samuel Richardson (1689–1761). A native of Derbyshire, he became a prosperous London printer. He was past fifty when he turned to novel writing. Bottom left, Aphra Behn (1640–89). She entered the English secret service, and was the first professional woman novelist and playwright in England. Right, Henry Fielding (1707–54). Born near Glastonbury, he earned money by writing plays to pay for his legal studies, and became a barrister, and later a J.P. He died at Lisbon whither he had gone for his health's sake. ENGLISH LITERATURE 41

Portrait of Richardson, National Portrait Gallery; of Fielding, after Hogarth

Plate 38   *Volume V*

MASTERS OF WIT AND DROLLERY. Laurence Sterne (1713–68), who was born at Clonmel, took holy orders, and was appointed to the living of Sutton, Yorks. There he lived quietly until 1759, when the first two volumes of " Tristram Shandy " brought him fame. Subsequently he spent much time in London and in continental travel. Right, Tobias George Smollett (1721–71), a Scotsman, born at Dalquhurn, Dumbartonshire, who from being a naval surgeon became the author of a number of novels of sea-life abounding in rollicking humour. ENGLISH LITERATURE 42

VIVACIOUS WOMEN NOVELISTS. Frances (Fanny) Burney (1752–1840), daughter of Charles Burney, a musician and author of Dr. Johnson's circle, was self-educated in her father's library. From 1786 to 1791 keeper of robes to Queen Charlotte, in 1793 she married General d'Arblay, a French emigré (d. 1818). In addition to her novels she wrote a diary covering seventy-two years. Right, Maria Edgeworth (1767–1849) who, born at Bourton, Oxon, spent most of her life on her father's Irish estate at Edgeworthstown. After 1803, visits to London and the Continent brought her into touch with literary and fashionable society, and she visited, and was visited by, Sir Walter Scott. ENGLISH LITERATURE 42

JANE AUSTEN (1775–1817). Daughter of a Hampshire rector, she was born at Steventon and died at Winchester. Her life was as uneventful and happily placid as that revealed in her novels. The first to be published was "Sense and Sensibility," which came out in 1811.
ENGLISH LITERATURE 43

SIR WALTER SCOTT (1771–1832). Most celebrated of his clan and race, he was famous first as a poet, then as a novelist. He was born, and lived for years, at Edinburgh, but the home he loved was Abbotsford, beside the Tweed. There he performed prodigies of industry, and there he died. He was buried in Dryburgh Abbey. This picture, by J. Watson Gordon, was painted in 1830, and shows Scott with his favourite dog Bran. ENGLISH LITERATURE 43

Plate 40   *Volume V*

LESSON 37

Irregular Verbs—2nd Conjugation

IN this Lesson we continue the irregular verbs in which irregularities occur in the tenses as well as in the principal parts.

The following are verbs of the second conjugation. Except in special cases the imperative is not given, as its first and second persons are identical with those of the present indicative.

1. ACQUÉRIR, to acquire, *acquérant, acquis.* Ind. Pres.: *j'acquiers, tu acquiers, il acquiert, nous acquérons, vous acquérez, ils acquièrent.* Imp.: *j'acquérais.* P. Def.: *j'acquis.* Future: *j'acquerrai.* Cond.: *j'acquerrais.* Subj. Pres.: *que j'acquière, que tu acquières, qu'il acquière, que nous acquérions, que vous acquériez, qu'ils acquièrent.* Imperf.: *que j'acquisse.*

Conjugate similarly *conquérir*, to conquer, *reconquérir*, to reconquer, *s'enquérir de*, to inquire about, and *requérir*, to request.

In the future and the conditional, each " *r* " must be pronounced separately, though the break in the trill must be very slight. This pronunciation is necessary to distinguish these tenses from the present and imperfect indicative.

2. COURIR, to run, *courant, couru.* Ind. Pres.: *je cours, tu cours, il court, nous courons, vous courez, ils courent.* Imperf.: *je courais.* Past Def.; *je courus.* Future: *je courrai.* Cond.: *je courrais.* Subj. Pres.: *que je coure, que tu coures,* etc. Imperf.: *que je courusse.*

Conjugate similarly *accourir*, to rush up, hasten; *concourir*, to concur, to complete; *discourir*, to discourse; *encourir*, to incur; *parcourir*, to run through; *recourir*, to have recourse; and *secourir*, to succour. In all these verbs also, the two " *r's* " of the future and of the conditional are pronounced separately.

3. CUEILLIR, to gather, to pluck, *cueillant, cueilli.* Ind. Pres.: *je cueille, tu cueilles, il cueille, nous cueillons, vous cueillez, ils cueillent.* Imperf.: *je cueillais.* Past Def.: *je cueillis.* Future: *je cueillerai.* Cond. Pres.: *je cueillerais.* Subj. Pres.: *que je cueille, que tu cueilles,* etc. Imperf.: *que je cueillisse.*

Conjugate similarly *accueillir*, to receive, to welcome; and *recueillir*, to collect.

4. MOURIR, to die, *mourant, mort*. Ind. Pres.: *je meurs, tu meurs, il meurt, nous mourons, vous mourez, ils meurent*. Imperf.: *je mourais*. Past Def.: *je mourus*. Future: *je mourrai*. Cond. Pres: *je mourrais*. Subj. Pres.: *que je meure, que tu meures, qu'il meure, que nous mourions, que vous mouriez, qu'ils meurent*. Imperf.: *que je mourusse*.

Mourir is conjugated with *être*. Both " *r*'s " of the future and of the conditional are to be pronounced distinctly.

5. TENIR, to hold, *tenant, tenu*. Ind. Pres: *je tiens, tu tiens, il tient, nous tenons, vous tenez, ils tiennent*. Imperf.: *je tenais*. Past Def.: *je tins, tu tins, il tint, nous tînmes, vous tîntes, ils tinrent*. Future: *je tiendrai*. Cond. Pres.: *je tiendrais*. Subj. Pres.: *que je tienne, que tu tiennes, qu'il tienne, que nous tenions, que vous teniez, qu'ils tiennent*. Imperf.: *que je tinsse*.

There are various idiomatic uses of the verb *tenir*. (*a*). *Tenir de* followed by a personal noun means to take after, to resemble. *Cet enfant tient de sa mère*, That child takes after his mother.

(*b*). *Tenir à* followed by a noun or preceded by " *y* " means to value, to set store by. *Ne perdez pas ce livre, j'y tiens*, Do not lose that book, I value it.

When followed by an infinitive, it means to be anxious to. *Je tiens à lui dire ce que j'en pense*, I am anxious to tell him what I think about it.

Tenir à ce que followed by a personal tense has the same meaning. It is followed by the subjunctive: *Je tiens à ce qu'il nous dise ce qu'il en pense*, I am anxious he should tell us what he thinks about it.

Tenir à used impersonally means, to depend on: *Il ne tient qu'à vous de réussir*, It only depends on you to succeed—i.e. It will be your fault if you do not succeed.

The derivatives of *tenir* are : *s'abstenir*, to abstain ; *appartenir*, to belong ; *contenir*, to contain ; *détenir*, to detain ; *entretenir*, to keep up ; *maintenir*, to maintain ; *obtenir*, to obtain ; *retenir*, to retain, to remember ; *soutenir*, to sustain ; *se tenir*, to stand. to hold oneself.

6. VENIR, to come, *venant, venu*, is conjugated like *tenir* and with *être*.

Venir is conjugated with *être* in its compound tenses.

The following are idiomatic uses of *venir*. (*a*). *Venir de* followed by an infinitive means, to have just ; *Je viens de le voir*, I have just seen him ; *il venait de sortir*, he had just gone out.

IRREGULAR VERBS—2nd CONJUGATION

(b). *Venir à* followed by an infinitive means to chance to, to happen to : *pendant que le marquis de Carabas se baignait, le roi vint à passer*, whilst the marquess of Carabas was bathing, the king happened to pass.

(c). There is also a reflexive form, *s'en venir*, to come along, to come away : *Nous nous en vînmes ensemble*, We came away together.

Derivatives conjugated like *venir* are : *convenir*, to agree, to suit ; *prévenir*, to warn ; *devenir*, to become ; *revenir*, to come back ; *intervenir*, to intervene ; *parvenir*, to reach, to succeed ; *se souvenir de*, to remember.

EXERCISE.

TRANSLATE INTO FRENCH : 1. Little Red Riding Hood (*Le Petit Chaperon Rouge*) set out to go to her grandmother's, who lived in another village. 2. The wolf that she met asked her where she was going. 3. The little girl said to him : " I am going to see my grandmother and to take (*porter*) her a cake (*une galette*) with a little pot (*le pot*) of butter (*beurre*) which my mother is sending her." 4. The wolf began to run with (*de*) all his might (*la force*) by the road which was the shortest, and the little girl went off by the longest road, loitering (*s'amuser*) to gather nuts (*la noisette*) and to run after butterflies (*le papillon*). 5. Puss in Boots (*le Chat Botté*) said to the Ogre (*Ogre*) : " I have been assured that you had the power (*le pouvoir*) to change (*changer*) yourself into (*en*) a rat, and a mouse (*la souris*) ; I confess (*avouer*) to you that I consider (hold) that quite impossible."—" Impossible ? " replied (*reprendre*) the Ogre, " you are going to see." 6. " It will depend only on you, Marquess " (*Monsieur le marquis*), said the King," to be (that you be, subj. pres. preceded by *ne*) my son-in-law " (*gendre*). 7. The Cat became (a) great lord, and no longer ran after mice, except (*que*) to amuse himself. (*se divertir*). 8. The fairy (*la fée*) said to Cinderella (*Cendrillon*) : " Go (thou) into the garden ; you will find there six lizards (*le lézard*) behind (*derrière*) the watering-can (*arrosoir*, m) ; bring them to me." 9. " I recommend you (*recommander*) above all (*surtout*) not to pass midnight ; if you remain (*demeurer*) at the ball a moment longer (more) your coach (*le carrosse*) will become (a) pumpkin (*la citrouille*) again, your horses mice, your footmen (*laquais*) lizards, and your old clothes (*les habits*, m), will resume (*reprendre*) their first form."

LESSON 38

Irregular Verbs—3rd Conjugation

IN this Lesson we deal with those verbs of the third conjugation in which irregularities occur both in tenses and in principal parts. It should be noted with regard to *savoir* that both this verb and *connaître* mean to know. *Connaître* means to know in the sense of to be acquainted with, and therefore applies to persons and places : *Je connais son frère,* I know his brother. *Savoir* means to know as the result of study : *il sait sa leçon.* *Savoir* is also used when the object is a fact or statement, or a pronoun referring to a fact or statement : *Savez-vous ce que je viens d'apprendre ?* Do you know what I have just learned ?

Savoir also means to know how to, and therefore to be able : *cet enfant sait déjà lire et écrire,* that child can read and write already. *Savoir* is frequently used negatively without *pas* or *point* : *Je ne sais ce que je dois faire,* I don't know what I ought to do.

1. S'ASSEOIR, to sit down, *s'asseyant, s'étant assis.* Ind. Pres. : *je m'assieds, tu t'assieds, il s'assied, nous nous asseyons, vous vous asseyez, ils s'asseyent.* Imperf. : *je m'asseyais.* Past Def. : *je m'assis.* Future : *je m'assiérai.* Cond. Pres. : *je m'assiérais.* Subj. Pres. : *que je m'asseye, que tu t'asseyes, qu'il s'asseye, que nous nous asseyions, que vous vous asseyiez, qu'ils s'asseyent.* Imperf. : *que je m'assisse.* Imperat. (positive) : *assieds-toi, qu'il s'asseye, asseyons-nous, asseyez-vous, qu'ils s'asseyent.* Imperat. (negative) : *ne t'assieds pas, qu'il ne s'asseye pas, ne nous asseyons pas, ne vous asseyez pas, qu'ils ne s'asseyent pas.*

There is a transitive form *asseoir,* to seat. The alternative conjugation, *je m'assois, je m'assoirai,* etc., is seldom used.

2. MOUVOIR, to move, *mouvant, mû,* f. *mue.* Ind. Pres. : *je meus, tu meus, il meut, nous mouvons, vous mouvez, ils meuvent.* Imperf. : *je mouvais.* Past Def. : *je mus.* Future : *je mouvrai.* Cond. Pres. : *je mouvrais.* Subj. Pres. : *que je meuve, que tu meuves, qu'il meuve, que nous mouvions, que vous mouviez, qu'ils meuvent.* Imperf. : *que je musse.*

The derivatives *émouvoir,* to move, to affect, *s'émouvoir,* to be affected, and *promouvoir,* to promote, take no circumflex accent in the past participle : *ému, promu.*

3. POUVOIR, to be able, *pouvant, pu.* Ind. Pres. : *je peux,* or *je puis, tu peux, il peut, nous pouvons, vous pouvez, ils peuvent.* Imperf. : *je pouvais.* Past Def. : *je pus.* Future : *je pourrai.* Cond. Pres. : *je pourrais.* Subj. Pres. : *que je puisse, que tu puisses, qu'il puisse, que nous puissions, que vous puissiez, qu'ils puissent.* Imperf. : *que je pusse.*

Only *puis* can be used interrogatively : *Puis-je ?* May I ? Can I ?

4. SAVOIR, to know, *sachant, su.* Ind. Pres. : *je sais, tu sais, il sait, nous savons, vous savez, ils savent.* Imperf. : *je savais.* Past Def. : *je sus.* Future : *je saurai.* Cond. Pres. : *je saurais.* Subj. Pres. : *que je sache, que tu saches, qu'il sache, que nous sachions, que vous sachiez, qu'ils sachent.* Imperf. : *que je susse.* Imperat. : *sache, qu'il sache, sachons, sachez, qu'ils sachent.*

5. VALOIR, to be worth, *valant, valu.* Ind. Pres. : *je vaux, tu vaux, il vaut, nous valons, vous valez, ils valent.* Imperf. : *je valais.* Past Def. : *je valus.* Future : *je vaudrai.* Cond. Pres. : *je vaudrais.* Subj. Pres. : *que je vaille, qu'il vaille, que nous valions, que vous valiez, qu'ils vaillent.* Imperf. : *que je valusse.*

Conjugate similarly *équivaloir,* to be equivalent, and *revaloir,* to repay. *Prévaloir,* to prevail, differs from it in the present subjunctive : *que je prévale.*

6. VOIR, to see, *voyant, vu.* Ind. Pres. : *je vois, tu vois, il voit, nous voyons, vous voyez, ils voient.* Imperf. : *je voyais.* Past Def. : *je vis.* Future : *je verrai.* Cond. Pres. : *je verrais.* Subj. Pres. : *que je voie, que tu voies, qu'il voie, que nous voyions, que vous voyiez, qu'ils voient.* Imperf. : *que je visse.*

7. VOULOIR, to wish, want, to be willing, *voulant, voulu.* Ind. Pres. : *je veux, tu veux, il veut, nous voulons, vous voulez, ils veulent.* Imperf. : *je voulais.* Past. Def. : *je voulus.* Future : *je voudrai.* Cond. Pres. : *je voudrais.* Subj. Pres. : *que je veuille, que tu veuilles, qu'il veuille, que nous voulions, que vous vouliez, qu'ils veuillent.* Imperf. : *que je voulusse.*

The *Imperative* is hardly ever used, except in the form *veuillez,* or *veuillez bien,* please, have the kindness.

Bien added to *vouloir,* gives the idea of consent : *Venez-vous avec nous ? Je veux bien.* Are you coming with us ? I am quite willing.

En vouloir à means to have a grudge against, to have designs on. *Il m'en veut d'avoir agi sans le consulter,* he bears me a grudge for having acted without consulting him.

Vouloir dire, literally, to wish to say, is the usual expression for to mean, to signify ; *Que veut dire ce mot ?* What is the meaning of that word ?

Key to Exercise in Lesson 37.

1. Le Petit Chaperon Rouge partit pour aller chez sa grand'mere, qui demeurait dans un autre village. 2. Le loup qu'elle rencontra lui demanda où elle allait. 3. La petite fille lui dit : " Je vais voir ma grand'mere et lui porter une galette avec un petit pot de beurre que ma mère lui envoie." 4. Le loup se mit à courir de toute sa force par le chemin qui était le plus court, et la petite fille s'en alla par le chemin le plus long, s'amusant à cueillir des noisettes et à courir après des papillons. 5. Le Chat Botté dit à l'Ogre : " On m'a assuré que vous aviez le pouvoir de vous changer en un rat et en une souris ; je vous avoue que je tiens cela tout à fait impossible."—" Impossible ? " reprit l'Ogre, " vous allez voir." 6. " Il ne tiendra qu'à vous, Monsieur le Marquis," dit le Roi, " que vous ne soyez mon gendre." 7. Le Chat devint grand seigneur, et ne courut plus après les souris que pour se divertir. 8. La fée dit à Cendrillon : " Va dans le jardin ; tu y trouveras six lézards derrière l'arrosoir ; apporte-les-moi." 9. " Je te recommande surtout de ne pas passer minuit ; si tu demeures au bal un moment de plus, ton carrosse redeviendra citrouille, tes chevaux des souris, tes laquais des lézards, et tes vieux habits reprendront leur première forme."

LESSON 39

Irregular Verbs—4th Conjugation

In this Lesson we give the irregularities of the French verbs of the fourth conjugation, *boire*, to drink : *dire*, to say : *faire*, to do. With the exception of *redire*, to say again, which, like *dire*, has *vous redites* in the present indicative, and *redites* in the imperative, all the derivatives of *dire* have -*disez* in the second person plural. They are : *dédire*, to retract, gainsay ; *contredire*, to contradict ; *interdire*, to forbid ; *médire*, to backbite ; *prédire*, to foretell (*vous prédisez, vous contredisez*, etc.).

IRREGULAR VERBS—4th CONJUGATION

1. BOIRE, to drink, *buvant, bu.*

Ind. Pres. : *je bois, tu bois, il boit, nous buvons, vous buvez, ils boivent.*

Imperf. : *je buvais.*   Future : *je boirai.*

Past Def. : *je bus.*   Cond. Pres. : *je boirais.*

Subj. Pres. : *que je boive, que tu boives, qu'il boive, que nous buvions, que vous buviez, qu'ils boivent.*

Imperf. : *que je busse.*

2. DIRE, to say, to tell, *disant, dit.*

Ind. Pres. : *je dis, tu dis, il dit, nous disons, vous dites, ils disent.*

Imperf. : *je disais.*   Future : *je dirai.*

Past. Def. : *je dis.*   Cond. Pres. : *je dirais.*

Subj. Pres. : *que je dise, que tu dises, qu'il dise, que nous disions, que vous disiez, qu'ils disent.*

Imperf. : *que je disse.*

3. FAIRE, to make, to do, *faisant, fait.*

Ind. Pres. : *je fais, tu fais, il fait, nous faisons, vous faites, ils font.*

Imperf. : *je faisais.*   Future : *je ferai.*

Past Def. : *je fis.*   Cond. Pres. : *je ferais.*

Subj. Pres. : *que je fasse, que tu fasses, qu'il fasse, que nous fassions, que vous fassiez, qu'ils fassent.*

Imperf. : *que je fisse.*

Faire, followed by an infinitive, means " to cause to be," " to get," " to have." *Il fait bâtir une maison*, he is getting a house built ; *je ferai relier mes livres*, I shall have my books bound.

In this construction, if the second verb has a direct object, the object of *faire* is indirect : *je le fais lire*, I make him read ; but *je lui fais lire un livre français*, I make him read a French book.

Faire, followed by an adjective used as a noun, means " to play the part of," " to pretend to be." *Il fait le sourd*, he pretends to be deaf.

EXERCISE.

TRANSLATE INTO FRENCH : 1. Little Mary, seated in an armchair (*le fauteuil*), was reading the story of Little Red Riding-Hood (*le Petit Chaperon Rouge*). 2. When the poor girl had done her work she used to go (and) sit down in the ashes (*la cendre*) ; that is why she was called Cinderella (*Cendrillon*).

3. Do not sit on the grass ; it is damp ; you would catch cold (*s'enrhumer*). 4. He spoke every moment (at each instant) of going away, but he always sat down again (*se rasseoir*), and we could not get rid (*se débarrasser*) of him. 5. To (*pour*) move his hearers (*auditeur*) the orator must himself be moved ; one does not move without being moved. 6. An army is a body animated (*animer*) by (*de*) an infinite number (*une infinité*) of different passions, which a skilful (*habile*) man sets in motion (*faire mouvoir*) for the defence of the fatherland (*la patrie*). 7. When we (*on*) cannot do what we wish, we must try to wish what we can. 8. We speak little when vanity does not make us speak. 9. We easily forget our faults when they are known only to (*de*) ourselves. 10. Perfect valour is to do without witnesses (*le témoin*) what we should be capable of doing before everybody. 11. Weak people (*la personne*) cannot be sincere. 12. We are nearer loving those who hate us than those who love us more than we (*ne*) wish. 13. A philosopher has said that few people (*gens*) know how to be old. 14. Vanity makes us do more things contrary (*contre*) to our taste than (does) reason. 15. What we know is little in comparison with (*de*) what we do not know ; and sometimes even what we do not know is just what we ought to know. 16. To know that one knows nothing (it) is to know a great deal. 17. The man who sells himself is always paid more than he (*ne*) is worth. 18. Great thoughts come from the heart.

LESSON 40

Incomplete Verbs

THE following verbs, and a few others of rare occurrence, are incomplete or are now obsolete except in some only of their tenses. *Eclore*, to be hatched, to open (of flowers), is used in the third person singular and plural ; its compound tenses are conjugated with *être*.

FAILLIR, to fail, to miss, to escape narrowly. Past Part. : *failli*. In practice, the use of this verb is limited to the Past Definite, *je faillis*, etc. ; and the Past Indefinite, *j'ai failli*, etc. *Il a failli en mourir*, He was near dying of it.

GÉSIR, to lie. Present Participle : *gisant*. Ind. Pres. : *il gît, nous gisons, vous gisez, ils gisent*. Imperf. : *je gisais*, etc.

INCOMPLETE VERBS

Ouïr, to hear, still occasionally used in the compound tenses. Past Participle : *ouï*. It is usually followed by *dire—j'ai ouï dire*, I have heard say.

Seoir, to become, to befit ; *seyant*. Ind. Pres. : *il sied, ils siéent*. Imperf. : *il seyait, ils seyaient*. Future : *il siéra, ils siéront*. Cond. Pres. : *il siérait, ils siéraient*.

Seoir, to be situated, *séant, sis, sise*.

Braire, to bray. Ind. Pres. : *il brait, ils braient*. Future : *il braira, ils brairont*. Condit. : *il brairait, ils brairaient*.

Frire, to fry, is commonly conjugated with the different tenses of *faire*, to make, *je fais frire*, I fry (make to fry). It may, however, be used in the singular of the Ind. Pres., *je fris, tu fris, il frit ;* throughout the whole of the Future, *je frirai*, etc. : the Cond. Pres. *je frirais*, and in the Imperat., *fris*.

Traire, to milk, *trayant, trait, traite*, has no Past Definite. Ind. Pres. : *je trais, tu trais, il trait, nous trayons, vous trayez, ils traient*. Imperf. : *je trayais*. Future : *je trairai*. Cond. Pres. : *je trairais*. Imperat. : *trais, qu'il traie, trayons, trayez, qu'ils traient*. Subj. Pres. : *que je traie, que tu traies*, etc.

Vocabulary

un arsenal, arsenal	*un hôte*, host
une aventure, adventure	*une hôtesse*, hostess
le bout, end	*le jambon*, ham
le bruit, noise	*la lampe*, lamp
le camarade, comrade	*le lendemain*, next day
le chapon, capon	*le lieu*, the place
le charbonnier, charcoal-burner	*la mine*, appearance, look
le chemin, road	*le mot*, word
le chevet, head (of a bed)	*la peine*, difficulty
la couronne, crown	*le pistolet*, pistol
le couteau, knife	*le plafond*, ceiling
le coutelas, cutlass	*la sabre*, sword
le déjeuner, breakfast	*le sens*, sense, meaning
le diamant, diamond	*le sentier*, path
le dogue, mastiff	*le soin*, care
un escalier, staircase	*le souper*, supper
la fente, chink	*le soupçon*, suspicion
le feu, fire	*la tranche*, slice
le fusil, gun	*le traversin*, bolster
la gorge, throat	*la valise*, valise
une hésitation, hesitation	*le voyageur*, traveller

(329)

haut, upper (after noun)
malheureux, unhappy
montagneux, hilly, mountainous
pieds nus, barefooted
practicable, practicable
précieux, precious
riche, rich
arriver, to arrive, happen
causer, to chat
chercher, to seek, look for
comprendre, to understand
consister, to consist
coucher, lie down, sleep
découvrir, uncover
déplaire, displease
descendre, go down
déterminer, determine
échapper (*s'*), escape
écouter, listen
égarer, led astray [away
emporter, to carry away, take
entrer, enter
étendre, to stretch
éveiller, awaken
examiner, examine
hurler, howl
inviter, invite
laisser, leave
marcher, walk
monter, come up
omettre, omit
oser, dare
passer (*se*), pass by, go by
pendre, hang

perdre, lose, undo
poser, lay down
prier, request, beg
promettre, promise
raconter, relate
rassurer (*se*), regain confidence
respirer, breathe
rester, remain
retirer (*se*), retire
saisir, seize
trouver, find
tuer, kill
veiller, watch
voyager, travel
ne pas se faire prier, to require no pressing
à peine, scarcely
au contraire, on the contrary
au dessous de, beneath
auprès, near
aussitôt, immediately
autrement, otherwise
dehors, outside
dès que, as soon as
devant, in front, ahead
doucement, gently
du moins, at least
en bas, below, downstairs
eh bien ! well
enfin, at length, now, finally
près de, near to
tant que, as long as
tranquillement, quietly
voyons ! let us see, let us settle

Key to Exercise in Lesson 39.

1. La petite Marie, assise dans un fauteuil, lisait l'histoire du Petit Chaperon Rouge. 2. Quand la pauvre fille avait fait son ouvrage, elle allait s'asseoir dans les cendres ; c'est pourquoi on l'appelait Cendrillon. 3. Ne vous asseyez pas sur l'herbe ; elle est humide ; vous vous enrhumeriez. 4. Il parlait à chaque

instant de s'en aller, mais il se rasseyait toujours, et nous ne pouvions (pas) nous débarrasser de lui. 5. Pour émouvoir ses auditeurs il faut que l'orateur soit ému lui même ; on n'émeut pas sans être ému. 6. Une armée est un corps animé d'une infinité de passions différentes qu'un homme habile fait mouvoir pour la défense de la patrie. 7. Lorsqu'on ne peut faire ce que l'on veut, il faut essayer de vouloir ce que l'on peut. 8. Nous parlons peu quand la vanité ne nous fait pas parler. 9. Nous oublions aisément nos fautes lorsqu'elles ne sont sues que de nous. 10. La parfaite valeur est de faire sans témoins ce qu'on serait capable de faire devant tout le monde. 11. Les personnes faibles ne peuvent être sincères. 12. Nous sommes plus près d'aimer ceux qui nous haïssent, que ceux qui nous aiment plus que nous ne voulons. 13. Un philosophe a dit que peu de gens savent être vieux. 14. La vanité nous fait faire plus de choses contre notre goût que la raison. 15. Ce que nous savons est peu de chose en comparaison de ce que nous ne savons pas ; et quelquefois même ce que nous ne savons pas est justement ce que nous devrions savoir. 16. Savoir qu'on ne sait rien, c'est savoir beaucoup. 17. L'homme qui se vend est toujours payé plus qu'il ne vaut. 18. Les grandes pensées viennent de cœur.

LESSON 41

On the Adverb

ADVERBS (*les adverbes*) may be either (a) single and simple words—that is, words not formed from others by the addition of a suffix ; (b) single words derived from adjectives by the addition of a suffix ; or (c) expressions made up of several words. In this last case they are called adverbial phrases (*locutions adverbiales*).

The chief will be found in the following lists :

1. ADVERBS OF TIME.

alors, then	*après-demain*, the day after to-
après, after	morrow
aujourd'hui, today	*ensuite*, afterwards
autrefois, formerly	*hier*, yesterday
aussitôt, immediately	*jadis*, formerly
auparavant, before	*jamais*, ever, never

avant-hier, the day before yesterday

bientôt, soon

cependant, meanwhile

déjà, already

demain, tomorrow

depuis, since

désormais, henceforth

dorénavant, henceforward

encore, again, yet, still

enfin, at last

la veille, the day before

l'avant-veille, two days before

le lendemain matin (*soir*) next morning (evening)

longtemps, long

maintenant, now

parfois, at times

puis, then

quand, when

quelquefois, sometimes

souvent, often

tard, late

tantôt, by and by, a short time ago

tôt, early

toujours, always, still

le lendemain, next day

le surlendemain, two days after

la veille au matin (*soir*) the morning (evening) before

Tard cannot be used as an adjective. "You are late" is "*Vous êtes en retard.*"

2. Adverbs of Place.

ailleurs, elsewhere

alentour, around

auprès, near

dedans, inside

dehors, outside

dessus, above

dessous, below

derrière, behind

devant, before, ahead

ici, here

là, there

loin, far

où, where

d'où, whence

partout, everywhere

partout où, wherever

Y is a pronoun when it means not "there" but "to it," "to them," etc. In any case, however, its place in the sentence is always that of a conjunctive pronoun. "There" is to be translated by *y*, not by *là*, when it refers to a place mentioned before. After "it is," etc., *là* is to be used.

3. Adverbs of Quantity.

assez, enough

autant, as much

beaucoup, much, many

bien, much, many

combien, how much

davantage, more

guère, but little

moins, less

peu, little, few

plus, more

trop, too much   [many!

que, how! how much! how

When these adverbs are used in connexion with a noun, the preposition *de* is always required between the adverb and the noun : *Il a beaucoup de livres*, He has many books.

Bien is the only one that takes the definite article as well as *de* :
Il a bien des livres, He has many books.

When the noun is understood, and replaced by a pronoun, that
pronoun must be *en : A-t-il beaucoup de livres ? Oui, il en a
beaucoup,* Has he many books ? Yes, he has many.

Davantage (more) comes always at the end of a sentence. It
may be preceded by *en* (before the verb) like any other adverb of
quantity : *Il a assez d'argent ; ne lui en donnez pas davantage,*
He has enough money ; do not give him any more.

Beaucoup must never be preceded by any other adverb. If a
stronger expression be required, some other word must be used,
such as *infiniment, excessivement,* etc.

4. ADVERBS OF AFFIRMATION, NEGATION AND DOUBT.

oui, si, yes	*non,* no
certes, certainly	*ne, pas, point,* not
même, even	*guère,* little
cependant, however	*peut-être,* perhaps

Oui is the ordinary affirmative adverb. *Si* is used either by
way of contradiction or in answer to a question put negatively.
It is frequently preceded by *mais,* which makes it more emphatic.
It may also be emphasized by placing *fait* after it. The English
equivalent of *si* is commonly " yes " plus an auxiliary : *Est-ce
que vous n'allez pas à Paris ? Si.* Are you not going to Paris ?
Yes, I am.

Even in French, *si* is very frequently followed by the verb
used in the previous statement or question : *N'avez-vous pas lu
ce roman ? Si, je l'ai lu,* Have you not read this novel ? Yes, I
have read it.

Owing to its contradictory force, *si* is hardly a polite expression
and, except in familiar conversation had better be replaced by
some other formula, such as : *Je vous demande pardon,* I beg
your pardon.

In " indirect speech," *oui* and *si* and *non* are preceded by *que :
Pleut-il ? Je crois que oui,* Is it raining ? I think so (yes).

Ne is the only simple negative. Except in certain idiomatic
constructions, where its use is pleonastic, it seldom occurs alone.
It is used in connexion with *pas, point* (which is rather stronger
than *pas*), *nul, nullement, ni, aucun, aucunement, guère, jamais,
plus, rien, personne : Nul n'est prophète en son pays,* no one is a
prophet in his own country. *Il n'a aucune envie de partir,* He has
no wish to go away.

Ne is frequently used without *pas* or *point* in connexion with the verbs *cesser*, to cease ; *oser*, to dare ; *pouvoir*, to be able, and *savoir*, to know :

Cet enfant ne cesse de nous tourmenter, that child does not cease worrying us. *Il ne peut parler*, he cannot speak. *Je ne sais s'il réussira*, I do not know whether he will succeed. *Je n'ose vous adresser ma demande*, I dare not make my request to you.

A sentence in which *peut-être* occurs admits of three constructions :

(a) *Peut-être* may begin the sentence, and in this case the subject and verb may take the same places as in interrogative sentences : *Peut-être ses amis l'ont-ils vu pour la dernière fois*, perhaps his friends have seen him for the last time.

(b) *Peut-être* may be placed after the verb in a simple tense, or between the auxiliary and the past participle in a compound tense : *Nous lui écrirons peut-être demain*, we shall perhaps write to him to-morrow.

(c) When *peut-être* begins a sentence, it may be followed by *que*, and does not then require any change in the order of the subject and verb : *Peut-être qu'il ne vous a pas compris*, perhaps he has not understood us.

5. ADVERBS OF MANNER.

A few adverbs of manner are simple forms, such as *bien*, well ; *mieux*, better ; *mal*, badly ; *pis*, worse ; *ainsi*, thus. The majority of them are derivatives ending in *ment*, and formed from adjectives according to the rules given in our next Lesson.

LESSON 42

Formation of Adverbs

THERE are three methods of adverbial formation from adjectives in French : 1. Adverbs from adjectives ending in a vowel, add *ment* : *facile*, easy ; *facilement*, easily ; *obstiné*, stubborn : *obstinément*, stubbornly ; *poli*, polite : *poliment*, politely ; *dû*, due : *dûment*, duly ; *éperdu*, distracted : *éperdument*, distractedly. Exceptions :

The circumflex accent on the following adverbs *assidu, assidûment*, assiduously ; *cru, crûment*, crudely ; *résolu, résolûment*, resolutely ; *indu, indûment*, unduly ; the adverb from *gai* (gay) may be written *gaîment* or *gaiement*. Note also *traître, traîtreuse-ment* (treacherously) and *impuni, impunément* (with impunity).

The following adjectives ending in *e* take an acute accent before the additional *ment ;* *aveugle, aveuglément,* blindly ; *commode, commodément,* conveniently ; *incommode, incommodé-ment,* inconveniently ; *énorme, énormément,* hugely ; *conforme, conformément,* conformably ; *immense, immensément,* immensely ; *opiniâtre, opiniâtrément,* stubbornly ; *uniforme, uniformément,* uniformly.

2. To form adverbs from adjectives ending in a consonant, add *ment* to the feminine form : *faux,* false : *faussement,* falsely ; *frais,* fresh : *fraîchement,* freshly ; *actif,* active : *activement,* actively ; *nouveau,* new : *nouvellement,* newly. Exceptions :

The following adjectives take an acute accent on the *e* of the feminine form preceding the termination *ment : commun, com-munément,* commonly ; *confus, confusément,* confusedly ; *diffus, diffusément,* diffusely ; *exprès, expressément,* expressly ; *importun, importunément,* importunately ; *inopportun, inopportunément,* inopportunely : *obscur, obscurément,* obscurely ; *opportun, oppor-tunément,* opportunely ; *profond, profondément,* deeply ; *précis, précisément,* precisely.

The adverbs corresponding with *gentil* (nice) and *bref* (brief) are *gentiment* and *brièvement*.

3. To form adverbs from adjectives ending in *ant* or *ent,* change *nt* into *m,* and add *ment : prudent,* prudent : *prudemment ; constant,* constant : *constamment,* constantly. Exceptions :

Lent, présent and *véhément* become *lentement* (slowly), *présente-ment* (at the present time), and *véhémentement* (vehemently).

The following adverbs are derived from adjectives either wholly obsolete or seldom used : *grièvement,* grievously ; *journelle-ment,* daily ; *notamment,* notably ; *nuitamment,* by night ; *sciem-ment,* wittingly. The last syllable but one of adverbs ending in *amment* or *emment* has no nasal sound, but is pronounced like *a : prudemment,* pru-da-ment ; *constamment,* con-sta-ment.

In French an adverb must never be placed, as it frequently is in English, between the subject and the verb : *Je le vois souvent,* I often see him.

Its position is generally after the verb if the verb is in a simple tense, and between the auxiliary and the past participle if the verb is in a compound tense : *Nous en parlons rarement,* We rarely speak of it. *J'ai bien dormi,* I have slept well.

Many adverbs of time and place, however, and adverbial phrases come after the past participle : *Je lui ai parlé hier*, I spoke to him yesterday. *Nous l'avons envoyé ailleurs*, We sent him elsewhere.

Exercise.

Translate into French : 1. Men do not arrive immediately at the knowledge of truth. 2. There is nothing more vexatious (*fâcheux*) than uncertainty (*incertitude*, f.). 3. If we had lived only two centuries earlier, we should have had no idea of steam-engines (*la machine à vapeur*), of railways, of the telegraph (*le télégraphe*). 4. Laziness goes so slowly that poverty soon overtakes (*atteindre*) it. 5. The reason of the strongest is always the best. 6. Young people must speak little and listen much. 7. The happiness of the wicked (sing.) does not last (*durer*) long. 8. That thief is accused of having entered (*s'introduire*) a house by night. 9. Let him come on Friday or Saturday ; those are the days when I am most usually (*ordinaire*) at home in the evening. 10. And now, answer me frankly, what is there (of) true in this accusation ? 11. I have always wondered (asked myself) why the French, who are so smart (*spirituel*) at home, are so stupid (*bête*) when travelling (*en voyage*). 12. An extraordinary good fortune (*le bonheur*) has constantly accompanied that brigand (*le brigand*) to (*jusqu'à*) this day. A price is set on his head (his head has been put to price) ; nevertheless he continues with impunity his dangerous trade (*le métier*). 13. He is extremely generous (*généreux*) ; money costs (*coûter*) him but little to earn (*gagner*), and he spends (*dépenser*) it easily with the poor. 14. He ordinarily wears (*porter*) a costume (*le costume*) of very great elegance (*élégance*, f.) ; his linen (*le linge*) is always of dazzling (*éclatant*) whiteness (*la blancheur*).

French Conversation.

Would you direct me to the library, if you please ? *Voulez-vous avoir la bonté de m'indiquer le chemin de la bibliothèque ?*

Certainly, sir ; with pleasure. *Certainement, monsieur ; avec plaisir.*

It is in this street, is it not ? *Elle est dans cette rue, n'est-ce pas ?*

No, monsieur ; it is opposite the railway station. *Non, monsieur ; elle est en face de la gare.*

Take the first turning to the right and then the second to the left. *Prenez la première rue à droite et puis la seconde à gauche.*

Thank you, mademoiselle. *Merci bien, mademoiselle.*

LESSON 43

Minor Parts of Speech

IN French the prepositions *à, de* and *en* must be repeated
before every complement. All prepositions except *en*
require the verb coming after them to be in the infinitive.
En is followed by the present participle : *Il ne partira pas sans
venir nous voir*, he will not go away without coming to see us.
C'est en voyageant que j'ai appris la géographie, it is by (in)
travelling that I have learnt geography. In, or at, when
followed by the name of a town, is expressed by *à*. When
followed by the name of a country, continent, or large island,
it is expressed by *en* : *Il demeure à Paris*, he lives in Paris.
Son père est en France, his father is in France.

The prepositions in most frequent use are :

à, to, at	*envers*, towards
après, after	*excepté*, except
à travers, through	*hormis*, except
attendu, considering	*malgré*, in spite of
avant, before (time)	*moyennant*, in consideration of
avec, with	*outre*, in addition to
chez, at the house of	*par*, by, through
concernant, concerning	*parmi*, amongst
contre, against	*pendant*, during
dans, in	*pour*, for, in order to
de, of, from, with	*sans*, without
depuis, since	*selon*, according to
derrière, behind	*sous*, under
dès, from, as early as	*suivant*, according to
devant, before (position)	*sur*, on, upon, about
durant, during	*sauf*, save
en, in	*touchant*, concerning, touching
entre, between	*vers*, towards
	vu, seeing, considering

The preposition *à* is used to form prepositional phrases, of
which the most common are :

jusqu'à, till, to, as far as	*quant à*, as for, as to
par rapport à, with regard to	*grâce à*, thanks to

(337)

The preposition *de* is used to form the following prepositional phrases :

autour de, around, about	*au-travers de*, through
au-dessus de, above	*à moins de*, unless
au-dessous de, below	*à l'insu de*, unknown to
à l'égard de, with regard to	*en dépit de*, in spite of
au-devant de, towards, to meet	*en face de*, facing
à côté de, beside	*faute de*, for want of
du côté de, in the direction of	*le long de*, along
à force de, by dint of	*près de*, near
à fleur de, flush with	*proche de*, adjoining
auprès de, near	*vis-à-vis de*, opposite
au delà de, beyond	*au-dedans de*, inside
à l'abri de, sheltered from	*au-dehors de*, outside

Speaking generally, " in " is to be translated by *dans* when followed by an article, a possessive, or a demonstrative, and by *en* when there is no such determinative : *Elle rencontra un loup dans le champ*, she met a wolf in the field. *En hiver la terre est couverte de neige*, in winter the ground is covered with snow.

Before expressions of time, *dans* expresses " time when," and *en*, " time how long": *Je ferai cela dans une heure*, I shall do that in an hour's time (from now). *Je ferai cela en une heure*, I shall do that in an hour (it will take me an hour).

Durant and *pendant* both mean during ; but *durant* implies the whole of a period, and *pendant* a point of time during a period : *Nous sommes restés à Paris durant tout le siège*, we remained in Paris during the whole siege. *C'est pendant le siège que s'est livrée cette bataille*, it was during the siege that this battle was fought.

Vers implies actual movement towards : *Elle leva les mains vers le ciel*, she raised her hands towards heaven. *Envers* is used figuratively, in connexion with feelings, sentiments, etc. : *Il s'est montré reconnaissant envers nous*, he has shown himself grateful to (towards) us. *Vers* also approximates " time when " : *Nous arriverons vers midi*, we shall arrive about noon.

Approximation of " time how long," and of number or quantity generally, is expressed by *environ : Nous y resterons une heure environ*, we shall remain there about an hour.

Personal pronouns coming after a preposition usually refer to persons. Consequently, an English preposition followed by a neuter pronoun " it," " them," is commonly rendered by the corresponding adverb : *Ouvrons la boîte pour voir ce qu'il y a dedans*, let us open the box to see what is in it.

Conjunctions. The chief simple conjunctions are :

car, for	*ni*, nor
cependant, however, yet	*non plus*, either
comme, as	*or*, now
donc, therefore, then	*ou*, or
et, and	*pourtant*, nevertheless, yet
mais, but	*quand*, though
que, that	*puisque*, since
parce que, because	*quoique*, although

A great number of conjunctive phrases (*locutions conjonctives*) are formed by the addition of *que* to certain adverbs or to certain prepositions. Some of these are followed (*a*) by the indicative ; others (*b*) by the subjunctive ; and others (*c*) again by the indicative or the subjunctive according to their meaning :

(*a*) *à cause que*, because
  à ce que, according to what
  ainsi que, as
  à mesure que, in porportion that
  après que, after
  attendu que, considering
  peut-être que, perhaps
  tandis que, whilst
  vu que, seeing that
  au lieu que, whereas
  aussitôt que, as soon as
  autant que, as much as
  depuis que, since
  dès que, as soon as
  pendant que, whilst
  outre que, besides

  tant que, so long as
  jusqu'à ce que, until
(*b*) *afin que*, in order that
  à moins que—ne, unless
  avant que, before
  bien que, although
  de crainte que—ne, lest
  de peur que—ne, for fear
    that
  en cas que, in case
  non que, not that
  pour que, in order that
  pourvu que, provided
  sans que, without
  soit que, whether
  supposé que, supposing

(*c*) *de manière que*, in such a way that ; *de (en) sorte que*, so that ; *si ce n'est que*, except that ; *si non que*, unless ; *tellement que*, so that.

These last conjunctions require the indicative when actual fact is indicated, and the subjunctive when a purpose or contingency is expressed : *Il a bien travaillé de sorte que son père est content de lui*, he has worked well, so that his father is pleased with him. *Travaillez de manière que votre père soit content de vous*, work in such a way that your father may be pleased with you.

The conjunction " for " meaning " because " must be distinguished from the preposition " for " meaning " on behalf of," " instead of," etc. : *Ce n'est pas pour vous que j'ai acheté ces livres car vous ne lisez jamais*, it is not for you I have bought those books, for you never read.

Que is used to avoid the repetition of *comme*, as ; *quand*, when ; and *si*, if. In the last of these cases it is followed by the subjunctive : *Comme (quand) il fait beau temps et que nous n'avons rien à faire nous allons nous promener*, as (when) it is fine and we have nothing to do, we are going for a walk ; *Si nous n'avons rien à faire et qu'il fasse beau temps nous irons nous promener*, if we have nothing to do and (if) it is fine, we shall go for a walk.

Puisque and *depuis que* both mean " since " ; but the former introduces a motive, and is nearly synonymous with " because," whilst the latter refers to a point of time : *Je le lui donnerai, puisque je le lui ai promis*, I shall give it to him, since I promised it him ; *Il m'a écrit deux fois depuis qu'il est en France*, he has written to me twice since he has been in France.

EXERCISE.

TRANSLATE INTO FRENCH : 1. (The) Charity is patient, gentle and benevolent (*bienfaisant*). 2. The compass (*la boussole*) was not discovered (*trouver*) by a mariner (*marin*), nor the telescope (*le télescope*) by an astronomer (*astronome*). 3. Neither (the) gold nor (the) greatness (*la grandeur*) make(s) us (*rendre*) happy. 4. (The) man is unhappy only because he is wicked (*méchant*). 5. Obey (sing.) if you wish to be obeyed one day.

Interjections. Apart from a great many words and phrases that are frequently used as exclamations, the chief interjections are : *Ah !* Oh ! *Aïe !* Oh dear ! *Bah !* Nonsense ! Never mind ! *Bis !* Encore ! *Chut !* Hush ! *Crac !* Bang ! *Eh !* Hallo ! *Fi !* Fie ! *Gare !* Look out ! *Ha !* Ah ! *Hélas !* Alas ! *Hein !* What ? What's that ? *Hola !* Hi ! *Hum !* Hem ! *O !* O ! *Pst !* Hist ! An expression which is often heard, and which a literal translation quite fails to render, is *Mon Dieu !* It has about the same strength as the English " Goodness ! " " Why ! " *Allons !* which literally means " let us go," is used like the English word " Come ! "

KEY TO EXERCISE IN LESSON 42.

1. Les hommes n'arrivent pas immédiatement à la connaissance de la vérité. 2. Il n'y a rien de plus fâcheux que l'incertitude. 3. Si nous avions vécu seulement deux siècles plus tôt nous

n'aurions eu aucune idée des machines à vapeur, des chemins de fer, du télégraphe. 4. La paresse va si lentement que la pauvreté l'atteint bientôt. 5. La raison du plus fort est toujours la meilleure. 6. Les jeunes gens doivent parler peu et écouter beaucoup. 7. Le bonheur du méchant ne dure longtemps. 8. Ce voleur est accusé de s'être introduit nuitamment dans une maison. 9. Qu'il vienne vendredi ou samedi ; ce sont les jours où je suis le plus ordinairement chez moi le soir. 10. Et maintenant, répondez-moi franchement, qu'y a-t-il de vrai dans cette accusation ? 11. Je me suis toujours demandé pourquoi les Français, si spirituels chez eux, sont si bêtes en voyage. 12. Un bonheur extraordinaire a constamment accompagné ce brigand jusqu'à ce jour. Sa tête est mise à prix ; pourtant il continue impunément son dangereux métier. 13. Il est extrêmement généreux ; l'argent ne lui coûte guère à gagner, et il le dépense facilement avec les pauvres. 14. Il porte ordinairement un costume d'une très grande élégance ; son linge est toujours d'une blancheur éclatante.

LESSON 44

Use of the Articles

THE definite article is required before all nouns used in their widest sense—that is to say, in a way that includes all the individuals or objects of a given class. In accordance with this principle (a) abstract nouns, and (b) nouns indicating material take the definite article : *L'hypocrisie est un hommage que le vice rend à la vertu*, hypocrisy is a homage that vice pays to virtue. *Le platine est plus pesant que l'or*, platinum is heavier than gold. Titles immediately preceding proper nouns require the definite article : *Le règne de la reine Victoria en est un des plus longs de l'histoire*, Queen Victoria's reign is one of the longest in history. When proper nouns are qualified by an adjective, that adjective must be preceded by the definite article : *La pâleur du petit Pierrot inquiétait la vieille Marguerite*, little Pierrot's pallor troubled old Margaret.

The definite article, with the preposition *à*, is used to express some peculiarity or distinctive feature : *Il y avait parmi les passagers, de jeunes Anglaises aux brillantes spirales de cheveux blonds*, there were amongst the passengers some young English girls with brilliant coils of fair hair. In descriptions of personal appearance, the verb *avoir* and a noun with a definite article are frequently used : *Elle a les cheveux blonds, les yeux bleus, le teint frais, et les lèvres vermeilles,* she has fair hair, blue eyes, a fresh complexion, and ruddy lips. The definite article is used distributively to express measure and weight : *Ce vin coûte deux francs la bouteille,* this wine costs two francs a bottle.

The definite article is used before the names of continents, countries, and provinces : *La Suisse, la Belgique, le Danemark et le Portugal ne sont pas au nombre des grandes puissances ;* Switzerland, Belgium, Denmark and Portugal are not amongst the great powers.

Exception : After the preposition *de*, the definite article is not used when it is intended to form an adjective phrase only : *La plupart des vins de France sont moins forts que ceux d'Espagne et de Portugal ;* the greater part of French wines are less strong than those of Spain and of Portugal.

With feminine names of countries, " in " and " into " are expressed by *en* without the definite article. Also the preposition *de* is used alone, after verbs expressing coming from those countries, such as *arriver de, venir de*, etc. : *S'il part d'Amérique le vingt-trois juin, il arrivera en Europe vers le premier juillet,* If he leaves America on the 23rd of June, he will arrive in Europe about the 1st of July.

The definite article is not used before numerals denoting the order of succession of sovereigns, etc. It is also omitted before nouns in apposition : *Louis seize, petit-fils et successeur de Louis quinze, monta sur le trône en* 1774, Louis the Sixteenth, the grandson and successor of Louis the Fifteenth, ascended the throne in 1774.

The definite article is not used in French, as it is in English, when a comparative is repeated :

Plus vous serez gai, plus longtemps vous vivrez, the gayer you are, the longer you will live.

Indefinite Article. This is omitted after *quel*, what, and *sans*, without : *Quel beau tableau,* what a fine picture ; *Je ne puis écrire sans plume,* I cannot write without a pen ; before nouns in apposition : *Nelson, célèbre amiral anglais, naquit en* 1758, Nelson, a famous English admiral, was born in 1758 ; before nouns serving as predicative complements to such verbs as *être*, to be ;

devenir, to become ; and *paraître*, to seem ; and also before nouns serving as the second accusative after such verbs as *faire*, to make ; *se faire*, to become ; *se montrer*, to show oneself ; *nommer*, to appoint ; *croire*, to believe : *Le père du maréchal Ney était tonnelier*, Marshal Ney's father was a cooper.

Partitive Article. The partitive article *du, de la, des* is used as a general rule before any noun indicating a certain portion of anything or a limited number of objects, whether the English equivalents " some " and " any " be expressed or only understood : *J'ai passé des jours heureux à la campagne*, I have spent (some) happy days in the country.

Before a noun preceded by an adjective, the preposition *de* alone is to be used : *De riantes prairies s'offraient à nos regards charmés*, smiling meadows presented themselves to our delighted gaze. When a noun taken partitively is the object of a negative sentence, *de* alone is to be used : *Je n'ai pas d'argent*, I have not any money. *Il ne porte jamais de chapeau*, he never wears a hat.

Before an adjective the partitive article is used to indicate distinction or opposition. Thus, *donnez-moi de bon pain* means simply, give me some good bread ; but *donnez-moi du bon pain* means, " give me some of the good bread "—not the bad.

In negative sentences the definite article is to be used before the complement, if that complement is followed by an adjective or an adjective clause. Thus, *Je n'ai pas d'argent* means I have no money ; but *Je n'ai pas de l'argent pour le dépenser follement*, I have no money to spend extravagantly, implies that I have money, but that it is not to be squandered.

The position of the article before *quelques* should be noted : *Je ne regrette pas les quelques francs que cela m'a coûté*, I do not regret the few francs which that has cost me.

Tout (*toute, tous, toutes*) is the only adjective which, when accompanied by an article, always precedes it. *Il a perdu toute l'affection qu'il avait pour moi*, he has lost all the affection which he had for me.

KEY TO EXERCISE IN LESSON 43.

1. La charité est patiente, douce et bienfaisante. 2. La boussole n'a point été trouvée par un marin ni le télescope par un astronome. 3. Ni l'or ni la grandeur ne nous rendent heureux. 4. L'homme n'est malheureux que parce qu'il est méchant. 5. Obéis si tu veux qu'on t'obéisse un jour.

Our Course in French is continued in Volume 6.

LESSON 27

Physical Aspect of Middle America

FROM the United States tapers, to the south, the Mexican plateau, which narrows to the isthmus of Panama. Here the grain of the land produces the western mountain rim, flanking the Pacific ocean, the connexion between the Rockies and the Andes. Here are the Mexican Republic and the states of Central America, of which British Honduras is a British colony. Eastwards lies the American Middle Sea ; its accidental labels— Gulf of Mexico, Caribbean Sea—disguise its real character, for it is as definite a unit as the Mediterranean.

Coming south from the level Mississippi plains, where from St. Louis, for example, for over 500 miles the land slopes on the average downwards less than 1 foot per mile to the Gulf coast, it might be expected that this dominant flatness would continue under the waters ; this is not the case. The flatness continues some 70 miles or so to a continental shelf, but farther seawards the solid surface drops somewhat suddenly into the north-western basin of the Middle Sea, which is a mile deep within 100 miles of the shore. This basin is the Gulf of Mexico ; its eastward edge is intricate ; north-east is the flat peninsula of Florida, 350 miles in length, over 100 miles wide, and nowhere higher than 500 feet above sea level ; south-west is the slightly less flat peninsula of Yucatan ; in both the flatness continues well out to sea in a widening of the continental shelf. Between the two peninsulas is the western end of Cuba, which is curved in sympathy with them to form a rampart to the basin, which is deep near the Cuban shore, and which spills out, in the narrow Yucatan Channel, to the Central Basin.

The Central Basin, which lacks a topographic label, is ledgeless, for the deep waters fringe the high lands, except along the south-east. There a submarine rim continues from the bulge of Honduras, which is a wedge of the continental shelf, through the submarine banks to Jamaica and Haiti. The basin spills out between eastern Cuba and Jamaica and in the narrowing of the Windward Passage. Across the basin a submarine ridge comes to the surface as the Cayman Islands. The south-eastern basin, the largest of the three, is more definitely ledgeless, for even along the north coast of South America the continental shelf is narrow; half of its boundary is continental, and half is a curved ridge from Haiti through Puerto Rico and the Leeward and Windward Islands to the junction with the continental island of Trinidad.

The Middle Sea is thus bounded on the north-east by the West Indies, which are the relics, the unsubmerged peaks, of an ancient land-mass older than the Andes, a middle-world east-west earth crinkle, which lies just within the tropics. The larger islands compose the Greater Antilles, which do not immediately drop to

SKETCH MAP OF THE MIDDLE AMERICAS

the depths of the Atlantic Ocean, for beyond a deepish channel is an almost continuous ridge, which rises to the sea surface as the coral isles and islets of the Bahamas. The Bahama Sea is relatively shallow and spills out as the Florida Channel, wherein the Gulf Stream is narrowed sufficiently to ensure the speed and driving force which make it a river on the ocean surface.

Three definite basins fringed by mountains form the Middle Americas. Here is one of the great world cemeteries. The curious may examine the parallel between this museum of the dead and the other Middle Sea, a museum of the moribund, both on the fringe of the white man's world, like scum edging a vortex swirl.

Both are still necessary passage ways for the white man's cargoes, because at the extremity of each he maintains a lock—the Panama and Suez Canals, dismal portals to his world.

The oldest of the monuments await complete identification and classification—they are hidden in the forest fastnesses of the continental area ; but the chiefest monument is probably the place-name Vera Cruz, the symbol of the graveyard of the power and authority of his Catholic Majesty of Spain, for Spain exterminated a people and began the re-population of the region with its present half-breeds, and began, also, the world lust for gold as a weapon for dominance over men and women.

Among the minor ruins are the negro republic of Haiti, the decayed but once magnificent domiciles of the early planters, and —if they still persist amid the tropic rains and rank vegetation— the scrap heaps of metal deserted by those who first failed to cut a trans-isthmian canal. As a museum the land abounds in fables associated with men like Montezuma, Las Casas and Drake, which still delight the young in mind. In a wider sphere the pride of place must be accorded to the negro element in the population, for the movement for the emancipation of the slaves.

Fittingly, the present produce of the area is decadent or obsolescent. Mexico mines gold and silver. Cuba produces cigars. The islands generally, and latterly the coast strips, produce sugar canes and bananas and other fruits. Honduras produces mahogany. The Bahamas supply sponges. Trinidad has an asphalt lake. Lime-juice and pine-apples come from the islets. All these are exotics ; they owe their importance—such as it may be—to consent, and fashion is changing ; there is no assured future market for a single one of them.

One thing, however, of permanent value comes thence : it is the Gulf Stream. From the Florida Channel issues this warm river, which, with the help of wind and tide and ocean swirl, brings to north-west Europe its annual winter vapour-bath of warm surface waters and of warm wet lower cloud-laden layers of air, and keeps away from British waters, from the North Sea, and from the Channel, the ice floes which would otherwise come down from the Arctic basin.

The population totals some thirty millions, of whom half inhabit Mexico. The mainland is scantily peopled ; some of the islets are as densely peopled as the Channel Islands. The towns are in general small, though the usual map in an atlas tends to a crowd of place-names. Mexico, a capital city, has nearly a million inhabitants, and is comparable with Cleveland ; Guadalajara, with less than 200,000 people, is the next town in Mexico. Havana, the celebrated Cuban capital, contains rather more than half a million folk, and compares with Singapore. The only other places with populations in excess of 100,000 are the capitals Guatemala and Port au Prince. Kingston, the chief place in Jamaica and the headquarters of British interests, is, to our standards, a small town with some 60,000 folk.

Communications are extensive, especially by sea round the shores of the basin. Railways happen in most of the larger islands, across the isthmus between the two oceans, and in Mexico, with connexions to the U.S.A. across the boundary of the Rio Grande. In the latter country the railways are of the rank of those of Chile or South Africa in comparison with the numbers of the population.

LESSON 28

Southern States of Latin America

THE triangular wedge of lowland which makes the major portion of the inland valley of the Amazon is to be contrasted with the oblong lowland of the lower Plate valley. The triangle has its longest side west-east ; the oblong lies mainly north and south. Meridian 65° W., from Oran south to the coast close to Bahia Blanca, is the western edge of the lowland, where in the lee of the Andes aridity is prevalent ; meridian 55° W., some 600 miles to the east, is crossed by the in-and-out political boundaries as well as by the edge of the Brazil heights ; between them, from 21° S. to 41° S., some fourteen hundred miles of lowland complete the oblong, most of which fails to reach an elevation of 500 feet above the level of the sea.

A corresponding oblong in North America, with the Mississippi as a north and south axis roughly on meridian 90° W., to match the Parana axis on 60° W., would reach from 40° N., roughly the line of the Ohio and the lower Missouri, to Yucatan across the Gulf of Mexico, with the Gulf coast, Galveston and New Orleans across the middle of the oblong. In both cases the equatorial half of the oblong is of small importance. In the north it is the seaway of the gulf ; in the south it comprises Paraguay and the northern part of Argentina, El Gran Chaco. The valuable areas are the polar halves of the oblongs, each roughly a 10° square.

In the summer both have temperatures in the neighbourhood of 75° F. The north, however, has slightly colder winters, for the frost line is roughly the northern edge ; in both the warmest winters reach 55° F. The rainfall is similar both in quantity and in seasonal distribution, for the equatorial edges tend to a summer rain maximum, the north being slightly the wetter. Both areas are peopled mainly by descendants of immigrants from Europe, though the negro problem is acute in the north. In the south the Italian workers have been exploited as were the negroes ; yet the Italians return to their native shores, while the negroes were mainly fixed to the land on their emancipation. The major difference lies in the distribution of the population. The people of the United States are not concentrated within the oblong ; there is no northern parallel to the agglomeration of folk along the Plate river. From La Plata or Montevideo to Santa Fé the riverine shores are densely peopled to form the chief populated area of the South American continent. On the other hand, the distribution of folk is more even in the north, especially east of the Mississippi.

The northern oblong includes the bulk of the cotton belt, much of the maize belt and some of the wheat belt, chiefly winter wheat ; the southern oblong contains practically the whole of the effective area of the southern continent. There is some production of cotton and cane sugar, but the major products are wheat and meat and wool, and in this respect Argentina and Uruguay are to be classed with corresponding lowlands in the southern hemisphere, in south-east Australia. Buenos Aires is to be compared with Sydney rather than with New Orleans. The remainder of Argentina lies south of the oblong, and includes the plateau country between the Andean summits and the accidental sea edge, where the South Atlantic forms a border on the wide eastern continental shelf. For 20° of latitude, some 1,500 miles farther south, the land is reminiscent on a larger scale of Sweden ; parallel rivers trench the land in almost direct courses down the slopes to the shore. Here is Patagonia, as unimportant as the north of Canada. and similarly disregarded in political and administrative circles as relatively unimportant attached

Territories. North of it, in the south-west corner of the oblong, the lowland pampas, the natural grassland, rises to the plateau level. In the far south, in the detached Tierra del Fuego, beyond Magellan Strait, the eastern portion of the island is Argentinian. Eastwards, some 400 miles away on the outward edge of the submarine shelf, lie the British Falkland Islands, in latitudes similar to Wales. East of the forested slopes the vegetation is poor steppe grassland with temperatures similar to those of Britain, but with a scanty rainfall, especially nearer the coast. The Andes, being higher than the Pennines, interfere with the prevailing westerly oceanic winds, and the east is the driest section of the country. The people are separately labelled as Patagonian Indians, among whom a few colonies of Europeans manage to persist on the frontiers of civilization. Patagonia is scantily peopled.

SOUTH AMERICA'S SOUTHERN STATES

The Argentine as a whole is about a third of the area of Brazil; Paraguay is about twice the size of British Guiana, and Uruguay about twice the size of French Guiana. Uruguay, on account of its compactness, its almost completely lowland character, and its situation on the Plate, is the most densely peopled state of the continent; the total population is about two millions. Paraguay contains fewer than a million folk and is comparable both in size and population with Italian Somaliland. Argentina has a population of 12,000,000, rather more than Canada ; it is somewhat more extensive than Mexico, and contains but two-thirds of the population of that country.

Centres of Population. The chief place is Buenos Aires, with more than 2,000,000 inhabitants, the largest city and seaport of the continent, the fourth largest city in the Americas. Across the estuary Montevideo has half a million people, and is comparable, slightly to its advantage, with San Francisco. All the other places are small. The river port of Rosario, with about half a million people, is about the size of Sheffield ; La Plata, an outport on the estuary, is fourth—it is slightly larger than Quebec. Asuncion, the Paraguayan capital, well upstream on the Paraguay, has rather fewer inhabitants than La Plata. Cordoba, the largest town of the interior, has a population roughly equal to that of Denver, and contains more folk than either of the two last-mentioned riverine towns. With the exception of Tucuman in the far north-west, and Santa Fé, which are both roughly equivalent to Ottawa, and Bahia Blanca, no other place has a population of more than 100,000.

Products. The wheat crop of the Argentine is roughly two thirds that of Canada and twice that of Australia ; the maize crop is the second largest in the world, though little more than a tenth of that of the United States. The Argentine produces more wine than Portugal.

Tobacco is grown both in Paraguay and Argentina, though neither country produces as much as Canada or Brazil. Cotton is grown on the scale of the cotton supply from Uganda ; the yield is less than that of Peru, Mexico or Brazil. Argentina has many horses, almost one per head of the population ; the total is two-thirds that of the United States and four times that of Australia. It has half as many cattle as the United States, and Uruguay has as many cattle as Canada. Paysandu and Fray Bentos, towns on the Uruguay, are almost household words in the lands where the produce of the great meat-packing establishments is utilized. Paraguay has almost as many cattle as New Zealand.

The Argentine occupies an important position in the wool trade. Australia, of course, is the chief producer of wool, and the Argentine competes with the United States for the second place ; each of them produces 50 per cent more wool than New

Zealand which in turn surpasses the production of the Union of South Africa. Uruguay comes next, with about half the yield of the Argentine.

Despite the implication of its name, Argentina does not produce appreciable quantities of silver. The quantity of cane sugar produced is roughly equal to that of Australia. The area is one of limited interests—wheat, wool, meat—primary produce for the white man's use in the northern hemisphere. Seaports are important and are the chief reason for town aggregations ; river traffic proceeds by the Plate river to railway terminals, and an extensive system of railways crosses the lowlands. The trans-Andean, trans-continental railway is of greater political significance than commercial importance, for Argentina ends at the Andes.

LESSON 29

The Amazon Basin in Geography

THE core of this section of the South American continent is the monstrosity, the Amazon river. North are the Guiana highlands and the valley of the Orinoco ; south-east lie the Brazil highlands and the valley of the São Francisco river. A rough axis is the Amazon, which flows from about 76° W. to 50° W., i.e. roughly 1,800 miles as the crow flies, almost along parallel 6° S. from the west to the east.

On the Pacific, from 10° S. to 5° S., the coast bears almost N.W.–S.E. in the neighbourhood of Trujillo. Within 200 miles seaward from the shore the undersea land surface slopes steadily down to a depth of more than a mile ; within a similar distance landward the sub-aerial land surface slopes upwards in places to heights in excess of three miles. Here is a land bastion, a youthful excrescence of the earth pushed up and folded between the greatest of the oceans and the relics of one of the ancient con-tinents—on the one side the great sea, on the other the great basin, for the Amazon valley to the east is a basin.

The headwaters of this mighty stream flow in mountain valleys almost parallel to the axis of the upthrusted disturbance ; they emerge on to the almost flat triangular basin, of which the three sides are the heights, and the eastern corner is at the constriction at Obidos. The Andean edge is some 600 miles long, and from it great rivers, such as the Madeira, flood the plain. From the Guianan edge the Putumayo, the Japura and the Negro-Branco flow in a general direction almost at right angles to the line of the Madeira. From the edge of the Brazilian massif there are few large rivers, for the Madeira is both close to and parallel with the edge. East of Obidos, at the apex of the triangle, the Tapajoz, the Xingu and the Tocantins flow from the massif in roughly parallel north-flowing streams to the Amazon.

Such is the heart of the South American continent, a land of excesses beyond the present powers of humanity to utilize. It is an area of superlatives. It is the largest area of humidity, far exceeding in extent, if not in precipitation, the wet zone of north-east India ; west, beyond the uplift, is an almost desert coast ; north, on the far slopes from the Guianan heights down to the Caribbean coast, is a comparatively dry area of summer rains in July ; south-east, near Cape San Roque, is a similar area of smallish summer rains in January. Both these lands receive on-shore trade winds, which yield their moisture at the period of the zenithal sun. The triangle lies between them, always humid. It is one of the hottest areas in the world ; because of the clouds, the world's protection from the sun's extravagance, it lacks the excessive heat of the Sahara under the zenithal sun, yet it has perpetually the discomforts of monsoon time in India.

We may imagine the atmosphere as a sheath of fluid stuff, which tends to accumulate in dense nodules over the great waters along the polar edges of the tropics of Cancer and Capricorn, with a broad intertropical patch of less dense air between. Within this sheath the spinning globe runs frictionally against the lowest levels, at a speed which is in the neighbourhood of 1,000 miles an hour from west to east. The nodules move faster than the land, and the anti-cyclones, as these nodules are named, move with the earth eastward. Between them the earth moves faster than its sheath, and the less dense air lagging with a load of water well warmed by excessive insolation is recorded, humanly, as the trade winds. Where the speeds coincide is the Belt of Calms, the doldrums. This lag of air, a frictional lag in the atmospheric lower levels, is met by the bastioned basin, the triangle of the Amazon, with its terminal western and highest wall athwart the line of motion. Here is the extreme of equatorial climatic phenomena. The result is the selvas, the hot, wet forest, the extreme manifestation of vegetational luxuriance, the

CRETACEAN REPTILES. Above, the Trachodon (" rugged-tooth ") dinosaurs walked on two feet, using their forefeet to support their massive bodies only when feeding on grass and leaves. The megalosaurus, seen in the lower illustration, was carnivorous, possessing formidable teeth and strong claws. GEOLOGY 18

Reconstruction in the American Museum of Natural History and Natural History Museum, South Kensington

CRETACEAN MONSTERS. While the chalk beds were being formed out of the foraminiferal ooze, the land was roamed over by monstrous creatures, larger than any that existed before or since. Two of these are illustrated above in reconstruction : Monoclonius, a herbivorous stegosaur, and (right) Tyrannosaurus, a fearsome carnivore. GEOLOGY 19

THE NEEDLES. A colossal bed of chalk lies beneath the surface of a great part of eastern and southern England. It is well exposed along the coasts of Kent and Sussex, and also in the Isle of Wight—largely composed of chalk—where this photograph of the famous Needles was taken. Beyond the outermost of the three sharp-pointed pillars of white chalk may be seen the Needles lighthouse. **GEOLOGY 19**

LONDON'S CHALKY BASE. Some 250 feet below London's streets, separated 700 feet in thickness, which comes to the surface in the Chilterns and North the rain-water is retained in the chalk, which thus constitutes a vast natural and a fifth of London's water is obtained by way of

Plate 42   *Volume V*

THE GIANT'S CAUSEWAY. This promontory of columnar basalt on the north coast of Antrim, Northern Ireland, really comprises three causeways—the Little, the Middle or Honeycomb, and the Grand (shown in this photo)—separated from each other by upthrusts of shapeless basalt called whindikes. Some 40,000 polygonal basalt pillars (diameter 15–20 ins.) are closely packed in the Causeway area. GEOLOGY 20

Photo, W. Lawrence

from them by layers of clay, grey sand and shingle, is a bed of chalk, 600 to Downs. Below the chalk is a layer of gault, and as this is impervious to water, reservoir. An inch of rain yields 14½ million gallons over one square mile. artesian wells sunk down to the chalk. GEOLOGY 19

MAUSOLEUM OF THEODORIC. Succeeding his father as king of the Goths in 473, Theodoric (c. A.D. 454–526) became virtually king of Italy in 493. He died at Ravenna and was buried in the splendid mausoleum shown here.

HISTORY : MEDIEVAL 27

Photo, Alinari

SIXTH CENTURY COSTUME. These mosaics (left) from the church of S. Apollinare Nuovo in Ravenna, though they depict two martyred saints, give an admirable presentation of the style of court dress in the age of Theodoric. HISTORY : MEDIEVAL 27

Photos, Alinari

Plate 44

Volume V

relic of conditions which pertained in a younger, hotter world. Here is a museum of primordial conditions, where men have not multiplied exceedingly, as in China or India; the native races lack numbers, as they lack intelligence. The white man can do little with this exuberance.

The fringing lands are the coastal margins. In the Age of Discovery, when the few mariners saw strange things and Europe

SKETCH MAP OF BRAZIL AND ADJOINING STATES

marvelled at the rare exotics these wanderers brought home, access was by sea, and the fringe lands were slightly known. The known area is now a little larger, but it matters much less.

The coastal states begin in the north-west with Colombia, a curious nodal state including a Pacific coast beyond the upthrust, an interior tangle of the Cordillera, and the north-west corner of the inland triangle, for the Putumayo is a boundary, and the

M5

tropical grassland and gallery forest of the valley of the Magdalena and a Gulf coast. Eastwards lies Venezuela, with the drowned lagoon of the Maracaibo between spurs of the Cordillera, a narrow coastal strip to the Caribbean, the llanos of the Orinoco valley, and a southern boundary on the Guianan edge of the triangle. Off-shore is Trinidad. This southern boundary continues east as the south of the Guianas : British, then Dutch, and finally French, the sole relics of western European acquisitions on the continent. In general, the Guianas comprise a series of north-looking valleys between spurs from the ancient heights. The coastal strip is wide.

The coastal strip south of Para is the major portion of the extensive state of Brazil. North of the corner the coastal plain is wide, but on the South Atlantic it narrows and almost disappears, until it reaches in the far south the lagoon coast near the Rio Grande do Sul. The inland boundary of Brazil includes portions of the components of the Plate river, the Uruguay, the Parana, and the Paraguay ; along the last river it crosses the swamps of the lowland west of the plateau of Matto Grosso. Interior Brazil is reached on the north by the Amazon, on the south-west by the Plate, and elsewhere directly from the sea.

Areas and Populations Brazil has an area almost half that of the whole continent, rather greater than that of the United States ; it contains 40 millions of inhabitants, about half the total for the continent. The people fringe the great rivers and the coast. Colombia has a seventh the area and a fifth the population of Brazil ; the upper Magdalena valley is a centre of population. Venezuela is a little smaller than Colombia and has but two-fifths as many inhabitants, who live on the coastal strip and not in the llanos. The Guianas are small and are the least densely populated of the states of Latin America. Together their area is less than half that of Venezuela, and the total population is but half a million, a fifth of that of Venezuela. British Guiana is the largest.

The chief aggregations of people in South America are outside the area of this section. Rio de Janeiro, one of the famous cities of the world, with a harbour of notable beauty, has a population of $1\frac{3}{4}$ millions.

Production of Coffee. São Paulo, in the coffee country, almost due west of Rio, but inland, has 1,120,000 folk, and is comparable with Hamburg. Next to it come four Brazilian ports—

Porto Alegre and Para (Belem), about the size of Newcastle, and, slightly larger, about the size of Portland (U.S.A.), Bahia (San Salvador) and Pernambuco (Recife). Elsewhere only Bogota (Colombia) and Caracas (Venezuela) exceed 200,000 in population. The other capitals—Georgetown, Paramaribo, Cayenne, and the Amazon river port Manaos—are small. The statistical records indicate that Brazil produces maize in quantity half the crop of Argentina and as much as Rumania, and rice to the quantity grown in Madagascar.

The Brazilian coffee crop dominates the world ; the nearest competitor is Colombia, where the yield is but a sixth of that of Brazil. The whole crop is now in excess of the world's needs, and demand seems likely to decrease. Brazil is the chief American source of the cacao bean. Venezuela yields about a quarter as much as Brazil. In the last decade Brazil has greatly increased its production of tobacco, and is now second to the United States, with about a seventh of the total yield of that country, and with a third the yield of Soviet Russia. Raw rubber from Brazil has declined both in total quantity and, more particularly, in relative importance ; the drop is from a third to a thirtieth of the world's requirements. The cotton produced in Brazil is rather less than that of Egypt.

Brazil supplies manganese ; the Guianas (British and Dutch) yield bauxite (aluminium ore). Venezuela has jumped into importance as a source of petrol in the last decade ; a tenth of the world's supply now comes from that country, a quantity equal to the supply from Russia and twice the amount obtained from Iran. Brazil and British Guiana supply some cane sugar.

LESSON 30

South America's Pacific Fringe

FOR over four thousand miles, through 65 degrees of latitude, from Cape Horn northwards, the littoral of South America stretches along the shores of the deepest and largest of the oceans. The southern end, Cape Horn, is as far to the south of the equator as to the north are Belfast, Danzig, Moscow, or Port Nelson on Hudson Bay. Here are the Andean Latin-American states, Chile, Peru, Ecuador and Colombia, to which must be added the coastless Bolivia. Their total area is less than three-quarters of the area of Brazil and less than a third of the total area of the continent. Relatively in area, if Ecuador is 1, Chile is 2½, and Bolivia 5, with Colombia and Peru almost equal at 4.

They include more than twice as many inhabitants as Argentina, and less than a third of the total population of South America, Relatively in population, if Ecuador is 1, Chile is 2, and Bolivia 1½, with Peru 3 and Colombia 4. Compared with Mexico, they contain together 50 per cent more people in rather less than three times the area.

The greater part of the 25 million inhabitants are Indians , usually they are illiterate, apathetic, inert, and without useful qualities, except the negative ones of dull utility as beasts of burden and doers of chores. In addition there exists a fairly numerous section of people of mixed breed, European crosses with the native races. The whites, or as some writers dub them, the reputed whites, form about one-eighth of the population, generally as an aristocracy of landholders.

It is reported that the people of Chile have been the most successful of all the peoples of South America in developing towards a new race of more or less mixed origin with definite characteristics ; although the lower orders, the peasants and workers, are illiterate crosses.

The whole area is a museum of antiquities, for the people are a backwash relic, and their monuments, the fabled monuments of the Incas which excited the cupidity of the Spaniards, are of archaeological interest. The more recently discovered relics, such as the remains of a great wall across the deserted Andean valleys, excite a mild curiosity. The records of earlier populations are scanty, but the evidence which exists suggests that in the last half century there has been no influx of settlers, or foreign-born, into these lands ; in fact, in Chile the increase in population during 50 years is below the increase to be normally expected from natural causes. Including Bogota, in Colombia, there are only nine towns with a population in excess of 100,000. Santiago, the Chilean capital, has half a million inhabitants and rivals Montevideo. Valparaiso, the Chilean port, is only half the size of Rosario. La Paz, in Bolivia, has 200,000 folk, and surpasses Ottawa in numbers but not in the character of its inhabitants. Quito, in Ecuador, is smaller still. Less reputable records state that Lima, the Peruvian capital, is at the 373,000 mark. Smaller places line the coast ; they are Maracaibo, Guayaquil, Callao, the port of Lima, Arica, Iquique, Antofagasta, Valdivia and Puerto Montt.

The records state that Chile produces as much wheat as Algeria or Egypt, a tenth the production of Argentina ; less maize than Canada ; and about a tenth as much wine as Argentina. Peru, Ecuador and Bolivia are recorded as producers of small quantities of coffee, together about a tenth of the yield of Colombia. Ecuador provides about 4 per cent of the world's cacao beans, about as much as either Venezuela or San Domingo. Relatively negligible quantities of tobacco are grown in Chile and Colombia, and of rubber are obtained from Bolivia, Ecuador and Peru. Peru provides the world with as much cotton as Mexico, and with half as much as Brazil. Chile and Peru supply wool, much of which is due to the indigenous llama.

Production of Minerals. Chile has coal mines ; the yield, though small, is important for the extensive Chilean railways, and also in relation to the small coal supplies of the Southern Hemisphere. During the last decade Chile has developed a copper industry until it follows the United States as the second most important producer of copper in the world ; the yield is about a sixth of the world's total and is about six times as large as the product of Spain. Bolivia has made similar advance in connexion with tin ; that country is now second to Malaya, and produces a quarter of the world's supplies, more than is obtained in the Dutch East Indies. Negligible quantities of gold are mined in each of the five states. Peru mines silver to the same extent as Canada, about a fifth as much as Mexico ; Bolivia mines a quarter as much as Peru, and Chile a quarter as much as Bolivia. The precious metals, on which Spanish dominion was based, existed in fabled inexhaustible stores only relatively to the amount of these metals then in circulation ; the richer and more extensive ores of Africa and North America have made these South American supplies of minor importance. Bolivia produces 10 per cent of the world's antimony, as does Mexico ; these supplies are important since the major supply comes from China in very fluctuating amounts. Peru is a minor source of petrol ; the total is about 1 per cent of the world's supply.

The total utilities of the area are of relatively small importance. With the few mineral exceptions these lands contribute little of value to the white man's world. It might be claimed that the

Chilean nitrate of the Atacama desert, a mineral on which Chile has become prosperous, is an exception, but the chemist has decided that synthetic nitrogen is more important than nitrogen obtained from Chile. The yield of this mineral source of fertilizers, despite the fact that the consumption of fertilizers has increased as the areas of large-scale farming have increased, has remained steady for 30 years on the average, although the annual range of fluctuation is astonishingly large : for example, the output in 1929 was double that of 1927, yet but little more than that of 1917, while the yield in 1925 was no larger than that of 1911.

As a whole, the invaders of this littoral have arrived from the Pacific, and depend on oceanic communications, which were improved when the Panama Canal came into effective use. They spread eastwards but slowly and in scattered groups. In the south, where Argentina lies beyond the mountains, Chile stops at the mountainous water-parting; farther north, where Brazil lies to the east, the east side of the Andes was for long practically a no-man's land,

SOUTH AMERICA'S WESTERN LANDS

and the western republics spread beyond the mountains. Bolivia acquired portions of both the Amazon and the Paraguayan lowlands. Peru contains the head-waters of the Amazon, the whole of the Ucayali, and extends to the Putumayo ; Ecuador likewise has a portion of the Amazon lowlands drained by many of the smaller headstream tributaries of the Amazon. On the whole, however, these lowlands and eastward extensions do not count ; even in Argentina the eastern slopes of the Andes are relatively unproductive.

The Andean backbone unifies these states, while the ocean margin diversifies them. Colombia, north of the equator, is hot and wet and forested. At Ecuador begins the arid strip which extends south to Valparaiso, where the prevailing trade winds are off-shore, rainfall is slight, temperatures are high on the lowland, and where the more genial temperatures of the plateau settlements, as at Quito, are less warm but still endure tropical conditions, with days roughly equal to nights in length and a minimum of twilight. Southern Chile is forest ; the oceanic westerlies bring abundant rains, and temperatures are like those of Britain with less variation. Throughout, the highest peaks are cold and inclement, and the change in climate and vegetation vertically from the coast inland is rapid.

The parallelism between the Andes and the Rockies is noteworthy. The great inland basin of the north, the area of the Great Salt Lake, has its counterpart in the Titicaca area in the boundary between Peru and Bolivia ; the larger lake is joined by the Desaguadero 180 miles long to Lake Poopo, and the whole provides some 350 miles of navigable waterways which are self-contained. The longitudinal valleys of the western Rockies— the Californian basin, for example—are paralleled by the great longitudinal valley of Chile, in which settled life is easy. Here, in central Chile, as in California, the climate is genial and is characterized by winter rainfall and summer droughts, and the products are wheat, and wine, and luscious fruits. Here the greatest railway of the west runs north and south, crossing the trans-Andean line at Santiago ; other railways run inland from the coast, as from Antofagasta to La Paz.

LESSON 31

The World's Polar Extremities

THE top and bottom of the world, as it were, are the polar areas. The top, or north, is the Arctic Ocean; the bottom, or south, is Antarctica, a continental land mass. If a circle be drawn slightly smaller than a sixpence, a concentric circle twice as far across, about the size of a penny, and the common centre be marked with a dot, then the dot is a pole, the inner circle is lat. 60° and the outer circle is the equator. If the pole be 90° N., then within the smaller circle is the Arctic Ocean with its shorelands, while between the circles lies the rest of the northern hemisphere, the home of practically the whole of the world's people.

Within the smaller circle are found a few utilities, chiefly on a small scale. In Spitsbergen (Svalbard) coal of excellent quality, almost as good as the best anthracite, is mined. The reserves are estimated to exceed nine billion tons. Mining is simple, since galleries, not shafts, lead to the seams; the coast is near, and neither water nor fire-damp makes the work dangerous, and ventilation is easy; the main difficulty is the short navigation period, from June to September. The coal tends to oust coal supplies from Britain in Norwegian markets. Based on the coal industry are permanent winter residents, settlements, wireless stations, and regular mail steamers. In Alaska, near Cape Lisburne, coal and petroleum await extraction.

Klondike and Dawson lie within the circle, and on the coast. Nome has gold veins in the low hills and gold in the gravel of the streams. Here an open roadstead has been made safer for shipping by breakwaters and by dredging; coastal driftwood is hauled inland by tractors to be used in making corduroy roads (roads with logs laid across to reinforce the surface). Only for five months is the mean temperature above freezing point. A narrow gauge railway goes inland for 460 miles. Dog haulage was first used; now power is based on petrol. Wireless is the usual means of communication, since navigation is confined to the period June to October, when the coast is free from drift ice.

Fauna of the Arctic. Just outside the smaller circle, in the Bering Sea, lie the Pribilof and Commander Is., respectively belonging to the U.S.A. and Russia, which are the two chief rookeries of the fur-bearing seal. Elsewhere, in the Arctic, the seal is a source of fat and clothing for the local inhabitants ; it is the chief game animal, in the sea, of the Eskimo. The whale has almost disappeared from the Arctic ; whalers now frequent Antarctic waters. The land animals are the musk ox, the caribou, reindeer, bear and the Arctic fox. The musk ox is herbivorous ; it feeds on the scanty grass tundra of northern Greenland, and is able to obtain its food from under a thin snow cover. It is dying out and is much less use to the natives than the reindeer, which feeds on lichen. The reindeer is a game animal in America and Greenland, a domestic animal in Asia ; it has been introduced into Alaska and Labrador.

The caribou is the chief game animal of the Eskimo on the land, for the Eskimo plans his life and movements so as to be able to hunt the caribou on its routes of migration from the uplands, which it frequents in the summer, to the lower lands, its winter home. Arctic fox pelts are becoming the main economic need of the Eskimo in those areas where the increase in the frequency of visits from the white man has, on the one hand, restricted the numbers of wild animals, and, on the other hand, introduced the Eskimo to exotic necessities ; for civilized Eskimos in northern Alaska need the white man's weapons, tools, whaleboats, his clothing and his food. Antarctica has whales off its shores and penguins on the coast ; it lacks quadrupeds.

Climatic Conditions. The polar areas include all the lands of the midnight sun. At lat. $66\frac{1}{2}°$, on midsummer day, the sun does not set, but is continuously above the horizon for almost 72 hours. As the latitude increases the period of continuous sunlight increases ; at 70° it is two months, at 80° four months, and at 90° six months. Symmetrically, about midwinter, continuous lack of sunlight endures for similar periods.

During the period of continuous sunlight in the north the sun is at its diurnal highest in the south of the sky at noon, and at its diurnal lowest in the north of the sky at midnight ; on midsummer day, June 21, at $66\frac{1}{2}°$ the difference between highest and lowest is 47°, at 70° it is 40°, at 80° it is 20°, and at 90°, 0°.

The apparent motion of the sun in the sky is a sort of wave motion with successive noons at the crests of the waves and successive midnights at the troughs of the waves, and with a wave amplitude of twice the polar distance of the place of observation ; crests and troughs follow each other at twenty four-hour intervals, slightly higher in the sky from December to June, and slightly lower from June to December. As everywhere, the sun is above the horizon exactly half of each year, but the doses of sunlight increase in length and decrease in frequency towards the poles. With the increase in length there is also an increase in steadiness, for the wave amplitude is smaller. The difference in insolation between noon and midnight is less nearer the pole. The daily range of temperature during the continuous sunlight tends to be small. The period of continuous lack of sunlight is incorrectly labelled the period of darkness, for there are periods of moonlight ; the continuous lack of insolation tends to a steadiness of daily temperature.

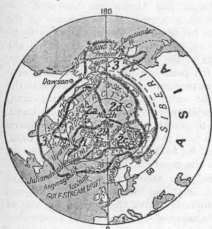

It happens, therefore, that winter conditions are often more favourable for human movement than summer conditions. In summer the melted ice limits travel, and mosquitoes and other insects, including butterflies, swarm as nowhere else in the world. In summer also, wherever soil appears, plant life appears also, and there is the grass tundra for the musk ox and the lichen tundra for the reindeer and caribou. Here happens a marginal land for cultivated plants with a suitable period between sprouting and seedtime.

The dominant climatic factor is, however, not the sun, but the permanent load of ice, either on the land, as in Antarctica and Greenland, or on the sea, as in the Arctic. Taking the year as a whole the polar regions are the coldest places in the world, for though in Siberia, outside the Arctic, it is probable that the maximum pole of cold occurs, yet this great cold is confined to the winter, and the yearly mean in Siberia is not so low as in Antarctica. Climatic variations depend next upon the oceans and the character of the ocean currents. The Gulf Stream drift of the north Atlantic keeps the north of Europe ice-free in summer, while lower latitudes off east Greenland are infested with drift ice ; off north-west Greenland Peary found summer navigation relatively easy. If the sea ice does not melt, then the climatic effect of the warmer sea waters is negligible ; although the ice south of the Ross Sea is partly afloat, and partly anchored on the continental shelf, it is climatically part of the continent.

When extensive patches of land are free from ice and snow in the summer, the climate tends to continental extremes, which may be modified by the nearness of ice-free waters and thus become a modified maritime climate. Where ice persists the air is dry ; there is no cloud blanket ; winds tend to move more rapidly and freely. Scott said of the Antarctic, " blizzards are our bugbear." Walking against a blizzard is only possible with crampons (iron shoe spikes to grapple the frozen ground), and with the body almost horizontal in the teeth of the snow-filled whirl. The edge of a blizzard is often clear cut, for a man may stand unaffected and see, two yards away,

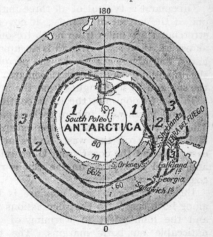

men blown down and heavy articles spun like feathers. In the north, where ice and water meet more frequently, the air is moisture-laden and the bugbear is, not the blizzard, but fog—fog in summer.

Regional Divisions. The polar areas are not uniform. Three main regions are defined : (1) where the warmest month has a mean temperature of 32° F., freezing point ; (2) where the warmest month lies between 32° and 41° F. ; (3) where the warmest month lies between 41° and 50° F. In the south the first region includes

Antarctica, its edge marked roughly as the mean limit of drift ice ; the second includes the S. Shetlands, S. Orkneys, S. Georgia and Sandwich Is. ; the third includes Tierra del Fuego and crosses the Falkland Is., although it is suggested that these areas should not be included in the true polar areas ; the boundary of the third region is roughly 50° S.

In the north, region one is inland Greenland ; two includes all the rest of the Arctic islands, except the coast of southern Greenland, which is in three. The last also includes the littoral of the Arctic Ocean, except Norway, and the southern half of Iceland.

Region two is subdivided into four : (a) includes the Canadian Islands ; (b) the Greenland northern shores ; (c) Spitsbergen and Novaya Zemlya ; (d) the Asiatic quadrant.

Greenland is typical of all three major regions. This island is one of the largest of islands ; it covers some 860,000 sq. miles, stretches 1,650 miles from north to south, and is about 800 miles across at its widest. Inland is an upland dome of ice some mile and a half above sea level ; the periphery begins at the edge of the inland ice and is a transition area penetrated by arms from the sea and by ice tongues from the interior.

Inland (region one) the ice is continuous except in the south-east and north-west, where rock appears above the ice surface. The coast is in general ice-free except for a long stretch along Melville Bay on the west, and south of Angmagsalik on the east. Round the coast from Upernivik on the west northwards and round to $66\frac{1}{2}$° N. on the east is region 2b ; the rest of the coast is in region three.

Inland, in region one, pressure is high, with lower pressure along both coasts, so that depressions travel south over the seas and the föhn effect (a warming of descending air) is usually noticeable on both margins. The temperature rises sharply away from the land ice, and on the margin clouds and fog prevail with a decreased speed of the blanketed winds. On the margin the sea effect is pronounced ; the coastline is cooler in summer and warmer in winter than the areas farther inland. Region two tends to aridity, region three has 40 inches of rain, as a maximum, in the extreme south ; there trees attain a height of 12 feet ; farther north their height decreases.

Reindeer, fox and hare occur all over the margin, the musk ox, lemming, wolf and ermine only in region two. The chief of the five species of seal, the fiord seal, provides fuel, light, food, clothing and a covering for the kayak (canoe). Salmon abound.

The island is ruled by a Danish official staff ; Norwegians have certain rights of trading and fishing. The population includes 400 whites and 16,000 others, most of whom are half-breeds. Greenlanders, the only pure Eskimos, are isolated at Etah and Angmagsalik. The winter settlements are of primitive low stone and turf houses ; in summer the people camp on their seasonal hunts. Tobacco, coffee, Eskimo newspapers—for few are illiterate —betoken the influence of the white. The kayak is the vehicle for water transport and fishing, the dog sledge for hunting ; fiord seal are mainly hunted in region three from the kayak, in region two from the ice. Closest settlement occurs in the south, near Julianehaab, where garden cultivation is possible.

The Arctic is impracticable for the world's shipping. The North-east passage and the North-west passage can be made. The North-east passage almost follows the shortest distance from London to Japan ; this distance along one of the world's great circles is almost a straight line when drawn on the map in page 362 ; from London it skirts the west of Norway, crosses Novaya Zemlya and skirts the Japanese islands. The North-west passage through Baffin Bay to Bering Strait is more tortuous, for the land intervenes. A great circle from the Great Lakes of Canada to Britain roughly marks the sea route from the English Channel to Hudson Bay ; a great circle from Lake Superior to the Caspian Sea crosses Greenland, skirts the North Cape, and crosses the White Sea, a simple curve on the polar map. These great circles will probably become the air routes of the future.

LESSON 32

The African Continent

AFRICA is in some respects a symmetrical continent ; it lies evenly athwart the equator. Cairo is 30° N., Durban is 30° S. ; the northern portion is roughly bisected by 10° E., Gambia is 15° W., and Eritrea 35° E. It is the largest land mass except Asia, being larger than either North or South America ; it is three times as big as Europe and contains fewer than a third of the people of Europe ; except South America, it has fewer persons to the square mile than any populated continent, so long as the island of Australia is counted as part of the " continent " of Australasia.

Physically, the south is an elevated plateau, most of which lies between half a mile and a mile above sea level. Here, on the west, there is little coastal fringe or continental shelf ; the plateau edge ends sharply near the sea. In the east the shelf is also narrow, but Mozambique is almost entirely a coastal lowland. Across the deep Mozambique Channel is the French island of Madagascar, with a steep bastion wall to the east of its central mountain massif and splayed lowlands on its west coast. In the south-east of the mainland the Drakensberg Mts. present a scarp face to the Indian Ocean in Natal and Swaziland ; from their western slopes the Vaal-Orange flows west, and finally reaches the Atlantic after a three-hundred-mile passage through useless, rocky, arid country. The Limpopo curves round their northern edge to the swampy eastern lowlands, where it receives the Olifants. The north-west section of the plateau is drained by the tributaries of the Zambezi, which follows a trench course below the Victoria Falls till it emerges on the widest part of the eastern lowland.

North-east beyond the river in Lake Nyasa begins the great Rift Valley, which continues through Lakes Tanganyika and Rudolf to the Red Sea and terminates in Palestine. The rift occurs on the western side of the elevated eastern portion of equatorial Africa, where many peaks rise to a height exceeding $2\frac{1}{2}$ miles ; these include those of the mountain range Ruwenzori (some peaks over 16,000 ft.) and Kilima Njaro (19,300 ft.). Here, crossed by the equator, is Lake Victoria (Victoria Nyanza), filling a shallow plateau depression as one of the world's largest sheets of fresh water ; from it issues the Nile.

Western equatorial Africa, in a square roughly 15° each way, is the Congo basin. The north-west corner of the square is mountainous and culminates in Cameroon Mt. (13,400 ft.). A gentle tableland connects these heights with the Uganda plateau and forms the northern edge of the basin. The sweep of the riverine waters curves round three sides of the square. The main stream follows the eastern edge, cuts across westwards parallel to the Ubangi and curves round across the corner ; it receives short streams from the east, long streams—such as the Lomami and the Kasai—from the south and the interior of the square, and short streams from the north-west. The Congo challenges comparison with the Amazon, from which it differs in two important particulars : its basin is squarish, not triangular, and its slopes drain westwards, so that the laggard winds descend seawards. Also the rainfall régime of the Congo differs from that of the

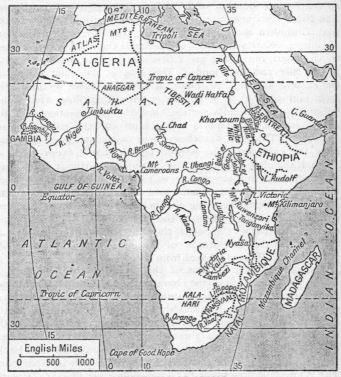

SKETCH MAP OF AFRICA

Amazon, though both rivers flow in the region of constant equatorial rains and hot, wet forests.

Northern Africa has in the north-west the Atlas Mts., which belong to the great Eurasian east-west fold mountain system ; they are, strictly, not African. In the south-east the continuation of the central heights is mountainous Ethiopa, with an arm

(367)

to Cape Guardafui ; across the intervening area and joining them
is a height of land through Tibesti and Ahaggar. The rest of the
north is a low plateau, reaching a coastal lowland in Tripoli and
in Senegal, with isolated lower elevations in N. Nigeria and
French Guinea. South-west are the minor coastal rivers, such
as the Senegal, Gambia and Volta, and the greater Niger-Benue.
The Niger rises near Sierra Leone, curves with a mighty sweep
past Timbuktu and enters the sea at the other end of the Gulf
of Guinea. North-east from the Benue is the Chad basin, drained
by the Shari, one of the great basins of internal drainage.

The Nile and Its Floods. The Nile is the chief feature of
the eastern section. Normally, a river has three sections : the
mountain section of steep slopes and rapid flow, and valley
tributaries ; the middle section ; and the plain section near the
mouth, where the slope is a minimum and the tributaries are
sluggish. The Nile has these three normal features upstream
from the cataracts ; the normal mouth should occur south of
Wadi Halfa, but the lower Nile is unique ; without tributaries,
the river flows in a ten-mile or so wide trench without the usual
fluviatile activities ; it is harnessed and controlled, and is little
other than a water-bringing channel for a desert land. The real
river comprises the system of the main stream, the White Nile,
the chief tributaries the Sobat, the Blue Nile and the Atbara—all
three from the mountains of Ethiopia—and the occasional
tributary the Bahr el Ghazal from the desert.

The annual phenomenon of the all-important Nile flood is
due to two causes : first, the character of the heavy early summer
rains on the Abyssinian mountains which flood the valleys of
the three tributaries, particularly of the Blue Nile, owing to the
large run-off of water from the mountains ; and secondly, the
character of the valleys themselves, for they tend to be deep
gorges with narrow sides, because lateral erosion of the river banks
is at a minimum. The floods dam the White Nile at Khartoum.
The White Nile flow tends to be normally river-like, as the water
supply comes from the constant equatorial rains of the Lake
Victoria area, and the lake itself tends to act as a regulator to the
outflow. When the White Nile is dammed the lowland areas,
where the river is known locally as the Bahr-el-Jebel, are flooded
and marshy. The Nile, Niger and Zambezi have deltaic outlets.

Climatically, the symmetry of African conditions is unique.
The high-pressure belts, where the heavy anti-cyclones tend to

move from west to east faster than the earth revolves below them, occur both north and south. As the world tilts seasonally on its axis relatively to the sun, to bring in turn the so-called summer and winter seasons, the main axis of the belt swings laggardly to the north or south in sympathy with the tilt, with the result that the north, or Mediterranean, coast in July and the south, or Cape, coast in January, lie within the belt. The consequent aridity, cloudlessness and brilliant sunshine in these summer months, coupled with the inevitable rain of the cool season, are characteristic of these areas of winter rains and summer drought. Between the high pressures is the equatorial low pressure with the laggard winds and the rising air ; this means convectional rains, especially when insolation is high, and the equatorial area has constant rains while the edges near the tropics have summer rains. Normally, the water for the rain should come inland from the Indian Ocean, borne by the trade winds ; the spinning world should spin into a wet, hot, steamy, clammy atmosphere ; but the Indian Ocean is not normal in summer, for the winds there become monsoons in summer and the south east trade tends to swirl away from Africa towards India, and, also, the eastern heights tend to condense the moisture on the coastal lowland.

Madagascar is narrow enough to have extensive summer rain throughout, but the continent has its summer rain heaviest inland from the coast on the inland side of the heights. These rains in Ethiopia provide the Nile flood water, and in the south provide water for the upper Congo and the upper Zambezi. On the west the water supply comes from the Gulf of Guinea, and the Guinea Coast has heavy summer rains. The sequence from north to south (or south to north)—winter rains, no rains, summer rains, constant rains, summer rains, no rains, winter rains—is symmetrical. The no-rain areas are the Sahara and Kalahari deserts. Snow falls on the heights even on Cameroon Mt., and lies on Kilima Njaro, but the snow rarely endures, even on the Atlas, for long, and there are no snow-fed rivers such as the Ganges or Indus.

The natural vegetation is symmetrical. It is Mediterranean with the winter rains, hence Cape and Algerian wines ; it is summer rain grassland, not prairie-like, for there are no winter frosts, but savannah-like or park-land ; hot wet forests occur with the constant rains. The effect of elevation is important, because the predominant plateau of the south limits the size of the

Kalahari and allows the veld, summer grassland, to extend far south to the Transvaal, 500 miles farther away from the equator than in the Sudan. The interfluvial uplands of the Congo basin are open park-land similar to the Brazil uplands. but the Congo forest is not nearly so extensive as the Amazon forest ; it lies entirely west of the rift valley.

Distribution of Population. The unique canal of the lower Nile is lined by a dense population similar to that of the Low Countries. Elsewhere the people are scattered, with the greatest density in a zone which stretches from the Gulf of Gambia round the Gulf of Guinea and across to Mozambique. In this zone the people are Sudan or Bantu negroes.

The whites or Indo-Europeans are few in number, widely scattered in the extreme north-west and in the south. In the north they represent attempts at colonization from Spain, France and Italy ; in the south they are descendants from Dutch or British colonists, or a conglomerate of exploiters of mineral wealth.

Half as many people as there are in India are spread over the continent. They supply the world with primary products, the most valuable of which are precious minerals—valuable only because the white man esteems them. They lack wealth and purchasing power, and count for very little in the white man's scheme of things.

The white man has sunk much capital in this continent. The railways are ambitious in conception, notably the Cape to Cairo scheme and the Benguella railway. The plantations are probably as futile. Orange groves, rubber plantations, cotton fields served by waters from expensive Nile dams and barrages, all will probably, in the long run, be of little worth, for all are marginal efforts to produce raw materials, etc., in a white man's scheme dominated by one stupid idea—keep the machinery moving, make more and more things whether they are needed or not ; their temporary success depends solely on an exploitation of the black man and his lands.

Our Course in Geography is continued in Volume 6.

Survey of the Cretaceous Period

(See plate 41)

THE Cretaceous is the third and last period of the Mesozoic Era; it is named from *creta*, Latin for chalk, the formation which is the most extensive of the Cretaceous series. The lower beds are largely of sand and estuarine origin and therefore of a terrestrial character, composed of clays intercalated with layers of sand, particularly in the series present in western Europe. On the other hand, the great mass of the Cretaceous deposits are of marine deposition, oceanic in character and world-wide in extent. They are chiefly composed of great beds of soft limestone in the form of chalk, and comprise one of the most extensive and massive of all the sedimentary strata now existing.

The Cretaceous facies, as presented in western Europe, extend from Britain (Upper Cretaceous) to northern France, Belgium, north Germany and the south Baltic area, Bohemia and Saxony. This area in Cretaceous times constituted a largely land-locked sea, into which were poured the waters from large rivers from a vast continent to the north. This Cretaceous sea was separated from a great world-wide ocean to the south by an ancient mountainous ridge stretching from what is now Brittany, through the Auvergne and south Germany, to Bohemia. There were then no Pyrenees, Alps or Apennines, nor any Downs in England.

South of this ancient ridge exists the world-wide oceanic deposit, the main Cretaceous beds, extending from Portugal across southern Europe to the Carpathians and south Russia to south-west Asia, including the whole of the Mediterranean area and north Africa, and then extending eastward across Arabia to India, Tibet, south China and Japan. All this area was part of the great Cretaceous ocean that covered the equatorial regions and divided the large land areas of the northern continent from those of the southern. All except the north-eastern portion of the North American continent was under a vast Cretaceous bed, which in the west reached 13,000 feet in thickness.

The great equatorial ocean was the cause of the remarkable diversity which began in Cretaceous times between the fauna and flora of the northern continent and the southern. Later on, in the Tertiary Era, this became more marked, and it persists to this day in Australia, the last remnant of the great southern continent of Cretaceous times. South Africa and South America became united to the northern land-mass in later Tertiary times, but not Australasia, the sole representative of the great Gondwana Land of the Mesozoic Era.

The Lower Cretaceous series are represented in England by the Hastings beds, which consist of Ashdown Sand, the lowest; Wadhurst Clay above, and Tunbridge Wells Sand at the top. Above these is the Weald Clay—the whole attaining in south-east England a thickness of nearly 2,000 feet.

The Hastings beds have a total thickness of about 1,000 feet. The Ashdown Sands reach to 400 feet in Ashdown Forest, and compose Crowborough Beacon; they thin out into clays near Hastings. The Wadhurst beds consist of shales and hard clays, and vary between 150 and 160 feet in thickness between Hastings and Wadhurst. They provided much iron ore from medieval times down to the last century, when the last iron-furnace was extinguished at Ashburnham. The Tunbridge Wells Sands consist of calcareous grit, sandstones, shales, clays and sands, the whole attaining a thickness of nearly 400 feet, but thinning out eastward. All the series just mentioned are well shown in the cliff-face between Hastings and Fairlight.

The Weald Clay consists of blue and brown clays intercalated with beds of shelly limestone, calcareous sandstone and sands, the whole reaching to a thickness of about 900 feet. These are well shown along the cliffs of the Isle of Wight, extending along the back of the island from the Atherfield rocks south of Brixton, along Brixton Bay, to Brook. The Weald Clay also extends from Hythe to the Vale of Wardour in the west, but is only exposed in the hollow between the North and South Downs and in some small areas, particularly in the Isle of Wight. Farther west, it appears in a great mass at Swanage, where its beds reach a total thickness of over 2,000 feet. From there it crosses the Isle of Purbeck to Worbarrow Bay, where the beds are about 1,200 feet thick. The Wealden formation rapidly thins out northward and westward, being little more than 50 feet thick in the Vale of Wardour, where it is last seen.

The deposits of the Wealden series indicate that a great fresh-water basin, known to geologists as the Wealden Lake, covered the southern counties from Dorset to Kent, and also the Channel area to Dieppe and south-eastward to Paris. Early in Cretaceous times the sea penetrated from the south-east, and deposited a great bed of chalk over the whole of the Wealden beds.

The Lower Greensand formation is evidence of the coming of this sea—the sands and thin layers of limestone following the muddy deltaic and freshwater deposits of the Wealden series. The Lower Greensand, or Vectian, as it is sometimes called, from the Isle of Wight (Lat. *Vectis*), where it is well exposed, is represented, in succession upwards, by the Atherfield, Hythe, Sandgate and Folkestone beds. They consist of green, yellow and grey sands, together with layers of clay, limestone and ironstone—the whole attaining a thickness of about 500 feet in Surrey, 250 feet near Sandgate, and thinning out in other directions. The Hythe beds contain layers of hard limestone known as " ragstone," which is valuable for building purposes. These deposits were laid down during the gradual submergence of the land which began late in Lower Cretaceous times ; and so beds of alternating sands, clays and limestones bear witness to a succession of vacillations ere the great transgression of the sea gave the area an oceanic character.

In north-east England marine conditions prevailed during Lower Cretaceous times ; hence a very different facies is presented in the contemporaneous beds revealed in Norfolk, Lincolnshire and the East Riding of Yorkshire. These are evidence of the existence of a narrow arm of the sea extending over the greater part of the present North Sea and linked up with the sea which then covered north and east Russia by way of Spitsbergen—in those days more tropical than arctic. Fossils, particularly ammonites, found in this district of England are singularly like those found in the Russian area just mentioned, whereas they are totally dissimilar to those ammonites and molluscs found in the contemporaneous beds of southern England. An elevated ridge which appears to have extended from the Charnwood Forest area of Leicestershire to the Ardennes, and part of which is now far beneath London, is believed to have separated these two areas.

The deposits of this northern marine series of beds consist of dark clays and shales, the chief of which is the Speeton Clay, well exposed at Speeton Gap, south of Filey, in Yorkshire. These beds are exposed from Caistor to Tealby, to Spilsby, Candlesby and Willoughby at the south of the Lincoln Wolds, attaining in places a thickness of nearly 100 feet. Thence they extend south to the Hunstanton and Downham Market area of Norfolk, and reappear in a few isolated areas farther south, e.g. at Biggleswade.

Fossils of the Period Fossils are prolific of both flora and fauna in favoured situations, the former in Lower Cretaceous times being very similar to the Jurassic forms. They were of a type that denoted a warm climate even in Greenland and Spitsbergen. Conifers and cycads, together with the ferns *Alethopteris* and *Sphenopteris*, predominated, but plants which were the ancestors of our flowering trees and shrubs had appeared.

While the reptilian ichthyosaurs and plesiosaurs were declining in numbers, the great dinosaurs increased enormously, attaining a great variety of species—more particularly the *Cetiosaurus brevis, Megalosaurus Bucklandi,* the sea serpent *Mosasaurus* and the famous Iguanodon. Numerous remains of *Iguanodon Mantelli* have been found in the Tilgate beds in Sussex, and numbers of complete skeletons in Belgium Large numbers of ammonites and cephalopods flourished in the sea, together with fishes—in particular, the *Hybodus* and *Lepidotus Fittoni ;* while the *Lepidotus Mantelli* frequented the great Wealden Lake.

The Isle of Wight Wealden beds yield fossils of most of the above species, including bones and footprints of the Iguanodon and Hypsilophodon ; while the so-called " lobster bed," with numbers of the crustacean *Meyeria magna,* forms part of the Atherfield Clay.

LESSON 19

Ancient Albion's Chalk Formations

(See plates 41–43)

THE outstanding feature of the Cretaceous period was the wide spread of sea over land, the greatest encroachment taking place during the deposition of the various beds composing the Upper Cretaceous series. The gradual process occupied millions of years ; thus we find a succession of facies of a very different character revealing the conditions of deposition. The lowest, consisting chiefly of dark bluish marine clays, intercalated in places with sands and chert beds, indicate the wearing down of the land and cliff face of those days, and the deposition of the argillaceous sediment along the margin of the encroaching sea-bed. This deposit is known as *Gault*. Above, following this, is a sandy deposit of greenish and sometimes yellowish hue produced by the wearing away of hard rocks of a former age and the redepositing of them along the sinking shore line of Cretaceous times. This deposit is the Upper Greensand and, together with the Gault, is palaeontologically known as *Albian* and geologically as *Selbornian*. These are followed by the great series of calcareous deposits, known collectively as the chalk, which is divided into Lower Chalk or Cenomanian ; Middle Chalk or Turonian ; and Upper Chalk or Senonian and Campanian, the second terms being now used as a rule.

Gault is essentially an arenaceous deposit of marine sediments with occasionally sandy marls, overlain with Upper Greensand. The whole is now regarded as one formation and attains a thickness up to about 300 feet, reaching 200 feet at Maidstone and increasing westward through Kent and Surrey to Hampshire, where, near Selborne, it is nearly 250 feet in thickness. It appears in Wiltshire and the Isle of Wight, where along the famous Undercliff the Gault clays, sands and chert beds attain a thickness of 240 feet. It is also well displayed at Folkestone in the Warren undercliff bordering East Wear Bay. In Dorset and Devon the Gault is well shown in parts of the cliffs between Lyme Regis and Sidmouth, where it attains a thickness of about 150 feet and is prolific in fossils. In various localities between these towns and the Blackdown Hills the Gault appears above the Triassic and Liassic formations. In Berks and Oxon the Gault clays and marls reach 300 feet in thickness. North-eastward this thins out to 150 feet in Cambridgeshire and to 60 feet in the Stoke Ferry area of Norfolk. Farther north the Gault clays change into the thin beds of " red chalk " so strikingly exhibited in the cliff face at Hunstanton, where they are, however, only between 3 and 4 feet thick. These beds appear in Lincolnshire, where at Willoughby they total about 12 feet thick, and reappear in Yorkshire, where at Speeton Gap they attain a thickness of 30 feet, but thinning out westward. Farther north than Bedfordshire the Upper Greensand and distinctive Gault deposits are gradually replaced by clays, which finally become the reddish marls known as Red Chalk.

Chalk is probably the most easily recognized of all deposits ; it is a very friable limestone, composed chiefly of foraminiferal ooze. The shells of these tiny organisms, deposited in the course of millions of years on the ocean floor, gradually built up the massive beds, over 2,000 feet thick, which are now largely high and dry around the shores of Britain, and from which it was called Albion (Lat. *albus*, white). This foraminiferal deposit is still taking place in the bed of the Atlantic and elsewhere, the genus *Globigerina* entering largely into its composition now as it did then. There are several varieties of chalk, deposited after long intervals of time, and, therefore, under different conditions and after considerable evolution of life forms.

The Lower Chalk has at the base a sandy marl with glauconite grains giving it a greenish hue similar to the Greensand facies ; the Lower Chalk is also known as Grey Chalk, owing to the amount of clayey material in its composition. Numerous fossil sponges, ammonites, particularly *Schloenbachia varians*, and many other fossils occur. Above are deposits of soft grey marl with belemnites in profusion. This constitutes the Cenomanian zone, the name being given because the beds were first recognized in the Le Mans area of the ancient Cenomanni. The Lower Chalk extends over most of the area of south-east England, beneath the superimposed strata, from Wiltshire and Dorset to Norfolk and Suffolk, being absent only in the Wealden and Lower Greensand area of Surrey, Sussex and Kent. It consists collectively of a bed about 250 feet thick in Wiltshire, decreasing gradually to about 60 feet at Hunstanton, and thinning out further in Lincolnshire and Yorkshire. It is well presented at Folkestone, and also in the Culver Cliffs of the Isle of Wight, where the Lower Chalk attains a thickness of about 200 feet. In Europe it extends eastward into northern France, Belgium, and Germany to Bohemia, while southwards it covers most of southern Europe.

The Middle Chalk or Turonian consists of a massive bed of white chalk resting upon a layer of hard nodular chalk, which in turn overlays the soft marl of the Lower Chalk series. The lower portion of this white chalk is without flints, while the upper part is often stratified with flints ; it is well presented in cliff faces on the south and east coasts and attains various thicknesses—150 feet at Compton Bay, nearly 200 feet in the Culver Cliff of the Isle of Wight, at Ballard Cliff in Dorset about 120 feet ; and gradually thickening eastward it reaches nearly 250 feet near Dover. On the east coast the Middle Chalk series are presented in Norfolk and Lincolnshire about 100 feet thick, but near

Speeton in Yorkshire they increase to over 200 feet. Generally they overlie the Lower Chalk series throughout south-east England and elsewhere.

The Upper Chalk series are remarkable for the layers of black flints with which they are stratified. These flints are siliceous concretions which often contain silicified fossil shells and fragments as a central nucleus.

The massive white face of the Upper Chalk approaches the surface over an extensive area of England. This colossal bed of chalk is exposed at various places round the English coast, and in many railway cuttings and numerous quarries. At the Needles and cliffs of Afton Down in the Isle of Wight it is well presented, attaining a thickness of over 1,300 feet. Westward in Dorset it averages about 1,000 feet, and it also appears throughout the Sussex chalk area, reaching to about 900 feet in thickness. It comprises the cliff face of Thanet and the North and South Forelands, extending from St. Margaret's Bay to near Walmer, the thickness of the bed in these areas being about 500 feet. In Suffolk and Norfolk the Upper Chalk reaches about 1,100 feet ; in Yorkshire, where it is well presented at Flamborough Head, it is over 1,000 feet thick.

The Upper Cretaceous beds are but little in evidence in Scotland, having been saved from denudation in a few isolated areas by subsequent lava flows in Mull and the adjoining Morvern district. The same applies to Ireland, where the Upper Cretaceous beds appear as an encircling fringe of white cliff and vale beneath the great plateau of black basalt which covers Antrim and the adjoining districts.

The Campanian facies of the Upper Chalk constitutes the last and uppermost of the Cretaceous series found in England, but there is yet another deposited later, the Danian, named from East Denmark, where it is well shown, though found also in Sweden and a few patches elsewhere in northern Europe. The Danian represents the only transition beds remaining which connect the Cretaceous with the Eocene, some of the fossil types of the former passing up into the latter ; thus is bridged the immense break between the last period of the Mesozoic era and the first of the Tertiary.

Flora and Fauna. The flora of the Cretaceous period had already begun to assume the types prevailing today, and while the ferns such as *Asplenium* and *Gleichenia*, cycads, palms and various conifers such as juniper and others of earlier periods flourished, angiosperms had appeared in profusion. Dicotyledons must have been evolved earlier, for they are found perfected and in abundance at this period—the oak, beech, plane, poplar, fig, maple, willow, magnolia, gum tree, cinnamon, buckthorn, ivy, laurel, walnut, alder, cassia, and many others indicative of the long period of time that must have been spanned by the Upper Cretaceous age, probably at least twenty million years.

It is the fauna of this age which exhibited such an amazing development, particularly in reptilian forms. These evolved into giant species and the largest land animals that ever existed, but all save a few diminutive types vanished toward the close of the period. Such were the huge land reptiles, the dinosaurs. The herbivorous *Brontosaurus* attained a length of 80 feet and a weight of between 30 and 40 tons. Other herbivores were the stegosaurs (plated lizards) such as *Monoclonius*. Giant carnivorous dinosaurs preyed upon these—*Tyrannosaurus*, 30 feet long, and the *Allosaurus*. The sea also had its giant reptiles, the *Mosasaurus* attaining 75 feet in length, and the great seasnake, the *Discosaurus*, a length of 40 feet; others were the *Dolichosaurus* and the *Coniosaurus*. The air had its great reptiles, the *Pterosauria*, of which the strange pteranodon and the *Ornithocheirus* are examples.

Great toothed birds such as the *Hesperornis*, 6 feet in length, the *Apatornis* and *Ichthyornis*, smaller varieties resembling the ostrich, but all with reptilian skulls, were plentiful; only remains of the *Enaliornis* have so far been found in the English Cretaceous beds. Small mammals continued to maintain an existence, but remains of them are very rare, doubtless because the Cretaceous deposits are largely marine.

The worldwide semi-tropical climate of those times was particularly conducive to flourishing life; even in north Greenland tropical ferns, figs and magnolias flourished. The seas teemed with life all tending to abundance of giant forms. The cephalopods, ammonites and belemnites were most prolific and remarkable both for size and variety : *Baculites, Toxoceras, Ancyloceras, Hamites, Scaphites, Ptychoceras, Crioceras, Hoplites, Helicoceras, Nautilus, Belemnites minimus, Ammonites inflatus*, and *Turrilites*. The lamellibranchs also attained profusion, the Hippurites largely composing the great worldwide beds of hippuritic limestone extending over southern Europe, south-west Asia, India, Texas, Mexico, and California. Other species were *Trigonia*, *Nucula* and *Inoceramus*. The brachiopods *Terebratula* and *Rhynchonella* were most prolific, together with sponges, more particularly *Ventriculites*, *Camerospongia* and *Doryderma ;* while the sea-bottom was covered with sea-urchins, chiefly *Echinoconus*, *Ananchytes*, *Cardiaster*, *Marsupites* and *Micraster*. Innumerable teeth of various species of sharks, *Lamna*, *Oxyrhina* and *Otodus*, are found, together with fossil remains of modern species of teleostean fishes such as cod, herring and salmon.

Apart from its lime products, the Upper Cretaceous system of porous chalk strata is of great economic value as a source of reserve water supply ; for since these beds are usually over clay beds which are non-porous, vast natural reservoirs are thus created and are well adapted for artesian well sinking where synclines exist, as in the Thames basin and many areas in south-east England. Experiments in Queensland and other parts of Australia and in the United States, where surface water is scarce, have shown that large areas may be made fertile by thus tapping these vast reservoirs in the Cretaceous rocks.

LESSON 20

First Periods of the Cainozoic Era

(See plate 43)

THE Tertiary or Cainozoic era (Gk. *kainos*, recent, *zoe*, life) is the era of recent life-forms as distinct from those of the Mesozoic era, which terminated with the Upper Cretaceous times. The Cainozoic era embraces the last ten to possibly twenty million years, and it is divided into four periods, as follows : (1) Eocene—" Dawn of recent " species ; (2) Oligocene—" Few recent " species ; (3) Miocene—" Less recent " species ; (4) Pliocene—" More recent " species. The first two compose the Lower Cainozoic or Palaeogene division and the last two the Upper Cainozoic or Neogene division. Some authorities add two periods to the Neogene division ; these are : Pleistocene—" Most recent " species ; Neocene—" New " species. Other authorities allow these two periods to constitute the Quaternary era, the present Age of Man.

Throughout the Mesozoic era the vast central sea or ocean known as the Tethys had occupied the great Mediterranean basin, north Africa and the whole of central Asia as far as China. There were no Himalayas in those days, no Caucasus, Alps, Carpathians, Balkans or Apennines, no Pyrenees or Atlas mountains, and no Downs or Pennine range in England. Over this area, from the ancient mountains of Wales, the west of England and Scotland, which linked up with Scandinavia, to the southern boundary of what is now the Sahara, was this vast waste of waters, which had increased considerably during the Cretaceous period.

A great uplift of the sea bed had set in toward its close and a resuscitation of volcanic activity ; these were involved in seismic stress and strain which, toward the middle of the Tertiary era, were to result in the colossal crustal folds and the formation of the above-mentioned mountain ranges. But some millions of years intervened before the great calcareous deposits rose above the sea level here and there, thus producing peninsulas and islands, which at a later age were to produce the numerous countries surrounding the modern Mediterranean littoral.

One such island had risen in a large and partially enclosed sea, which covered south-east England, the north of France from Normandy to the Ardennes and the Netherlands ; this sea is therefore known as the Anglo-Gallic basin. The island rose as a great dome, attaining a height of over 1,000 feet, and extended from Hampshire to Artois, across what is now the Strait of Dover, and is known as the Wealden Island. It was composed of a great anticlinal fold of chalk ; subsequent denudation eroded the centre down to the Wealden strata, forming the valley of the Weald and leaving the escarpment of the remaining chalk beds to constitute the North and South Downs.

Eocene Classification. Meanwhile the lowest of the Eocene beds were beginning to form as shallow water deposits and, later, as estuarine and deltaic sediments—the result of the denudation here and in the mountainous regions to the north and west. These deposits were gradually spread over south-east England, northern France and Belgium, composing one vast extending layer of various kinds of sands and clays, which in Eocene times attained a thickness of over 1,500 feet in south-east England.

These beds are classified and constituted as follows :

Thanet Beds. Immediately overlying the Cretaceous are the lowest of the series, composed of sands, pale or greenish, with some sandy marl and numerous fossils ; the beds are well exposed in the cliffs of Thanet and Pegwell Bay and attain a thickness of 60 feet, thinning to 50 feet in Kent and vanishing in Surrey.

Woolwich, Reading and Oldhaven Beds. These consist of marine and estuarine sands with grey clays, attaining a thickness of between 100 and 130 feet ; between Reading and the Isle of Wight at Whitecliff Bay.

London Clay. This is a bluish-grey clay changing to a brown tint on atmospheric contact and containing layers of septarian nodules. The clay attains a thickness of about 500 feet beneath London, but thins out and becomes more sandy towards the west, being only 50 feet thick at Newbury. It remains thick in the Hampshire area, reaching nearly 300 feet thick at Portsmouth and in the Whitecliff and Alum Bay area of the Isle of Wight. Its abundant fossils are a curious mixture of marine and land types; these include fishes, molluscs, crustaceans, turtles, crocodiles, sea-snakes, sharks, remains of birds, small plants, palms, modern trees and many varieties of mammals.

Bagshot Beds. Sands which have been largely eroded and therefore remain in patches over the London Clay, compose these beds ; they are present over the Bagshot, Aldershot, Farnborough, Wokingham and Ascot areas and attain a thickness approaching 150 feet in the Bagshot district. North of the Thames they are much more denuded, occupying small areas at Highgate, Hampstead and Harrow, on the high ground. In the Hampshire area and that of Alum Bay in the Isle of Wight the light coloured sands are laminated with clays and attain thicknesses varying between 300 and 600 feet.

Bracklesham and Bournemouth Beds. Composed of laminated clays and sand, these beds are between 200 and 300 feet thick. They are well presented at Bracklesham Bay in Sussex, at Whitecliff Bay in the Isle of Wight, at Bournemouth and at Hengistbury Head. The sands and clays of this series exceed 500 feet in thickness in this area.

Barton Beds. These consist of alternating layers of sands and clays. They are nearly 200 feet thick at Barton, where they are well shown to the east of Christchurch, and also at Alum Bay and Whitecliff Bay, where they exceed 300 feet.

Oligocene Period in England. Above the Eocene series are further thinly bedded deposits of sand, clay, marls and thin limestone layers in the Isle of Wight and New Forest areas.

These are the only representatives of the Oligocene period in England, but in Germany they constitute thick and extensive beds forming a long and important geological period. During this time nearly the whole of south-east England and northern France had been lifted above the sea and, consequently, there were no deposits ; the German area, on the contrary, which had remained uplifted during the Eocene period, became submerged during the Oligocene and so obtained the deposits missed in the Eocene.

The Oligocene is practically a later continuation of similar Eocene conditions, which in the above small areas are represented by the following series :

The Headon and Brockenhurst Beds. These are composed of clays and sands intercalated with thin beds of limestone, the whole comprising a marine facies and approaching 150 feet in thickness. Well exposed at Headon Hill and Whitecliff Bay ; extending beneath the New Forest, Brockenhurst and Lyndhurst.

The Bembridge Beds. Composed of freshwater marls over the Bembridge limestone, which in turn overlies the Osborne marls, these beds form three divisions of freshwater and brackish deposits, which together attain a thickness of about 200 feet.

The Hamstead Beds. Composed of marine deposits of marls and clays with numerous fossils of land plants, indicating an estuarine origin, the beds altogether attain a thickness of about 250 feet.

In addition to the Hamstead Beds, which are the uppermost of the series, there are in the Bovey Tracey area of Devonshire a series of freshwater sands and clays which, from the fossil plants found embedded, suggest formation in late Oligocene times, though they have been ascribed to the succeeding Miocene period.

Over southern Europe the Eocene deposits were most extensive and attained a thickness of 3,000 feet in many areas. They consisted largely of nummulitic limestone, so named from the great proportion of the remarkable nummulites, or disk-shaped foraminifers, entering into its composition. These massive beds extend from the Pyrenees to the Caucasus and Egypt.

Volcanic Eruptions. A great recrudescence of volcanic activity occurred in Eocene times over large areas of northern Britain and Ireland, which were then united in a land mass, probably with Iceland and Greenland. From Mull to the volcanic cone of far St. Kilda, possibly to the Faroes, and from the Antrim mountains to Skye, vast lava sheets were spread out from the great volcanoes rivalling the present Etna in magnitude, and of which Ben More of Mull is but a denuded stump. This volcanic activity synchronized with the general upraising of north-west Europe. An area over 2,000 square miles in extent, comprising nearly the whole of Antrim and much of Down and Derry, is covered by two immense sheets of basaltic lava totalling over 1,000 feet in thickness, overlying the chalk beds of the preceding period. Along the Antrim coast the gigantic black cliffs formed by the basalt are a most impressive feature, particularly along the northern coast, where the basaltic lava forms many picturesque and symmetrical columns generally hexagonal or pentagonal, and divided horizontally into countless perfect-fitting sections. Over 40,000 of these gigantic pillars are visible in the district known as the Giant's Causeway.

Similar outpourings extended over what is now the sea as far as Mull and other islands of the Inner Hebrides, of which the beautiful Staffa is the most famous (*see* volume 2, plate 41). The eruptions were spread over long intervals of time—probably more than a million years.

Fossil Remains. The great saurians and amphibians, such as the *Brontosaurus*, *Megalosaurus*, *Stegosaurus*, *Mosasaurus*, the plesiosaurs, ichthyosaurs and pterosaurs completely vanished and only a few diminutive species remained. The ammonites, belemnites, hamites, hippurites and many other varieties died out entirely. In their place totally different types of animal life have not only appeared, but attained perfection and differentiation. It is as if another world of life was entered which had already existed for several millions of years. Birds had appeared in great variety, though fossils are scarce, while mammals had completely supplanted the saurians.

This fauna was adapted for a warm climate, the most noteworthy types being various tapir-like animals, the *Palaeotherium*, *Coryphodon*, *Lophiodon*, *Paloplotherium*, and *Pachynolophus* of the rhinoceros type, the *Hyracotherium*, a cony-like creature, and the carnivorous *Palaeonictis* and *Arctocyon*. The *Dinoceras*, *Arsinoitherium* and *Hyaenodon* are further examples of the strange creatures that had supplanted the colossal dinosaurs. A stranger had appeared in the form of the lemuroid *Microchaerus*, the first known primate and possible ancestor of Man.

Our Course in Geology is continued in Volume 6.

LESSON 18

Position of Pronouns

W E have seen that in a principal clause, if the verb is separable, the particle belonging to it comes last when we are using a simple tense (e.g. present : *ich sehe ihm zu*, I watch him ; imperfect : *ich sah ihm zu*, I watched him). We have seen further that in a compound tense the particle and the verb come at the end of the sentence (e.g. *ich habe ihm zugesehen*, I have watched him). At the end of Lesson 17 (volume 4, page 424) we noted that in the sentence *der Mann wird morgen mit der Butter in die Stadt kommen*, the position of *in die Stadt* is fixed. The reason is that *in die Stadt kommen* is really treated as if it were a separable verb. This is shown by the accent. The main accent in a separable verb is on the prefix ; the main accent in the phrase *in die Stadt kommen* is on *Stadt.*

Hinkommen means to come to a place. In the two sentences *ich komme morgen mit der Butter hin* and *ich komme morgen mit der Butter in die Stadt*, *hin* and *in die Stadt* are interchangeable as far as position goes. If we now use the future tense, *ich werde morgen mit der Butter hinkommen*, and *ich werde morgen mit der Butter in die Stadt kommen*, we see that *hin* and *in die Stadt* still occupy the same position in the sentence structure.

Let us now take the simple case of a transitive verb, i.e. a verb which can take a direct object. *Trinken* (to drink) is a transitive verb ; *Bier* (beer) is a possible direct object. In the sentences *ich trinke mit meiner Tante Bier, ich trank mit meiner Tante Bier, ich habe mit meiner Tante Bier getrunken, ich werde mit meiner Tante Bier trinken, Bier* is treated exactly as if it were a separable particle. (It is, of course, possible, and perfectly good German, to say *ich trinke Bier mit meiner Tante*, though it would be unusual to say *ich habe Bier mit meiner Tante getrunken*, because that would stress the word aunt. The fact that the usage fluctuates merely shows that in such phrases as *Bier trinken* there is still more freedom of usage than in such phrases as *hinkommen*.) A complement, or an adverbial phrase, or a direct object, which is felt to be closely connected with the verb is usually treated as if it were a separable particle.

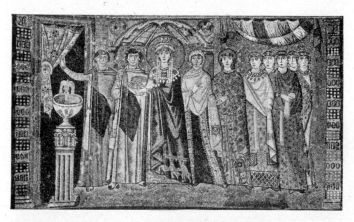

JUSTINIAN AND THEODORA. These mosaics in the choir of San Vitale at Ravenna show Justinian with his empress, Theodora, making dedicatory offerings. Below is the emperor attended by his armed bodyguard, civil ministers, and S. Maximian, bishop of Ravenna ; and above, Theodora and her entourage.

HISTORY : MEDIEVAL 28

Photos, Alinari and Anderson

MAHOMET AND THE BLACK STONE. The " black stone " that is built into the
wall of the Kaaba was an object of worship to the pre-Islamic Meccans, and
Mahomet, though bent on abolishing idol-worship, was reluctant to ruin his birth-
place by destroying its sanctity, and so found a place for the Kaaba and the Stone in
Islam.   Here we see him rededicating the latter for Moslem worship.   This example
of statesmanlike tolerance was frequently copied by the Prophet's successors.
HISTORY : MEDIEVAL 28

From F. R. Martin " Miniature Painting of Persia, India and Turkey "

CHARLEMAGNE AS CHURCH BUILDER.   Charlemagne was a great builder,
and German Romanesque may be said to date from his reign.   This sculpture from
his shrine depicts the emperor offering the newly-built cathedral at Aachen (Aix-
la-Chapelle) to the Virgin Mary. HISTORY : MEDIEVAL 30

Plate 46   *Volume V*

CAROLINGIAN COSTUME. How ninth century courtiers dressed is shown in detail in this miniature depicting Charles the Bald accepting the gift of his illuminated Bible from the canons of St. Martin at Tours in 869. The clergy wore elaborate stoles, the king and courtiers garb of Roman fashion, the royal mantle being of embroidered cloth of gold.

HISTORY: MEDIEVAL 31

Bibliothèque Nationale, Paris

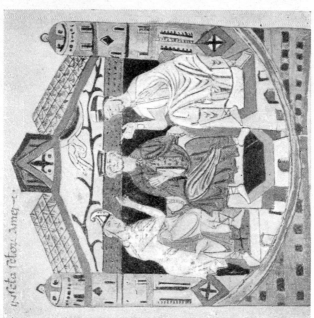

LOUIS I, THE DEBONAIR (778–840). Third son of Charlemagne, he became Roman emperor on his father's death in 814. This miniature portrays him wearing the closed Byzantine crown. HISTORY: MEDIEVAL 31

From a MS. in the Bibliothèque Nationale, Paris

OTTO II AND THEOPHANO. This ivory diptych shows Otto II (955–983) with his Byzantine wife Theophano. HISTORY: MEDIEVAL 32

Cluny Museum; photo, Giraudon

Plate 48

Volume V

The following examples should now be analysed :—

Er steht gern früh auf, he likes rising early. *Das Haus brannte bis auf den Grund ab*, the house burned down to the ground. *Er ist gestern in London angekommen*, he arrived in London yesterday. *Das Kind fiel die Treppe hinunter*, the child fell down the stairs. *Er besah mit seiner Frau das Haus*, he looked at the house with his wife. *Er hat mit seiner Frau das Haus besehen*, he has looked at the house with his wife.

Now consider the following sentences :

Er warf seine Mütze in die Luft, he threw his cap into the air. *Er hat seine Mütze in die Luft geworfen*, he has thrown his cap into the air. *Er traf auf der Strasse den Arzt*, he met the doctor in the street. *Er traf den Arzt auf der Strasse. Er hat auf der Strasse den Arzt getroffen. Er hat den Arzt auf der Strasse getroffen.*

In the first example, *er warf seine Mütze in die Luft*, it is the direction of the throwing rather than the object thrown which is closely connected with the verb, hence *in die Luft* comes last in the simple clause and before the main verb in the compound clause. In the next example both constructions are possible. It all depends whether the speaker feels that *den Arzt* or *auf der Strasse* are more closely connected with the verb. The more usual construction would be *Er traf den Arzt auf der Strasse ;* that is to say, *auf der Strasse treffen* would be considered the verb rather than *den Arzt treffen*, the manner of the meeting rather than the person met.

Position of Personal Pronouns. The personal pronoun, when used as direct or indirect object, is placed immediately after the verb in a simple clause, and after the auxiliary in a compound clause. Examples : *Ich sprach ihn gestern auf der Strasse*, I spoke to him yesterday on the street ; *ich habe ihn gestern auf der Strasse gesprochen. Ich werde ihn morgen in der Stadt sprechen*, I shall speak with him tomorrow in the town. *Er kaufte ihr zu ihrem Geburtstag eine neue Perlenschnur*, he bought her a new string of pearls for her birthday, *er hat ihr zu ihrem Geburtstag eine neue Perlenschnur gekauft. Ich tat es leider nicht zur rechten Zeit* (*zur* stands for *zu der*), unfortunately I did not do it at the proper time, *ich habe es leider nicht zur rechten Zeit getan.*

When there are two personal pronouns in the sentence, one a direct, the other an indirect object, it does not really matter which comes first. We can thus say *er hat mir ihn vorgestellt*, he introduced him to me, or *er hat ihn mir vorgestellt*, though the latter might be more usual. If, however, the direct object is *es*, this pronoun almost invariably comes first : *ich habe es ihm gesagt*, I told it to him. *Ich habe ihm es gesagt* would usually mean I told *him*, not somebody else.

Position of Reflexive Pronouns. The reflexive pronoun of the third person is *sich*. It is used for all genders, both numbers, and is indeclinable. In a simple tense clause *sich* comes immediately after the verb, in a compound tense clause immediately after the auxiliary. If a reflexive verb is used together with a pronoun taking the place of the indirect object, the reflexive comes first.

Examples : *sich verloben* (to become engaged to). *Er hat sich mit meiner Tochter verlobt*, he has become engaged to my daughter. *Sie hat sich mit meinem Sohn verheiratet*, she has (become) married (to) my son. In a simple tense the sentences would run as follows : *Er verlobte sich mit meiner Tochter. Sie verheiratete sich mit meinem Sohn. Sich* plus personal pronoun is the indirect object. Examples :

Er hat sich ihm aufgedrängt (*sich aufdrängen*, to force one self on to someone), he forced his company on him. *Der Soldat hat sich ihm ergeben* (*sich ergeben*, to surrender), the soldier has surrendered to him.

The same order is used with the reflexive pronouns of the first and second person. Here is part of the conjugation of a reflexive verb ; *sich freuen*, to be pleased.

	PRESENT.	PERFECT.
Sing. 1.	*ich freue mich*	*ich habe mich gefreut*
2.	*du freust dich*	*du hast dich gefreut*
3.	*er freut sich*	*er hat sich gefreut*
	sie freut sich	*sie hat sich gefreut*
	es freut sich	*es hat sich gefreut*
Plur. 1.	*wir freuen uns*	*wir haben uns gefreut*
2.	*ihr freut euch*	*ihr habt euch gefreut*
3.	*sie freuen sich*	*sie haben sich gefreut*
	FUTURE.	CONDITIONAL PERFECT.
Sing. 1.	*ich werde mich freuen*	*ich würde mich gefreut haben*
2.	*du wirst dich freuen*	*du würdest dich gefreut haben*
3.	*er wird sich freuen*	*er würde sich gefreut haben*
	sie wird sich freuen	*sie würde sich gefreut haben*
	es wird sich freuen	*es würde sich gefreut haben*

Plur. 1. *wir werden uns freuen*   1. *wir würden uns gefreut haben*

2. *ihr werdet euch freuen*   2. *ihr würdet euch gefreut haben*

3. *sie werden sich freuen*   3. *sie würden sich gefreut haben*

These models will serve for any other tense. Note that a reflexive verb cannot have a passive form, and also the occurrence of *sich* with *er*, *sie*, *es*, and the plural *sie*.

Examples : *Ich habe mich über seinen Brief gefreut*, I was pleased with his letter. *Ich habe mich gestern über seinen schönen Brief gefreut*, I was pleased yesterday with his nice letter. *Du hast dich sehr schnell angezogen* (*sich anziehen*, to dress), you have dressed very quickly. *Er hat sich über dein Benehmen gewundert* (*sich wundern*, to be surprised), he was surprised at your behaviour. *Wir haben uns um zwölf Uhr getroffen* (*sich treffen*, to meet), we met at twelve o'clock. *Ihr habt euch unnötigerweise geärgert* (*sich ärgern*, to be annoyed at), you were unnecessarily annoyed. *Sie haben sich sehr gut auf der Reise verstanden* (*sich verstehen*, to understand one another), they got on very well on their journey.

LESSON 19

Subsidiary Clauses

IN this Lesson we deal with subsidiary or subordinate clauses. In these the order differs somewhat from that which obtains in main clauses. It will be observed, however, that the only part affected is the verb. The chief subordinate conjunctions (i.e. conjunctions which introduce subordinate clauses) are : *als* (when) ; *bevor* (before) ; *bis* (until) ; *da* (as, since) ; *damit* (so that) ; *dass* or *dasz* (that) (Note the distinction between *das* and *dass*. *Das* is a relative pronoun standing for *welches* ; *dass* is the conjunction " so that." In English we do not distinguish the two functions of " that " in our orthography. In the sentence " The chicken that I killed," *that* is a relative pronoun, and in German would be given by *das* ; in " I knew that he was lying," *that* is a conjunction, and would be given in German by *dass* ; *ehe* (before) ; *falls* (in case) ; *indem* (whilst) ; *nachdem* (after) ; *ob* (if) ; *obgleich*, *obschon*, *obwohl* (although) ; *seit* (since) ; *seitdem* (since) ; *während* (while) ; *weil* (because) : *wenn* (when) , *weshalb*, *weswegen* (why) ; *wofern* (unless). Sometimes two words are used as a conjunction (cf. English " as if ") : *als ob* (as if) ; *bis dass* (until) ; *auf dass* (so that) ;

dadurch dass (literally " thereby that ") ; *ehe dass* (before) ; and a few more that are less common.

Rule : In a subordinate clause the verb goes to the end of the sentence. Examples : *Ich sah ihn, als er nach Hause kam*, I saw him when he came home. *Das Haus brannte ab, bevor die Feuerwehr kam*, the house burned down before the fire-engine arrived. *Ich werde warten, bis er zu mir spricht*, I shall wait until he speaks to me. *Sie ging fort, da sie müde war*, she went away because she was tired. *Der Vater gab dem Kinde Geld, damit es sich etwas kaufen konnte*, the father gave money to the child so that it could buy something. *Er brülte, dass die Wände wackelten*, he roared so that the walls shook. *Der Zug fuhr ab, ehe ich zum* (*zum* stands for *zu dem*) *Bahnhof kam*, the train departed before I arrived at the station. *Gib ihm das Buch, falls er kommt*, give him the book in case he comes. *Der Schutzmann lief in das Zimmer, indem der Einbrecher aus dem Fenster sprang*, the policeman ran into the room whilst (at the moment that) the thief jumped out of the window. *Die Sonne schien, nachdem der Regen vorüber war* (*vorüber sein*, to be over, to cease), the sun shone after the rain had ceased. *Er wusste nicht, ob es erlaubt war*, he did not know whether it was permitted. *Er ging ohne Hut aus dem Hause, obgleich es stark regnete*, he left the house without a hat, although it rained heavily.

NOTE. There is no distinction in meaning in *obgleich, obwohl, obschon*. *Obgleich* is the most common, *obwohl* rather less common and largely confined to literary language, *obschon* is somewhat pedantic. Instead of saying *Obgleich es regnete* or *obschon es regnete*, we can also say *Ob es gleich regnete* or *Ob es schon regnete*. Instead of *obgleich* and *obschon* we also find *wenngleich* and *wennschon*. These are usually separated, and only used in literary language : *Wenn es gleich regnete, wenn es schon regnete*. In these last instances the sense approaches to " even if."

Examples : *Es ist lange her, seit er in England war*, it is a long time since he has been to England. We could also say : *Es ist lange her, seitdem er in England war*. *Er ging im Garten spazieren, während ich meine Arbeit beendete*, he went for a walk in the garden whilst I finished my work. *Er konnte nicht mitkommen, weil er krank war*, he could not come because he was ill. *Ich werde zehn Mark von ihm borgen, wenn ich ihn sehe*, I shall borrow ten marks from him when I see him. *Kein Mensch wusste, weshalb er sich erschossen hatte*, nobody knew why he had shot himself. *Wofern* will not be met with very frequently, as it is more usual to substitute *wenn nicht : Ich werde kommen, wofern es regnet ; ich werde kommen, wenn es nicht regnet,* I shall come if it does not rain, unless it rains. *Es schien fast, als ob er den Verstand verloren hätte,* it almost seemed as if he had lost his reason. (It will be noticed that the verb after *als ob* is in the subjunctive.) *Er las das Buch, bis dass es zu dunkel wurde,* he read the book until it became too dark. (It would be more usual to say *bis* instead of *bis dass*.) *Der Mann arbeitete sehr, auf dass er früher fertig werden sollte,* the man worked very hard so that he should be finished earlier. *Er fiel in das Wasser, dadurch dass er sich nicht festhielt,* he fell into the water through not holding on tightly (literally, thereby that he did not hold on tightly). *Die ganze Stadt wartete auf der Strasse, ehe dass der König ankam,* the whole town was waiting on the street before the king arrived.

We have seen in Lesson 16 (volume 4, page 421) that the order of subject and verb is changed in a principal clause if anything precedes the subject. The same rule holds good if the subordinate clause comes before the main clause, which is a very frequent occurrence. Thus in the sentence *er fiel in das Wasser, dadurch dass er sich nicht festhielt,* the usual order would be : *dadurch dass er sich nicht festhielt, fiel er in das Wasser. Er ist in das Wasser gefallen, weil er sich nicht festgehalten hat,* he has fallen into the water because he has not held tight ; it is better to say, *weil er sich nicht festgehalten hat, ist er in dass Wasser gefallen,*

It will have been noted in the various examples that the auxiliary verb comes last. Thus : *Er weint, weil ich gehe,* he cries because I am going. *Er weint, weil ich gegangen bin* (*bin* is the auxiliary verb), he cries because I have gone. *Er weinte, weil ich gegangen war,* he cried because I had gone. *Er weint, weil ich gehen werde,* he cries because I shall go. *Er weint, weil ich gegangen sein werde,* he cries because I shall have gone. *Er weint, weil ich gehen würde,* he cries because I should go. *Er weint, weil ich gegangen sein würde,* he cries because I should have gone. From the examples just given it will have been seen that the rest of the verb does not alter its relative position.

Study the word-order of the following :

Der Löwe war alt geworden und konnte nicht mehr jagen. Er lag in seiner Höhle und nährte sich von den Tieren, die kamen, um sich nach seinem Befinden zu erkundigen. Eines Tages kam der Fuchs vorbei. Der Löwe bat ihn einzutreten, aber der Fuchs weigerte sich. " Ich sehe," sagte er, " die Fusspuren von vielen

Tieren, die sich zu dir in die Höhle begeben haben, aber ich sehe keine Fusspuren, die wieder aus der Höhle herausführen."

This is translated : The lion had become old and could no longer hunt. He lay in his cave and lived on (*sich nähren*, to nourish oneself) the animals that came in order to inquire after his health. One day the fox passed. The lion begged him to enter, but the fox refused. "I see," he said, "the foot-prints of many animals that have gone to visit you in the cave, but I do not see any foot-prints that lead out of the cave again."

LESSON 20

Direct and Indirect Speech

IN the short story which we studied in the preceding Lesson the speech of the fox is given directly. This is called direct statement. It could also have been given indirectly ; that is, it could have been reported by somebody else. This would be indirect statement or speech, reported statement or speech. Before we deal with the rules governing indirect speech, we will re-tell the story in indirect speech, so that an example is to hand and can be studied before formulating the rules. *Ein Mann erzählte* (a man told), *dass der Löwe alt geworden sei und nicht mehr jagen könnte. Er läge in seiner Höhle und nährte sich von Tieren, die kämen, um sich nach seinem Befinden zu erkundigen. Eines Tages sei der Fuchs vorbeigekommen. Der Löwe habe ihn gebeten einzutreten, aber der Fuchs habe sich geweigert. "Ich sehe," habe er gesagt, "die Fusspuren von vielen Tieren, die sich zu dir in die Hohle begeben haben, aber ich sehe keine Fusspuren, die wieder aus der Höhle herausführen."*

1. The first rule to note is that the verbs in the reported speech are put into the subjunctive. Other examples of this rule are :

DIRECT SPEECH.	INDIRECT SPEECH.
er kommt	*er sagt, dass er komme*
sie liest	*sie sagt, dass sie lese*
ich gebe	*ich sage, dass ich gebe*

In the first person singular present the indicative has the same form as the subjunctive, therefore there is no difference in the form of the verb.

du sprichst	*er sagt, dass du sprechest*
ihr gebt	*er sagt, dass ihr gebet*

2. The indirect speech is put into the tense of the direct (or supposed direct) speech. This is different from English usage, where we follow the sequence of tense. If we turn the English sentence " I said ; he is going " into indirect speech we might say : " I said that he was going," " he was going " appearing in the same tense as " I said." If the direct statement, *Ich sagte : er geht*, is turned into indirect speech, we would usually obtain : *Ich sagte, dass er gehe*. *Gehe* is the third person present subjunctive, and we use this tense because in the direct (or supposed direct) speech this statement was also in the present. Hence, " He said that I had come " would be : *Er sagte, dass ich gekommen sei*, where *gekommen sei* is the subjunctive of *gekommen bin*. The supposed direct statement would have been : *Er sagte : Ich bin gekommen*. *Er sagte, dass ich gekommen sei* would, of course, only occur if the statement *Ich bin gekommen* is used without reference to the person who is speaking. If *er* and *ich* are the same people, as presumably in the statement " He said : I have come," then, as in English, the " I " would become " he " in indirect speech. Thus : *Er sagte : Ich bin gekommen*, but *Er sagte, dass er gekommen sei*.

3. In an indirect speech beginning with the conjunction *dass*, the conjunction can be left out. The word order is then the normal word order of the principal clause, in spite of the fact that the indirect statement is made in a subsidiary clause. Examples :

Er sagte, dass er gekommen sei or *Er sagte, er sei gekommen*.

Sie bat, dass er ihr das Geld geben möge (she requested that he might give her the money) or *Sie bat, er möge ihr das Geld geben*.

These rules do not always work out as they should, and the general principle that in indirect speech we should use the subjunctive mood of the identical tense that would be necessitated if the statement were made in direct speech is often broken. All first persons singular present are the same for the indicative and the subjunctive ; the same applies to the first and third persons of the plural of the present tense, and frequently also to the second person plural. If, therefore, we wish to show a form which is definitely subjunctive, we frequently have to employ an imperfect tense instead of a present tense. Thus : *Er sagte :*

" *Ich gehe* " would more frequently appear as *Er sagte, dass er ginge*. If the perfect tense is formed with *haben* (as in *ich habe geliebt*), the same difficulty occurs, since only the second and third persons singular present have a really distinctive subjunctive. But in the imperfect tense, the modification of the vowel shows clearly we are dealing with a subjunctive tense (*ich hatte*, but *ich hätte*). The same applies to the present and imperfect tenses of *werden*. But in the imperfect the modification of the vowel would show clearly the subjunctive (*ich wurde*, but *ich würde*).

The usually observed rule, therefore, is to use the present subjunctive in the third person singular (not always in the second person singular, although that would usually be distinctive with *haben* and always with *werden*), and the imperfect subjunctive elsewhere. Thus :

I said I was coming : *Ich sagte, dass ich käme* or *ich sagte, ich käme*. He said he was coming : *Er sagte, dass er komme* or *er sagte, er komme*. In both cases the original (or supposed) direct statement was in the present : I said, " I am coming." He said, " I am coming."

I have loved : *Ich habe geliebt*. I said that I had loved : *Ich sagte, dass ich geliebt hätte* or *ich sagte, ich hätte geliebt*. I shall love : *Ich werde lieben*. I said that I should love : *Ich sagte, dass ich lieben würde* or *ich sagte, ich würde lieben*. But : He has loved : *Er hat geliebt*. He said that he had loved : *Er sagte, dass er geliebt habe* or *er sagte, er habe geliebt*. He will love : *Er wird lieben*. He said that he would love : *Er sagte, dass er lieben werde* or *er sagte, er werde lieben*.

These rules are rather complicated, and Germans themselves are unable to remember them instinctively and to apply them properly. The present tense being frequently unable to express the subjunctive, and the imperfect being then used, the idea has arisen that there is really, as in English, a sequence of tense. We therefore find the imperfect often used even when the present provides a perfectly adequate subjunctive. *Ich bin gekommen* : I have come. I said I had come : *Ich sagte, dass ich gekommen sei*. (This is the correct formation according to our rules. It is heard in good southern German, and is the literary form.) But : *Ich sagte, dass ich gekommen wäre* is the form current in the north of Germany, and is also written in good German.

Our Course in German is continued in Volume 6.

Medieval History's Stormy Dawn

THE accepted date, arbitrary but convenient, for marking the division between ancient and medieval history is A.D. 476. We must briefly recall the conditions at that time. The Roman Empire covered the whole civilized world of which the West had any knowledge, a world professedly Christian, though the conflict between the Catholic and Arian Christianity was still fierce. It embraced in Europe all that lay west of the Rhine or south of the Danube ; in Asia all that lay west or south of the Euphrates and the Persian Gulf ; in Africa, Egypt and the whole Mediterranean littoral. It ignored Arabia at one end, and had cut Britain adrift at the other. It claimed, but could not exercise, authority over the barbarians beyond these bounds in Europe—Teutonic on the Rhine and upper Danube, Slavonic or Mongolian on the lower Danube, and beyond the Euphrates lay the Neo-Persian empire which had succeeded the Parthian.

Within the empire, the Visigoths, who had invaded Italy in force in the first decade of the fifth century, had left it to occupy Spain and south-western France under their own kings. Vandals, too, had settled in Spain, but had later transferred themselves to Africa, where they set up a pirate or brigand state. The Roman legions in Italy were no longer Roman but barbarian warriors, captained by Sueves, Vandals, Scythians, and, finally, by Odoacer, chief of the tribe of the Heruli. The Ostrogoths, on the Danube, threatened to dominate the eastern empire.

Such were the conditions when the chaos in Italy gave to Odoacer the opportunity to remove Romulus Augustulus, the child-emperor who ruled in Italy, and invite the emperor Zeno at Byzantium to appoint him official Regent in the West.

Gothic Rule in Italy. Odoacer ruled well, and seemed to be on the way to establish a Teutonic kingdom of Italy, when the alarmed Zeno tried to eliminate two menaces at once by persuading the young king of the Ostrogoths, Theodoric, that Italy was a more promising field for him and his people than the Balkan peninsula. With the emperor's sanction—was not Odoacer a rebel ?—Theodoric with the whole Ostrogothic people poured into Italy, overthrew Odoacer, killed him, and in fact—though always as the loyal minister of Zeno—set up a Gothic kingdom in Italy, where (493–526) he ruled with a wisdom, justice, and moderation (despite some cruelties in his last years) which entitle him to a high place among the great princes of history. Ravenna, rather than Rome, had been the capital of Italy, and fine building had been carried on there. The mausoleum which Theodoric erected during his reign still exists. He also built three churches for Arian worship, which, with others built by his successors and finished by the Emperor Justinian, are famous for mosaics.

Theodoric was a statesman, a diplomatist, and a soldier, a builder whose work might have created a new western empire had a second Theodoric followed him. But at his death the Ostrogoths broke up into factions ; the Emperor of the East, Justinian, in the vain hope of reviving a unified Roman empire, sent armies to Italy under two great commanders—first Belisarius, who had already exterminated the Vandal kingdom, and then Narses— who after long and hard campaigning almost annihilated the Ostrogothic forces and drove the remnant out of Italy. They disappeared completely, and an imperial viceroy called the Exarch was established at Ravenna, although he was never accorded sufficient support to make him an efficient ruler.

Clovis, King of the Franks. Meanwhile, however, another Germanic dominion, far more barbaric than Visigoth or Ostrogoth, was establishing itself from the Rhine over all the country which we now call France. Along the mouths of the Rhine and the Meuse, in the flat expanses of Champagne and Lorraine, and on the left bank of the middle Rhine, clustered the two great divisions of the Frankish nation, the Salian and Ripuarian Franks. The Scandinavian branch of the Teutons, of whom we have met Goths, Vandals, and others, had all long ago adopted the Arian form of Christianity, which rejected the orthodox doctrine of the Holy Trinity ; but the German Franks had remained heathens till, just before our story begins, their brisk young king, Chlodwig, or Clovis, embraced the faith of his Christian wife, Clotilde, and at his bidding the majority of his subjects embraced it likewise. A fact of immense importance for the future history of Gaul and Europe was that the Christianity which won his allegiance was not of the Arian but of the Trinitarian or Catholic type. With the downfall of the Goths in Spain, Arianism perished in 587.

Orthodoxy secured for Clovis the goodwill of the Catholic clergy, and through them of the subject Romanized population through the whole of western Europe, and was doubtless one cause of the rapid extension of the Frankish kingdom. In the year 507, as the fervent champion of orthodoxy against Arianism, he challenged the Visigothic king to battle, and defeated and slew him on the plains of Poitiers. The Visigothic monarchy survived for some time south of the Pyrenees, but within Gaul it retained only a corner of territory on the west of the Gulf of Lions, called Septimania.

Clovis died in the year 511; his sons and descendants, the Merwing or Merovingian kings of the Franks, continued his policy of profitable religious warfare, and after some campaigns, conducted with varying success, finally added the fruitful provinces of Burgundy to the Frankish kingdom, which now included the whole of modern France—save for the little strip of Septimanian territory—and also the Netherlands, the Rhinelands, and an indefinable extent of country beyond the Rhine. It was certainly in the seventh and eighth centuries the most powerful of all the barbarian kingdoms; but Frankish custom always divided it between brothers, who invariably fought each other for supremacy.

Coming of the Lombards. Fifteen years after the expulsion of the Ostrogoths from Italy, the Lombards, or Langobards, another Teutonic horde, under the ruthless Alboin, arrived in the peninsula (568). An uncouth and barbarous people, they were for generations a miserable substitute for the far more advanced Ostrogoths, and their religion, if they had any, was either Arian Christianity or absolute heathenism. Pope Gregory I (590–604), justly called the Great, a man of an extraordinary breadth of view, to whose initiative an immense amount of missionary work, including the conversion of England, was due, even while he was planning his campaigns of spiritual conquest, was living, as he bitterly complained, " between the swords of the Lombards "; and the fierce enmity between the Papacy and the Lombard kings was not appeased even by the conversion of the latter to Catholic Christianity.

The conquest of Italy by the Lombards was only partial. From their capital at Pavia they ruled the greater part of the valley of the Po. Tuscany was theirs, and most of the country on the flanks of the Apennines, divided into the two great duchies of Spoleto and Benevento. But the city of Naples, the toe and heel of Italy, the island of Sicily, and—in the north-east corner of the land—the all but impregnable city of Ravenna, the seat of the imperial Exarch, were still in the imperial allegiance. Rome was, of course, also nominally imperial ; but all through these centuries the Popes, who had many a theological battle with the Eastern emperor, were showing an increasing tendency to make Rome their own subject city, and to rule it and the Western Church independently of Constantinople ; though the final separation of the Latin Papal or Catholic Church from the Greek or Orthodox Church of the East had not yet arrived.

During the same period the little city amid the mudbanks of the Adriatic, which was afterwards to be known as Venice, was quietly increasing in wealth and power, holding the Lombard barbarians at bay and professing unbounded loyalty to the distant Byzantine emperor—being comfortably beyond his reach. But the days of her greatness were still far off.

LESSON 28

Byzantium and the Moslem Menace

(See plates 45 and 46)

THOUGH Justinian (A.D. 527–565) attempted to reassert the imperial authority in the West by destroying the Ostrogothic power in Italy, the power actually recovered by Byzantium was very meagre and shadowy. The reunion of East and West had ceased to be practicable. In his reign the Eastern empire was at its height, and he is commemorated in the West by mosaics in the churches at Ravenna. Here, also, in the church of San Vitale, his Empress Theodora is depicted in gorgeous robes with her court ladies. An actress whose reputation was notorious, Theodora was a woman of forceful character, whose loyalty to her husband and influence over him never waned after her marriage. While capable of courage and energy, she was self-indulgent and extravagant to a degree.

In the age of Justinian, his capital, Constantinople, was the scene of vast building activities. The great cathedral, St. Sophia (see Volume 2, Plate 10), is the grandest memorial of his reign. Though many churches were erected, and palaces enlarged and redecorated on splendid scale, other building operations engaged his attention. The residential quarters of Constantinople in his day looked much like those in a modern city, with fine houses for the wealthy, and for the workers blocks of flats, the ground floors of which were devoted to shops. An elaborate system of drainage was installed. Huge underground cisterns for water supply were constructed within the city. One of the largest of those built by Justinian was the famous " Palace of Waters," an underground hall, the roof supported by 420 pillars set in rows. A parallel has been drawn between Justinian and " Le Roi Soleil," Louis XIV of France. Both were magnificent builders and patrons of the arts ; both were much influenced by priests and women ; both made ambitious conquests and ended by reducing their states to practical bankruptcy.

Apart from the obliteration of the Vandal kingdom by Belisarius, his heroic general, the extensive military operations of Justinian's reign were grandiose but of little practical value. His deserved and enduring title to fame rests upon his great work of codifying and giving a permanent shape to the vast mass of laws and precedents which the Roman legal system had been accumulating for hundreds of years ; so that the Code of Justinian became the basis of practically every legal system in Europe, with the one notable exception of England.

Campaigns Against the Persians. For half a century after Justinian's death in 565, the restive Slavonic and Mongolian barbarians on the Danube, and the aggression of Persia in Asia, gave the Eastern emperors enough occupation. Between 613 and 620 the victorious Persians practically conquered Syria and Egypt, overran Asia Minor, captured and sacked Jerusalem, and threatened Constantinople, which was at the same time threatened from the rear by the Mongolian Avars. Nevertheless, in the truly heroic fashion displayed at intervals by the Eastern empire, crusading armies were raised, and in a series of brilliant campaigns between 622 and 628 the Emperor Heraclius drove the Persians completely behind the Tigris. But even while Heraclius was delivering the Western world from this Oriental peril, another storm-cloud was arising in a new and most unexpected quarter.

Arabia had always stood outside the influence of the neighbour civilizations—Egyptian, Syrian, Greek or Roman. The Arabians were still nomads or primitive agriculturists. Traditionally, they claimed descent from the father of the Hebrew race through

Ishmael, the son of the bondwoman ; but their already distorted religion had been further distorted by all sorts of miscellaneous accretions, till, in the sixth century, it was a sort of conglomerate of fetish worship and demon worship, with occasional borrowings from Judaism, Christianity, and miscellaneous Eastern religions. In the city of Mecca were a temple and a stone, called the Kaaba, which were general objects of veneration traditionally associated with Adam and Abraham.

Rise of Mahomedanism. In these very unlikely surroundings arose the prophet Mahomet, who, when already of mature years, became possessed with the idea that he had a mission of regeneration to accomplish. The archangel Gabriel appeared to him in a vision. He began to preach moral and religious doctrines, by no means elevated, but still infinitely higher than anything to which the Arabs had been accustomed. He was met first with scoffings, then with persecution. In the year 622 he was obliged to take flight from Mecca ; this year of the Prophet's flight, which is called the Hijra, or Hegira, is reckoned as the first year in the Mahomedan era, the equivalent of A.D. 1 in the Christian era.

But the Prophet found followers ; they grew in numbers ; their leader claimed, and they believed, that his pronouncements were inspired. They made war upon the unbelieving city of Mecca ; they were victorious over the Meccans ; and the Kaaba was converted into the sacred shrine of the new faith. The Prophet and his followers set themselves to compel submission to his authority at the sword's point. When the Emperor Heraclius was engaged in his struggle with the Persians, both he and the Persian king received missives inviting them to recognize and submit to the Prophet of Allah—missives which the Persian received with contumely and Heraclius with polite but hardly veiled contempt. Neither of them imagined that an obscure Arabian fanatic was about to turn the world upside-down.

Mahomet's death was a shock to his faithful followers ; but the ablest of his disciples, Abu Bekr, was chosen as the first khalif, or successor of the Prophet. Rivals naturally sprang up ; they were vigorously suppressed, but the faith which had first established itself by the sword was fanatically resolved to spread itself by the same means. The Moslems, organized after Abu Bekr by the great Omar, advanced against the West and against the East, offering to all opponents the three alternatives, conversion, submission and tribute, or death. The first energies of Islam were directed against the Persians ; its arms were carried across the Euphrates and across the Tigris. Following this eastward advance, the Moslems turned upon Syria, which was a portion of what was still called the Roman Empire, absorbed it piecemeal, burst upon Egypt, and in 641 captured its capital city, Alexandria.

The progress of Mahomedanism was as rapid in Africa as it had been in Asia ; in no part of his dominions overseas could Heraclius from Constantinople offer an adequate resistance. Physically and intellectually he was no longer the same man who had hurled back the Persian power. After his death his successors proved to be no better able to deal with the situation. Outside of Europe little remained to the empire except Asia Minor. The Saracens, as the followers of the Prophet began to be called, built fleets which dominated the Mediterranean, carried their faith westward among the Berber tribes on the African coast, flung themselves even upon Sicily, and at the end of the century were on the point of invading Spain.

The khalifate, the leadership of Islam, had fallen into the hands of a family called the Ommayads. Under them the Saracen dominion had been extended over the whole East to the farther confines of the Persian empire ; Arab invaders early in the eighth century planted themselves even in the Punjab, though they established no permanent dominion in the Indian peninsula.

The house of Heraclius had failed to defend Africa and Asia east of the Taurus mountains against the Moslem deluge. Nevertheless, Constans, the grandson of Heraclius, fought manfully against the Saracens, and at least held them in check, though he failed to recover lost territory. The vigour of their attack was, in fact, weakened by internal dissensions among the faithful and struggles for the khalifate. A great body amongst the Moslems maintained that the true succession lay with the house of Ali, the son-in-law of the Prophet, husband of his daughter, Fatima ; this section came to be variously known as the Shiites or Fatimites. Opposed to them were the more orthodox Sunnites, so called because they accepted as their rule not only the Koran but the Sunna, i.e. collections of traditional sayings and doings of Mahomet put together in the 9th century. For a time, therefore, the attack upon the Empire was relaxed.

Constans then turned his attention once more, with some degree of temporary success, to an attempt at recovering supremacy in Italy. While he was in the West, the Saracen attack was renewed.

Constans was assassinated, and was succeeded by his young son Constantine, called Pogonatus, the Bearded. So vigorous was the onslaught at this time that the Saracens pierced the Taurus, overran Asia Minor, and threatened Constantinople itself. Victory, however, fell to Constantine, who first succeeded in shattering the enemy's fleet, and then routed their land forces.

Though Constantine drove the Saracens back out of Asia Minor, he was unable to carry a counter attack beyond the Taurus. Justinian II, a prince whose remarkable abilities were counter-balanced by ungovernable passions and a singularly cruel and capricious disposition, was killed in a military revolt; and once more there was a brief succession of emperors raised to the purple by one military faction only to be overthrown by another.

At about this time the Mongol Bulgars effected their definite settlement in the Danube valley. Slavonic tribes, also, of the Aryan stock had for a long time past been spreading themselves over the whole of the Balkan peninsula. The Mongol Bulgars dominated, and gave their name to Bulgaria; but, in fact, the Mongol stock soon mingled with and became absorbed in the Slavonic stock, so that even from a very early stage the Bulgarians must be looked upon not as Mongols but as Slavs.

LESSON 29

Clash of Cross and Crescent

EARLY in the eighth century the Mahomedan attack on Christendom was renewed. The vigorous Walid became khalif in 705. Under his rule the power of the khalifate increased, and great was the glory of Islam. He not only excelled in wisdom and chose able ministers to rule under him, but was also a generous patron of the civilized arts and architecture. In Damascus, his capital, the Great Mosque was erected during his reign in its present form. In military operations, though the troubles at Constantinople enabled his troops to overrun Asia Minor, his main energies were directed to establishing his power in the further East. In 715, however, he was succeeded by Suleiman, and Suleiman determined to make a grand attack upon the Christian empire at Constantinople.

The first onslaught was checked at Amorium, in the centre of Asia Minor, by the imperial general Leo, called the Isaurian— the Isaurians being a race of mountaineers of eastern Asia Minor. But Leo saw that the Saracens were not to be held back by the struggles of isolated generals. The chaos at Constantinople must cease if an organized resistance was to be offered. From Amorium he hurried to Constantinople, where the last emperor who had been raised to the purple was wise enough to abdicate voluntarily in favour of a man able to deal with the situation. Leo was acclaimed emperor as Leo III (717–741), and at once set about a vigorous organization of the defences of Constantinople.

Islam's Defeat in the East. Suleiman's armies poured across Asia Minor ; his fleet dominated the Aegean Sea ; his troops were carried over to Europe, and Constantinople was shut in upon the west as well as upon the east. But through the winter Constantinople defied attack, and Leo's ships, issuing from the Golden Horn, broke up the Persian fleet. As the spring of 718 advanced the Bulgarian king was induced to lend his aid. He attacked the Moslem force on the west, and inflicted upon it a great defeat. Leo himself had by this time dealt a heavy blow to the forces on the other side of the Dardanelles. The Saracens in Europe were already in straits from failure of supplies. The siege was raised ; the remnants of the army were embarked in the fleet, and most of the fleet went to the bottom in a storm.

Leo's great defence of Constantinople was decisive in the East. In the following years the Saracens were completely expelled from Asia Minor, though the empire never effectively recovered what had already been lost, all territory in Asia beyond the Taurus mountains. Leo's successors held what he had won. Islam was rent by the khalifate battle, which paralysed it for aggression in the East. The Ommayad dynasty was overthrown and its place taken by the Abbasids about 750, and the khalifate acquired a new splendour with Bagdad instead of Damascus as its capital ; but before that development Islam in the West had struck the great blow which planted in Spain a Moorish dominion that endured for nearly eight hundred years.

Moorish Invasion of Spain. The khalifate in the East had little or no control over Islam in the West, the African Moslems, collectively called Moors. The Visigothic kings in Spain had no better control over their nobles. In 711 a Moorish host crossed the Strait of Gibraltar (Jebel-Tarik, the name of the Moslem captain), annihilated the Visigothic army on the Guadalete and overran the peninsula. The Goths were driven into the remote mountains, and were almost, though not quite, exterminated. Masters of Spain, and reinforced by more swarms from Africa, the Moors a few years later poured through the Pyrenees into southern France ; but in 732 they were met at Poitiers (or Tours) by the gathered forces of the Franks under Charles Martel (the Hammer), who drove most of what was left of them back through the Pyrenees, which they never recrossed.

After his repulse of the Saracens the great emperor Leo and his descendants ruled the Eastern empire with vigour and high ability for some sixty years. They are known as the iconoclasts (idol-breakers) from their zealous endeavours to purge the Church of what they accounted idolatry ; unfortunately they smashed vast quantities of fine statues. Their reign ended when Irene, widow of Leo IV, usurped the imperial authority in 780. Throughout her regency for her son and her own reign (797–803) she was an ardent image-worshipper, summoning the Council of Nicaea in 787 to reverse the decisions of the Council of Constantinople, which had forbidden image worship.

The Franks were loyal to the line of the Merovings, though the kingdom was habitually divided between different members of the family. But the whole line had degenerated into feeble incompetence before the middle of the seventh century, and whether there was one king or more, from that time the real rule was in the hands of some great noble officially known as mayor of the palace. This mayoralty became, in effect, hereditary in a Rhineland family, the Arnulfings. They had extended the Frankish dominion over the Germans on the east of the Rhine, when Charles Martel (whose descendants were called Karlings or Carolingians) secured the succession in 720 ; but their hold over southern and western France was precarious, while for some years Charles was more concerned with consolidating the conquests on the east.

Hence it was not till twelve years had passed that he could draw the Franks together and deliver Western Christendom from the Mahomedan menace by his triumph at Poitiers in 732. Even then it was only by hard fighting that he was able to make the whole south secure before his death in 741. The puppet king died, and no Merovingian heir was forthcoming ; but Charles refused the crown and continued to rule with the title of duke of the Franks. He was succeeded by his two sons, Pepin the Short and Carloman, who worked in unprecedented harmony till Carloman retired into a monastery and left Pepin sole ruler in 747. The brothers had found a young Merovingian prince, Childeric, in a monastery, and, so to speak, legalized their position by crowning him.

Pepin and the Papacy. During the last hundred years the Papacy had been in continual conflict with the unruly Lombards, who had produced only one memorable prince, Liutprand. Charles Martel had been honoured and respected by successive popes on account both of his martial power and of his distinguished zeal in Christianizing the more barbarian German tribes ; but he had turned a deaf ear to their appeals for his intervention against the Lombards. Now in 751 Pepin was elected king by the Franks gathered in a national assembly. But he had already made Childeric the anointed king, and conscience and religious sentiment must be reconciled to his deposition ; so Pepin put to the pope as the supreme authority in religion and morals the question, whether the royal title should not accompany the exercise of the royal authority. In answer, Pope Stephen II crossed the Alps, and at St. Denis crowned and anointed the new sovereign in 754. Later popes claimed this as an admission that their authority extended to the deposition and appointment of kings ; thus began the temporal power of the Papacy.

Pepin, however, could no longer resist the appeal of the complaisant Papacy for his intervention against the aggressive Lombard, who had already annexed Ravenna and permanently expelled the imperial exarch. Accordingly, to the joy of the Franks, he descended on Italy, vanquished the Lombard king, who swore allegiance to him as over-lord, handed over Ravenna and other recent Lombard conquests to the Papacy, and withdrew over the Alps to complete his work of consolidating his Frankish kingdom, from which he expelled the last remnant of Saracens in Septimania, and where he had to bring to submission the rebellious dukes of Aquitaine on one side and Bavaria on the other. The kingdom he left to his sons when he died in 768 was incomparably the largest and most powerful in Europe. This dominion was parted between his two sons, Charles and Carloman ; and it was only after three years of constant quarrelling that the death of Carloman in 771 left Charles the Great (Charlemagne) undisputed king of the Franks.

LESSON 30

Charlemagne
and the Holy Roman Empire

(See plate 46)

CHARLES THE GREAT, Carolus Magnus (742-814), universally
known through legend and literature as Charlemagne,
the first of the Carolingian monarchs, had been king of
the Franks for thirty years before the grateful and astute Pope
Leo III was (by his own account) inspired to crown him emperor
of the Holy Roman Empire at Rome on Christmas Day, 800.
Charles himself is the most striking if not the greatest figure,
as the birth of the Holy Roman Empire is the most striking
event, in the whole course of medieval history.

During those thirty years he had been conquering, organizing,
evangelizing at the sword's point, educating, building up the
widest dominion ever ruled in Europe by any one man except
Russian Czars or by Napoleon at the zenith of his power. Out
of his system, though in changed form, was later developed feudalism, the political and social framework of Europe for centuries
to come. The revival of a Roman empire in the West, associated
by its very title with the Church of the West, begot the
unrealizable idea of a Christendom united under two heads, the
spiritual and the temporal, the Pope and the Emperor, which,
in fact, eventually brought an almost unceasing conflict between
the two instead of unity, because no dividing line could be drawn
between the spiritual and temporal functions. And all this strife,
instead of unity and peace, was born, we may say, on that fateful
Christmas morning.

Charles began his career as a conqueror in 773, by lowering to
an appanage of the French crown the Lombard kingdom, which
his father, Pepin, had been content to reduce to vassalage—
excuse being provided by a quarrel between the Lombard
king and the Pope ; this partisanship interrupted Charles's first
campaign against the hitherto unsubdued Saxons. Most of the
Lombard dukes and counts, with the notable exception of Spoleto
in the south, took the oath of allegiance and gave little further
trouble. Saxony presented a more serious task ; much like that

which had proved too difficult for the Romans when they tried to carry their borders beyond the Rhine in the days of Augustus and Tiberius. West Saxony was apparently subdued and compelled to accept Christianity in 776 ; but while Charles was campaigning in Spain the Saxons again revolted. Charles reconquered them in 779 and baptized them by the thousand, but had to return three years later, smiting them with fire and sword and massacring some thousands in cold blood ; yet they fought on stubbornly till, in 785, they submitted again. This time the conquest was effective—though there were some sporadic revolts later—and Saxony was organized as a province of the Frank kingdom. The Spanish expedition against the newly established emirate (soon to be the Cordova khalifate, independent of Bagdad) of the Ommayad Abderrahman, in 778, gave rise to the famous legend concerning Charles's commander, the paladin Roland. This legend is embodied in the " Chanson de Roland " and is the foundation of the vast traditional literature about Charlemagne. Roland's defeat and death at Roncesvalles by the Gascons—whose country he and his army invaded, returning from Spain across the Pyrenees—when the Franks were killed to a man, made a great theme for minstrels ; in time it became embodied in lengthy poems, in which all the incidents of the expedition and final defeat were magnified. Roland was glorified into one of the world's heroes, he and his army being regarded as martyrs in a Holy War—because the expedition was against Islam in the first place—instead of as military trespassers in the territory of the Gascons.

Charles's aim, however, was not the conquest of Spain but the establishment of a strategic frontier along the Ebro, behind which the Moors were gradually driven and confined by treaty in 812. Without being brought formally into the Frank kingdom, Slavonic tribes beyond the Elbe readily acknowledged the Frankish supremacy ; but it was not without much campaigning that the Khan of the Mongol Avars in Hungary was also subdued.

When, therefore, Pope Leo III hailed Charlemagne as Roman emperor and Caesar, he was really giving expression to an accomplished fact. Then besides, a woman, Irene (*see* Lesson 29, page 400), was seated on the imperial throne at Byzantium, and it seemed naturally right for popes, who claimed a spiritual supremacy over the whole Christian Church, to transfer their temporal allegiance to a Catholic prince from one who repudiated the papal claim and at the best of times upheld the heresies of the Church in the East.

Charles, as emperor, embarked on no new projects of expansion. His acceptance of the crown imperial was also the acceptance of a tremendous responsibility. He had still to complete, so far as one man already nearing sixty could do so, the work of imperial organization based upon the Frankish system blended with still persistent survivals of the bygone Roman system.

The title of emperor added nothing to the dominions of the king of the Franks, within which the Franks were the dominant race ; and Charlemagne's favourite capital was still Aachen, which was in a conveniently central position in the Frankish Rhineland. Here he himself directed the building of a great city, in which his courtiers recognized a second Rome. " Here," in the words of a Latin poem of the period, " shall be the forum and the holy senate, which shall deal justice to the people and dictate the law to it." Here rose the royal palace, the theatre, the marble building enclosing the hot baths, and the famous basilica church, dedicated to the Virgin, the finest ornament of the city, from which it received its French name, Aix-la-Chapelle.

Racial Divisions of the Empire. Charles's government was an autocracy in which the king's word was law. Franks were naturally more likely to be appointed to offices of state than others, but they had no monopoly, and no privileges as Franks. Geography made three more or less racial divisions in the empire : Germans almost untouched by Latinism, east of the Rhine as far as the Slavonic border ; thoroughly latinized Celts and slightly latinized Teutons, west of the Rhine, the former preponderating ; Latins south of the Alps, with a mainly Lombard aristocracy. Those three strongly marked divisions never really amalgamated ; they separated into German, French, and Italian. But the central wedge from the Rhine mouth to the Alps, where the races were most mixed, gravitated sometimes to one side, sometimes to the other ; and the Rhône basin, Provence, the one time Roman Provincia of Gaul, might have become Italian instead of French had a united Italian kingdom ever emerged to absorb it—much as Catalonia, between the Ebro and the Pyrenees, was absorbed in the later Spanish kingdom of Aragon. The Frankish name survived both in France, and, more appropriately, east of the Rhine, in Franconia ; but cleavage did not set in while the great emperor lived.

CHARLEMAGNE AND THE HOLY ROMAN EMPIRE

In the empire the emperor was without question supreme, recognizing no antagonism between the Papal functions and his own. Had they clashed, the Pope would have given way as a matter of course. Charles ruled as a faithful son of the Church, but as the undoubted head of Western Christendom, and not challenging the Eastern empire in its own sphere, deeply as the East resented his assumption of the imperial title. He ruled also as king of the Franks, summoning twice a year the General Assembly to hear and approve his projects. The whole dominion was divided into governorships, in which the governor, appointed by himself and removable at his pleasure, was responsible to him for the maintenance of law and order. If they were not bishops, they bore the title of duke, count, or, in border provinces, margrave (count of the marches). Commonly they were local nobles. There was no right of succession to governorships, though the succession of son to father was a natural development which came later. The danger of the rise of powerful and ambitious families probably led to an extensive employment of clerics. Ecclesiastical officials predominated in Charles's Court, and the double character of Church and State working together in perfect harmony was maintained. Under a strong and self-reliant monarch of a dominating personality, in a heterogeneous empire, the system was sound ; but it had in it the germs of disintegration. To carry on the work, another Pepin or Charles Martel was needed ; but the Karlings who followed fell away from the standards of their mighty ancestry.

While Charles lived, however, he seemed to have revived in the Holy Roman Empire that Roman peace which had been the moral justification of the old empire's existence. Great though he was as conqueror and organizer, it may be that his best title to be called great lies in his perception of the hitherto unrecognized value of education, when learning was practically a monopoly of the churchmen. He not only cultivated the society of learned men—he strove to bring learning within the reach of those to whom it had been denied, by founding schools and gathering teachers as well as scholars. Like his great contemporary, Harun al Raschid, at Bagdad, Charlemagne needs no legends or mythical trappings to warrant his inclusion among the few emphatically great men of history.

LESSON 31

Emergence of the Western Kingdoms

(See plates 47 and 48)

WHEN Charlemagne died in 814 at the age of 71, in his palace at Aachen, his only surviving son Louis crowned himself emperor and also king of the Franks. This he did as by indisputable right, though his elder brother's son was king of Lombardy ; he himself had long been king of Aquitaine. Clearly, Charles had intended that after his death there should be one supreme emperor, but that the Frank kingdom should be divided, according to the immemorial habit, among his sons, on each of whom he bestowed a kingdom during his own lifetime ; but the two elder and more capable of his sons died before him. Louis the Pious—to avoid confusion, we keep that form of Ludwig or Lewis for princes and others who are reckoned as French— also known as the Debonair, was a somewhat tragic example of that type of piety of which our own Edward the Confessor was later to provide another. It unfitted him hopelessly for the personal responsibilities of the imperial office, which he was at least twice anxious to resign in favour of retirement to a monastery. He sanctioned the death of his nephew Bernard, king of Lombardy, who came to him under safe-conduct, and was haunted for the rest of his life by this sin. His sons, on whom he bestowed kingdoms, were in perpetual revolt, knowing that if they were defeated they were secure of pardon and reinstatement. In the last year of his life he succeeded in breaking a revolt in which his eldest son Lothar had for once taken no active part. Consequently, when Louis died, Lothar (who was already king in the Rhineland, which took from him the name Lotharingia, Lorraine) became emperor as his eldest son.

Soon, however, he and his two brothers, Lewis called the German, and Charles the Bald, the Benjamin of the family, were fighting again ; but the three came to terms, in the Treaty of Verdun (843). The emperor kept a great central kingdom from the Rhine mouth on the north to the Rhône mouth on the south, together with Italy ; Lewis was king of the Germans eastward of it, Charles the Bald king of all Gaul, or France, west of it.

Lothar gave his own eldest son Lewis the kingdom of Italy. This Lewis (not his uncle, Lewis the German) became emperor in 855, but continued to be preoccupied with Italy. In 875 he died, leaving no heir. Two years later Charles the Bald and Lewis the German, who had been constantly fighting each other, both died. The successor of Lewis was his son Charles the Fat ; in 884 the sons of Charles the Bald were dead, and their heir was the infant afterwards known as Charles the Simple. In loyalty to the Carolingian dynasty the west Franks, being in need of an active king, not a baby, gave their crown to the incapable Charles the Fat, who had already secured the imperial crown, the Italian crown, which went with it, and Lotharingia.

In 887, Charles, having surrendered the German crown to his rebellious—and illegitimate—cousin, Arnulf of Carinthia, died. The west Franks, refusing to acknowledge Arnulf, elected the distinguished warrior Odo, count of Paris, king. From that time no king of France—as we may thenceforth call the Western kingdom—owned allegiance to an emperor, or himself wore the imperial crown. And for some time to come the imperial authority was in abeyance, though the title was occasionally borne by some rival prince with a claim to Carolingian descent.

While the kings were fighting to snatch territory from each other, little attention was given to external foes or to the duties of government except by Lewis as king of Italy. That was left to the dukes and counts. When one died, it saved trouble to pass the governorship on to his son, so that by the end of the century their families had come to regard the succession as a hereditary right, and the disintegrating legalist theory of feudalism was generally established. All the land was the king's, but he had distributed it among magnates who held their territories from him by hereditary right, but under the pact of allegiance. They were required to do homage to him as his " men," and to render him military and other services upon conditions equally binding on both parties, failure in which justified, on one side, renunciation of allegiance, and, on the other, forfeiture of territory. Similarly, within the county or dukedom the big landholders held their land from the duke or count as his men (vassals) : and so on. Everyone held his land as tenant or vassal of some overlord who was himself the vassal of another, the overlord being, in the final stage, the king's vassal. In the system, however, as it prevailed on the Continent, the vassal's allegiance was rendered to his immediate overlord, not to the over-lord's overlord. Thus a duke's vassals would follow him against the king, and their vassals would follow them.

There was another most important result of the kings' pre-occupation with their mutual quarrels. The individual nobles were left to defend their own territories against invaders ; and all through the century the Northmen from Denmark, Norway, and, to a less extent, Sweden were swarming along the coasts and thrusting up the estuaries, robbing and pillaging, but avoid-ing pitched battles in the open. The nobles learnt to build impregnable strongholds and to pursue the raiders with mounted men, with the consequence that castles and armoured cavalry became the prominent features of medieval warfare and the measure of the military power of every noble. Paris itself was saved from sack at the Northmen's hands by the skilful military defensive tactics of its count, Odo, before he was raised to the French throne. Early in the next century, in 911, one of their chiefs, Rolf or Rollo, acquired the duchy of Normandy.

Saracenic Influence in Europe. In the reign of Lewis of Italy the menace of the Saracen power had revived. Saracen fleets dominated the Mediterranean ; Saracens swarmed into Sicily (which, with the " foot " of Italy, was still attached to the Eastern empire) and conquered it ; they planted pirate fortresses on the mainland, and retained possession of Sicily and Sardinia for about two centuries.

This western extension of Arabic influences is important. The Saracens brought Arabic culture as well as Saracenic arts and products to the ports of Christendom. For 200 years they held Malta (the Maltese language is still a corrupt Arabic dialect), and in the 9th and 10th centuries, while they were also masters of Sicily, they bequeathed the Saracenic style of architecture to their successors, the Norman kings of Sicily. In the 10th century the Saracens, with their Arabic culture, were the distributors of learning in Europe. Arabic medicine was studied at the medical schools of Salerno and Bologna. Arabic ideas pervaded the universities, just as the artistic craft of the Saracenic glassworkers and damasceners filled the Italian marts, where separate booths were reserved for Oriental traders. Even in France, where the decisive victory of Charles Martel against Islam at Tours had put a stop to the tide of Arab conquest, the Saracens still kept some influence in Provence, where the mountains of Les Maures preserve the name of the Moors, while the lays of the troubadours have affinities with Arabic poetry. In Moorish Spain Arab culture was the cynosure of all eyes. By the Moors many important buildings were erected there, from the mosque of Cordova begun in 786, to the Alhambra at Granada, in the 14th century. Arabic possesses a vast literature, and its momentous service at this time, when Europe was steeped in blind illiteracy, was that it prepared the way for the Renaissance revival of learning.

Cleavage in the Church. During the struggle the Eastern empire had failed to make effective intervention on behalf of its subjects, but in 867 the adventurer Basil the Macedonian, groom and boon-companion of the drunken emperor Michael, murdered his master, seized the crown of the Caesars, and founded an imperial dynasty which reigned at Constantinople for some two hundred years. Basil won the throne by crime, but he was an able ruler. Just before the murder of Michael, the Synod of Constantinople pronounced the final separation of the Eastern and Western Churches (867), confirming the spiritual as well as the temporal cleavage. This pronouncement was the outcome of the long-standing quarrel between Rome and Constantinople on the question of authority, which had now reached a climax. Each of the Churches has been under the other's ban of heresy ever since.

LESSON 32

Feudalism Takes Shape in Europe

(See plate 48)

IN the preceding Lesson we saw how France and Germany first came into being definitely in 843, when, by the Treaty of Verdun, the three sons of Louis the Pious divided his territory into three : Germany east of the Rhine went to Lewis ; France, composed of Neustria and Aquitaine, to Charles the Bald ; and the state between them, comprising most of Belgium and all Burgundy, together with Lombardy, to Lothair. In this last kingdom lay Charlemagne's capital of the Holy Roman Empire, Aachen. At the end of the 9th century Odo was reigning in the West as elected king of the French. The titular king of the Germans, acknowledged as a Carolingian, was the great-grandson of the first German king Lewis, Arnulf's small son, Lewis the

Child. Germany included the five dukedoms corresponding to the five German "nations": Lotharingia, with Friesland (the Netherlands), on the west; in the centre, from north to south, Saxony, Franconia, and Swabia; and on the south-east, Bavaria. Provence was independent, and Berengar was king of Italy.

Saracens who did not acknowledge the Bagdad khalifate were still in full possession of Sicily, but Byzantium had recovered its hold on Calabria in Italy. In the unsubdued north of Spain Christian kingdoms were rising and already very gradually pushing back the Moors. The Bagdad khalifate, for all its glory, was being outshone by the brilliant period of the Moors in Spain. The brilliance was due, as at Bagdad, to a fusion of races in which the Arab played a subordinate part. In Spain, the Arab element was quite inconsiderable, and the main factors were African Berbers, Christian Goths and Jews. While the early khalifs of Damascus took very little interest in letters or philosophy, their descendants of Cordova were distinguished by their cultivation and support of literature, their encouragement of philosophers and of poets.

The Mahomedan world at this period, with one khalif at Bagdad, another in Africa, and a third at Cordova, was too much rent to be aggressive in Europe; and a pedant, Leo VI, reigned peacefully at Byzantium over an empire where the administrative machine ran smoothly without interference. Outside the empire, Danes and Norsemen were continuing their depredations, but the Vikings were independent adventurers, not the armies of the kings of Denmark or of Norway. In England, Alfred had permitted colonies of Danes to settle in the Danelagh. East of the Elbe the Slavonic peoples were outside the empire, while in Hungary the Ugrians or Magyars, people of non-Aryan or Mongolian stock, had absorbed the Avars and were now threatening Bavaria.

French Dynastic Details. France presents us, from this time, with the picture of typical feudal monarchy. Odo himself was a noble among other nobles, many of whom were more powerful than he, when he was elected king, simply because he had shown himself to be the man who could best discharge a critical task at a critical moment. The rest swore allegiance, but his power of controlling them depended on their loyalty and readiness to support his authority against recalcitrants. When he died, his brother Robert might have secured the succession, but chose instead to set the crown on the one available representative of the old royal house, Charles the Simple, who was now (899) eighteen. Charles was neither stern enough nor cunning enough to inspire fear ; and in conjunction with Rudolf of Burgundy, the same Robert of Paris who had set him on the throne—and had then been made " duke of France " with greatly enlarged estates—deposed him. Robert was killed in battle, Rudolf was made king, Charles was starved to death in captivity. When Rudolf died in 936, Robert's son, Hugh the Great, instead of seizing the crown himself, preferred to enjoy more real power as a sort of Mayor of the Palace, and recalled Louis (IV), the young son of Charles—who had been carried away to England and safety —to the throne, with the prestige of the Carolingian line. Louis and his son Lothaire, who followed him, were both capable and vigorous princes, but both died young. When there was no Carolingian left to succeed, Hugh Capet, the son of Hugh the Great, was elected king of France in 987. The dynasty endured with intervals till 1848.

Conditions in Germany. In Germany, Arnulf had been what Germany had most needed, a strong king and emperor, whose supremacy the dukes were ready to acknowledge. Lewis the Child could be no more than a figurehead. The Magyars took their opportunity to make devastating raids ; Lewis died in 911, a year after suffering a heavy defeat at their hands, and the German Diet, following the French example, elected as German king Conrad, count of Lower Franconia. Conrad died in 918, and the Franconians supported the election of the sturdy Saxon duke, Henry the Fowler. Having no rival whose power he need fear, he was careful to avoid arousing jealousy, to rule the princes rather as president of a confederation than as a sovereign ; he beat off the Magyars and exacted from them a ten years' truce ; he planted agricultural colonies, which were also organized commercial centres, between the Elbe and the Vistula. Each colony had a walled town, within which a tenth of the colonists resided to form a garrison, the other colonists being responsible for the maintenance of the garrison's farms. These garrison towns proved effective strongholds against Magyar raids. He strengthened his own duchy by his internal administration. Though never crowned Emperor, he is reckoned on the list as Henry I.

His son, Otto the Great (936-73), abandoned the cautious policy of Henry. He meant to be a second Charlemagne, a real head of the Holy Roman Empire, with a full appreciation of what that implied. His election was almost a matter of course, but in many parts of Germany there was armed refusal to acknowledge a youth of twenty as master. By 941 rebellion was crushed; in the course of it three of the dukes had been killed. Otto took the Franconian dukedom, and gave Bavaria to his brother Henry and Swabia to his own son, thus making his own house far the most powerful in Germany. But in every duchy he appointed a Count Palatine, as minister for the crown. His power after this was as incontrovertible even as Charlemagne's before his coronation as Emperor. For the consummation of his ideals, it remained that he should exercise decisive control over the degenerate Papacy, for he himself was in entire accord with his brother Bruno, archbishop of Cologne, in desiring the purification of the Church, as conceived by the new school of fervent churchmen at Cluny.

Pope John XII gave him his opportunity by appealing to him against Berengar, king of Italy. Otto came, had himself crowned Emperor in Rome, and then dictated his terms to John (962). Finally, Otto deposed John, put in his place a new Pope, Leo VIII, of his own choosing, and left Italy in 967. In 973 he was succeeded by his son Otto II, a youth of eighteen, for whom he had procured as bride a Byzantine princess of the Eastern empire, Theophano, with the imperial Italian lands as marriage portion.

When Otto the Great died, he had made the Czech kingdom of Bohemia tributary, and carried the north-eastern bounds of the organized empire from the Elbe to the Vistula; and the whole eastern border had been portioned into marks—margraviates—independent of the German dukes and closely bound to and dependent on the German crown. He had reduced the dukes to a secure obedience, he was master of Italy, the clergy were under his control, and he had forced the Papacy to recognize his supremacy.

Otto II wished to make Italy, not Germany, the centre of the restored empire. He had first, however, to make his authority in Germany decisively felt. This duly accomplished, the next step, with a view to a " Holy War " against the infidel Saracens in Sicily, was to do the same in south Italy; but he died suddenly while he was in the midst of preparing a mighty expedition with this object, in 983, leaving as his successor the infant Otto III, whose title had already been conferred by the German Diet. Otto's immediate project perished with him, and for some years the affairs of the empire were conducted by a regency.

LESSON 33

Early Monarchs of Medieval Germany

(See plates 49 and 50)

WHILE France was making ready for the Capet monarchy, and the great rulers of the Saxon line were restoring the Holy Roman Empire in Germany and Italy, the Eastern empire had enjoyed a long period of comparative repose and mechanical prosperity, unvexed by the divided Saracen powers except in Mediterranean waters. A period of revived activity followed during the minority of the emperors Basil II and Constantine VIII, under the associate emperors Nicephorus Phocas and his nephew and murderer, the Armenian, John Zimisces. After the death of Romanus II in 963, Nicephorus Phocas had married the young widow Theophano. Tiring of him, she conspired with her lover, John Zimisces, to effect his assassination. In spite of great military successes—the recovery of Crete and Cyprus and subjection of half Syria—the brutal Nicephorus was exceedingly unpopular with clergy and court, and his murder was generally condoned. John proclaimed himself, without opposition, the associate emperor of Theophano's two children, but Theophano herself was imprisoned in a convent (969).

Under John, Byzantine policy changed. In 971 he co-operated with Boris II of Bulgaria in expelling the invading Russians with their leader, Prince Sviatoslav, and concluded, after two victories, a treaty which not only converted the Russian people into allies, but also to the Orthodox Christian faith. Basil, coming of age at the time of John's death in 976, ruled in fact as sole emperor, though in form as the colleague of his studious brother Constantine, from 976 to 1025. He continued John's work, winning the doubtfully honourable title of the " Bulgar slayer " by a victory over Bulgaria, which for the time extinguished that kingdom and added much to the great power of the Eastern empire, of which he reorganized the Asiatic portion. But he left no male heir. With his death (1025) passed the revived strength of the Eastern empire. In 1028 Constantine died, and for the next 26 years the emperors were the three successive husbands of his daughter Zoe. Her more admirable sister Theodora reigned for only three years, and in 1057 the Macedonian dynasty ended with her death.

(415)

We must now turn to France, where Hugh Capet reigned for eleven years, with less power as the crowned king than he had enjoyed as the king's controller and leader of the baronage. But the dynasty remained sufficiently firm, son succeeding father, each king reigning thirty years or more for several generations, free from family disputes as to the succession, strengthening itself by alliance with the Church and by avoiding direct conflict with the powerful nobles, though exercising little control over them. Thus dukes of Normandy or Aquitaine or counts of Flanders or Anjou became virtually independent princes, ruling over vassals who were prone to display towards them the same spirit of turbulent independence which they themselves were apt to show towards the crown. The dynasty, however, was so securely established that the accession of an infant heir, Philip I, in 1060, was undisputed.

In Germany and Italy the reign of Otto III (983–1002) is a curious interlude. A thirteen years' regency, chiefly directed by bishops, had its troubles, but they were successfully pacified ; and at the age of sixteen Otto, a born idealist, fostered and educated by idealists, and son of an idealist, became head of Christendom, and set about the realization of his ideals with all the enthusiasm and self-confidence of an abnormally clever boy. He went off at once to Italy to be crowned emperor, taking with him his dearest friend and cousin, Bruno. While he was on the way the Pope died. Bruno was at once made Pope as Gregory V, and the two young men started to establish the kingdom of God upon earth, hand in hand, sharing the same ideals. But Gregory died. Otto put in his place another idealist, Gerbert of Aurillac, a fervent reformer of the Cluniac school, who, as Sylvester II, immediately quarrelled with the nationalist German bishops. Otto's own dreams, which centred not in Germany but in Italy, were far too fantastic to be possible of realization ; he died at the age of no more than twenty-two in 1002, and Sylvester died the next year. Germany's new emperor was Henry of Bavaria, grandson of the great Otto's younger brother.

Henry II was in a stronger position than any other of the German princes. He had no touch of the genius which, whether practical or erratic, had been present in each of the Ottos ; but he was level-headed, shrewd, resolute, imperturbable, and pious enough to be termed " the Saint." Like Henry I, he concentrated on Germany and the working of the political machine,

BASIL II (c. 957–1025). Emperor of the Eastern Roman empire from 976 till his death, he conquered the Bulgarians with such ruthlessness that he became known as " Bulgaroctonus "—" the Bulgar slayer." This miniature from a contemporary psalter depicts him in imperial costume with obsequious officials on their knees before him. HISTORY : MEDIEVAL 33

S. Mark's, Venice; from Schlumberger, " L'épopée byzantine "

HENRY II (973–1024).   German king and Roman emperor.   Elected
emperor in 1002, he was an able ruler and so devoted a servant of the Church
that he won the title of " the Pious " and was canonized in 1146.   This miniature from a manuscript at Munich shows him and his consort, Cunegonde,
being presented to Christ by SS. Peter and Paul, with, below them, Germany
between Rome and Gaul.   HISTORY : MEDIEVAL 33

From Schlumberger, " L'épopée byzantine " (Hachette)

Plate 50   *Volume V*

THE CONQUEROR'S BIRTH-PLACE. The mighty castle of Falaise, seen in this photograph, was one of the favourite seats of the Norman dukes; and here Arletta, the tanner's daughter, bore to Duke Robert in 1027 the illegitimate son who in due course succeeded to the dukedom and won the English crown.
HISTORY : MEDIEVAL 34

NORMANS AT SEA. The Normans of Normandy used ships of practically the same build as those of their Norsemen forbears. The vessel seen here is carrying Normans across the Channel to England.
HISTORY : MEDIEVAL 34

Bayeux Tapestry

THE CRUSADERS' GOAL.
The Church of the Holy
Sepulchre in Jerusalem, cover-
ing the supposed site of
Calvary and the rock tomb in
which the body of the dead
Christ was laid, was founded
in 335 by the emperor Con-
stantine and rebuilt by the
Crusaders.

HISTORY: MEDIEVAL 35

HENRY IV AT CANOSSA. In 1076 the Papacy for
a brief moment triumphed over the Empire, when
Henry IV (emperor 1056–1106) found it advisable to
abase himself at Canossa before Gregory VII.
Canossa was in the domains of the countess Matilda,
one of the pope's most ardent supporters, and this
MS. shows the emperor kneeling before her.

HISTORY: MEDIEVAL 35

Vatican Library, MS. Lat. 4922; photo, Giraudon

BARBAROSSA. Frederick I
(c. 1124–90), German king and
Roman emperor, known as
Barbarossa from the redness
of his beard, was crowned
emperor in 1155. His years
were passed in conflict with
his vassal states and the
Papacy. He was accidentally
drowned in Cilicia on the
3rd Crusade.

HISTORY: MEDIEVAL 36

Relief at Reichenhall, Bavaria

Plate 52   *Volume V*

without indulging in any grandiose schemes, but with undeniable success, cultivating the goodwill of the German clergy. He recognized the independence of both Bohemia and Poland, and established very friendly relations with Stephen, the great king and in some sort creator of the power of the Magyar kingdom of Hungary. But the interventions in Italy which were forced on him met with little success, though Germany enjoyed peace and prosperity under his cautious sway.

He was the last of the house of Henry the Fowler. When he died he was succeeded by Conrad II (1024–39) the Salic, of Swabia, who founded a new dynasty. In the fifteen years of his rule, Conrad succeeded, despite strong opposition, in greatly increasing the power of the crown as against the dukes and counts, by multiplying the nobles of secondary rank, who had no overlord but himself ; he also in part succeeded, where his predecessor had failed, in establishing his authority in northern Italy ; and, despite his own unpopularity, he left the succession secured to a son who, though young, was thoroughly trained for his great and difficult position, while combining the father's practical qualities with the lofty ideals of an Otto.

Henry III the Black was twenty-one when he succeeded Conrad, and only thirty-eight when he died. During that period he raised the empire to a greater height of power than it had known since the time of Charlemagne. Conrad had recovered on the eastern side some of the authority over Bohemia and Poland which Henry II had abrogated ; he had also acquired the crown of Provence, which, commonly spoken of as the Arelate, remained an integral part of the empire for some centuries. The disorders in Hungary after Stephen's death and the aggressiveness of Bohemia made it imperative for Henry III to spend the first years of his reign in bringing them under the imperial obedience, though as dependencies outside the imperial system. His prestige was raised by these successes and by the generosity of his treatment of opponents, who could not ascribe his magnanimity either to cunning or to fear.

Having established an unwonted concord in Germany, he turned in 1046 to Italy and the Papacy. The secular authority of the German kings had almost disappeared under Henry II, and though Conrad had restored it in the north, the difficulties of his task in Germany had prevented him from doing so in the south, where Greeks and Lombard dukes were in perpetual conflict, while Saracens and Norman adventurers added to the complications.

Italian nobles, however, who could afford to disregard or defy Conrad, became discreet when one who was so secure in Germany crossed the Alps. Henry assumed the supreme authority as a matter of course, summoned two synods, and after himself appointing in succession two zealous Cluniacs, both of whom died, nominated as Pope his cousin Bruno, Bishop of Toul, who only after he had received full canonical election—a significant point—accepted the office. Bruno, as Leo IX, inaugurated a new line of Popes devoted to the Cluniac doctrines, and a new era in the history of the Papacy (1048).

Henry at the time of his early death was at the very height of his power, but he had not consolidated his great work. He died leaving an infant heir. The next generation was to witness not the spiritual and temporal harmony promised by his reign, but the opening of a prolonged conflict between the temporal and spiritual powers for supremacy in both spheres.

LESSON 34

The Norman Century of Conquest

(See plate 51)

THE last years of the great emperor Henry III inaugurated a new era, to which various names are given. Primarily, it centres on the rival claims to the supreme authority in Christendom of the spiritual power of the Papacy and the temporal power of emperors and kings—the conflict of the empire with the Papacy. It is also called the Crusading Era, or the Age of Chivalry. A new importance attached to the personality of the popes and the claims of the Papacy for some two and a half centuries.

Going from west to east, we will now get some idea of the position in 1048. In Spain the Christian kingdoms of Castile, Navarre, and Aragon, which had not yet absorbed the Carolingian county of Catalonia or Barcelona, had emerged, and were pushing back the Moorish power, which acknowledged an Ommayad khalifate at Cordova. In France the Capet monarchy was estab-lished, but the power of the French kings was very circumscribed. Their territory included a part of upper Burgundy, but the Arelate, as well as the Rhineland, was definitely attached to the empire. Scandinavia stood outside the general European system. Knut (Canute) had failed to consolidate an Anglo-Scandinavian empire, and Edward the Confessor was on the English throne. The dominion of the German king extended from the Rhineland to the Slavonic eastern marches; and in his capacity as emperor he was sovereign of Italy also, though the Greeks in the south still acknowledged the Byzantine sovereignty, and Saracens, who acknowledged a Fatimid khalifate in Egypt, were in full possession of Sicily. At Byzantium the Macedonian dynasty was flickering out in a melancholy decadence. Finally, in Asia there was still an Abbasid khalif at Bagdad; but he was a puppet in the hands of the barbarian Seljuk Turks, the most fanatical of the peoples who had embraced Islam. These Turks now dominated Syria, and were on the point of absorbing almost the whole of Asia Minor, though Palestine was still in the hands of the tolerant Egyptian khalifate, and was resorted to by streams of Christian pilgrims from the West. The change wrought by the Seljuk conquest of Jerusalem in 1076 was to be made the occasion, though it was not the cause, of the first Crusade.

Line of Cluniac Popes. For five-and-twenty years after the accession of Leo IX in 1048, a series of popes, all ardent reformers imbued with the doctrines of the Cluniac school, were restoring the lost moral ascendancy of the Papacy, and giving new force to its admitted claim to the spiritual sovereignty of Catholic Christendom. There was no challenge as yet to the imperial authority, Henry III and Leo being in complete harmony, though Leo refused to accept the emperor's nomination as valid without canonical election by the Church. But the right of the emperor to require that a pope's election should be submitted for imperial ratification, which had been recognized since the days of Otto the Great, was ignored in 1062 at the election of Alexander II, when Henry IV was twelve and the German government was in the hands of a regency. The indignant anti-Cluniac German ecclesiastics disputed the validity of the election and procured that of an anti-pope, Honorius, who, however, was practically unrecognized outside Germany. But the fact was significant of the attitude the new school was adopting towards the temporal authority. The clash, however, did not come till Alexander's successor was on the papal throne.

The Cluniacs had the loftiest conception of the clergy as the organized servants of God consecrated to the task of establishing the kingdom of God upon earth, having as their head the divinely appointed successor of St. Peter. The Church's divine authority over the laity was the logical consequence of their office, but to justify that high claim it was necessary that the Church herself should be purged. Abuses, laxity of morals, laxity of discipline, worldliness, must be reformed ; above all, simony and nepotism—the purchase and sale of ecclesiastical offices and the advancement (otherwise unwarranted) of relations—must cease, and the celibacy of the clergy, which more than anything else made them a class apart from the laity, must be rigidly enforced. The reforming emperors, from Otto I to Henry III, had been in harmony with the Cluniac popes of their own appointment, who would have been powerless without their support, and with whose reforming aims they were in full sympathy, their own authority being unchallenged. The fact that the spiritual power needed the support of the fleshly arm was too obvious. But the line of Cluniac popes which began with Leo IX saw in this the need for establishing for themselves a temporal authority independent of imperial support, for which the only basis they possessed was their sovereignty in the Patrimony of St. Peter, the central Italian provinces bestowed on them centuries before by Pepin and Charles the Great.

The most effective move in this direction was their alliance with the Norman adventurers, descendants of the Northmen who had settled in Normandy under Rollo. The Normans had developed a distinctive type of their own, which, though their numbers were too few for them to form politically a nation, made themselves, but not the duchy of Normandy, a force in the European system. Wherever the clash of arms sounded in Europe, and there was hire to be had, parties of Norman adventurers were to be seen approaching the field of action. They were born warriors and born lawyers, the strictest of overlords and the most turbulent of vassals ; always ambitious and always greedy. Lastly, they were always most punctilious in their regard for the Church and the requirements of piety. The Cluniac reformation was brought to Normandy in 1001, and in the next sixty years many monasteries were built. Since Normandy offered no scope for ambitious adventure, the Normans went abroad in search of it, as knights-errant instead of as vikings.

Scenes from the famous Bayeux tapestry represent Norman episodes at this period, when their duke William—William the Conqueror—was on the point of providing them with an outlet in England, after having defeated Conan of Brittany in 1064 and won his coveted lands ; but for fifty years before the conquest which most concerns English history, they had been swarming into south Italy, where the incessant fighting invited profitable adventure, the most distinguished of them being the numerous brothers of the Hauteville family. By the middle of the century they had been rewarded by acquiring, with the emperor's acquiescence—for they were diplomatists as well as warriors—the counties of Apulia and Capua, and were already more powerful than any of the Lombard dukes or their Greek rivals.

When Leo became pope, he regarded the Normans as a menace, came into collision with them, and suffered an overwhelming defeat at their hands. But the Normans used their victory with astute magnanimity. They wanted not the humiliation of the Papacy, but its alliance. Each could be of invaluable service to the other ; the pious Normans desired only to be the Church's trusted—and favoured—champions. Five years later, in 1059, under Leo's successor, Nicholas II, the alliance was struck. Robert Guiscard, the head of the Hautevilles, received the dukedoms of Apulia and Calabria as papal fiefs, and, also as a papal fief, the island of Sicily—when he should recover it from the infidel Saracens. In 1071 his younger brother Roger began the long process of conquest. In the same year Robert expelled the Greeks from Bari, their last stronghold in Italy—and the Eastern emperor Romanus was overwhelmingly defeated by the Turk Alp Arslan, with the result that all but a fragment of Asia Minor was turned into the Seljuk sultanate of Roum.

The prestige of the Papacy in 1073, when Alexander II had died, was probably higher than it had been at any time since the death of the great pope Gregory I. The man who had stood beside and perhaps inspired the policy of every pope for five-and-twenty years was the cardinal-archdeacon Hildebrand, who, as Gregory VII, was, in effect, elected to succeed Alexander by popular acclamation. The irregular election was condoned by the ratification of Henry IV, who was now twenty-three ; but in 1075 Gregory threw down the direct challenge, which the young emperor, elated by the successful issue of a conflict with the Saxons, was prompt to take up.

LESSON 35

The Papacy and the First Crusade

(See plate 52)

WITH the accession to the papal chair of the greatest of the popes, Gregory VII (also known by his name of Hildebrand), in 1073, the idea of the supreme value of the Papacy reached its highest development. After two centuries, during which Rome seemed to be sinking into degradation, and was at one time in danger of capture by Saracens, Europe recognized that the fall of the Papacy would leave an impossible vacuum, that there was nothing to take its place, and that the bishop of Rome must be reinstated in full dignity. The age was longing for reform, and the strength of Gregory VII lay both in the appeal he made to this new desire for morality and in the practical wisdom of many of his deeds. His political insight had shown itself in his support of the Normans in Sicily, and in their conquest of England, William the Conqueror receiving the papal blessing. The Normans were characteristically loyal to the Church and prime movers subsequently in that migration to Palestine known as the First Crusade.

Gregory's vision, in place of the Holy Roman Empire with its dual leadership, was a United States of the World with the pope as the supreme head over kings and rulers. He also attempted to purge the Church of two great evils : the corruption of the monastic ideal and simony. The first he dealt with mainly by enforcing celibacy on the clergy ; the second by striking at its root, the system of lay investiture which had made bishops, through the bonds of feudalism, tools of kings. In respect of spiritual functions the obedience of bishops and abbots was due to the pope ; on the other hand, they were also territorial magnates in their own countries responsible to the head of their State. Bribery entered into their appointment by emperor or king.

Princes had not only made their own ecclesiatical appointments ; they had conferred spiritual authority by investing their nominees with the ring and crosier, the symbols of it, evoking protest at this usurpation of a purely spiritual function.

In 1075, Gregory issued a decree pronouncing ex-communication against all who bestowed or received lay investiture. Henry retorted by investing a new archbishop of Milan, and followed this up by declaring Gregory's deposition from the Papacy by his own imperial authority.

Gregory summoned the emperor to appear before him to answer for his crimes, and on his refusal absolved all his subjects from their oath of allegiance, excommunicating him, and finally calling on the Germans to elect a new emperor. Panic-stricken by signs of revolt in Germany, Henry repaired to Canossa, in the domain of Gregory's devoted adherent, Matilda of Tuscany, where the pope was that winter staying. According to a picturesque but not too well substantiated account, for three days the emperor stood in the snow, a penitent clad only in his shirt, knocking vainly at the gate of the castle for admittance to receive forgiveness. On the fourth day he made submission to Gregory.

Rival Emperor and Pope. Such depths of humiliation, however, produced a reaction not only in Henry, but in public opinion in Germany. Gregory's pride had overreached his wisdom. Within a month the emperor was planning to overthrow his humiliator. He returned to the practice of lay investiture, and Gregory renewed the excommunication, and in consequence a rival emperor was elected. Germany was plunged into a new civil war, and Henry's rival was killed in battle ; a second rival was elected, but also received only half-hearted support. The German and Lombard anti-papalists elected an anti-pope.

Henry, leaving Germany, descended into Italy and marched on Rome, where Gregory, steadfastly defiant but inadequately supported, since the Norman Guiscard was fighting the Greeks in Illyria, was besieged for three years. When at last the city was betrayed to the enemy Gregory retired to the impregnable castle of St. Angelo, while Henry mastered Rome and set up the rival pope, Clement, who crowned him emperor. In 1084 Guiscard returned with a mixed army of Normans and Saracens in defence of Gregory, drove Henry out, sacked Rome, and withdrew Gregory—leaving the Eternal City practically deserted—to safer quarters in the south at Salerno, where he died in 1085.

The papalists, who refused to recognize the anti-pope Clement, found a leader as uncompromising as Gregory in Urban II, whom they elected to the Papacy in 1088. The emperor was too deeply involved in ceaseless struggles with his German rebels, among whom was numbered his eldest son and heir Conrad, to take decisive measures in Italy; and then an opportunity was offered to Urban, which he grasped with both hands.

In 1081 an able and astute emperor, Alexius Comnenus, assumed the diadem at Constantinople. He wanted aid from the West to recover the lost dominions in Asia. The West cared less than nothing about the Eastern empire, but might rise to the idea of a Holy War against the infidel. The Turks, in possession of the Holy Sepulchre, were subjecting pilgrims to persecutions in which the Arabs had never indulged. This gave Alexius the excuse he needed. There was no potentate who had either the prestige or the leisure to organize a war for the Cross against the Crescent, but Alexius appealed to Urban. By answering the appeal the pope would definitely assume the character of Christendom's leader in the sight of the world.

Council of Clermont. A great Council of the Church was, therefore, summoned (1095) to meet at Clermont. A vast multitude assembled, nobles and knights, clergy and commoners; and when, in an atmosphere of passionate emotion, Urban made his final fervid appeal, the universal cry rang out—*Deus Vult,* It is the will of God. The First Crusade was launched; Christendom was united, and the man who had united it was not the emperor, as in past times, but the pope. The first wave of Crusaders, under Peter the Hermit and Walter the Penniless, consisted of ill-armed enthusiasts, of whom not one reached the goal, but in 1097 a vast host of regular troops had gathered at Constantinople and passed on into Asia Minor. In July, 1099, the Crusaders captured Jerusalem, Urban died, and the Latin kingdom of Jerusalem was born.

Meanwhile the defeat of Henry IV was complete. Every would-be rebel could make the excommunication his warrant, and rebellion was endless. The sentence was never withdrawn. Conrad died, but when Henry himself died in 1106 he had already been practically deposed by his second son and successor, Henry V, between whom and Urban's successor, Paschal II the struggle was renewed. It went on unabated till in 1122 the Concordat of Worms settled the investiture question by requiring the ecclesiastics to render homage and service for their lands but retained for the Church their investiture with the symbols of their spiritual office. The basic question of the ultimate supremacy as between emperor and pope was left untouched

After the First Crusade was launched, Alexius hoped for a

substantial force from the West which he could turn to account
for the recovery of more than Asia Minor, factions being rife
among the Turks.   The army which assembled at Constantinople
had other views.   Half its leaders hoped to carve principalities
for themselves out of Asia, and the other half had Jerusalem
as their single objective.   Asia Minor had to be cleared first and
handed over to Alexius, but once past the Taurus their obligations
to him ended ; and there was no single leadership. After a long and
desperate siege, Antioch fell to Bohemund of Otranto, Robert
Guiscard's second son.   Raymond of Toulouse concentrated on
the coast.   It was a depleted force that finally, under Godfrey,
commonly though erroneously called de Bouillon, stormed and
captured Jerusalem.   Feudal theory required that the conquest
should be organized as a kingdom, the kingdom of Jerusalem,
though Godfrey, when elected, accepted the office but not the
title and royal crown adopted by his successor, Baldwin.

The Latin Kingdom. The Latin kingdom was a narrow strip of
coastal territory extending from Ascalon and Jerusalem to Antioch
and thence to Edessa.   The kingdom was, in fact, a long line of
fortresses with some ports, including Acre (captured in 1104), the
frontier between Christendom and Islam, with a small permanent
garrison mainly consisting of the two new orders of military
monks, the Templars and the Knights of St. John.   But a line
of such length so sparsely garrisoned could hardly escape being
penetrated if Islam should unite in a concentrated attack.   And
so though the kingdom held its own for forty-five years after
the capture of Jerusalem under its elected kings, Baldwin I,
Baldwin II, and Fulk of Anjou, its great northern outpost,
Edessa, was captured by the Turks in 1144. This event opens the
second stage of the Crusading era.

LESSON 36

Barbarossa's Restless Reign

(See plates 52 and 53)

O N the death of Henry V without a direct heir, the Saxons
and Bavarians secured the imperial succession for
Lothair of Saxony, the defeated candidate being Henry's
nephew Conrad of Weiblingen (the name later corrupted into
Ghibelline) and Franconia. Lothair, an elderly man, had no male

(425)

heir ; but Henry the Proud of Bavaria, of the House of Welf (later corrupted into Guelph), was his son-in-law. The rivalry between the Ghibellines and the Guelphs was a primary source of trouble through the next century and a half. When Lothair died in 1137, Conrad was the successful candidate, but he was not established as emperor, owing to civil wars, until 1143.

The influence of the Papacy was in abeyance at the moment owing to internal dissensions ; and Roger II of Sicily, nominal vassal of the popes, had been able to wring from them the title of king, while he had also been able to bring under his sway not only the family dukedoms of Apulia and Calabria, but also most of the counties of south Italy which in effect formed part of the Norman Sicilian dominion. The kingdom of Roger has been called the first modern state ; but it was like no other state in history. Into the strange medley of Greek, Saracenic and medieval Italian institutions the Normans introduced the feudal system of the North with Byzantine variations as to the divine right of the ruler to question whose word was sacrilegious. The Norman rule, was, however, in the main tolerant, interfering little with local conditions. Under Roger II, though French was the court language, the Sicilian culture was for a time cosmopolitan— perhaps because the king had a passion for geography fostered by an able collaborator, Idrisi, an Arab from Spain. The chief literary figures were Greeks, while the architect of the church of La Martorana at Palermo was George of Antioch, Roger's admiral, a Saracen who had embraced Christianity.

The church of S. Giovanni at Palermo is another gem of Arabo-Norman culture. Palermo remained essentially the Saracenic city upon which Norman colour had been laid, but Messina became Latinized with a certain Greek element. Roger likewise planted agricultural colonies of Italians here and there in the island, organized into communes. Some of these colonies were composed of northern Italians, mostly Lombards, and there are still places in eastern Sicily where a dialect with western Lombard elements is spoken. Meanwhile England was passing through the appalling anarchy of Stephen's reign. In Spain Crusaders counted fighting the Moors a frequent equivalent for fighting Saracens in Syria. Such was the general position when Europe was startled by the fall of Edessa in 1144, and the voice of Bernard, abbot of Clairvaux, the most powerful spiritual influence of the day, was raised to call Christendom to a new Crusade.

The Second Crusade. Louis VII of France eagerly, and the emperor Conrad reluctantly, answered the appeal. Conrad, when he had gathered a mighty army, would not wait for Louis, and his transit into Asia Minor was pleasantly agreed to by the Eastern emperor Manuel Comnenus (1148). Louis followed next year, and was joined by Conrad, but with no more than a remnant of his forces, which had suffered disaster in the mountains of Roum. A remnant of the combined force reached Damascus, but failed to take it, and the final remnant escaped ignominiously home. Thus ended in failure the Second Crusade.

In 1152 Conrad died, and the rivalry of the two great houses was for the time adjusted by the election of his nephew Frederick of Swabia, called Barbarossa (his mother was a Guelph), the one man whose participation in the Second Crusade had earned him marked distinction. No other man could have satisfied and pacified the perpetual German unrest as he did in the first two years after his accession. But Frederick was not satisfied to be German king; intense conviction of his imperial responsibility urged him to the restoration of the imperial ideal.

In 1154 he turned to the troubled land of Italy, where the imperial and papal authority alike were at a very low ebb ; in the south, Roger king of Sicily had long been defiant of both ; in the north the great cities had made themselves independent of their overlords ; Rome itself had set up its own commune, repudiating the papal sovereignty. The late series of inefficient popes had, however, now come to an end with the election of the one English pope in the entire series of popes, Nicholas Breakspear (a native of Hertfordshire), as Adrian IV, who upheld every claim that Gregory VII himself had ventured to make.

The call for intervention in Italy was premature ; the pacification of Germany was not yet complete, and the emperor had to hurry back over the Alps. Adrian was left to work out a policy of his own—which he did with remarkable success—while Frederick was completing his interrupted task in Germany, to all appearance triumphantly. In 1158 he returned to Italy, primarily to enforce submission on the cities headed by Milan which had formed the Lombard League to resist expected encroachments on their autonomy. It took Frederick three years to crush the resistance of Milan. While the struggle was still going on, Adrian died. An avowed anti-imperialist, Alexander III, was elected as his successor in the papal chair.

Four years later Frederick's work had to be done over again. The League had revived under new leadership. In 1166 Frederick Barbarossa swept irresistibly down on Rome ; the pope, having excommunicated the emperor, fled to the Normans in the south ; and then the army was smitten by a pestilence so terrible that Frederick could only make the best of his way home with the survivors. Papal anathemas encouraged disaffection in Germany ; the Guelphs were papalists by tradition ; the loyalty of Henry the Lion was doubtful and he was lord of nearly half Germany, as his father-in-law Henry II of England was lord of half France (to the great inconvenience of king Louis) : papalist sympathy was growing among the German clergy. It was not till 1174 that Frederick could venture on a return to Italy, leaving Germany very insecure—but the League and Alexander were stronger, more defiant, and more determined than ever. After two years' campaigning Frederick's army was shattered in a great battle at Legnano by the stubborn resistance of the League's burgher infantry to the charges of his mail-clad cavalry (1176).

Treaty of Constance. Frederick had believed in the righteousness of his cause, though he may have been shaken when his conquering army perished ten years before like Sennacherib's. Legnano did not of itself make victory impossible, but it did convince him that he had been in the wrong. Being a great man, he dared to act on that new conviction and to seek the pope as a suppliant for pardon. Alexander, being of a like greatness, understood him. Final details of the ensuing settlement involved long negotiation but were at last embodied in the treaty of Constance in 1183. Full autonomy was restored to the cities, with little more than a nominal allegiance to the emperor.

Barbarossa had returned to Germany, where the widening breach between him and Henry the Lion soon developed into open war. Despite the surrender in Italy, which would have been fatal to a smaller man, the emperor was completely victorious. Henry was left little more than Brunswick ; Bavaria went to the Austrian Wittelsbachs, and half Saxony to the Brandenburg margravate. It seemed that the emperor was to end his days in peace. But the East, where he had made his name at the outset of his career, was to claim him again at its close, for in 1187 the Seljuk Sultan —Saladin—captured Jerusalem, and the news led to the Third Crusade, in which Barbarossa was first to take the field.

Our Course in Medieval History is continued in Volume 6.

LESSON 19

Percentages and Fractions

ALL fractions in Latin with 1 for numerator are denoted by ordinals, with or without *pars* : ⅓ = *tertia*, or *tertia pars* ; ¼ = *quarta*. All fractions with a numerator less by one than the denominator are denoted by cardinals with *partēs* simply : ⅔ = *duae partēs* ; ⅝ = *quinque partēs*. All fractions with 12, or its multiples, for a denominator, are denoted by the parts of an *As* (*see* below), which is taken as the whole : *Hērēs ex asse* = heir to the whole estate. *Hērēs ex triente* = heir to a third. *Hērēs ex sēmisse* = heir to a half. All other fractions are denoted by the cardinal for a numerator, and the ordinal for the denominator : 4/7 = *quattuor septimae*.

Most of the Roman weights and measures were divided by fractions which were originally parts of the *As* or pound weight, containing twelve ounces. The *As* was thus divided :

Unciae, i.e. Ounces.		Fractions of As.
12	As, *a pound*	1
11	Deunx (de -uncia), *an ounce off*	$\frac{11}{12}$
10	Dēxtāns (dēsextāns), *a sixth off*	$\frac{5}{6}$
9	Dōdrāns (dēquadrāns), *a fourth off*	$\frac{3}{4}$
8	Bēs, or Bessis (dui-assis)	$\frac{2}{3}$
7	Septunx (septem unciae), *seven ounces* ..	$\frac{7}{12}$
6	Sēmissis, or Sēmis (semi-assis)	$\frac{1}{2}$
5	Quincunx (quinque unciae)	$\frac{5}{12}$
4	Triēns, *a third*	$\frac{1}{3}$
3	Quadrāns, *a fourth*	$\frac{1}{4}$
2	Sextāns, *a sixth*	$\frac{1}{6}$
1	Uncia, *an ounce*	$\frac{1}{12}$

Other fractions used were *Sescuncia* (1½ ounces), *Sēmuncia* (½ ounce), *Sīcīlicus* (¼ ounce), *Sextula* (⅙ ounce), *Scripulum* ($\frac{1}{24}$ ounce).

Interest on Money. After 80 B.C. legal interest was fixed at the rate of $\frac{1}{100}$ of the capital per month, called Centesima

LATIN 19

(sc. *pars*)—i.e. 12 per cent per annum. Lower rates than this were denoted by the fractional parts of the *As* (the Centesima being taken as the As). Thus, reckoning the percentage as per annum :

12 per cent = *ūsūrae centēsimae*, or *assēs ūsūrae*.
11 per cent = *ūsūrae deuncēs*.
8 per cent = *ūsūrae bessēs*.
5 per cent = *ūsūrae quincuncēs*.
1 per cent = *ūsūrae unciae*.

Higher rates than 12 per cent were denoted by distributives :
24 per cent = *bīnae centēsimae*.
60 per cent = *quīnae centēsimae*.

Although the *dēnārius* (= 10 asses) was the silver coin in most frequent currency, the ordinary unit of reckoning was the *sestertius*, or *nummus* (= ¼ denarius, or 2½ asses). The Roman sign for 2½ was IIS—i.e. II + S(emis). This is now written HS, and is the usual abbreviation for a sestertius. Thus, 7,000 sesterces = *septem mīlia sestertium* (shortened from *sestertiōrum*).

This shortened form *sestertium* was taken for a neuter singular noun, meaning 1,000 sesterces, and so we get such forms as
Sestertia decem = 10,000 sesterces.

For sums of a million sesterces and upwards adverbial numerals are used—e.g. 1,000,000 sesterces = *deciēs centēna mīlia sestertium* (or, more usually, just *deciēs sestertium*).

2,300,000 sesterces = *ter et vīciēs sestertium*.

To distinguish the meanings, strokes were usually added to the numerals—e.g. HS$\overline{X}$ = *decem mīlia sestertium* (10,000) ; HS $|X|$ = *deciēs sestertium* (1,000,000).

The following passage " How to procure contentedness," by Jeremy Taylor, should be turned into Latin prose with the aid of a dictionary, afterwards correcting the attempt by the Latin version given below.

If then thou fallest from thy employment in public, take sanctuary in an honest retirement, being indifferent to thy gain abroad or thy safety at home. If thou art out of favour with thy prince, secure the favour of the King of kings, and then there is no harm come to thee. And when Zeno Citiensis lost all his goods in a storm, he retired to the studies of philosophy, to his short cloak and a severe life, and gave thanks to fortune for his prosperous mischance. When the north wind blows hard and it rains sadly, none but fools sit down in it and cry : wise people defend themselves against it with a warm garment or a good fire and a dry roof. When a storm of a sad mischance beats upon our spirits, turn it into some advantage by observing where it can serve another end, either of religion or prudence, or more safety or less envy ; it will turn into something that is good, if we list to make it so.

LATIN VERSION OF THE FOREGOING.

Honore amisso in honestum otium quasi in templum defugito, neve pluris lucrum foris quam domi securitatem facito. Et studio regio verso, modo tibi faveat Deus, nihil tibi damno fuerit. Zeno enim Citiensis re inter procellam amissa ad sapientiae studium togamque brevem et duriorem victum ubi recesserat, fortunae gratias egit quod sibi ita opportune nocuisset. Et aquilone acri, tristi imbre, soli stulti sedentes flent, sapientis est se toga, igne, tecto defendere. Et ubi malae fortunae tempestas in nos inciderit, decet hoc ipsum in lucrum vertere, spectato an ad aliud quid prosit, sive ad fortiores sive ad sapientiores reddendos, sive ad securitatem dandam, sive ad invidiam arcendam. Omnia enim in melius verti potuerint, modo ipsi hoc velimus.

LESSON 20

Some Irregular Verbs

I F the verb in the principal clause is in a *primary* tense (i.e present, future, or true perfect), the verb in the subordinate clause will be (*a*) in the present subjunctive if present time be denoted ; (*b*) in the perfect subjunctive if past time be denoted, e.g. : *Rogavi ut illi ignoscatur* = I have asked that he may be pardoned. *Cognoscam cur venerit* = I will ascertain why he came.

But if the verb in the principal clause is in a *historic* tense (i.e. imperfect, simple past, or pluperfect), the verb in the subordinate clause will be (*a*) in the imperfect subj. if present time be denoted ; (*b*) in the pluperfect subj. if past time be denoted, e.g. : *Rogavi utrum adesset* = I asked whether he were present. *Non dubium erat quin fugisset* = there was no doubt that he had fled.

Infinitive Mood. The infinitive is an indeclinable verbal noun. It is used as object, as predicate and as subject, so far as a substantive in the acc. or nom. case would be so used. It is not properly used as a genitive, dative, or ablative, or as an acc. after a proposition. The gerund (also a verbal noun) is used instead.

1. As subject : *Dulce et decorum est pro patria mori* = dying for country is sweet and comely.

2. As object : *Vincere scis : victoria uti nescis* = you know how to conquer, but not how to use your victory.

3. As predicate to a subject in the nom. case : to express the occurrence of actions without marking the order of time Often used in narration for a finite verb, hence called historic infinitive, e.g. : *Clamare omnes* = all cried out. *Rex primo nihil metuere, nihil suspicari* = the king at first feared nothing, suspected nothing.

Gerunds and Supines. 1. These are the cases of the infinitive. As mentioned above, the gerund is used to express the gen., dat., abl., or acc. after a preposition, of the verbal noun : e.g. *Breve tempus satis longum est ad bene honesteque vivendum* = for living well and honourably, a short time is long enough. *Fugiendo vincimus* = we conquer by fleeing. *Videndi et audiendi delectatio* = the delight of seeing and hearing.

2. The supine in *-um* is an acc. after verbs of motion. It often has a direct, more rarely an indirect, object : e.g. *ibo lusum* = I will go to play. *Deos atque amicos it salutatum ad forum* = he goes to hail the gods and his friends at the forum. *Non ego Graiis servitum matribus ibo* = I will not go to serve Grecian matrons.

NOTE. This supine, with *iri* (pass. infin. of *eo*), forms the fut. infin. pass. : e.g. *rectum iri*.

3. The supine in *-u* is used in the abl. to qualify adjectives in a way which may be classed under the head of " part concerned " (abl. of respect) : e.g. *Formae terribiles visu* = forms terrible to see. *Mirabile dictu* = wonderful to say.

The Gerundive. 1. The gerundive is confined to transitive verbs. It is usually substituted for the gerund when the gerund has an object expressed ; the object is then attracted into the case of the gerundive, which is made to agree with it in number and gender. *This is very important :* e.g. *Caesar comitiali morbo bis inter res agendas correptus est* = Caesar was twice seized with epilepsy in the midst of transacting business.

Often used (like the supine in *-um*, or the fut. ptc.) to express purpose, instead of *ut* with the subj. : *Missus est a senatu ad* *animos regum perspiciendos* (translate " for the purpose of discovering "). *Hi septemviri fuerunt agris dividendis* (" for dividing lands ").

NOTE. The gerundive is used from *utor, fruor, fungor, potior,* all these verbs being originally transitive.

2. The impersonal gerundive implies necessity, principally in intransitive verbs. This is the usual construction for expressing " must," and the agent is usually put in the dat., not in the abl. with *a* or *ab* : *Bibendum est mihi* = I must drink (literally, it is to be drunk by me). *Suo cuique judicio utendum est* = each must use his own judgement.

3. The gerundive is often used as a mere attribute or adjective, meaning obligation, destiny, desert or possibility.

Deus et diligendus est nobis et timendus = God is both to be loved and feared by us.

Eis otium divitiaeque, optanda alias, oneri miseriaeque fuere = to them leisure and riches, things desirable in other circumstances, were (for) a burden and a misery.

Irregular Verbs. The following comprise the first section of the most important irregular verbs of the third conjugation.

CONSONANT VERBS

Stems with Back Consonants, -sī. -tum (five, -sum)

dīco	*dīxī*	*dictum*	say
dūcō	*dūxī*	*ductum*	lead
cingō	*cīnxī*	*cīnctum*	surround
coquō	*coxī*	*coctum*	cook
fingō	*fīnxī*	*fīctum*	fashion
pingō	*pīnxī*	*pīctum*	paint
jungō	*jūnxī*	*jūnctum*	join
tegō	*tēxī*	*tēctum*	cover
-stinguō	*stīnxī*	*stīnctum*	quench
tinguō	*tīnxī*	*tīnctum*	dye
unguō	*ūnxī*	*ūnctum*	anoint
trahō	*traxī*	*tractum*	draw
vehō	*vexī*	*vectum*	carry
vīvō	*vīxī*	*vīctum*	live
struō	*struxī*	*structum*	pile
-laciō	*lexī*	*lectum*	entice
-speciō	*spexī*	*spectum*	espy
fluō	*flūxī*	*flūxum*	flow

fīgō	*fīxī*	*fīxum*	fix
mergō	*mērsī*	*mērsum*	drown
spargō	*spārsī*	*spārsum*	sprinkle
tergo	*tērsī*	*tērsum*	wipe

Stems with Point Cons., -sī, -sum.

| *claudō* | *clausī* | *clausum* | shut |

Similarly, *dīvidō, laedō, lūdō, plaudō, rādō, rōdō, trūdō,* and *vādō.* Also :

cēdō	*cēssī*	*cēssum*	yield
mīttō	*mīsī*	*mīssum*	send
quatiō	(*quassī*)	*quassum*	shake
flectō	*flexī*	*flexum*	bend
nectō	*nexī*	*nexum*	bind

Stems with Lip Cons., -sī, -tum.

| *carpō* | *carpsī* | *carptum* | pluck |

Also *rēpō, scalpō, serpō, nūbō* (*nūpsī*), and *scrībō* (*scrīpsī*).

Stems with -m- or -r-, -sī, -tum (one, -sum).

| *cōmō* | *cōmpsī* | *cōmptum* | adorn |

Also *dēmō, prōmō, sūmō, temnō, premō* (*pressī, pressum*), *gerō* (*gessī, gestum*), *ūrō* (*ūssī, ūstum*).

Stem various, -uī, -tum (one, -sum).

| *cumbō* | *cubuī* | *cubitum* | lie down |
| *ēliciō* | *ēlicuī* | *ēlicitum* | entice forth |

Also *strepō, fremō, gemō, tremō,* and *vomō.*

| *rapiō* | *rapuī* | *raptum* | seize |
| *alō* | *aluī* | *altum* | nourish |

Also *colō* (*coluī, cultum*), *cōnsulō, occulō, pōnō* (*posuī, positum*), *gīgnō* (*genuī, genitum*), *texō* (*texuī, textum*), *serō* = I join (*seruī, sertum*), and *metō* (*messuī, messum*).

Present Stem anomalous, -vī, -tum.

linō	*lēvī*	*litum*	smear
sinō	*sīvī*	*situm*	allow
cernō	*crēvī*	*crētum*	sift, discern
crēscō	*crēvī*	*crētum*	increase
			(*intrans.*)
spernō	*sprēvī*	*sprētum*	despise
sternō	*strāvī*	*strātum*	strew
serō	*sēvī*	*satum*	sow
nōscō	*nōvī*	*nōtum*	know
pāscō	*pāvī*	*pāsum*	feed
suēscō	*suēvī*	*suētum*	be accustomed

quiēscō	quiēvī	—	rest
cupiō	cupīvī	cupītum	desire
petō	petīvī	petītum	ask
quaerō	quaesīvī	quaesītum	seek
terō	trīvī	trītum	rub
arcessō	arcessīvī	arcessītum	send for
lacessō	lacessīvī	lacessītum	provoke

-i, -sum (one, -tum).

| pandō | pandī | pānsum | spread |
| | | (pāssum) | |

Also *scandō, prehendō, -cando, -fendō, vertō (vertī, versum), bibō (bibī, bibitum), vellō (vellī or vulsī, vulsum)*.

| findō | fidī | fissum | cleave |
| scindō | scidī | scissum | tear |

LESSON 21

More About Irregular Verbs

IN this Lesson we continue the irregular verbs in Latin. The following, while apparently of the fourth conjugation, are really third : *capiō, cupiō, faciō, fodiō, fugiō, jaciō, pariō, rapiō, sapiō, quatiō,* compounds of *speciō* and *laciō, gradior, patior, morior ;* and in some tenses *orior* and *potior.* In their present stem forms they usually retain the *-i,* but not before *i,* final *e,* and short *er :* e.g. *capiam, cape, capere, capiendum. Morior* and *orior* have future participles—*moritūrus* and *oritūrus. Orior* is conjugated like *patior,* except a few forms which follow the fourth conjugation : *oriri, orirer,* etc. *Potior* follows the fourth, but occasionally wavers between third and fourth : *poterer* and *potirer.*

IRREGULAR VERBS : THIRD CONJUGATION.
Perfect reduplicates ; Supine, *-tum* or *-sum.*

pendō	pependī	pēnsum	weigh
tendō	tetendī	tēnsum	stretch
		(tentum)	
dīsco	dīdicī	—	learn
pōscō	popōscī	—	demand
currō	cucurrī	cursum	run

pungō	*pupugī*	*pŭnctum*	prick
tundō	*tutudī*	*tŭnsum*	thump
		or *tŭsum*	
fallō	*fefellī*	*falsum*	deceive
parcō	*pepercī*	*parsum*	spare
pariō	*peperī*	*partum*	bring forth
cadō	*cecidī*	*cāsum*	fall
caedō	*cecīdī*	*caesum*	cut, beat
canō	*cecinī*	*cantum*	sing
pangō	*pepigī*	*pāctum*	fasten
tangō	*tetigī*	*tāctum*	touch
pellō	*pepulī*	*pulsum*	drive
tollō	(*sustŭlī*)	(*sublātum*)	raise

-*i* with lengthened stem-vowel, -*tum* (three -*sum*)

faciō	*fēcī*	*factum*	do, make
jaciō	*jēcī*	*jactum*	throw
linquō	*līquī*	-*lictum*	leave
vincō	*vīcī*	*victum*	conquer
agō	*ēgī*	*āctum*	do, drive
frangō	*frēgī*	*frāctum*	break
legō	*lēgī*	*lēctum*	choose, read
fugiō	*fūgī*	*fugitum*	flee
edō	*ēdī*	*ēsum*	eat
fodiō	*fōdī*	*fōssum*	dig
fundō	*fūdī*	*fūsum*	pour
capiō	*cēpī*	*captum*	take
rumpō	*rūpī*	*ruptum*	break
emō	*ēmī*	*emptum*	buy

U-Verbs.
-*ī*, -*tum*.

| *acuō* | *acuī* | *acŭum* | sharpen |

Also, *arguō* (prove), *exuō* (put off), *induō* (put on), *imbŭo* (tinge), *minuō* (lessen), *statuō* (set up), *trĭbuō* (assign). *Metuō* (fear) and *nuō* (nod) have no supine.

luō	*luī*	*luitum*	wash, atone
		or *lŭtum*	
ruō	*ruī*	*rŭtum*	rush, fall
solvō	*solvī*	*solŭtum*	loosen
volvō	*volvī*	*volŭtum*	roll

MORE ABOUT IRREGULAR VERBS

DEPONENTS.

Pres.	Infin.	Pf. Ptc.	
fungor	*-ī*	*fūnctus*	perform
amplector	*-ī*	*amplexus*	embrace
nītor	*-ī*	*nīsus*	strive
		or *nīxus*	
patior	*-ī*	*passus*	suffer
ūtor	*-ī*	*ūsus*	use
gradior	*-ī*	*grēssus*	step
lābor	*-ī*	*lāpsus*	glide
morior	*-ī*	*mortuus*	die
queror	*-ī*	*questus*	complain
fruor	*-ī*	*fruitus* (*frūctus*)	enjoy
loquor	*-ī*	*locūtus*	speak
sequor	*-ī*	*secūtus*	follow
apiscor	*-ī*	*aptus*	obtain
comminiscor	*-ī*	*commentus*	devise
expērgiscor	*-ī*	*experrēctus*	wake up
fatiscor	*-ī*	*fēssus*	grow tired
īrāscor	*-ī*	*īrātus*	be angry
nanciscor	*-ī*	*nactus*	obtain
nāscor	*-ī*	*nātus*	be born
oblīviscor	*-ī*	*oblītus*	forget
paciscor	*-ī*	*pactus*	bargain
proficiscor	*-ī*	*profectus*	set out
ulciscor	*-ī*	*ultus*	avenge

IRREGULAR VERBS : FOURTH CONJUGATION.
-uī or -īvī, -tum.

aperiō	*aperuī*	*apertum*	open
operiō	*operuī*	*opertum*	cover
saliō	*saluī*	(*saltum*)	leap
sepeliō	*sepelīvī*	*sepultum*	bury

-ī -tum.

comperiō	*comperī*	*compertum*	find
reperiō	*repperī*	*repertum*	discover
veniō	*vēnī*	*ventum*	come

-sī, -tum (one, -sum).

fulciō	*fulsī*	*fultum*	prop
sanciō	*sanxī*	*sanctum*	consecrate

vinciō	*vinxī*	*vinctum*	bind
hauriō	*hausī*	*haustum*	drain
sentiō	*sēnsī*	*sēnsum*	feel

DEPONENTS.

assentior	*-īrī*	*assēnsus*	agree to
experior	*-īrī*	*expertus*	try
metior	*-īrī*	*mēnsus*	measure
opperior	*-īrī*	*oppertus*	wait for
ōrdior	*-īrī*	*ōrsus*	begin
orior	*-īrī*	*ortus*	rise

LESSON 22

Exercises in Latin Idiom

SIMPLE verbs are not so often used in Latin as verbs compounded with a preposition, the preposition either strengthening or changing the meaning. The following are the chief changes of prepositions in composition : *A, ab* become *ā-* before *m, v* (*āmittō, āvocō*) : *abs-* before *c, t* (*abscēdō, abstergō*) ; *ās-* before *p* (*āsportō*) ; *au-* before *f* (*auferō*). But *āfuī* (from *absum*). *Ad* becomes *a-* before *gn, sc, sp* (*agnōscō, ascendō, aspiciō*). It remains *ad-* before *b, d, h, j, m, v,* and vowels, but is assimilated before other consonants : *afferō, assistō*.

Con- (for *cum*), and *in*, become *com-, im-,* before *p, b, m* (*compellō, imbuō*), and are assimilated before *l, r : collūdō, irruō*. They remain unchanged before other consonants, except that : *Con-* becomes *co-* before *h, gn,* and vowels : *coeō, cognōscō*. Also, *ignōscō. Ob, sub,* are assimilated before *c, g, p, f : occurrō, sufferō ;* except *suscipiō, suscitō, suspendō, suspiciō*. They remain before other sounds, except *sustineō, sustollō, sustulī, surripiō*.

Note *omīttō, ostendō*.

E, ex are assimilated before *f : efferō. Ex-* before vowels, *h, c, q, p, s, t ; e-* before other consonants : *educo, evoco. Trans-* becomes *trā-* before *d, j, n ; trādō, trājiciō, trānō. Dis-* (inseparable prefix) is assimilated before *f : differō*. It becomes *dī-* before *s* with consonant (*dīstringō*) and certain consonants

(438)

(*dīruō*). Note *dirimō* for *disimō*. *Re-, sē-* (inseparable prefixes) add *d* in *reddō, redeō, redhibeō, redimō, redoleō, sēditiō* (noun).

In addition to the changes in the prepositions there is a vowel change in the verbs themselves in becoming compounds : e.g. *concutio* (*quatiō*), *collīdō* (*laedō*), *explōdō* (*plaudō*), *exigō* (*agō*), *conficiō* (*facio*), *confiteor* (*fateor*), *retineō* (*teneō*), etc. The student must look these up for himself in the dictionary, as he comes across them in his reading.

IDIOMATIC SENTENCES TO BE PUT INTO LATIN.

1. Socrates was called to trial on the charge of corrupting youth, but in reality because he had become suspected by those in power. 2. He is too wise to err, too good to be unkind. 3. He came to such a pitch of folly that he could not be persuaded to eat. 4. It was resolved to send ambassadors to ask what was the meaning of these repeated insults. 5. I hear that she died four years after returning home : I fear that her children are in very poor circumstances. 6. If you help me, I shall rejoice ; if not, I shall not take it ill.

LATIN VERSION OF THE ABOVE.

1. Socrates in judicium vocatus est quod corrumperet juventutem, re tamen ipsa quia in suspicionem magistratibus venerat. 2. Sapientior est quam qui erret, melior quam qui inclementer agat. 3. Eo stultitiae venit ut illi non persuaderi posset ut ederet. 4. Placuit legatos mitti qui rogarent quid vellent hae tot contumeliae. 5. Nuntiatum est mihi illam anno quarto postquam domum rediisset mortuam esse : cujus liberi timeo ne pauperrimi sint. 6. Si mihi subvenies (*note tense*), gaudebo : sin minus, haud aegre feram.

TRANSLATION.

THE GREAT ERUPTION OF VESUVIUS. August 24th, A.D. 79.
Extract from letter of Pliny the Younger to Tacitus.

Nec multo post illa nubes descendere in terras, operire maria. Cinxerat Capreas et absconderat : Miseni quod procurrit, abstulerat. Tum mater orare hortari jubere, quoquo modo fugerem ; posse enim juvenem : se et annis et corpore gravem bene morituram, si mihi causa mortis non fuisset. Ego contra, salvum me, nisi una, non futurum : dein manum ejus amplexus, addere gradum cogo. Paret aegre, incusatque se, quod me moretur ;

jam cinis, adhuc tamen rarus. Respicio ; densa caligo tergis imminebat, quae nos, torrentis modo infusa terrae, sequebatur. Deflectamus, inquam, dum videmus, ne in via strati comitantium turba in tenebris obteramur. Vix consederamus, et nox, non qualis illunis aut nubila, sed qualis in locis clausis lumine extincto. Audires ululatus feminarum, infantium quiritatus, clamores virorum. Alii parentes, alii liberos, alii conjuges vocibus requirebant, vocibus noscitabant. Hi suum casum, illi suorum miserabantur. Erant qui metu mortis mortem precarentur. Multi ad deos manus tollere : plures, nusquam jam deos ullos, aeternamque illam et novissimam noctem mundo interpretabantur.

ENGLISH VERSION OF ABOVE.

Not long afterwards that cloud descended (*historic infinitive*) over the land and covered the sea. It had encircled Capreae and blotted it out : it had removed from our sight the promontory of Misenum. Then my mother begged, exhorted, ordered me to flee in whatever way I might, (saying) that a young man could, and that she, weighed down with years and weakness of body, would die happy, if she had not been the cause of my death. I on the other hand (affirm) that I will not be saved unless with her : then clasping her hand, I urge her to quicken her step. She obeys reluctantly, and blames herself for delaying me. Now there are ashes, as yet, however, few and far between. I look back : thick darkness overhung us in the rear, and kept following us, pouring over the land like a flood. " Let us turn aside," I say, " while we can see, lest being knocked down in the street we be trampled upon in the darkness by the crowd of our companions." Scarcely had we sat down when night (was upon us), not a mere moonless, cloudy night, but such night as there is in a closed room when the light is extinguished. You could hear the wailing of women, the cries of infants, the shouts of men. Some were seeking by the voice, by the voice were recognizing parents, others children, others wives. These were pitying their own fate, those that of their loved ones. There were some who, through the fear of death, prayed for death. Many raised their hands to the gods : while more still imagined that there were no longer any gods anywhere, and that this was the final and everlasting night for the world.

LESSON 23

More Miscellaneous Idioms

Questions to which an affirmative answer is expected are introduced in Latin by *nonne ;* when a negative answer is expected, by *num ;* but when the answer is absolutely an open matter, by the enclitic *ne* added usually to the first word of the sentence, e.g. *Num putas bis bina esse quinque ?* = you surely don't think that twice two are five, do you ? *Nonne Caesar erat imperator maximus ?* = was not Caesar a mighty general ? *Putasne me patris similem esse ?* = do you think that I am like my father ?

The above are all *direct questions.* In *indirect questions*—i.e. questions depending on a verb—the verb in the question is subjunctive. " Whether " and " if " in such sentences are rendered by (1) *utrum,* followed by *an* or *ne ;* (2) *num*—e.g. *Rogavit utrum haec vera essent annon* = he asked whether this was true or not.

Note. Distinguish between " whether " thus introducing an independent clause and " whether " used to express a condition ; the latter is *sive,* a compound of *si* = if :

Haec, sive vera sunt sive falsa, nullo modo me movent = whether —i.e. if—this is true or false I am not troubled by it.

Miscellaneous Idioms.

English.	Latin.
Calpurnia married Caesar.	Calpurnia Caesari nupsit (lit., *veiled herself for Caesar*).
Caesar married Calpurnia.	Caesar Calpurniam in matrimonium duxit.
He is the best scholar in the school.	Discipulorum, si quis alius, ille optime discit.
I prefer a thousand deaths.	Malo sexcenties mori (the Latins always said *six hundred times* in such sentences).
I fear you are wrong.	Timeo ne erres.
I fear you are not wrong.	Timeo ut erres.
I will do it if I can.	Hoc si *potero* (*fut.*) faciam.

It does not fall to the lot of everybody to visit Naples.

Non cuilibet contingit Neapolim videre.

There are some who think you are mad.

Sunt qui putent te insanire.

I am sorry to say this.

Invitus hoc dico.

He perished in his youth.

Juvenis mortuus est.

I have asked him to come to see me as quickly as possible.

Rogavi eum ut quam celerrime veniat me visum (*supine*).

I cannot write for weeping.

Prae lacrimis scribere non possum.

One uses one tent, another another.

Alius alio tabernaculo utitur.

All the best citizens are present.

Optimus quisque civis adest.

It is all over with me.

Actum est de me.

You ought to have done it before.

Antea te hoc facere oportuit (*note the pres. infinitive*).

On the march.

Ex itinere.

On horseback.

Ex equo.

He departed without asking what I had done.

Discessit, neque quid fecissem rogavit (*or*, Ita discessit ut non rogaret, etc.). But not *sine* with gerund.

With your usual kindness.

Pro tua clementia.

In front was the sea, in our rear the enemy.

A fronte mare, hostes a tergo imminebant. (Note the " back to back " construction, called Chiasmus, *mare* and *hostes* being the two means, *a fronte* and *a tergo* the extremes.)

He came sooner than he was expected.

Opinione celerius venit.

The House divided on the motion.

Pedibus in sententiam iverunt.

Once every four years.

Quarto quoque anno.

I am on the point of going.

In eo sum ut proficiscar.

In the open air.

Sub divo.

The sisters loved one another.

Sorores altera alteram amaverunt.

I was within an inch of death.

Minimum abfuit quin morerer.

Mind you come.

Cura (or Fac) ut venias, or simply Cura venias. (*Cura* is imperative of *curo, curare*.)

He is not a fit person for you to converse with.

Non est aptus quocum colloquaris.

I cannot walk even a mile, not to mention seven.

Ne mille passus quidem ambulare possum, nedum septem (millia passuum).

At one time he is wise, at another a perfect fool.

Modo sapiens, modo stultissimus est.

I asked him what time it was, but he made me no reply.

Mihi interroganti quota hora esset, nihil respondit.

I am writing this letter on the 1st of April.

Has literas (or hanc epistolam) Kalendis Aprilibus scribebam. (Epistolary imperfect, because to the reader the writing is *past*.)

It would be tedious.

Longum est.

It would have been better.

Melius fuit.

All the world knows that you are not convinced.

Nemo est quin sciat tibi non persuasum esse.

Instead of thanking me, he abused me.

Quum gratias mihi agere deberet, mihi maledixit.

" This, then, is the reason why pay has been granted to the soldiers : nor has it escaped our notice that this gift will be daubed with the poison of our enemies. The liberty of the people has been sold : our soldiery is removed for ever and banished from the city and from the republic : no longer do they give way even for winter or the season of the year and visit their homes and possessions. What do you think is the reason for this prolonged service ? "

In Oratio Obliqua. Hoc illud esse quod aera militibus sint constituta ; nec se fefellisse, id donum inimicorum veneno illitum fore. Venisse libertatem plebis ; remotam in perpetuum et ablegatam ab urbe et ab republica juventutem : jam ne hiemi quidem aut tempori anni cedere ac domos ac res invisere suas. Quam putarent continuatae militiae causam esse ?

(Livy.)

The top of the mountain.	Summus mons.
From day to day.	Diem de die.
To be brief.	Quid plura [dicam] ?
As far as I know.	Quod sciam.
No letter from you.	Nulla tua epistola.
Every fifth year.	Quinto quoque anno.
To make many promises.	Multa polliceri.

LESSON 24

Terminology and Translation

I N this Lesson we define the terms attached to various rhetorical figures and idiomatic constructions that are in common use in Latin, and the student would be well advised to memorize their definitions, since many of them are frequently found in the best English literature.

Asyndeton. The annexing of words without a conjunction : e.g. *di, homines* (gods and men).

Aposiopesis. A sudden stopping on the part of the speaker, as though unwilling or unable to proceed : e.g. Aeneid I, 135 : " *Quos ego—sed motos praestat componere fluctus.*"

Hendiadys. The presentation of one and the same notion in two expressions : e.g. " with might and main." *Chlamydem sinūsque* (the folds of the cloak : literally the cloak and the folds).

Enclitic. A word or particle which always follows another word, so united to it as to seem a part of it : e.g. *-que, -ve.*

Patronymic. A title expressing descent from a father or ancestor : e.g. *Alcides* = son of Alceus ; *Anchisiades* = son of Anchises.

Syncope. The shortening of a word by casting out an inner vowel ; as, *patri* (*pateri*).

Synesis. A construction in harmony with the sense rather than with strict syntax : e.g. *subeunt juventus auxilio tardi* = the young men come up slowly to the rescue. Here *subit* and *tarda* would have been strictly needed.

Crasis. The contraction of two vowels into one long vowel or into a diphthong.

TERMINOLOGY AND TRANSLATION

Zeugma. The using of one verb in two different senses : e.g. Aen. I, 264 : *mores et moenia ponet.*

Oxymoron. An apparent contradiction in terms : e.g. *splendide mendax : insepultam sepulturam* (a mockery of burial).

Periphrastic Conjugation. The participles in *urus, dus* may be conjugated with all the tenses of *sum :* e.g. to form fut. subj. of *amo, " amaturus sim."*

Litotes. Understatement, saying less than one means : e.g. " a citizen of no mean city " ; *non innoxia verba* (deadly words).

Hysteron-proteron. The idea, logically second, being put first : e.g. *moriamur, et in media arma ruamus.*

Chiasmus. Contrast obtained by reverse order : e.g. *urbi Caesarem, Brutum Galliae (dederunt).*

TRANSLATION.

The following passage, " The Golden Age," is from Virgil's Eclogues, or Pastoral Poems. In it the poet expresses the general hopes of a new era of peace and prosperity in language suggestive of the return of a bygone age of gold, connecting this age with the birth of a boy expected in this year, B.C. 40.

> At tibi prima, puer, nullo munuscula cultu
> Errantes hederas passim cum baccare tellus
> Mixtaque ridenti colocasia fundet acantho.
> Ipsae lacte domum referent distenta capellae
> Ubera, nec magnos metuent armenta leones.
> Ipsa tibi blandos fundent cunabula flores.
> Occidet et serpens, et fallax herba veneni
> Occidet ; Assyrium vulgo nascetur amomum.
> At simul heroum laudes et facta parentis
> Jam legere et quae sit poteris cognoscere virtus,
> Molli paulatim flavescet campus arista,
> Incultisque rubens pendebit sentibus uva,
> Et durae quercus sudabunt roscida mella.
> Pauca tamen suberunt priscae vestigia fraudis,
> Quae tentare Thetim ratibus, quae cingere muris
> Oppida, quae jubeant telluri infindere sulcos.
> Alter erit tum Tiphys, et altera quae vehat Argo
> Delectos heroas ; erunt etiam altera bella,
> Atque iterum ad Trojam magnus mittetur Achilles.
> Hinc, ubi jam firmata virum te fecerit aetas,
> Cedet et ipse mari vector, nec nautica pinus

Mutabit merces : omnis feret omnia tellus.
Non rastros patietur humus, non vinea falcem ;
Robustus quoque jam tauris juga solvet arator ;
Nec varios discet mentiri lana colores,
Ipse sed in pratis aries jam suave rubenti
Murice, jam croceo mutabit vellera luto ;
Sponte sua sandyx pascentes vestiet agnos.
' Talia saecla,' suis dixerunt, ' currite ' fusis
Concordes stabili fatorum numine Parcae.

ENGLISH VERSION.

On thee, child, the earth shall begin to lavish without aught
of tillage her simple gifts, straggling ivy twined with foxglove, and
colocasia (the Egyptian bean) with smiling bear's-foot. Of their
own accord the she-goats shall bring home their udders swollen
with milk, and the herds shall not dread the mighty lions. Thy
very cradle shall pour forth flowers to caress thee. The serpent,
too, shall perish ; perish likewise the treacherous poison-plant.
Eastern spice shall spring up everywhere. But so soon as thou
shalt be able to learn the exploits of heroes and the deeds of thy
father and what their manly virtue is, gradually the plain shall
turn yellow with waving corn ; on wild brambles shall hang the
ruddy grape, and sturdy oaks exude the dew-born honey. Yet
shall there lurk a few traces of early guile, to bid men tempt the
sea with barks, gird cities with walls, and cleave the earth with
furrows. Then shall be a second Tiphys (helmsman of the
Argo) and a second Argo to carry the chosen heroes ; there shall
be the old wars repeated and a great Achilles sent again to Troy.
Next, when thy full-grown strength has made thee a man, even
the merchant shall quit the sea, and the pine-built ship shall not
exchange its wares : every land shall bring forth everything. The
ground shall not endure the hoe, nor the vineyard the pruning-
hook : the stout ploughman, too, shall now loose his oxen
from the yoke. Wool shall not learn to assume divers colours,
but by Nature's gift (ipse) the ram in the meadows shall exchange
his fleece for sweetly-blushing purple and for saffron dye. Of
its own accord scarlet shall clothe the browsing lambs. " Ages
like these, run on ! " said the Parcae to their spindles, uttering in
concert the fixed will of Fate.

This Lesson completes our Course in Latin.

MATHEMATICS

LESSON 35
Linear Ratios

I F M is the mid-point of a line AB, then M divides the line AB equally into a " one to one " ratio. Stepping up a dimension from a line to a triangle, i.e. from AB to ABC, Fig. 1, having M, N, and P respectively the mid-points of the sides, the lines AN, BP, and CM, the medians of the triangle ABC, intersect at the common point G, and G divides each median into a " two to one " ratio, for $GC = 2GM$, and so on.

Similarly, Fig. 2, O is the common ortho-centre on the perpendiculars from the vertices, and S is the circum-centre of the triangle, and a " two to one " ratio holds, for $OC = 2SM$, $OA = 2SN$, and $OB = 2SP$.

But G lies on the line SO between S and O and divides the line SO into a " two to one " ratio, for $GO = 2GS$. The nine-point centre T lies also on the line SO and divides it into a " one to one " ratio, for $ST = TO$. G divides ST into a " two to one " ratio, for $SG = 2GT$. The radius of the circum-circle of ABC is twice the radius of the NP circle.

SO is a unique line determined in position by the shape of ABC and in size by the lengths of the sides of ABC, and it summarizes the " two to one " ratios which are consequent to the stepping-up of a dimension.

We may step up another dimension from the triangle to the orthogonal tetrahedron, which has each of a pair of opposite edges at right angles to each other. We should expect cases of a " three to one " ratio.

G is the centre of gravity of the triangle ABC. We may expect a " three to one " ratio in connexion with the C.G. of the solid. ABCD is the plan of an orthogonal tetrahedron, on ABC horizontal and with D as vertex. M, N, etc., are the mid-points of the six edges of the solid. (Fig. 3.)

AM, QL, and PN are equal and parallel.

NL, DK, and PQ are equal and parallel.

DK is at right angles to AM.

Hence PQLN is a rectangle, as are MNKQ and PMLK.

But P, M, N, L, K, Q are the corners of an octahedron, and

the circum-centre of the sphere which surrounds the octahedron is at R, where the diagonals of the three rectangles intersect.

Hence P, K, etc., are co-spheric.

Hence the circle through PMN, i.e. the N.P. circle of the base ABC, is a small circle of the sphere in question, which we will label the mid-point sphere, the M.P. sphere. Also the circle through KQL is a small circle to this sphere.

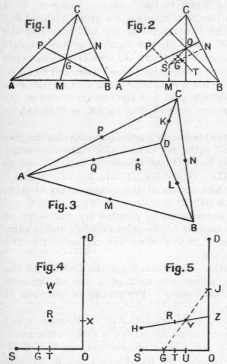

Fig. I

Fig. 2

Fig. 3

Fig. 4

Fig. 5

These two small circles are equal, for the radius of each is half the radius of the circum-circle to the base ABC, and the perpendicular to the face ABC through R leaves ABC at T, the N.P. centre of ABC, and reaches W, the circum-centre of the triangle KQL which is equal to the triangle MNP in a different orientation. TW = half the height of the tetra-hedron from D to ABC. The length of RT, therefore, divides the vertical height into a " three to one " ratio ; this vertical height is the distance from the corner D to the orthocentre of the opposite face of the tetrahedron. R is a unique point in the solid, for the perpendicular distance of R from any face divides the distance from that face to the opposite corner in a " three to one " ratio.

In Fig. 4 SGTO is repeated from Fig. 2 for the triangle ABC. DO is perpendicular to SO ; in DO find X, which divides DO

NORMAN RELIC IN SICILY. Byzantine and Arabian (Saracenic) characteristics distinguish the church of S. Giovanni degli Eremiti in Palermo, founded in 1132 by Roger II. It is conspicuous by its five red cupolas and its cupola-crowned bell tower, and is notable also for its Arabo-Norman cloister, of rather later date than the church. HISTORY: MEDIEVAL 36.

DYNASTS OF THE REACTION. Alexander I of Russia (1777–1825), became czar on the murder of his father, Paul I, in 1801. After Napoleon's fall, he formed the Holy Alliance of Russia, Austria and Prussia. Centre, Ferdinand II (1810–59), who succeeded to the throne of the Two Sicilies in 1830, and whose cruel and despotic nature found expression in a system of government described by Gladstone as the "negation of God." He once commanded his capital to be bombarded hence his nickname of "King Bomba." Right, Ferdinand VII (1784–1833), nominally king of Spain from 1808 and actually from 1814, was a bigoted despot only kept on his throne by French bayonets. MODERN HISTORY 23

Plate 54

Volume V

into a " three to one " ratio. R is the M.P. centre ; then RXOT is a rectangle and RX equals $\frac{3}{4}$ of GO, whence D and R and G are collinear ; whence R divides the line joining any vertex to the C.G. of the opposite face into a " three to one " ratio.

R is the C.G. or " mean-centre " of the solid.

The line SO, from the circum-centre to the orthocentre of a face, is unique to that face and projects perpendicularly to H, the circum-centre of the solid, and Z, the orthocentre of the solid. (Fig. 5.) The line HZ is unique to the solid.

T, the N.P. centre of the face, is unique to the face and projects to R, which is unique to the solid, so that R divides HZ in a " one to one " ratio.

Take U in SO, so that OU = UG = GS and so that U projects into HZ at Y ; then Y divides HZ in a " one to two " ratio. Let GY produced cut OD in J, then YG = YO = YJ, and J divides ZD in a " one to two " ratio. YJ is a third of HD. HD = the radius of the circum-sphere of the solid. RS = RO. Half HD = the radius of the M.P. sphere of the solid. YG = YO = YJ = a third of HD = the radius of the twelve point sphere of the solid ; the twelve points are the centroids of each face, the orthocentres of each face, and the points of trisection nearest Z, the orthocentre of the solid, of the joins from Z to the corners of the solid.

Solids of Revolution. A stone swung round at the end of a string describes a circle, and the length of the path or orbit of the stone is 2π times the length of the string. A line rotated round one end as a hinge covers the area of a circle of which the radius is the distance between the two ends of the line.

A rectangle rotating round one side pushed straight through a mass of clay would make a cylindrical hole or pipe of which the diameter of cross section would be twice the length of one side of the rectangle.

A rotating rectangle thus makes a cylinder of revolution. If the rectangle has long sides A and short sides B, then its area is AB. The cylinder of revolution which it generates has a surface area comprised of two circles, each area πB^2, and a curved figure which would flatten to a rectangle 2π B long by A wide, i.e. a total surface area of $2 \pi B^2 + 2 \pi AB = 2 \pi B (A + B)$. The volume of the cylinder would be πAB^2, i.e. π B times the area of the generating rectangle.

The solid of revolution generated by an equilateral triangle in rotation round one of its axes of symmetry would be a cone, a solid with a circular base, a vertical height, and a slant height. The slant height of the cone would equal the diameter of the circular base and one of the sides of the generating triangle. The vertical height would be $\frac{1}{2}\sqrt{3}$ of the slant height. The area of the generating triangle, if its base were C, would be $\frac{1}{4}\sqrt{3}\ C^2$. The area of the circular base of the cone would be $\frac{1}{4}\ \pi\ C^2$.

Since a cone is a pyramid, the volume of the cone would be $\frac{1}{24}\sqrt{3}\ \pi\ C^3$, i.e. $\frac{1}{6}\ \pi\ C$ times the area of the generating triangle. The curved surface of a cone, if a cut is made along the slant height from base to vertex, can be flattened to a portion of a circle of radius equal to the slant height, Fig. 6.

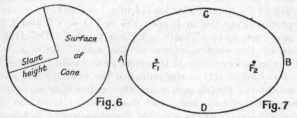

Fig. 6   Fig. 7

The portion of the circle depends upon the length of the circumference of the base. In this case the circumference of the base is π C. The circumference of a circle of radius equal to the slant height is 2π C, hence in this case the curved surface of the cone is equal in area to twice the circular base. Any right-angled triangle of shorter sides D and E rotated round either D or E will generate a cone. If D be longer than E the results may be tabulated as follows :

Hinge	Area of Circular Base	Vertical Height	Slant Height	Area of Curved Surface	Area of Generating Triangle	Volume of Cone
D	πE^2	D	$\sqrt{D^2+E^2}$	$\pi E\sqrt{D^2+E^2}$	$\frac{1}{2}$ DE	$\frac{\pi}{3}$ DE^2
E	πD^2	E	$\sqrt{D^2+E^2}$	$\pi D\sqrt{D^2+E^2}$	$\frac{1}{2}$ DE	$\frac{\pi}{3}$ D^{2}E

If a scalene triangle be rotated round its shortest side as hinge the solid would not be a whole cone, the base would be a hollowed-out conical surface, of which the slant height would equal the base of the triangle.

LINEAR RATIOS

The mechanical construction of an ellipse is illustrated in Fig. 7. AB and CD are two lines which bisect each other perpendicularly at O. If AB and CD are equal a circle may be drawn with centre O, passing through A, B, C, and D. If AB and CD are unequal the curve with centre O, which passes through A, B, C, and D, is not a circle, but an ellipse. The lines AB and CD are the axes of the ellipse, the major axis being greater than the minor axis.

The curve is defined in relation to two points in the major axis labelled the foci. The foci are symmetrically placed with reference to the minor axis. The turning points of the curve are at the ends of the axes. The curve is determined by the condition that the sum of the distances of a point on the curve to both of the foci is constant, and equal to the major axis. Obviously, the shape of an ellipse is not constant, for the two axes are independent, and ellipses on the same major axis may almost vanish to a straight line or expand until they are almost circular.

The quick method of drawing an ellipse is to erect a pin at each of the foci, fasten between them a length of thread equal to the major axis, and, with a pencil so placed as to stretch the thread always to its maximum, trace the curve which the pencil sliding round the thread will make.

The parabola is an open curve with one focus such that any point on the curve is equidistant from the focus and from the directrix. The ellipse is a closed curve such that any point on the curve has unequal distances from the focus and the directrix ; the distance from the focus is always the same fraction of the distance from the directrix.

Drill. 1. Practise drawing ellipses until the shape is familiar. Check by measurement the fact that the sum of the two focal distances of any point is a constant for the curve.

2. Graph the equations : $\frac{1}{4}x^2 + \frac{1}{4}y^2 = 2$; $\frac{1}{4}x^2 + \frac{1}{2}y^2 = 2$ on the same axes. 3. In Fig. 5 if SO = a inches, HS = b in., OZ = c in., find the radius of the circum-circle of the face ABC.

Revision. 1. The general term of a sequence is $\frac{1}{4}K^2 - \frac{3}{4}K$. (a) Write the first three terms : (b) write the tenth term ; (c) find the sum of the first ten terms ; (d) find an expression for the sum of T terms. 2. The frustum of a pyramid is what is left after the top portion has been sliced off by a cutting plane. Draw the plans of frustums of a square pyramid which has eight edges (a) when the cutting plane bisects the sloping edges ; (b) when the cutting plane divides one pair of sloping edges to cut

off the top third and the other pair to cut off the top two-thirds.
3. Prove that the angle in a semicircle is a right angle.

Expansion. In Fig. 3 R is the circum-centre of the sphere
which surrounds the octahedron MNPQLK. Investigate the
other possible spheres, the mid-point sphere and the inscribed
sphere, of the octahedron.

Solutions to Problems in Lesson 34:

Drill. 1. EK = a ninth AM. 2. DM = $\frac{3}{4}\sqrt{3}$ times AC.

Revision. Scale of % profit on cost jumps by $4\frac{1}{9}$ for each
penny difference in the S.P. from $6\frac{2}{3}$ for S.P. 2s. to 60 for S.P. 3s.

Expansion. See above.

LESSON 36

Mathematical Building and Counting

IMAGINE that you have a number of tetrahedra and octahedra,
of which all the faces are equal equilateral triangles, and
imagine that you are building with them as with a child's
blocks. Fig. 1 shows the original tetrahedron and the subsequent
layers. You will find that wherever two faces touch, there is
a face from each kind of solid. To make a solid with edges of
two units requires one octahedron and four tetrahedra. The
next layer requires three octahedra, six tetrahedra with points
upwards, and one tetrahedron with point downwards in the
middle. The next layer requires six octahedra, ten tetrahedra
with points upwards, and three tetrahedra with points downwards.
It will be obvious that the tetrahedra with points downwards
are hidden within the solid when the layers are put together.

The next layer may be visualized from the figure, for a back
row is required in addition to the lowest layer shown in the
figure : this layer will require ten octahedra, fifteen tetrahedra
pointing upwards, and six tetrahedra which will be hidden.

As a result of mere counting of the blocks used, we have
achieved numbers in the sequence 1, 3, 6, 10, 15. This suggests
the sequence for the summation of the first N natural numbers
of which the general expression is $\frac{1}{2}N(N + 1)$. In this sequence
the next term after 15 is 21. From this we conclude that in the
next layer used in building we should require 15 octahedra, 10
tetrahedra which would be hidden, and 21 tetrahedra which
would be visible on the faces of the built up solid.

Hence we can tabulate the results as shown here.

The results can be checked. One of the octahedra has a volume equal to that of four of the tetrahedra. Hence the volumes of the successive layers are 1, 7, 19, 37, 61, which are the respective first differences of successive cubes.

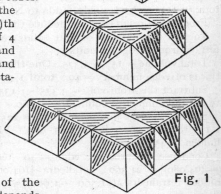

In general terms, the volume of the $(N + 1)$th layer is the sum of 4 times $\frac{1}{2}(N + 1)N$, and $\frac{1}{2}(N + 1)(N + 2)$ and $\frac{1}{2}N(N - 1)$; for the octahedra $2N^2 + 2N$ and for the tetrahedra $N^2 + N + 1$, which total $3N^2 + 3N + 1$, which is the difference between $(N + 1)^3$ and N^3.

Fig. 1

The total number of the small solids required depends on a new series based upon the sequence 1, 3, 6, 10, 15, 21, i.e. on the sequence 1, 4, 10, 20, 35, 56. For example, when 35 octahedra are used there will be 56 visible and 20 hidden tetrahedra, i.e. a volume equivalent to 216 ($140 + 56 + 20$) tetrahedra and a solid of edge 6.

Length of Edge of Solid.	Volume in terms of Unit Tetrahedron.	Octahedra.	Composition of Layers Tetrahedra.		
			Visible.	Hidden.	
1	1		1		
2	8	1	3		
3	27	3	6	1	
4	64	6	10	3	
5	125	10	15	6	
N	N^3	$\frac{1}{2}N(N-1)$	$\frac{1}{2}N(N+1)$	$\frac{1}{2}(N-1)(N-2)$	
N + 1	$(N + 1)^3$	$\frac{1}{2}(N + 1)N$	$\frac{1}{2}(N + 1)(N+2)$	$\frac{1}{2}N(N-1)$	
50	50^3	$\frac{1}{2}.50.49$	$\frac{1}{2}.50.51$	$\frac{1}{2}.49.48$	
	(125000)	(1225)	(1275)	(1176)	

The number of octahedra in the Nth layer is $\frac{1}{2}N(N - 1)$ and the number of octahedra used in all is $\Sigma\frac{1}{2}N(N - 1)$.

But $\Sigma N^2 = \frac{1}{6}N(N + 1)(2N + 1)$ and $\Sigma N = \frac{1}{2}N(N - 1)$; hence $\Sigma\frac{1}{2}(N^2 - N) = \frac{1}{6}N(N + 1)(N - 1)$.

Whence the numbers required are :

tetrahedra hidden $\frac{1}{6}(N - 1)N(N - 2)$

        visible $\frac{1}{6}(N + 1)(N + 2)N$

        total $\frac{1}{3}N(N^2 + 2) = \frac{1}{3}N^3 + \frac{2}{3}N$

octahedra $\frac{1}{6}N(N + 1)(N - 1) = \frac{2}{3}N^3 - \frac{2}{3}N$ tetrahedra ; and the total in terms of tetrahedra adds to N^3.

From these results we can deduce the following practical rules.

To find the number of unit solids required to build a large tetrahedron of edge 15 units.

Total volume $= 15^3 = 3,375$. One-third vol. $= 1,125$; add two-thirds of edge number $= 10$; total $1,135 =$ total of tetrahedra.

Subtract this from vol. $- 3,375 - 1,135 = 2,240$. Divide by 4 to get the number of octahedra $= 560$.

Square the edge number, i.e. $15^2 = 225$. Add this to the total $1,135$ to get $1,360$; halve this, 680. Visible tetrahedra $= 680$, hidden $= 455$.

Condense this process : edge $= 40$; tetrahedra $\frac{1}{3}(64,000 + 80) = (64,080) = 21,360$; octahedra $\frac{1}{4}(64,000 - 21,360) = 10,660$; hidden tetrahedra $\frac{1}{2}(21,360 - 1,600) = 9,880$; visible tetrahedra $= 11,480$.

Drill. 1. Extract builder's quantities for building in this manner a solid tetrahedral pyramid, edge 100 units.

2. Extract builder's quantities for building a tetrahedral pyramid one block thick with outside edges 60 units.

Revision. 1. Find the compound interest on £460 for $3\frac{1}{2}$ years at $2\frac{1}{2}$ per cent per annum (a) interest reckoned annually ; (b) interest reckoned half-yearly.

2. Find the difference between the simple and the compound interest on £830 for 6 years at 3 per cent per annum payable yearly.

3. If a sum of money quadruples itself in 50 years, what is the rate of compound interest per annum reckoned annually ?

4. At what rate of interest per annum reckoned half-yearly will £2,800 amount to £3,575 in 6 years ?

5. A rectangular tank is 12 ft. by $9\frac{3}{4}$ ft. by 5 ft. What is the longest length of wood which can reach from one corner to another corner ? What is the shortest ?

Expansion. Take a rectangular " brick " shape of wood. Letter the smallest face OABC, an adjacent face OADE, the base OEFC and the top ADGB. Use OE as an x-axis, OA as a y-axis and OC as a z-axis, with O as origin. Using the x, y, z notation as in plane graphs, find expressions for the eight corners, the twelve edges and the six faces. Take OE as 5, OA as 4 and OC as 3 units of length.

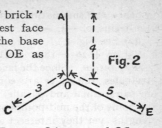

Fig. 2

Fig. 2 is a sketch of OE, OA and OC. Find expressions in terms of x, y and z for the lengths of the respective diagonals of the solid. Find numerical expressions for the diagonals OG and FB, and, by solving a simultaneous equation, find the position of their intersection.

Solutions to Problems in Lesson 35.

Drill. (1) See Fig. 3. (2) See Fig. 3. (3) $HD^2 = 4GJ^2 = 4 (GO^2 + OJ^2)$

$$= a^2 + 4c^2 + 4cb$$

$$SA^2 = 4c^2 + 4cb = \text{(radius required)}^2.$$

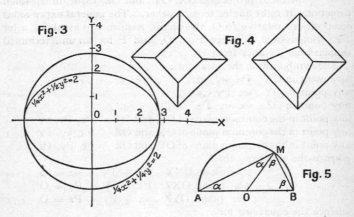

Fig. 3

Fig. 4

Fig. 5

Revision. (1) Sequence is $0, -\frac{1}{2}, -\frac{1}{2}, 0, 1, 2\frac{1}{2}, 4\frac{1}{2}, 7, 10, 13\frac{1}{2}$.

$$\text{Sum} = \Sigma\tfrac{1}{4}T^2 - \Sigma\tfrac{3}{4}T = \tfrac{1}{24}T(T + 1)(2T + 1) - \tfrac{3}{8}T(T + 1)$$

$$= \tfrac{1}{24}T(T + 1)(2T - 8) = \tfrac{1}{12}T(T + 1)(T - 4)$$

whence the summation series is o, $-\frac{1}{2}$, -1, -1, o, $2\frac{1}{2}$, $4\frac{1}{2}$, to ten terms, o, $-\frac{1}{2}$, $-\frac{1}{2}$ . . . . 7, 10, $13\frac{1}{2}$ = $37\frac{1}{2}$ (T = 9).

(2) See Fig. 4.

(3) $2^{a} + 2^{\beta} = 180$; AMB = $90°$ (*see* Fig. 5).

Expansion. Since the faces of the octahedron are not equilateral triangles, the edges are equal in six pairs ; but the edges are, in pairs, equal and parallel chords to the circumsphere, and the six joins of the mid-points of these pairs of chords are of different lengths, yet they intersect at R, hence the twelve mid-points are not co-spheric.

Similarly, the four heights of the tetrahedron are unequal, hence the perpendiculars from R to the faces of the octahedron are unequal and the feet of these perpendiculars are not co-spheric.

LESSON 37

Three-Dimensional Graphics

HERE follows an attempt to extend ordinary two-dimensional graphics into three dimensions. Fig. 1 shows in a pictorial projection OX, OY, and OZ, three dimensional directions at right angles to each other. The general expressions for positions relative to O, the origin, require two symbols, ω for zero dimensional distance from O, and P for an undetermined dimensional distance from O.

The symbolism is therefore for :

any point in OX   Px, ωy, ωz

any point in OY ωx, Py, ωz

any point in OZ ωx, ωy, Pz

any point in the common plane of OX and OY   Px, Py, ωz

any point in the common plane of OX and OZ   Px, ωy, Pz

any point in the common plane of OY and OZ ωx, Py, Pz

whence the equations for :

$$\text{the plane OXY} \quad Px + Py + \omega z = O$$
$$\text{the plane OXZ} \quad Px + \omega y + Pz = O$$
$$\text{the plane OYZ} \quad \omega x + Py + Pz = O$$

whence the equations for :

$$\text{line OX} \quad Px + \omega y + \omega z = O$$
$$\text{line OY} \quad \omega x + Py + \omega z = O$$
$$\text{line OZ} \quad \omega x + \omega y + Pz = O$$

(456)

In these equations ω indicates zero distance in the direction indicated and P any distance in the direction indicated, and these symbols ω and P are not operative in computations; they are positional symbols, not computative symbols.

Now a line parallel to OX at a distance d from it would lie on the surface of a cylinder which would cut the plane OYZ in the circle with O as centre and d as radius, whence $y^2 + z^2 = d^2$, so that the equation of a line parallel to OX would be

$$Px + y^2 + z^2 = d^2$$

The cylinder would cut the plane OXY in a line fixed by the solution of the simultaneous equation

$$Px + Py + \omega z = 0 \qquad Px + y^2 + z^2 = d^2$$

i.e. in the line

$$Px + y^2 + \omega z = d^2 \text{ or } Px + y + \omega z = d$$

whence the equation $x^2 + Py + \omega z = f^2$ would indicate a line parallel to OY in the plane OXY at a distance f from OY.

In Fig. 1 a brick 5 by 4 by 3 is put into position as shown. The numerical values 5 and 4 and 3 can now be substituted in the general equations.

The points are :

O	ω, ω, ω	A	$\omega, 4, \omega$
E	$5, \omega, \omega$	D	$5, 4, \omega$
C	$\omega, \omega, 3$	B	$\omega, 4, 3$
F	$5, \omega, 3$	G	$5, 4, 3$

the planes of OEDA $\quad Px + Py + \omega z = 0$

OCBA $\quad \omega x + Py + Pz = 0$

OCFE $\quad Px + \omega y + Pz = 0$

ABGD $\quad Px + y + Pz = 4$

DGEF $\quad x + Py + Pz = 5$

BGFC $\quad Px + Py + z = 3$

the lines   OE Px, ω, ω

OC ω, ω, Pz

OA ω, Py, ω

AD $Px, 4, \omega$

AB $\omega, 4, Pz$

BG $Px, 4, 3$

DG $5, 4, Pz$

FG $5, Py, 3$

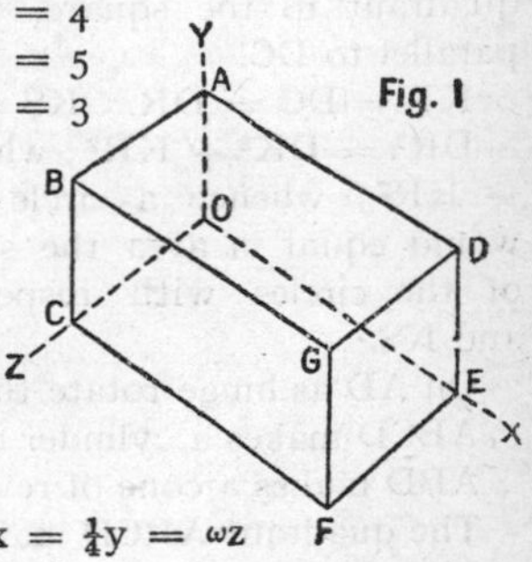

Fig. 1

the line OD $4x - 5y + \omega z = 0$ or $\frac{1}{5}x = \frac{1}{4}y = \omega z$

the plane of ODGC $\quad 4x - 5y + Pz = 0$

and the line CG $\quad \frac{1}{5}x = \frac{1}{4}y$, when $z = 3$

the line OB $\omega x + 3y - 4z = 0$ or $\omega x = \frac{1}{4}y = \frac{1}{3}z$

the plane of OBGE $Px + 3y - 4z = 0$

the line EG $\frac{1}{4}y = \frac{1}{3}z$, when $x = 5$

the line OF $3x + \omega y - 5z = 0$ or $\frac{1}{5}x = \omega y = \frac{1}{3}z$

the plane OFGA $3x + Py - 5z = 0$

the line AG $\frac{1}{5}x = \frac{1}{3}z$, when $y = 4$.

The line OG requires fuller attention.

Its equation must follow from the simultaneous solution of the equations for the planes ODGC, OBGE, and OFGA, and this yields the expression $\frac{1}{5}x = \frac{1}{4}y = \frac{1}{3}z$.

The line AF similarly requires the expression based on the equations for the planes AGFO, ABFE, and ADFC, $\frac{1}{5}x = \frac{1}{4}(4 - y) = \frac{1}{3}z$.

These expressions are jointly satisfied when $y = (4 - y)$, whence $y = 2$, which means that $x = 2\frac{1}{2}$ and $z = 1\frac{1}{2}$; and these are the co-ordinates of the intersection of the lines OG and AF in the middle of the solid.

Similarly, the lines BE and DC are in the plane BDEC and must satisfy the equation $3x + Py + 5z = 15$, i.e. $\frac{1}{5}x + Py + \frac{1}{3}z = 1$.

The expressions are:

for line BE $\frac{1}{5}(5 - x) = \frac{1}{4}y = \frac{1}{3}z$

for line DC $\frac{1}{5}x = \frac{1}{4}y = \frac{1}{3}(3 - z)$

which are equivalent expressions when $x = 2\frac{1}{2}$, $y = 2$, and $z = 1\frac{1}{2}$, and this point has already been determined as the mean centre of the solid.

Volume of a Sphere. In Fig. 2 ABCD is a square, ARC a quadrant to the square, DB a diagonal. KSRT is any line parallel to DC.

$KT = DC = DR$. $KS = KD$.

$DR^2 = DK^2 + KR^2$; whence $KT^2 = KS^2 + KR^2$: whence a circle with radius KT would equal in area the sum of the areas of the circles with respective radii KR and KS.

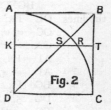

Fig. 2

On AD as hinge rotate the square.

ABCD makes a cylinder of revolution.

ABD makes a cone of revolution.

The quadrant ARCD makes a hemisphere of revolution.

The cone has a volume one-third the volume of its containing cylinder.

KT, KR and KS generate three concentric circles, of which the largest is equal in area to the sum of the areas of the two smaller; a Pythagoras relation.

Between the limits set by the hinge AD; $\Sigma\pi KT^2 =$ the volume of the cylinder of revolution; $\Sigma\pi KS^2 =$ the volume of the cone of revolution; whence $\Sigma\pi KS^2 = \frac{1}{3}\Sigma\pi KT^2$.

Also $\Sigma\pi KR^2 =$ the volume of the hemisphere of revolution and $\Sigma\pi KR^2 = \frac{2}{3}\Sigma\pi KT^2$, i.e. the volume of the hemisphere = two-thirds the volume of the cylinder.

But the volume of the cylinder $= \pi r^3$, where $r = DR = DC$. Hence the volume of the sphere $= \frac{4}{3}\pi r^3$.

Surface of a Sphere. In the limit, a sphere is composed of an infinite number of pyramids each with a vertical height equal to r, the radius of the sphere, and each with a base which is so tiny as to be indistinguishable from a plane n-gon; these bases are not necessarily of equal area or similar shape.

The total area of the bases equals the total surface of the sphere. The total volume of the pyramids is one-third of r times the total surface of the sphere, i.e. the area of the spherical surface $= 4\pi r^2$.

The volume and the surface area of a sphere are related by the differential relation: $v = \frac{4}{3}\pi r^3$; $s = 4\pi r^2$; i.e. $dv/dr = s$.

Drill. Using the notation above, find expressions for a point on the surface of a sphere; for a point of the equator of a sphere given that the poles are situated in OY and that the centres of the sphere, in both cases, are (a) at O and (b) at the point ω, a, ω. Find the expressions for the equatorial chord of which the extremities lie in the planes OYX and OYZ respectively.

Revision. 1. A (3, 5) and B (2, 7) are two points referred to rectangular co-ordinates. (a) Find the equation of AB, (b) Find the co-ordinates of the four points which divide AB in a " two to one " ratio.

2. A traveller receives a fixed salary plus commission of $2\frac{1}{2}\%$ on all orders in excess of a weekly average of £250. His weekly orders averaged £430 and his income was £725 for the year, which is reckoned as 50 weeks. What was his fixed salary?

3. A and B together earn £2 11s. in 6 days; B and C earn together £7 9s. 6d. in 13 days; A and C together earn £5 8s. in 18 days. What would each earn per day separately?

Expansion. Trace, on the same axes, the curves

(a) $\frac{1}{4}y^2 = \frac{1}{2}x$; (b) $\frac{3}{4}x^2 + \frac{3}{4}y^2 = 12$;

(c) $\frac{3}{4}x^2 + \frac{1}{2}y^2 = 4$; (d) $\frac{3}{4}x^2 - \frac{1}{2}y^2 = 4$.

Alter the scale of the axes so that the numbers along OX are increased by 3 and the numbers along OY are decreased by 2 and find the equations of the four curves in reference to the new position of the origin.

Solutions to Problems in Lesson 36.

Drill. 1. Edge 100 ; tetrahedra $\frac{1}{3}$ (1000000 — 200) = 333400 ; octahedra $\frac{1}{4}$ (1000000 — 333400) = 166650 ; hidden $\frac{1}{2}$ (333400 — 10000) = 161700 ; visible 171700.

2. A shell tetrahedron, edge P units, thickness one block, would enclose a space equal to a solid tetrahedron, edge (P — 3) units. Octahedra required = $\frac{1}{6}P^3 - \frac{1}{6}P$, less $\frac{1}{6}$ (P—3)^3 — $\frac{1}{6}$ (P—3), which simplifies to $\frac{1}{2}(3P^2 - 9P + 8)$. But in a tetrahedron the number of tetrahedra required exceeds twice the number of octahedra required by the number of units in the edge ; hence the number of tetrahedra for the shell is $3P^2 - 9P + 8 + 3$ = $3P^2 - 9P + 11$. Whence, when P = 60, 5134 octahedra and 10271 tetrahedra are needed, and all are visible.

The number $\frac{1}{2}(3P^2 - 9P + 8)$ depends on the difference between the P th. and the (P — 3) th. term in the sequence 1, 4, 10, 20, 35, etc.

Revision 1. (a) £41 11s. 5d. ; (b) £41 15s. 10d.

2. Difference per £1 = 0·014052. Ans. £11 13s. 3d.

3. 2·8%.

4. £1 becomes £1·27678. Ans. 4·2% p.a.

5. Longest : Required the sum of the squares of 12, $9\frac{3}{4}$, and 5 cu. ft. But $12^2 + 5^2 = 13^2$; $(4\cdot3\frac{1}{4})^2 + (3\cdot3\frac{1}{4})^2 = (5\cdot3\frac{1}{4})^2$. Ans. $16\frac{1}{4}$ ft. Shortest : $5^2 + 9\frac{3}{4}^2 = 11^2$. Ans. 11 (approx.).

Expansion. See above.

LESSON 38

Code Constants for Co-ordinates

THE code constants for rectangular rectilinear co-ordinates may be summarized in convenient form. Once the codal connexions have become familiar the code may be extended with considerable profit.

The straight line is the line AB in Fig. 1. The line AB cuts off OA and OB from the axes of reference, and the cut-offs are labelled intercepts. The slope of the line is measured by the tangent of the angle OAB.

The equation which represents AB in the code is $bx + ay = ab$, which may take the form

$$\frac{x}{a} + \frac{y}{b} = 1$$

or the form $y = b - mx$, where $m = b/a = \tan OAB$.

Changing the sign means substituting C for A, and the equation of BC is $- bx + ay = ab$.

E is the mid-point of AB, hence OE is parallel to BC, and the equation of OE is $- bx + ay = 0$.

F is the foot of the perpendicular from O to BC, and its slope is measured by tan FOC, i.e. tan OBA, which equals a/b, and the equation of OF is $y = -nx$, where $n = a/b$, whence $ax + by = 0$.

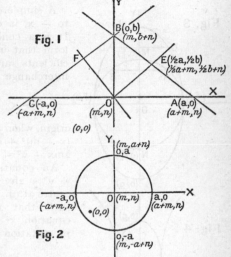

But OF is perpendicular to OE, and the equations $ax + by = 0$ and $- bx + ay = 0$ represent in the code two lines perpendicular to each other which intersect at the origin.

F may be found from the solution simultaneously of the equations $- bx + ay = ab$ and $ax + by = 0$, whence $x = - ab/(a^2 + b^2)$ and $y = ab/(a^2 + b^2)$. Whence interchanging the coefficients of the variables and changing the sign of one of them turn the line through a right angle.

Changing the sign only means obtaining the image of the line across an axis of symmetry which may be either axis of reference. In both cases the point of intersection of the line is found by the simultaneous solution of the two equations so obtained.

In Fig. 1 values are shown along the axes when the origin is shifted, so that the old origin now becomes m, n. The equation of AB now becomes y = c — mx, where m is still = b/a = tan OAB, such that the value of c must satisfy the condition laid down that A is now (a + m, n). c = (ab + an + bm) /a, and the equation is bx + ay = ab + an + bm.

The new equations are :

of BC   — bx + ay = + ab + an — bm
of OE   — bx + ay = + an — bm
of OF   ax + by = am + bn

In Fig. 2 is the circle with centre at the origin and radius = a. Its equation is : x² + y² = a².

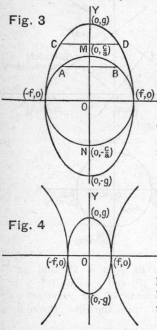

Fig. 3

Fig. 4

A simple change of sign, e.g. x to — x, is covered by the curve. It is a condition of the circular form that in its equation the co-efficients are equal, so that an interchange of coefficients has no consequence. In Fig. 2, values are indicated for a shift of the origin, when the equation becomes : (x — m)² + (y — n)² = a², i.e. x² — 2mx + y² — 2ny = a² — m² — n².

An equation such as x² — 2mx + y² — 2ny = 0 indicates a circle centre at (m, n) and with a radius r such that r² = m² + n². The equation x² + y² = 0 is one code presentation of the origin.

The equation x² = y² is a code presentation of two straight lines intersecting at the origin and bisecting internally and externally the angle XOY.

Another possibility is the equation ax² + by² = c, where a and b and c are unequal values. This possibility may be considered in relation to the circle.

In the exceptional case when a = b the equation is presented by the circle in Fig. 3, with centre at the origin and with radius = c/a. An ellipse is an oblique view of a circle.

Imagine that an oblique view of the circle be taken from a point so that the diameter along OX remains constant and that the diameter along OY, i.e. MN, be increased. The curve then becomes the ellipse, and a chord such as AB projects to CD. As a result, the x-values of A, B, C, D are equal in quantity, but the y-values of A and B have been equally enlarged. The precise value of the enlargement is a three-dimensional problem, which can be left for the moment; it will suffice that the result is an ellipse of which the equation is $ax^2 + by^2 = d$, where a and b and d are unequal.

A standard form of the ellipse equation is $m^2x^2 + n^2y^2 = m^2n^2$. Substituting in this equation the values in Fig. 3, we get the equation for the ellipse in Fig. 3 : $g^2x^2 + f^2y^2 = f^2g^2$. i.e. $x^2/f^2 + y^2/g^2 = 1$. In this form the equation indicates the result of the inequality of the coefficients; when the major axis of the ellipse is along the line OY, then the x-coefficient is the larger.

A change in the equation to $x^2/g^2 + y^2/f^2 = 1$ simply means slewing the ellipse through a right angle. Omitting the change of sign (for since the equation is of the second order, a change of sign here is inoperative, as in the case of a circle), this agrees with the result in the case of slewing a straight line through a right angle.

Shifting the origin so that the centre of the ellipse is now the point (m, n) gives rise to the equation $(x - m)^2/g^2 + (y - n)^2/f^2 = 1$. i.e. $f^2(x^2 - 2mx)^2 + g^2(y^2 - 2ny) = f^2g^2 - f^2m^2 - g^2n^2$.

An alteration in sign to the equation so that $x^2/f^2 - y^2/g^2 = 1$ gives rise to other possibilities. The form indicates at once that when $y = 0$, $x = f$; and that when $x = 0$, $y = g\sqrt{-1}$, which is an imaginary quantity. Further, since $x^2/f^2 = 1 + y^2/g^2$, when y increases x increases. Also when $y = 0$, $x = -f$, etc., and the curve is symmetrical about OY. This curve is shown in Fig. 4, where it can be seen that the curve lies outside the ellipse, so that a change of sign between the second order values alters the curve from an ellipse into a hyperbola.

Another reciprocal. When a quantity y is related to a second quantity x, one of the general code expressions for this relation is $y = f(x)$; y is a function of x.

When x increases it has an increment, δx, and there is a related increment of y, δy. These increments are in a ratio which is expressed in code $\delta y/\delta x$. The ratio $\delta y/\delta x$ becomes a constant when δx vanishes at the limit of experience. For example, let y = x², and let x = 3, then y = 9.

Take δx = 0·001, then δy = 0·006001 and δy/δx = 6·001. Take δx = 0·000001, then δy = 0·000006000001 and δy/δx = 6·000001. At the limit δy/δx = 6 ; if x = a, then at the limit δy/δx = 2a. But the ratio, at the limit, δy/δx = dy/dx, the differential coefficient of y. Obviously, the differential coefficient

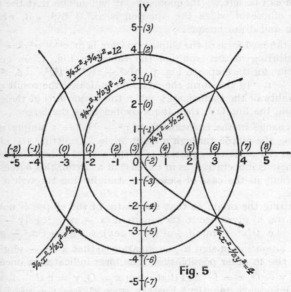

Fig. 5

is independent of the differing values of the increment of x. The code statement takes this form :

$$dy/dx = Lt_{\delta x \,=\, 0} \, \delta y/\delta x$$

Obviously, dx/dy = Lt$_{\delta y \,=\, 0}$ δx/δy. When y is a function of some x, then x is the inverse function of this y ; for example, when y = x², then x = ± y$^{\frac{1}{2}}$; dy/dx = 2x, and dx/dy = ± $\frac{1}{2}$y$^{-\frac{1}{2}}$ = 1/2x, i.e. 2x and 1/2x are reciprocal, and dy/dx and dx/dy are reciprocal. The code form for this fact is :

$$\frac{dy}{dx} \cdot \frac{dx}{dy} = Lt_{\substack{\delta x = 0 \\ \delta y = 0}} \left[\frac{\delta y}{\delta x} \cdot \frac{\delta x}{\delta y} \right] = 1.$$

(464)

Another example. Let $y = \sin x$. Then $dy/dx = \text{Lt}_{\delta x} = 0$ $(\sin(x + \delta x) - \sin x)/\delta x$. But $\sin (x + \delta x) - \sin x = 2 \cos (x + \frac{1}{2}\delta x) \sin \frac{1}{2}\delta x$, hence $dy/dx = \text{Lt}_{\delta x=0} \cos (x + \frac{1}{2}\delta x)$ times $\sin \frac{1}{2}\delta x/\frac{1}{2}\delta x$. But $\sin \frac{1}{2}\delta x = \frac{1}{2} \delta x$ when $\frac{1}{2}\delta x$ is very small at the limit of experience, hence $dy/dx = \text{Lt}_{\delta x = 0} \cos (x + \frac{1}{2}\delta x)$. But $\cos (x + \frac{1}{2}\delta x) = \cos x$ when $\frac{1}{2}\delta x$ is very small at the limit. Hence $dy/dx = \cos x$. Similarly, $dy/dx = - \sin x$, when $y = \cos x$.

Let $x = m \sin y$; it is required to find the differential co-efficient of y. $dx/dy = m \cos y = m(1 - \sin^2 y)\frac{1}{2} = m(1 - x^2/m^2)^{\frac{1}{2}} = (m^2 - x^2)^{\frac{1}{2}}$.

$$\text{Hence } dy/dx = \frac{1}{\sqrt{m^2 - x^2}} \text{ when } y = \sin^{-1}\frac{x}{m}$$

Drill. 1. Acquire familiarity with the curves in Figs. 1–4 by substituting numerical quantities for the literal values in the equations. Pay special attention to the turning points and the axes of symmetry of the curves.

2. Find differential coefficients of y with reference to x in the cases : (i) $y = \sin^{-1} x$; (ii) $y = \cos^{-1} x/m$; (iii) $y = \tan^{-1} x$; (iv) $y = x^{\frac{1}{a}}$.

Revision. 1. Factorize the following : (i) $20a^2 - a - 30$; (ii) $y^4 - 1 - 4 (y^2 - 1)$; (iii) $m^8 + m^4 n^4 + n^8$.

2. In a triangle $a = 100$, $B = 22\frac{1}{2}$, $C = 112\frac{1}{2}$. Completely solve the triangle and find the lengths of the perpendiculars from the vertices to the opposite bases, of the radii of all the circles related to the triangle, and of the join of the circumcentre to the ortho-centre.

3. Find the sum of the series $1\frac{1}{3}$, 2, $2\frac{2}{3}$ to 7 terms, and to N terms.

4. Find the geometric mean between 11 and 131.

Expansion. Carry the argument of this Lesson to the code co-ordinate presentation of equations of the second order containing a term in xy ; e.g. $3x - xy - 7y = 0$, $x^2 - 4xy + y^2 = 0$.

Solutions to Problems in Lesson 37.

Drill. Let the radius of the sphere $= R$. Point on the equator (a) $x^2 + \omega y^2 + z^2 = R^2$ (b) ; $x^2 + z^2 = R^2$, when $y = a$. Point on the surface (a) $x^2 + y^2 + z^2 = R^2$ (b) ; $x^2 + (y - a)^2 + z^2 = R^2$. Chord (a) $x + \omega y + z = R$ (b) ; $x + z = R$, when $y = a$.

Revision. 1. The four points are $(2\frac{1}{3}, 6\frac{1}{3})$, $(2\frac{2}{3}, 5\frac{2}{3})$, for internal section ; (1½, 8), (3½, 4) for external section. All these points satisfy the equation of AB : 2x + y = 11.

2. Total commission on £180 weekly = £225. Salary £500.

3. Per day A & B 8s. 6d. ; B & C 11s. 6d. ; A & C 6s. 0d. ; i.e. (A & B & C) 2 = 26s. ; whence A & B & C = 13s. 0d. daily ; i.e A 1s. 6d. ; B 7s. 0d. ; C 4s. 6d.

Expansion. Fig. 5. New equations (a) $y^2 + 4y — 2x + 10 = 0$; (b) $x^2 — 6x + y^2 + 4y — 3 = 0$; (c) $3x^2 — 18x + 2y^2 + 8y + 19 = 0$; (d) $3x^2 — 18x — 2y^2 — 8y + 3 = 0$.

LESSON 39

Three-Dimensional Graphics and Weighted Averages

GRAPHICS in three dimensions can be used for purposes of discovery and investigation. In Fig. 1 OX, OY, and OZ are axes of reference in three dimensions. In the plane XOZ, where $y = \omega$, take the point C in OX, so that its co-ordinates are (a, ω, ω). Through C take the line BA, $x + \omega y + \omega z = a$, so that B is (a, ω, γ) and A is $(a, \omega, -\beta)$.

Working in the plane XOZ and omitting ωy from the equations the line OA is $\beta x + a z = 0$
the line OB is $\gamma x — a z = 0$
the line BD, perpendicular to OA through B, is
$$a x — \beta z = a^2 — \beta \gamma$$
the point E, where BD cuts OC, is $\left(\dfrac{a^2 — \beta \gamma}{a}, \ \omega, \ \omega \right)$

M is the mid-point of OB and is $(\tfrac{1}{2}a, \ \omega, \ \tfrac{1}{2}\gamma)$
the perpendicular line to OB through M is
$$a x + \gamma z = \tfrac{1}{2} (a^2 + \gamma^2)$$
N is the mid-point of AB and is $(a, \ \omega, \ \tfrac{1}{2}(\gamma — \beta))$, the perpendicular line to AB through N is
$$z = \tfrac{1}{2} (\gamma — \beta)$$
these two perpendiculars intersect at P ; the values for P depend on the simultaneous solution of the equations for the perpendiculars and are $\left(\dfrac{a^2 + \beta \gamma}{2a}, \ \omega, \ \tfrac{1}{2} (\gamma — \beta) \right)$
the line EP is $a x + \dfrac{a^2 — 3 \beta \gamma}{\gamma — \beta} z = a^2 — \beta \gamma$

In Fig. 2 attention is concentrated on OC, EP, and a point V, vertically above E $\left(\dfrac{a^2 - \beta\gamma}{a}, \delta, \omega\right)$

OV is bisected at K $\left(\dfrac{a^2 - \beta\gamma}{2a}, \tfrac{1}{2}\delta, \omega\right)$

the line OV is $\delta x - \left(\dfrac{a^2 - \beta\gamma}{a}\right) y = O$ (ωz being omitted)

the line KL, perpendicular to OV, is

$$\left(\dfrac{a^2 - \beta\gamma}{a}\right) x + \delta y = \tfrac{1}{2}\left(\dfrac{a^2 - \beta\gamma}{a}\right)^2 + \tfrac{1}{2}\delta^2$$

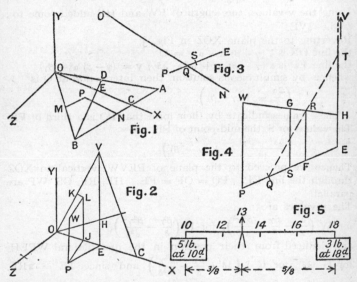

The point J in OX is the foot of the perpendicular from P to OX and is $\left(\dfrac{a^2 + \beta\gamma}{2a}, \omega, \omega\right)$.

The line JL in the plane XOY is parallel to OY and is $x = \dfrac{a^2 + \beta\gamma}{2a}$

this line cuts KL in L, and the simultaneous solution of the equations for KL and JL gives the values for L

$$\left(\dfrac{a^2 + \beta\gamma}{2a}, \dfrac{\delta}{2} - \dfrac{\beta\gamma}{\delta} + \dfrac{\beta^2\gamma^2}{a^2\delta}, \omega\right).$$

Whence the values for W, when PJLW is a rectangle in a plane parallel to OZ, are $\left(\dfrac{a^2 + \beta\gamma}{2a}, \ \dfrac{\delta}{2} - \dfrac{\beta\gamma}{\delta} + \dfrac{\beta^2\gamma^2}{a^2\delta}, \ \dfrac{\gamma - \beta}{2} \right)$.

VOAB are co-spheric with centre at W. OAB are cyclic with centre at P.

The line CV is $a\delta x + \beta\gamma y = a^2\delta$.

The perpendicular to CV from O, which cuts VE at H, is $\beta\gamma x - a\delta y = O$.

Whence, by simultaneous solution, H is

$$\left(\dfrac{a^2 - \beta\gamma}{a}, \ \dfrac{\beta\gamma}{a^2\delta}(a^2 - \beta\delta), \ \omega \right).$$

Using the y-values, the length of PW and HE added come to: $\frac{1}{2}\delta$, i.e. $\frac{1}{2}$VE.

Reverting to the plane XOZ in Fig. 3,

the line ON is $\frac{1}{2}(\gamma - \beta) x - a y = O$

the line EP is $a(\gamma - \beta) x + (a^2 - 3\beta\gamma) y = (\gamma - \beta) a^2 - \beta\gamma)$

whence by simultaneous solution, their intersection at Q is

$$\left(\dfrac{2a}{3}, \ \omega, \ \tfrac{1}{3}(\gamma - \beta) \right).$$

These values indicate by their form that PQ is a third of PE. The values for S, the mid-point of PE, are

$$\left(\dfrac{3a^2 - \beta\gamma}{4a}, \ \omega, \ \tfrac{1}{4}(\gamma - \beta) \right).$$

Thence we proceed to the plane of PEVW, vertical to XOZ through the line EP. PQ = QF = FE. HE, RF, GS, WP are parallel.

The y-values are :

for W $\left(\dfrac{\delta}{2} - \dfrac{\beta\gamma}{\delta} + \dfrac{\beta^2\gamma^2}{a^2\delta} \right)$, for H $\left(\dfrac{\beta\gamma}{\delta} - \dfrac{\beta^2\gamma^2}{a^2\delta} \right)$,

and deduced from their position in the quadrilateral WPEH,

for G $(\frac{1}{2}\delta)$, for R $\frac{1}{3}\left(\frac{1}{2}\delta + \dfrac{\beta\gamma}{\delta} - \dfrac{\beta^2\gamma^2}{a^2\delta} \right)$ and since TE = 2RF,

for T$\frac{2}{3}\left(\frac{1}{2}\delta + \dfrac{\beta\gamma}{\delta} - \dfrac{\beta^2\gamma^2}{a^2\delta} \right)$ whence the length of TH is

$\frac{1}{3}\left(\delta - \dfrac{\beta\gamma}{\delta} + \dfrac{\beta^2\gamma^2}{a^2\delta} \right)$ which is obviously a third of VH.

Since HR = $\frac{1}{3}$ HW and HT = $\frac{1}{3}$ HV, RT = $\frac{1}{3}$ WV.

Since QS = $\frac{1}{4}$ QE and SG = $\frac{1}{4}$ VE, and GS and VE are parallel, QGV are collinear and QG = $\frac{1}{4}$ QV.

Weighted Averages. The average height of two boys, one 5 ft. 3 in. and the other 5 ft. 5 in., is halfway between these values, their arithmetic mean, i.e. 5 ft. 4 in. If there be twelve boys each 5 ft. 3 in. and but one boy 5 ft. 5 in., the average height of the thirteen boys is 5 ft. 3 $\frac{2}{13}$ in.; the average has been pulled down towards the value which occurs most frequently.

Similarly, the arithmetic mean of 17 lb. and 20 lb. is $18\frac{1}{2}$ lb. If for any reason the 17 lb. is considered to carry greater weight by reason of its greater frequency or for any other reason whatsoever, then we may consider that the ratio of importance is as 5 is to 1, 5 of the 17 lb. to one of the 20 lb.; the mean then is but $17\frac{1}{2}$ lb. ($5 \times 17 = 20 = 105$; $105/6 = 17\frac{1}{2}$). It does not matter why the ratio of importance be selected; it may be as 19 of the heavier is to 6 of the lighter, in which case the mean is 19·28 lb. ($19 \times 20 = 380$; $6 \times 17 = 102$; $380 + 102 = 482$; $482/25 = 19·28$).

It is convenient to consider the effect of the ratio, i.e. the effect of the relative weights or importance attached to the values, in a simpler manner. Let the two measured quantities be A tons and $(A + E)$ tons, where the excess of the greater over the less is E tons. Let the weights attached to these measurements be in the ratio M of the greater to N of the less. Then M times the excess E is to be spread over $(M + N)$ cases and the weighted mean $= ME/(M + N)$ above A; whence it follows that the value of A indicates merely a starting point on a scale and does not enter into the calculation.

Consider this case quite generally. Stuff costing D per unit and stuff costing F per similar unit are mixed or compounded. If no other factor enters into consideration, then the cost per unit of the mixture is halfway between D and F, i.e. $\frac{1}{2}(D + F)$. If the cost of the mixture depends on the numbers of units mixed, for example, if there be P units @ D and Q units @ F, then the weighted mean, or cost per unit of the mixture, will be $(PD + QF)/(P + Q)$. The amount separating the mean from the cost $D = (PD + QF)/(P + Q) - D = (PD + QF - PD - QD)/(P + Q) = Q(F - D)/(P + Q)$.

The amount separating the mean from the cost $F = F - (PD + QF)/(P + Q) = (PF + QF - PD - QF)/(P + Q) = P(F - D)/(P + Q)$. This assumes that F exceeds D.

Obviously, the mean is separated from the ends, i.e. from D and F, by quantities proportional to P and Q respectively in relation not to the costs D and F but to the reverse costs F and D. Diagrammatically, the situation can be examined as a see-saw. (Fig. 5.) The heavier weight in a see-saw is nearer the balancing point. The heavier weight in a costing of a mixture

(469)

drags the mean towards the cost of the heavier weight in proportion to the weight of the other cost.

In a mixture of 3 lb. and 5 lb. of stuff the cost of the mixture per lb. will be $\frac{3}{8}$ of the difference between the costs nearer the cost of the 5 lb. ; if the costs be 10d. per lb. for the 5 lb. and 18d. per lb. for the 3 lb., then the mean cost per lb. will be $\frac{3}{8}$ of the difference 10d. from the 18d., i.e. 3d. more than the 10d., i.e. 13d.

Drill. 1. The total wages per day of 30 men and boys were £9 1s. 0d. Each man was paid per day 10s., each boy 3s. What would have been the total daily wages had the boys been paid a shilling more and the men a shilling less ?

2. An experiment was repeated ten times. The mean of the first five results was 1017, of the last six 1023, of the ten 1019. What was the mean of the first four ? How many individual results can you determine ?

Revision. 1. Differentiate with regard to x : $y = x^n$; $y = \log x$; $y = e^x$; $y = \sin x$; $y = -\cos x$; $y = \tan x$; $y = \sin^{-1} x$; $y = \tan^{-1} x$.

2. Differentiate with regard to x :
$y = 1/x^n$; $y = x^a \log x$; $y = e^{\sin x}$; $y = \sin^{-1} x^2$; $y = \sqrt{x^2 + a^2}$; $y = \sin^2 x$; $y = \sin^3 x$: $y = \sin^3 x . \cos x$.

Expansion. Across a piece of horizontally ruled paper draw a series of lines all at 60° with the horizontal to make plotting paper having as its basis not squares as in squared paper, but parallelograms which are equilateral and have angles 60° and 120°. Using this plotting paper and a piece of ordinary squared paper, explore the possibility of using the plotting paper instead of squared paper for the graphical solution of simultaneous equations and so forth.

Solutions to Problems in Lesson 38.

Drill. 2. (a) $1/(1-x^2)^{\frac{1}{2}}$; (b) $-1/(m^2 - x^2)^{\frac{1}{2}}$; (c) $1/(1 + x^2)$; (d) $\frac{1}{a} x^{(\frac{1}{a}-1)}$

Revision. 1. (a) $(4a-5)$ $(5a+6)$; (b) $(y-1)$ $(y+1)$ (y^2-3) ; (c) $(m^4 - m^2n^2 + n^4)$ $(m^2 - mn + n^2)$ $(m^2 + mn + n^2)$

2. Examine Fig. 6 geometrically to discover its unique relations first. $A = 45$; hence if $ACL = 90$, BLC is an isosceles triangle with base angles $22\frac{1}{2}$, and the circumcentre lies on KL produced ; also if $CMA = 90$, CMA is an isosceles triangle with base angles 45. If $NC = NA$, then $MNA = 90$, and the circum-

centre is at R, where NM produced meets KL. LCM is an isosceles triangle with base angles 45, hence AMC = 90. AD is the perpendicular to BC and meets MC produced in O, the orthocentre. AOC is an isosceles triangle with base angles $22\frac{1}{2}$, hence DO = DA, whence DO = RK. LC and RN are parallel. BC = a; CA = b = LC = LB; ML = MC = MA = $(\frac{1}{2}\sqrt{2})$b. BM = $(1 + \frac{1}{2}\sqrt{2})$b,

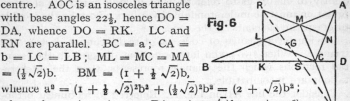

Fig. 6

whence $a^2 = (1 + \frac{1}{2}\sqrt{2})^2 b^2 + (\frac{1}{2}\sqrt{2})^2 b^2 = (2 + \sqrt{2})b^2$; whence b = a (0.541). c = BA = $(1 + \sqrt{2})$b = a (1.306) BLC and ACO are identically equal triangles, hence AD = BK = $\frac{1}{2}$a. Hence the circumradius = BR = a$(\frac{1}{2}\sqrt{2})$, LK = CD = $(b^2 - \frac{1}{4}a^2)^{\frac{1}{2}} = \frac{1}{2}(3 - 2\sqrt{2})^{\frac{1}{2}}a$ = (0.207)a. RO bisects KD at S; whence S is the N.P. centre and the N.P. radius = (0.354) a. s = $\frac{1}{2}$(a + b + c) = $\frac{1}{2}$a (1 + 0.541 + 1.306) = a(1.423). Area = BK.RK = $\frac{1}{4}$ a². The in-radius = a(0.176). The centroid, G, is $\frac{1}{6}$a up from BC. The perpendicular from B to CA produced is parallel to LC; its length is equal to BM, for the figure is such that BA and BO are symmetrical to an axis of symmetry BD.

3. To 7 terms $23\frac{1}{8}$; to N terms $\frac{1}{8}N^2 + N$.

4. 37.96.

Expansion. See later.

LESSON 40

Scales, Codes and Points of View

THE main burden of this Course, so far as it has gone, has been an introduction to a variety of codes in which Man records facts and relations, the things which he calls knowledge. No other subject of study revels in such a wealth of codal interpretations. All these codes must be related, for they vie in attempts to interpret the same things—each has its utility for its own purposes.

Now let us consider that very simple thing, a triangle. It is unique in size and shape. It can be exactly copied in size and shape; it can be regarded so that it looks like a line;

it can be examined by means of a mirror until it appears to have a decided bulge; scale drawings can be made of it; we can do all sorts of things to it, but it must preserve its identity sufficiently to enable us to refer to it again, and our codes of interpretation must be understandable by others who take the trouble to grasp the elements of the code.

Obviously, a change of code, or of scale, cannot destroy the triangle. When two codal interpretations disagree on the essential relations which the triangle represents, then the interpretations are incompatible.

Consider the line AB in Fig. 1. Referred to rectilinear orthographic axes of reference and to a definite and particular origin

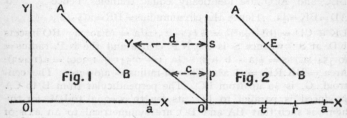

at O, the line AB as a picture may vanish from sight and be thought about as x + y = a. But this codal presentation is vague, for it implies, in this case, that the units of measurement along the axes of reference are both to the same scale, and it implies that the line AB produced will cut both axes at the point labelled, a, on their respective scales. Granted all these implications, we are able, without a picture or diagram, to know, e.g. that the perpendicular to the line AB from the origin is the line x = y, and that the orthogonal projections of AB to each of the axes will be equal. If, however, O is not the point (O, O), then the code presentation of AB becomes x + y = a + k, when referred to such axes and to an origin which values the point O as (m, n).

If, however, the origin is retained, but the angle XOY ceases to be a right angle, something must happen. The line AB can still be represented as x + y = a, provided the scales along the axes are still arranged so that AB produced cuts these axes at the points labelled a, but when that happens the scales are not equal. Copy Fig. 1 on squared paper and imagine the paper is distorted so that the angle YOX becomes 135°. This can be done by drawing the new OY through corners of original squares. Whenever the scales are kept equal, then the x-value of every point in AB will be altered (Fig. 2). Originally the point B was (r, p), such that r + p = a ; now it is (r + c, p).

In the picture OY has been slewed until it is almost parallel to AB ; were AB and OY parallel the equation representing AB would be x + Py = k, where P means that the y-value is indefinite and k equals the distance OE, the constant distance between AB and OY ; it is more convenient, however, to think of the constant distance between AB and OY not as the shortest distance between them, which is k, but as the constant distance between them in the direction which is indicated by OX, for then AB and OY are constantly separated by the distance, a. The equation then becomes x + Py = a. In the customary code this equation is written x = a, which is conventionally understood to represent a line ; the form here used introduces Py in order to make explicit the fact that we are thinking of a line. The expression x + Py = a, therefore, takes on a fuller meaning, a meaning which can be represented in a graph only by special examples. The expression ωx + Py = O (conventionally x = zero) represents the OY axis of reference, whatever and wherever it is ; the expression x + Py = a represents an image, a copy, a duplicate of OY, whatever it is, removed from OY to a parallel position and passing through the point (a, o). If AB be not parallel to OY, then the values of point B are now not (r, p), but (r + c, p), and the values of E the mid-point of AB are now not (t, s), but (t + d, s).

The slewing of OY means that when c = kp, d = ks, where k is a constant which varies with the amount of the slewing. The values are now B (r + kp, p)

E (t + ks, s)

But r + p = a = s + t
The values are now B (a — p + kp, p)

E (a — s + ks, s)

and the equation is x + y = a + kP, where kP is the indefinite value by which the scale along the old OY has been altered to get the corresponding scale on the new OY.

The slewing of OY leaves unaltered the y-values, but alters the x-values by a change which depends upon a factorial alteration of the OY scale.

It follows, then, that the equation x + y = a in its general form, a form which can be graphed only in particular examples, has a precise significance.

It represents a locus, a continuum of point positions, referred to two definite axes of reference.

These axes are $\omega x + Py = O$, where x and y are unknown variables ; and $Px + {}^\omega y = O$.

These axes intersect at O, which we label the origin, which is the point (ωx, ωy), commonly represented as (O, O). Along these axes points are labelled numerically, i.e. with constants, not variables, as a scale, one of which is a. Parallels to these axes are the lines $x + Py = m$ and $Px + y = n$. These parallels intersect at the point (m, n). If this point is on the line AB, then the sum of the constants m and n is a, and AB is the locus of successive intersections of parallels to the axes such that the sum of the intercepts on these parallels is a. The shape of AB depends entirely upon the shapes of the axes of reference. For example, let $\omega x + Py = O$ represent a plane axis of reference

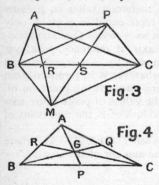

Fig. 3

Fig. 4

which is a circle marked with a definite y scale, then $x + Py = m$ is a set of concentric circles within this plane distant m from this axis of reference ; so that the centre of the circle of reference is the point in this plane where $Py = \omega y$; and let $Px + \omega y = O$ represent the other axis of reference which is a radius of the circle, then the origin of the system of reference is the zero point on the circular scale. Then the expression $x + y = a$ represents the locus of a (situated on the radius) to the scale point n on the circular axis of reference and m away from it, so that $m + n = a$, a pair of curious curves each with a turning point (a, O), (− a, O), which meet on the circular axis at (O, a) and (O, − a).

Plane Geometry. The relations below should be memorized.

(A) Two triangles of equal area are set on opposite sides of a common base. The base bisects the joins of their vertices, and conversely. In Fig. 3 ABC and MBC are the given triangles. BMCP is made a parallelogram. Then PA is parallel to BC, and SP = SM. Hence RA = RM.

(B) The longest of the three medians of a scalene triangle is from the mid-point of the shortest side.

In any triangle ABC let P be the mid-point of BC. When AB is less than AC, angle APB is less than angle APC, whence BG is less than GC. When G is the centroid, BQ is less than RC, etc.

(C) When a diagonal of a quadrilateral bisects its area it also bisects the other diagonal. Let ABMC be any quadrilateral bisected areally by BC Fig. 3, etc.

NOTE.—The expression $2s$ = the perimeter of a triangle.

(D) The sum of the distances from any point within a triangle to the three corners lies between s and $2s$.

In Fig. 4 let G be any point within ABC. Then AG + GB exceeds AB, but is less than AC + CB; GB + GC exceeds BC, but is less than CB + BA; GC + GA exceeds CA, but is less than CB + BA. Add these three and the result follows.

Drill. 1. The median of a triangle is less than half the sum of the two sides conterminous with it. Use MS in BMC.

2. The sum of the three medians of a triangle lies between $1\frac{1}{2}s$ and $2s$.

3. If a quadrilateral has a pair of parallel sides, the join of the mid-points of the other two sides bisects each diagonal of the parallelogram.

Revision. 1. Tabulate the integrals which correspond to the differentials given below in Solutions Revision 1 and 2.

2. A solid expands so that each linear foot measured within the solid in any direction increases by $1\frac{1}{2}$ per mille. This means that the expansion exceeds 1·45 per mille and is less than 1·55 per mille. Find the volume after expansion of 1,000 cu. ft. of this solid as accurately as the data of measurement permit.

3. If the relative ratings as producers of three men be A19, B20, C21, and B earns when paid on piece rates £5 per week, what will A and C earn? If, however, A's output is a standard which must not be exceeded, and the wages are constant, how long must B and C deliberately idle per day of 10 hours?

Expansion. Definition. Let A and B be the centres of two circles. Let O be the point in BA such that the difference between OA^2 and OB^2 is equal to the difference between the squares on the radii of the circles. Then a perpendicular to AB through O is called the radical axis.

Let O be the origin and the radical axis be the y-axis and the line of centres be the x-axis of a system of rectangular co-ordinates;

investigate (i) the equation of a circle with centre (3, O) and radius 2. (ii) The centre of a second circle, such that O is the radical axis. (iii) The equation of this second circle, and its radius. (iv) The equations of tangents to both circles from the point (O, 2). (v) The lengths of the tangents to the circles from the point (O, 2).

Solutions to Problems in Lesson 39.

Drill. 1. Team wage per person per day $= 6\frac{1}{30}$ sh.

Differences $10 - 6\frac{1}{30} = 3\frac{29}{30} = \frac{119}{30}$ $\left.\right\}$ 119 : 91

$\qquad 6\frac{1}{30} - 3 = 3\frac{1}{30} = \frac{91}{30}$ $\left.\right\}$ or 17 : 13

Team $= 17$ boys, 13 men.

Ans. 4 sh. more, i.e. £9–5–0.

2. Total scores, 10190 ; total first five $= 5085$; therefore last five $= 5105$. But last six total 6138 ; therefore the fifth was 1033. Therefore the first four totalled 4052. The mean of the first four was 1013. Only one individual result, the fifth.

Revision. 1. nx^{n-1} ; $\frac{1}{x}$; e^x ; $\cos x$; $\sin x$; $\sec^2 x$; $1/\sqrt{1-x^2}$; $1/1 + x^2$.

2. $- nx^{-n-1}$ or $- n/x^{n+1}$; ax^{a-1} $\log x + x^a \frac{1}{x} = x^{a-1}$ $(a \log x + 1)$; $\cos x \cdot e^{\sin x}$; $2x/\sqrt{1 - x^4}$; $x/\sqrt{x^2 + a^2}$; $2 \sin x \cos x$; $3 \sin^2 x \cdot \cos x$; $\sin^2 x (3 \cos^2 x - \sin^2 x)$.

Expansion. See above and later.

LESSON 41

Modern Technique of Geometry

GEOMETRY is concerned with the shape and size and relative position of lines, figures and solids. It was anciently developed as a rigorous training in deduction by pure reasoning in connexion with hypothetical considerations. A straight line is, or was, a hypothesis towards which every attempted drawn straight line was an approximation. All this was a necessary consequence of the fact that ancient drawings, unless elaborately carved or chiselled, were lacking in permanence. Ultra-modern geometry is neither more nor less hypothetical, yet it keeps the hypotheses in the background. It is premised that size is measurable in linear, square, and cubic units ; i.e. the hypothesis is the solid, the unit cube. It is premised that modern machinery can produce sufficiently accurate and permanent reproductions of the cube and the square and the straight edge, that it is not worth while to labour the fact that these reproductions are merely approximations.

On the basis of the cube we can assume, i.e. take for granted, squared paper. This assumption immediately requires the assumption or the inference of scales and similarity. Scales are inferred because squared paper may be of an infinite variety of sizes along the edge of unit square, hence every sheet of squared paper has its own scale. Similarity is inferred, for we assume that a fact which is true concerning the figure ABCD on one sheet of squared paper may be expected to be equally true when the shape of ABCD is drawn on a second sheet of squared paper.

It is also implied in the hypothesis of squared paper that the straight lines on the paper are arranged in two sets of parallels. The condition of parallelism, i.e. failure to meet, is assumed. Although squared paper is the common background, it follows that similarly made rectangular paper, with repetitions of a unit rectangle, or similarly made parallelogram paper with repetitions of a unit parallelogram may be, also, useful backgrounds. All this also implies the notion of symmetry whence the diagonal of a square is an axis of symmetry, and of reversed symmetry whence the diagonal of a parallelogram is an axis of reversed symmetry.

Once these assumptions are made, many of the theorems in Euclid become self-evident and the proofs which had to be learnt by heart by students of the last century are relegated to their proper home in a museum of antiquities. In the old days attention was focused upon the order of Euclid's propositions ; modern geometry has revised the order.

A triangle is a three-sided figure which has its corners at three different intersections in squared paper of the appropriate scale.

Euclid I, 4, the first theorem in the first book of Euclid, states : *"If two triangles have two sides and the included angle of the one, respectively equal to two sides and the included angle of the other, then the triangles are identities, i.e. are equal in all respects."*

Use parallelogram paper. Mark A ; along one line mark AB so that B is x units from A ; along the cross line through A mark AC so that C is y units from A. ABC is a triangle (Fig. 1) and it is an identity, it is unique ; all triangles so made on the parallelogram paper with the fixed scales used are but facsimiles of ABC. If the measured lengths be not x and y but ax and ay, where a is a constant ratio by which the linear scale of the paper used is altered, then the new triangle is not identical with ABC, but an enlarged or diminished copy of it, of the same shape, but not of the same size.

Euclid I, 5: *If two sides of a triangle are equal the angles which are opposite to them are equal ; and conversely*. (Euc. I, 6.) This is a special case of the last proposition, for every identity can have an image. Let ABC be a triangle on squared paper, and let ABD be the image of ABC ; then BCD is an isosceles triangle. Euclid I, 8: *If two triangles have the three sides of the one respectively equal to the three sides of the other, then the triangles are an identity*. This is another special case, for it is only necessary to

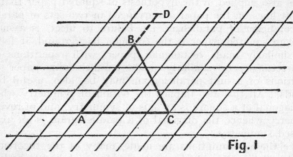

Fig. I

use the appropriate parallelogram paper, i.e. such a paper that one of the two triangles can be drawn as in Fig. 1, then the second triangle must fit the first and be a replica or must be a reversed image of the first to complete a parallelogram.

Euclid I, 13: *The angles which one straight line makes with another, upon one side of it, are together equal to two right angles, and conversely* (Euc. I, 14). This is implied in the conception that cubes fill space. Euclid I, 15: *If two straight lines cut one another the vertically opposite angles are equal*. This is implied in parallelogram paper.

Euclid I, 16: *If one side of a triangle is produced, the exterior angle, so formed, is greater than either of the two interior opposite angles ;* and (Euc. I, 32) *the exterior angle is equal to the sum of the two interior opposite angles*. This duality, a necessity under Euclid's limitations, follows immediately from the use of appropriate parallelogram paper (Fig. 1, DBC = BAC + BCA).

Similarly Euc. I, 17 : *Any two angles of a triangle are less than two right angles, and* (Euc. I, 32) *the three interior angles of a triangle are equal to two right angles.*

Euclid I, 18 : *The angle opposite the longer of two sides of a triangle is greater than the angle opposite the shorter of the two sides ; and conversely* (Euc. I, 19). Mark ABC on squared paper so that AB is greater than AC. Mark D in BC such that DAC has an image DAE (Fig. 3).

These propositions follow from the fact that (Fig. 2) a moving point P in MN gets nearer the point X as it moves towards N and later gets farther from X, so that at one point it is the nearest possible, and every point, excepting this one, in its path has a duplicate, i.e. an image ; the nearest point is Y, so that YX is

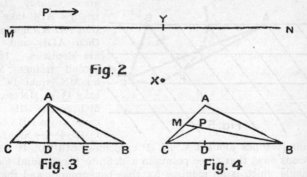

Fig. 2

Fig. 3   Fig. 4

perpendicular to MN ; the angle XPN increases to its maximum at XYN, when it is a right angle, and then decreases.

Euclid I, 20 : *Any two sides of a triangle are together greater than the third side, and* (Euc. I, 21) *if from the ends of a side of a triangle two straight lines are drawn to a point within the triangle the sum of them is less than the sum of the other two sides of the triangle, but the angle they contain is a greater angle than the vertical angle of the triangle.*

Set up ABC on squared paper and find D so that AD is a minimum. AB and AC exceed DB and DC. Set up any point P within ABC and produce BP to M in AC ; AB and AC together exceed MB and MC together, which exceed PB and PC together (Fig. 4). This is a special case which should be obvious from consideration of the moving point P in relation to MN (Fig. 2).

Euclid I, 24 : *If two triangles have two sides of the one equal to two sides of the other and the angles included between these sides unequal, then the third sides are unequal, as the angles are unequal, the greater opposite the greater.*

Use appropriate parallelogram paper and set up ABC. Within ABC take P so that BP is equal to BC ; then it is obvious that AC exceeds AP. Obviously this is but a special treatment : the values of AP in comparison with a fixed length AB when P is a moving point on the circumference of a circle with centre B and radius BC ; when P falls between A and B, AP is a minimum, etc. (Fig. 5).

Euclid I, 26 : *If two triangles have one side equal and the two angles adjacent to the equal sides respectively equal, then the triangles*

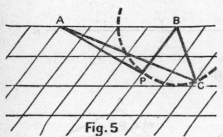

Fig. 5

are an identity. In one triangle ABC take D so that AD is a minimum ; then ADB and ADC are identities. In the second triangle MNP, let MN equal BC and take Q in MN so that MQ equals BD. Because angle DBA equals QMP, P lies along BA ; similarly P lies along CA, i.e. P coincides with A. It will be obvious now, that three points in a definite background form a triangle which is an identity for that background, and that the jargon and circumlocution with which these geometrical relations were clothed in the English translations of Euclid's Elements are at best merely museum specimens. Our technique has advanced, just as years ago the technique of arithmetic advanced with the invention of the zero and the decimal point. The theorems of Euclid set out above are incidental to the modern conception of squared and parallelogram paper. The curious may proceed similarly to investigate the remainder of Euclid's Elements at their leisure.

Drill. Fashion some parallelogram paper such that the unit is an equilateral parallelogram. (a) Draw any triangle so that two sides fall along the lines of the paper ; write out the facts concerning the mid-points of the sides of a triangle which appear to be obvious. (b) Draw an isosceles triangle with a diagonal

MODERN GREECE'S FIRST KING. In 1832 the Convention of London declared Greece to be an independent kingdom under the protection of Britain, France and Russia, and Prince Otto, son of Louis I of Bavaria, became its king. This painting by Peter Hess gives an impressive idea of Otto's entry in 1833 into Nauplia, then the seat of the administration. Athens became the capital of Greece in 1834. MODERN HISTORY 23

La Pinakothek, Munich

LOUIS PHILIPPE
(1773–1850). Head
of the Orleans branch
of the Bourbons, he
was king of the
French 1830–48.
MODERN HISTORY 24

LEOPOLD I (1790–1865). A
scion of the Coburgs, he first
married princess Charlotte of
England, who, however, died
after a year of marriage. In
1831 he became first king of
the Belgians. Uncle of Queen
Victoria, he was for years her
trusted adviser.
MODERN HISTORY 24

LOUIS NAPOLEON (1808–73).
Son of Louis Bonaparte by Hor-
tense, daughter of Josephine, he
was elected president of France
in 1848 and became emperor as
Napoleon III in 1852. The next
year he married Eugénie de
Montijo. After eighteen years
his empire crashed at Sedan and
he died in exile in England.
MODERN HISTORY 25

*From Flathe, " Restauration und
Revolution"*

LOUIS KOSSUTH (1802–
49). An ardent nationalist,
he led the Hungarian rising
of 1848 On its failure he
went into exile.
MODERN HISTORY 25

After Tietze

Plate 56

Volume V

of the parallelogram scheme as an axis of symmetry; write out the facts which seem to be obvious.

Revision. A cone and a sphere are made from the same metal. The cone is 3·03 cm. high with a base diameter = 2·997 cm. The sphere has a diameter 3·033 cm. The cone weighs 59·994 grams. Find, as accurately as the data permit, the weight in grams of the sphere.

Expansion. Draw seven parallel lines at varying distances apart. (Use squared paper.) Draw a circle so that a diameter AB has A on the first line and B on the seventh. Let O be the centre of the circle and P be a moving point on the circumference. Let MPN be a tangent of the circle which moves with P.

Let the angle AOP = α and the smaller angle between the tangent MPN and each of the parallels be β. Find an expression for β in terms of α.

Solutions to Problems in Lesson 40

Drill. 1. MS is the median in BMC. In MBP, BM + BP exceeds MP, i.e. BM + MC exceeds 2MS, whence, etc.

2. By 1 above the sum of the three medians is less than 2s. Since G is any point in the triangle, two-thirds of the sum of the medians exceeds s, whence, etc.

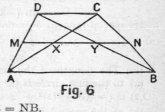

Fig. 6

3. In Fig. 6 ABCD is a parallelogram with AB and CD parallel. MA = MD, MXYN is parallel to DC, then XC = XA, YB = YD, NC = NB.

Revision. 2. The volumetric expansion is indicated by (1·0015)³, which lies between (1·00145)³ and (1·00155)³, i.e. between 1.00435 and 1.00465, i.e. as correct as may be, between 1·0044 and 1·0047. Ans. Between 1,004 and 1,005 cu. ft.

3. A £4¾; C £5¼. B works 19/20, idles 1/20 = ½ hr. C works 19/21, idles 2/21 = 20/21 hr.

Expansion. (i) The line $(y - k) = m (x - h) \pm a \sqrt{1 + m^2}$ touches the circle $(x - h)^2 + (y - k)^2 = a^2$, centre (h, k) radius a, for all values of m.

(ii) In Fig. 7 let (3, o) be the centre of a circle of radius, 2. The equation of the circle is $(x - 3)^2 + (y - o)^2 = 2^2 = 4$. The general equation of a tangent to this circle is $(y - o) = m (x - 3) \pm 2 \sqrt{1 + m^2}$.

The special equation of the tangents to this circle, from the point (0, 2) is obtained, first, by substitution to evaluate m, i.e. $2 = m(-3) \pm 2\sqrt{1 + m^2}$, whence $m = -\frac{12}{5}$ or O and, second, by replacing m by $-\frac{12}{5}$. It is $12x + 5y = 10$ or $y = 2$.

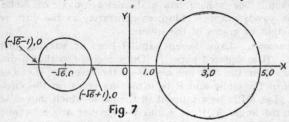

Fig. 7

(iii) If OY is the radical axis, the centre of the second circle is at the point $(-\sqrt{6}, O)$, for $3^2 - (\sqrt{6})^2 = 2^2 - 1^2$.
The equation of this circle is
$$(-x + \sqrt{6})^2 + (y - O)^2 = 1.$$
Its general tangent equation is
$$(y - O) = m(-x + \sqrt{6}) \pm \sqrt{1 + m^2}$$
Its special tangent equation from the point (0, 2) requires that $m = \frac{1}{5}(2\sqrt{6} - 3)$, and is
$$5y + x(2\sqrt{6} - 3) = 10$$
(iv) The (length of the tangent)^2 from (x^1, y^1)
(a) to the first circle is $(x^1 - 3)^2 + (y^1 - O)^2 - 4$; and from (O,2) is $(-3)^2 + (2)^2 - 4 = 9$.
(b) to the second circle is $(-x^1 + \sqrt{6})^2 + (y^1 - O)^2 - 1$; and from (O,2) is $(\sqrt{6})^2 + (2)^2 - 1 = 9$.
(v) Since the point has a value (O, d) the lengths of the tangent are :
$$\text{(a)} \quad \sqrt{9 + d^2 - 4} = \sqrt{d^2 + 5}$$
$$\text{(b)} \quad \sqrt{6 + d^2 - 1} = \sqrt{d^2 + 5}$$
i.e. the tangents to the circles from a point on the radical axis are equal in length.

Our Course in Mathematics is continued in Volume **6.**

Reaction's Triumph After Waterloo

(See plates 54 and 55)

AFTER the four great powers before whom Napoleon had gone down—Great Britain, Austria, Russia and Prussia—had disposed of the "disturber of European peace," the Vienna Congress under their influence returned to its task of restoring Continental equilibrium. The basic principle adopted was the replacement, with undiminished realms, of the legitimate dynasties of the pre-war days, wherever they had been dispossessed by revolutionary and imperial France. Between them the four great powers reconstructed the map of Europe to their own advantage. In restoring the Bourbon monarchy to France, they insisted upon the provision of a constitution, a course to which Louis XVIII agreed without demur. The other Bourbon kings, Ferdinand of the Two Sicilies and Ferdinand of Spain, were respectively restored to Naples and Madrid. France retained the pre-war boundaries, as laid down in the peace of Paris (1814), but was not admitted to the status of the four great powers, remaining under military supervision, and a war indemnity was levied on her as a defeated country. Otherwise all the princes of Europe were restored to autocracy. It occurred to no one to consider any but dynastic interests ; populations were transferred without consulting them.

The king of Sardinia recovered Piedmont ; William of Orange became king of Holland, with Belgium ; Austria received compensation elsewhere. German princes who had thrown in their lot with Napoleon were penalized for the benefit of Prussia ; a kingdom of Poland was revived for the Czar with the Grand Duchy of Warsaw, which Napoleon had presented to Saxony. Norway, which had been attached to Denmark, was transferred (as a separate kingdom) to Sweden, which surrendered Finland to the Czar. The Austrian empire recovered the north Italian duchies, with Venetia ; but the old Holy Roman empire was not revived. Instead, the German states were formed into a German Confederation with the Austrian emperor as president, but without including the non-German divisions of the Austrian empire. Metternich was the guiding spirit in both the German and Austrian governments for another generation. Britain retained Malta and Gibraltar, returned Minorca to Spain, but kept Ceylon and Cape Colony by agreement with the king of Holland ; the king of England was reinstated as king of Hanover, not as elector.

The four powers, as practically responsible for the peace of Europe, agreed to hold periodical congresses in order that all action might be co-operative. Czar Alexander was a visionary who at the moment believed in granting his subjects liberties so long as they used those liberties in exact accordance with his own wishes. He set the other despots the example of granting a constitution to his new kingdom of Poland. Several of the minor despots followed his lead, but, as the constitutions did not convey any effective power, the despots continued to act as despotically as before. Almost all of them accepted the Czar's invitation to join a (personal) Holy Alliance of Christian princes —from which the Sultan was of course excluded—pledging themselves to pursue Christian ideals in the government of their dominions, a pledge which as a matter of course they unanimously ignored ; so that, in practical effect, the Holy Alliance became a league of despots zealous to help each other in suppressing all movements towards such popular liberties as were in fact established in France and England, or that spirit of nationalism which resents subjection to an alien domination—a spirit which was active in Italy and among the Christian populations of the Turkish empire.

In every country which had been under the domination of the French republic the practice of France had implanted the conception of civic liberty. Spain, which had suffered most from the war—bridges broken, roads and villages ruined—was now ruled by a bigoted despot who had even succeeded in getting the Inquisition re-established. The Spanish liberal patriots knew that it was possible for an administration which was not priest-ridden to be efficient. They had also learnt from their English allies the value of parliamentary institutions. In central Europe, Metternich, though he felt fairly safe about Austria and the kingdom of Hungary, was more concerned about Germany and the large portion of Italy which had been reannexed to Austria in 1815. Germany was not the same country as it had been before the French Revolution. Under the Napoleonic scheme many small principalities had been absorbed into larger ones ; the left bank of the Rhine had been freed from feudalism and been brought under the French civil code, which guaranteed equal liberty to all men irrespective of birth. The southern states had followed suit. Now with the reaction the princes had again cut up Germany, denouncing the longing after a unified fatherland. In every town were created discontented bodies of students and democrats ready to flare into revolt.

The Italian situation had its own difficulties, partly owing to the civilization of the north of Italy and the backwardness of the south. Here again the allies cut to pieces the larger units formed under Napoleon's domination, distributing them under princes who were in some instances foreigners. Freemasons and Carbonari fraternized on both sides of the Alps ; Napoleon became almost a hero to many of the younger men, who formulated the political ideal of a secularized and unified Italy. On the Continent the aftermath of the French Revolution was not industrial troubles, as in England, but political and religious quarrels ; autocrats and the Church became close allies against democracy and liberalism.

The dynasts had the machinery for enforcing mastery in their own hands. Nationalism, however, in the alternative and quite distinct sense of passionate desire for unification among peoples of one stock—German, Italian, or Slav—was still a dream of idealists rather than an immediate political motive. The German Confederation and its Diet were not more than a League and its Council, of states under Austria's hegemony, and neither the German princes nor Metternich wished it to be more, since practically all were willing to follow Metternich's lead. In Italy, a large part of which formed part of the Austrian dominion, the kings of Sardinia and Naples looked to Austrian support in the suppression of liberal movements.

Throughout Germany, then, the constitutional movement known to its supporters as liberalism and to its opponents as the Revolution was silenced. Ferdinand of Naples (the " Two Sicilies ") was forced to accept a constitution which he repudiated as soon as he was assured of Austrian support. Ferdinand of Spain followed a similar course, both monarchs belonging to the most vindictively tyrannical type. Piedmont extorted a constitution from Victor Emmanuel of Sardinia, but his successor, Charles Felix, was enabled to cancel it by the aid of Austrian bayonets. Louis XVIII succeeded for a time in carrying on a government of moderates, so that in 1819 France was released from the fetters imposed on her at Vienna ; but from that time the ascendancy in the government passed to the king's brother and heir, Charles of Artois.

Monroe Doctrine. Meanwhile, all the Spanish colonies in America were in revolt. The prospect of European intervention there on behalf of Ferdinand of Spain was prevented by Castlereagh's successor, Canning, who on behalf of Great Britain recognized the insurgents as belligerents, while President Monroe at Washington promulgated the Monroe Doctrine (1823) that European interference with American affairs was not to be permitted.

The royalists were eventually defeated and a number of independent but very unstable republics, generally under military dictatorships, were set up. Brazil also declared itself an independent empire under the Portuguese crown prince, Pedro, who on his father's death in 1826 chose to retain Brazil and transfer the Portuguese throne to his daughter, Maria da Gloria, with her uncle Miguel as regent.

In the fourteen years following the Vienna Congress the dynastic reaction to the old order had all over western Europe the upper hand over the popular and nationalist movements ; even the Czar soon abandoned his brief faith in the development of liberal principles on the initiative of a benevolent autocrat, the Poles having shown—as throughout their history—no capacity for ordered self-government ; and on his death in 1825 he was succeeded by his brother Nicholas I, a conscientious believer in the most rigid autocracy, in whose eyes disobedience to the Divine authority of the autocrat was the unpardonable sin, though the autocracy of the Turk was another matter. It was largely owing to this distinction in the mind of Nicholas that the nationalist movement in Greece during the same period had a very different issue.

Greece's Fight for Independence. The Greek revolt against the Sultan's rule began in 1821, when Alexander was still on the Russian throne, in expectation of support from Turkey's age-long enemy Russia. The support was not forthcoming because Metternich persuaded him that to give it would encourage revolutionists. The European Congress then sitting at Verona banned intervention. In England and France there was lively sympathy for the Greeks, but both were committed to the doctrine of non-intervention. Byron, the poet, was foremost among the English sympathizers and volunteers in the cause of Greek freedom, and died at Missolonghi in 1824. The Greeks had many bold leaders but no common leadership. The balance of success in the barbaric warfare was on the whole in favour of the Greeks, owing to their greater skill at sea, till Sultan Mahmud called Mehemet Ali, pasha of Egypt, to his aid, at the moment when Nicholas succeeded Alexander.

It was obvious that Nicholas, intent on Russian interests, meant to intervene. Lest he should do so by himself and thereby dominate Constantinople, England and France persuaded him to an agreement for the three powers to force the belligerents to stop fighting. The attempt resulted in a collision, at Navarino, between the British and Egyptian fleets, in which the latter was sunk. England, under a new government, refused to be embroiled further, but could no longer resent independent action by the Czar, who invaded Turkey and forced the treaty of Adrianople on the Sultan (1829). That treaty established an autonomous Greek republic, and autonomy under Russian protection to the Trans-Danube provinces. Three years later, when Nicholas was much preoccupied with Poland, the powers combined to convert the autonomous republic into an independent constitutional monarchy under Otto of Bavaria, who in 1833 entered Nauplia.

LESSON 24

Tearing Up the Vienna Settlement

(See plate 56)

A T the opening of 1830 the only movement in Europe towards liberty, whether civic or national, that had been attended by success was the liberation of Greece, though both Spanish and Portuguese America had discarded European domination. England, indeed, was reverting to the reform movement, which had been nipped in the bud by the excesses of the French Revolution ; but in France Charles X (count of Artois, who had succeeded his brother Louis XVIII in 1824) and the monarchists were clearly aiming at the elimination of the constitution and recovery of the old-time absolutism. The Assembly and the city of Paris were restive ; but the country as a whole was pleased at re-established material prosperity, while patriotism was gratified at the assertion of France's position as a European power over the Greek question, and at the success of the campaign in Algiers (1830), which quelled the arrogance of the dey and laid the foundation of France's North African empire. In 1830, therefore, Charles felt strong enough to defy the opposition of the bourgeois constitutionalists.

He had already gagged the press by dint of royal ordinance, and in July he promulgated an electoral law which would have shorn the Senate and the Chamber of Deputies of effectual parliamentary rights. These ordinances violated the constitution and meant, in fact, a revolution to restore the absolutism of the days of " Le Roi Soleil." So confident were Charles and his reactionary minister Polignac of success that they made no preparations for a counter-revolution. Paris, however, responded by setting up a provisional government which elected the king's cousin, Louis Philippe of Orleans, lieutenant-general of the realm. Charles abdicated, naming his grandson as his successor, and himself took flight to England. France ignored his action and Louis Philippe, the " Citizen king," was raised to the throne as a constitutional monarch. The country accepted the new régime with placid acquiescence. The July Revolution of 1830 was effected without bloodshed. It was a bourgeois revolution in which only for a moment Jacobinism had threatened to gain the upper hand, and the new government of France was, to a certain extent, like the French people and like England, in sympathy with the liberal movements in the rest of Europe, though between the two countries there was no great cordiality.

Belgium in Revolt. Belgium had always resented its subordination to the kingdom of Holland by the Vienna Congress— the more because the Belgians were not on a constitutional equality with the Dutch. A scheme of Polignac's to absorb Belgium in the French monarchy had been foiled by Prussian veto. The revolution in France now encouraged the Belgian constitutionalists to demand independence and appeal to France for support. The rest of the powers regarded the Vienna settlement as sacrosanct ; Russia and Austria were, however, too busy with Poland to interfere. France and England held that it was open to modification. Holland refused the Belgian demand ; Dutch troops invaded Belgium and Prussia threatened to support them in arms ; France threatened counter-intervention. England, France and the Belgians agreed on Leopold of Saxe-Coburg as a prince to whom the crown might be given on constitutional terms. Holland remained obdurate, and not till the British fleet appeared on the scene did the Dutch evacuate Antwerp ; Leopold was crowned first king of the Belgians on June 4, 1832.

Open war was avoided, but the problem was not finally settled till 1839, by a treaty reluctantly accepted by William, king of Holland, which recognized Leopold as constitutional king of an independent Belgium, whose neutrality was guaranteed by Great Britain, France and Prussia—the " scrap of paper " which became so prominent in 1914.

In 1830 the people of Poland revolted against their Russian autocrat. The revolt was ruthlessly crushed by Czar Nicholas, and the Poles lost such semblance of their liberties as had survived the death of Alexander. In the same year Ferdinand II, later nicknamed Bomba from the savagery of his methods, succeeded to the throne of the Sicilies ; and in 1831 Charles Albert, a prince with nationalist and constitutional leanings, followed Charles Felix in Sardinia and Piedmont. A constitutional movement in the Papal states which divided Italy in two was suppressed by Austrian troops, though French troops were sent to Ancona as a check upon Austrian predominance, which, still under the strong personality of Metternich, was not to France's liking. In Germany Hanover's connexion with England was severed by the death of William IV in 1837, which gave the English succession to his niece Victoria but the Hanoverian to his brother Frederick—a bitter and stupid reactionary—since there the law of male succession prevailed.

In Portugal and Spain events followed a chequered course. After Pedro, emperor of Brazil, had passed on the Portuguese crown to his infant daughter, Maria da Gloria, under the guardianship of his reactionary brother Miguel, the latter promptly attempted to seize the crown for himself ; and a prolonged contest ensued, the constitutionalists supporting the child and finally expelling Miguel in 1834. In Spain Ferdinand died in 1833, leaving the crown by his own decree—in spite of the recently adopted Salic law—to his infant daughter Isabella, with the queen-mother, Christina, his fourth wife, as regent. His brother Carlos, like Miguel in Portugal, claimed the crown and the constitutionalists supported the child, her mother accepting the " Constitution of 1812," which they had endeavoured to force on Ferdinand ; but Carlos was not finally ejected till 1839.

Mehemet Ali. Meanwhile the Near Eastern problem was passing through another phase. The Treaty of Adrianople (1829) made Russia predominant in Constantinople, but the Porte was subjected to a new danger. The Sultan Mahmud, who had been forced to cede Greek independence, was not popular with his subjects—he had surrendered to the infidel and he was a reformer. Moreover, he had irritated the strongest of his viceroys, Mehemet Ali, pasha of Egypt, by refusing to convey Syria to him—the reward he was to have received for the quelling of the rebellious Greeks—a quelling he had failed to effect.

Mehemet, balked of his ambitions by the intervention of the powers in Greece, and bent nevertheless on gaining for himself Syria, invaded that province. Britain and France offered Sultan Mahmud advice ; the Czar offered him troops. Mehemet was ready to compromise ; the compromise was accepted, while Mahmud by the treaty of Unkiar Skelessi virtually placed himself under Russia's protection (1833). Five years later Mehemet renewed the challenge to his suzerain by withholding the Egyptian tribute. Mahmud accepted the challenge and dispatched an army against his recalcitrant vassal. Mehemet sent his son Ibrahim, an able soldier, to meet it. Mahmud died, leaving a young son, Abdul Mejid, Sultan. Ibrahim routed the Turks and threatened to march on Constantinople, while the Turkish admiral handed over his fleet to Mehemet.

The four great European powers were essentially interested. To Austria Russian domination in the Turkish empire was a menace to the Austrian position ; Russia had, since the days of Peter the Great, intended to dominate there ; France, since the Napoleonic conquests in Egypt, had wished to expand in that direction ; Great Britain did not wish any other power unduly to dominate or expand. Russian control of the Dardanelles was to be resisted, at all costs ; to Russian armies India might be accessible.

The powers, acting in concert, each watchful of the others, intervened with an offer to Ibrahim which he rejected. Thereupon the British fleet, being in a position to take immediate action, seized Acre, while Syria, which had no love for Mehemet, rose for the Sultan. As Napoleon's action had formerly been paralysed by his failure to capture Acre, so Ibrahim was now paralysed by the British seizure of it. Mehemet surrendered his claim on Syria in the Treaty of London (1841), while retaining his position as hereditary pasha of Egypt, the four powers participating in the treaty. This time, however, it was palpably England, not Russia, which had saved the Sultan; and England, not Russia, became the predominant influence with the Porte. In what was now becoming known as the Eastern Question, cordiality between Russia and England was impossible, owing to the growing conviction there that the Czar's real object was India.

To all appearance constitutionalism was established in all the western and northern states. In Austria Metternich had the separatist nationalism of the heterogeneous elements of the empire under irresistible control ; the German Confederation was satisfied with Austria's hegemony, and wanted no closer union ; while the material prosperity damped active discontent with the autocratic governments, which suppressed political freedom but were not actively tyrannical.

Second French Republic. Beneath the surface Italy was seething with hostility to the Austrian domination, and the Sicilies with hatred of their Bourbon monarchy. No one, however, suspected that red revolution was again imminent—still less (and least of all the French government) that the train was to be lighted in Paris.

Nevertheless, in February, 1848, without warning, the Orleans monarchy fell and the Second Republic took its place. The Paris mob rose in revolt, and there was a raging struggle in the streets for three days between them and the National Guard, who were loyal to the government. The Third Revolution, however, was in reality democratic and not republican. The Orleans monarchy died of dullness. It was true that the spread of the Industrial Revolution from England to Europe had revived in the city proletariat the old spirit of Jacobinism in the new form of Socialism—the hostility of labour to capitalism, not to the aristocracy—but this had no hold except in cities. The revolution was carried through by the bourgeoisie partly because Louis Philippe was showing indications of reversion to type, to absolutism, but much more because the whole country was weary of the persistent drabness of the government and the very secondary part it played in Europe, while the legend of France's glories in the days of Napoleon was being sedulously fostered. Within four years the Second Republic was turned into the Second Empire.

LESSON 25

Europe's Year of Revolutions

(See plate 56)

ON February 23rd, 1848, the Orleans government in France imagined itself secure, having vetoed a great public banquet of the parliamentary Opposition. Although the organizers announced that the banquet would not be held, the Paris mob paraded the streets and the city seethed with discontent. On the next day the king, having dismissed his eminently respectable minister, Guizot, abdicated, named his grandson as his successor, and, like him, disappeared to England, the natural home of refugees. Self-constituted committees proclaimed the Republic and summoned a National Convention, which carried on as a provisional government. In June, as the government failed to provide " work or bread " for the crowd of unemployed, the Paris mob rose again, but it was crushed in three days of fierce street fighting. The Convention settled down to the shaping of a constitution ; in December, Louis Napoleon Bonaparte, nephew of Napoleon I and son of his brother Louis, sometime king of Holland, was elected by enormous majorities first President of the Second Republic, as the re-embodiment of the Napoleonic Idea, a vague but prepossessing departure from the dullness of Orleanism.

The year 1848 was the " year of revolutions." Within three weeks from the fall of the French monarchy revolutions with every variety of motive were in progress over the greater part of Europe, and half the governments had either collapsed or were apparently on the verge of doing so. The German duchies of Schleswig and Holstein, attached to the Danish crown, were demanding separation ; all over Germany the princes were promising or granting constitutions, Frederick William IV of Prussia taking the lead and posing at the same time as the champion of German nationalism and unity, to be attained through the establishment of a constitution for the German Confederation, to be drawn up by a Pan-German parliament which assembled at Frankfort in May. Within the Austrian empire, Vienna, the German capital, demanded a constitution for Austria proper, the liberals obtained control of the city, and Metternich took flight to

England. The Hungarian Diet, led by the nationalist Louis Kossuth, demanded autonomy not only for Hungary, but for the Czechs in Bohemia and for the south Slavs. It went on to formulate its proposed constitution in the March Laws. Meanwhile the Young Czechs (nationalists) gained control in Prague. Vienna for the time sympathized, and early in April the panic-stricken emperor Ferdinand promised the concession of all the demands except those made by the south Slavs, which were incompatible with those of Vienna and Hungary.

Italian Unrest. In Italy Pope Pius IX had previously distinguished himself by liberal measures in the States of the Church ; Ferdinand II, king of Naples, was now frightened into granting a constitution, as Charles Albert, whose sympathies were liberal and nationalist, had already done in Piedmont. But in Italy the condition of any real progress was the emancipation of the whole peninsula from the Austrian domination. Charles Albert accepted the leadership and marched into Lombardy, which, with Venetia, rose against the oppressor. But here the Austrian government had an able commander-in-chief, Marshal Radetzky. He concentrated his troops in the strategic area known as the Quadrilateral, and waited his own moment ; while Charles Albert, whose gifts were those of a man of peace, not of war, also waited, till irritation at his inaction and mistrust of his leadership grew among the Italians, who were for the most part ardent republicans.

Meanwhile, the Pan-German parliament met at Frankfort, and began by proposing to include Bohemia among the German states, which was the last thing the Czechs desired. The emperor Ferdinand at Vienna, on the other hand, issued a constitution which exasperated instead of satisfying all the revolutionary forces. Vienna rose, the emperor escaped to Innsbruck, and the Viennese set up a provisional government.

Rehabilitation of the Hapsburgs. The Czechs replied to the Pan-Germans at Frankfort by calling a Pan-Slav conference whereby they alienated Vienna and the considerable body of German constitutionalists in Prague itself. Prince Windisch-grätz, the commander of the imperial troops, saw his opportunity, and, on his own responsibility, without orders, seized Prague and took over control as a military dictator in Ferdinand's name (June), resistance being out of the question. The Hungarian government, placed in control of the south Slavs, who detested Magyar even more than German domination, nevertheless set the Croat, Joseph Jellachich, in command of its army ; whereon he declared himself to be acting for the imperial government, which made haste to accept his services. Then in July Radetzky from the Quadrilateral attacked Charles Albert's forces and defeated them heavily at Custozza. Thus in two months the tables had been turned in favour of the imperial government in every quarter.

Before the end of the year the reversal had gone much farther. Radetzky in Italy, being actually master of the situation, suspended hostilities under an armistice, while dissensions weakened the Italians. The Pope, dismayed at the course of the revolution and by the assassination of his liberal secretary Rossi, abandoned liberalism and escaped to the Court at Naples, where Ferdinand II had cancelled the constitution and recovered his ascendancy, crushing the Sicilian rebels with a vindictive savagery which earned him the nickname of " Bomba " and caused the Bourbon house to be more bitterly execrated than ever.

Meanwhile, matters had not gone too smoothly in Vienna, and Ferdinand abdicated in favour of his nephew, Francis Joseph (1830–1916). Windischgrätz was master of Bohemia ; Hungary was completely isolated. It was announced that a new constitution for the whole of the Austrian empire was to be promulgated. Hungary replied by refusing to acknowledge the new " king " till he had sworn to the Hungarian constitution.

In Germany the Pan-German movement was breaking down ; the Frankfort parliament had elaborated a constitution, but its decisions had no binding powers behind them, and Frederick William in Prussia had deserted the cause by first intervening on behalf of Schleswig-Holstein and then admitting the Danish king's claim, following this by setting up a reactionary ministry in Prussia itself.

Accession of Victor Emmanuel. Before the autumn of 1849 the victory of reaction was complete. In Italy Charles Albert challenged Radetzky again, only to be hopelessly defeated at Novara in March. Rather than sign an ignominious peace he chose to abdicate and leave that to his son Victor Emmanuel, whom it would be impossible to reproach, because to fight would obviously be foolish. The Austrians gave the young king his choice of returning to the Austrian fold as a vassal, or paying the penalty of obstinacy in the armed occupation of Piedmont, coupled with the exaction of a heavy indemnity. He had the courage to choose the harder course, but Piedmont for the time was paralysed. Florence and Rome, which had both declared themselves republics, remained defiant. The French President tried to intervene, without pleasing either side ; the Austrians forced their way into Rome and restored the Pope ; Radetzky had completely subjugated Lombardy and Venetia.

The Hungarians, on the other hand, inspired by Kossuth and led in the field by their brilliant guerrilla commander Görgei, made so stout a resistance, with overwhelming odds against them, that the issue seemed doubtful till the imperial government appealed to the Czar for aid. The Russian hosts overwhelmed the Magyars by sheer weight of numbers, and then left the Austrians to trample on the smitten foe at leisure. In August all was over but the glutting of vengeance.

The scheme of German union collapsed. A Pan-German union must include Austria proper, but exclude the non-German portions of the Austrian empire ; to this the Austrian imperial government would not assent. The Frankfort parliament proposed to offer a German crown, without Austria at all, to Frederick William ; he rejected the proposal. Divers fresh proposals were made, all of which came to nothing. The old constitution of the German Confederation had never been dissolved, the reform movements ended in smoke, and in 1851 the former system, unaltered, once more came into full play.

Napoleon's Coup d'État. In France, however, the Republic, predominantly bourgeois, had displaced the constitutional monarchy but elected Louis Napoleon as its president, solely because he was his mighty uncle's nephew. He was expected to emulate that uncle, whom, though lacking the necessary genius, he nevertheless sought indeed to imitate. To do so he must make himself dictator and then emperor. As representative of the Napoleonic Idea he must convince the French people that he was the representative of stable and popular government at home, of glory and achievement abroad. His intervention in Italy had neither conciliated the clericals nor satisfied the democrats ; now he sought to increase his own popularity in the country by posing as the champion of democratic rights which the Chambers were seeking to curtail, thereby alienating the Chambers, in which a three-to-one majority was required to sanction his re-election as president in 1851. When the time came the majority was large but not large enough. But he had prepared for the *coup d'état* that, following precedent, was to secure him in defiance of the Chambers. The military chiefs were in the plot. He called for a law reviving universal suffrage ; the Assembly rejected it. On the night of December 1 the leaders of the opposition were arrested ; in the morning soldiers were patrolling the streets of Paris. Resistance was sharply stamped out, and a plebiscite triumphantly returned the " Prince President " to office. Twelve months later another plebiscite made him Napoleon III, Emperor of the French (December, 1852).

LESSON 26

Nation-Making of Bismarck and Cavour

(See plates 57 and 58)

D URING the French Second Empire (1852–70) under Napoleon III there came a series of international wars, the first being that which we are accustomed to think of as the Crimean War, a name that properly belongs only to its later phase. It originated in a dispute between Napoleon III and the Czar Nicholas as champions respectively of the Latin and the Orthodox Churches within the Turkish empire, certain privileges having been transferred from the former to the latter since the days of Catherine the Great. Napoleon demanded a re-transfer ; Nicholas would not hear of it. The Porte, reckoning on England's backing, refused to submit to Russian dictation. In June, 1853, Russian troops entered the trans-Danube provinces, as they were by treaty entitled to do. Nicholas did not realize that British public opinion was convinced of a secret Russian determination to win and use Constantinople as a bridge to India, and revived an earlier suggestion for a partition between Great Britain and Russia of the weakened Turkish empire. Though the result of this offer was entirely contrary to his expectation, the Czar remained convinced that a pacific British government would not intervene. But the war spirit was as high in France as was distrust of Russia in England. In November a Russian squadron sank the Turkish fleet at Sinope ; in March, France and Great Britain joined Turkey.

The Turks held up the Russians on the Danube. When the Turks were reinforced by French and British in midsummer, 1854,

(496)

the Russians fell back across the Pruth and Austrian troops entered the provinces. Nicholas would probably have assented to any terms that were not humiliating. But Napoleon wanted something more Napoleonic and England something more severe against the Russian menace ; so the two powers with Turkey launched an expedition against the Russian arsenal of Sevastopol.

War in the Crimea. The English organization was utterly inefficient for the conduct of the siege. The harbour was blockaded, but on the land side the investment could not be made complete. Incidents of the siege were the famous Balaclava charges ; the battle of Inkerman fought in a thick fog ; the terrible privations throughout the winter ; the arrival of an Italian contingent to assert Sardinia's European status ; the new organization of the base hospitals at Scutari which the world owes to Florence Nightingale, who arrived with her band of nurses to inaugurate the activities out of which arose the Red Cross ; the capture of the Malakoff fort by the French, which ensured the fall of Sevastopol in September, 1855.

Meanwhile, Nicholas—an honest man with the idea of autocracy —died and was succeeded by his son, Alexander II, who more resembled his uncle, Alexander I, with his Utopian visions, than his father. His desire was for peace. The allies had won all they could hope to win and the war was ended by the treaty of Paris (March, 1856), with Sardinia represented at the Peace Conference. Turkey, always ready to pledge herself to reforms, was guaranteed full sovereignty within her dominions, Russia surrendered her claims to protectorates, warships were excluded from the Black Sea, which was opened to commerce ; Napoleon was satisfied with the prestige he had acquired, and Great Britain with the security against Russian aggression which she conceived herself to have attained.

Charles Albert had failed as the champion of Italian aspirations, but his attempt and its failure had shown that emancipation from Austrian domination was the condition of escape from despotism, that disunited action could never be successful, and that united action was possible only under Sardinia's leadership. To his courageous and popular successor, Victor Emmanuel (1820–78), and his great minister Cavour (1810–61) it was also clear that—however strongly idealism or sentiment might resent the fact—the expulsion of Austria could not be effected without foreign aid.

The only foreign power whose self-interest might induce it to give Sardinia active aid against Austria was France ; Napoleon would be ready enough to combat Austrian influence in Italy, but not to help in creating a powerful and united Italian state ; and for whatever aid he might give he would demand his price. Cavour, however, had strengthened a sympathetic public opinion for Sardinia both in France and England by joining them in the Crimean War when Austria had held aloof, and was able to strengthen it further by giving prominence to the Italian griev-ances at the subsequent Peace Conference. In 1858 he came to a secret agreement with Napoleon. The conditions of French aid were that Austria must appear the aggressor, that the outcome of success should be an Italian confederation under the Pope's presidency, and France's reward the cession of Savoy and Nice.

Italian War of Liberation. Cavour had at least succeeded in exciting the interest of all Europe in the Italian question seething in Italy since Mazzini had inspired and founded the " Young Italy " movement, into which the patriot Garibaldi had flung himself in 1834. Manifestly both Sardinia and Austria were arming for a contest. In the former Garibaldi was raising troops of volunteers. Russia proposed a congress—from which Austria demanded the exclusion of Sardinia, and went on to an ultimatum requiring her immediate disarmament, thereby assuming the rôle of aggressor (April, 1859). France declared war ; Austria was defeated at Magenta and Solferino and promptly acceded to the terms offered by Napoleon at Villa-franca (July), in which he virtually deserted Sardinia, which could not stand out alone against the treaty of Zürich (November). Austria ceded Lombardy but not Venetia to Sardinia, which ceded Savoy and Nice to France. There was no Italian Con-federation ; but Napoleon could not prevent the minor central Italian states, which had rejected their rulers, from voting them-selves into the kingdom of North Italy.

Then on his own responsibility and against the orders of the official government, the brilliant condottiere Garibaldi (1807–82) organized the amazing volunteer expedition of the thousand " red shirts " which deprived Francis II, the successor of Bomba, of the throne of the Sicilies. Within two months of his landing in the island (May, 1860) Garibaldi was master of Sicily and was its elected dictator. He crossed to Italy, and his march on Naples was a triumphal procession. No one could tell what he would do next when he had finished with Francis. If he proclaimed a Sicilian republic it would be dangerous ; if he marched on Rome where the Pope still ruled, it would be fatal. Cavour must have troops on the spot. On the plea that the foreign troops in the Pope's pay were a menace, the king entered the papal states in arms ; the provinces by plebiscite transferred themselves to the northern kingdom. But the " Patrimony of St. Peter " was left intact to the Pope. Meanwhile, Garibaldi was in Naples and Francis II was holding out at Gaeta. Victor Emmanuel advanced into Neapolitan territory. Would he have to fight Garibaldi ? They met face to face ; and the Liberator hailed him as king of Italy. Both the Sicilies had already declared for union ; Gaeta was occupied in January. Only Venetia and Rome remained outside the new kingdom of Italy when it was formally proclaimed on March 17th, 1861, in which year Cavour died and Baron Ricasoli, an able statesman, who had laboured valiantly for the unity of Italy, succeeded him at the head of the ministry. He it was who modelled the organization of Italy on French lines—dividing the country into provinces, each with its prefect, under the Minister of the Interior.

Bismarck. Germany in 1851 had reverted to the system of the German Confederation in which the princes were for the most part dominated by the influence of Austria. But two things were contributing to a change transferring the hegemony to Prussia. One was the Prussian Zollverein or customs union into which most of the states had been drawn since its initiation in 1819, creating for them a common bond of commercial interests with Prussia as the senior partner, while Austria stood outside ; the other was the substitution for the erratic Frederick William, whose health gave way completely, of his brother William (1797–1888), first as regent and then as king of Prussia. For William found in Otto von Bismarck (1815–98) the minister who in the course of a few years made Prussia the first among the European powers by unscrupulous but extremely skilful statecraft. Bismarck meant himself to direct William, William to rule Prussia, Prussia to rule Germany, and Germany to rule Europe. Subsequently (1871) William I became the first German Emperor.

The revival of the army which a century previously had been the most efficient in Europe was in William's estimation the first essential. It was only by the help of a minister who was ready to over-ride the Prussian constitution that the necessary revenue could be raised. Bismarck did it, and the army was superbly organized under Von Moltke and Von Roon. The next step was to reconstruct the Confederation, with Austria excluded. Austria in 1863 propounded a reorganization scheme of her own. Prussia rejected it, but proposed a freely elected federal parliament. Then Austria and Prussia jointly took up the old Schleswig-Holstein question, invaded Denmark, and forced her to hand over the duchies, the respective administration of which the two powers appropriated (1864) ; while Russia was once more trampling on an insurrectionary Poland. Prussia had now tested her military machine. Bismarck only required security from adverse intervention before scraping the necessary quarrel with Austria. He duped Napoleon into believing that it would pay France to encourage a contest between Prussia and Austria ; he made a private pact with Italy that her opportune intervention should be rewarded by the recovery of Venetia. Then he quarrelled with Austria over the position in Schleswig-Holstein. Austria referred the question to the Diet of the Confederation. Bismarck demanded that a new Constitution should first be established— excluding Austria—and a federal parliament called to that end. Prussian troops entered Holstein ; Austria called on the Confederation to assert its authority in arms ; and Prussia withdrew from the Diet (June 14th, 1866).

Next day war was declared. The German princes were with Austria, but the Prussian army soon vanquished North Germany and Hanover ; although the Austrians defeated the Italians at Custozza, both Austrians and Bavarians were overwhelmed at Königgratz (Sadowa) and the victorious Prussian troops occupied the German principalities. The Seven Weeks' War was over before Napoleon could intervene ; the Peace of Prague was signed four weeks later. Venetia was ceded to the Italians (but not the Trentino) and Austria was permanently excluded from the German Confederation.

Our Course in Modern History is continued in Volume 6.

Bertrand Russell and Neo-Realism

MORE effective perhaps as a refutation of Idealism than the kind of Realism described in Lesson 20 (volume 4, page 515), and assuming in recent years great importance in philosophy, is the movement known as Neo-Realism. The most numerous advocates of Neo-Realism are to be found in America, but the Neo-Realist position has been effectively stated in England by Bertrand Russell. In his early book, " The Problems of Philosophy " (Home University Series), Russell was already pointing out that we have no direct knowledge in sense experience of what are called physical objects. The arguments which he brings forward in favour of this view may be briefly summarized as follow.

Returning to the case of the table (*see* Lesson 20), let us consider what sort of knowledge of it we actually do have. What is it precisely that we experience when, as we say, we perceive a table ? A shiny brown patch which we see, a cold hard something which we feel, a sharp hard noise which we hear when we rap the table, and so on. These entities—the shiny brown patch, the cold hard something, the rapping noise—are called sense data (sometimes *sensibilia*), " things given to the senses," and it is of these and not of tables and chairs that we have direct experience (what Bertrand Russell calls " knowledge by acquaintance ") when we come into contact with the external world. That the sense datum is not the same as what we call a physical object can be seen from a simple instance. If I put a shilling a foot away from me and a florin three yards away, the shining elliptical patch which is what I see in the place where the shilling is, is larger than the shining elliptical patch I see in the place where the florin is. Yet the florin is larger than the shilling. Physical objects, not being known by acquaintance, are said by Russell, in the book referred to, to be " known by description." Our knowledge of them, that is to say, is based on inference and involves some *a priori* knowledge.

Sense Data and Physical Objects. The problem raised by the recognition of the fact that what we directly apprehend when we have sensory experience of the external world are not physical objects, but are sense data, raps of sound, patches of colour, smell data, touch data, and so forth, is an exceedingly difficult one. In some way, it is true, we do know physical objects, but it seems very difficult to suppose that we know them directly by means of our senses. What, then, is the relation between the sense data which we experience by means of our senses and the physical objects with which in some way they seem to be connected ? If I hold up my finger and look at it, what I shall immediately apprehend is an oblong, pink shape. If I touch it, I shall feel something warm and firm. If I put it in my mouth when I am heated, I shall taste something salty. What, then, is the relation between the oblong, pink shape which is certainly not warm or firm or salty, between the warm, firm something which is certainly not pink, between the salty something which I taste, and my finger ?

Various suggestions have been made. It is said, for example, that the sense datum is part of the surface of the physical object. But if we take a case in which the surface of the physical object would not normally be said to have changed, and focus our attention upon the sense datum we actually apprehend, which, on this view, is alleged to be a part of the surface, then the datum perceptibly varies according to the position from which and the conditions under which we look at the alleged part. If, for example, we look at the alleged part from a greater distance, that which we actually see is different from what it is if we look at the part from a smaller distance. It differs again, if we look at it obliquely or if we put santonin into our eyes, and, most noticeably of all, it is different when we *touch* the alleged part. If the whole surface of the physical object does not change, then no part of it can change ; yet the datum, as we have seen, does continuously change, as we change our position of observation. It seems clear, then, that the datum cannot be identical with any *part* of the surface. Again, it is said that the relation between the object and the datum is that the object causes the datum. But, if we always directly apprehend the datum and never the object, we cannot know any of the properties of the object by direct experience. We could only at best infer them from our knowledge of the datum. We do not, therefore, know that the object has the property of being able to cause the datum. We do not, in fact, know by direct experience that the object exists at all. It is for these and other reasons that many writers are inclined to deny that there are physical objects which belong to the external physical world.

Russell's Later Views. In later books, " Our Knowledge of the External World " and " An Outline of Philosophy," Bertrand Russell dispenses with the physical object altogether. If, in experiencing the external world, we never do and never can meet with anything but sense data, what legitimate reason, he asks, is there for supposing that it contains anything but sense data ? To postulate a physical object as a hypothetical cause for the sense data, the cause being something which is never known, is like reintroducing Locke's unknown and unknowable substance to be the *cause* of our ideas and impressions.

But, if the external world consists of sense data, why, it may be asked, do we believe in physical objects ? Because we correlate together, in virtue of their resemblance to each other and in accordance with the laws of perspective, numbers of sense data which we proceed to regard as being those caused by or associated with one physical object.

Sense data are not enduring entities, but have only a momentary existence. Moreover, they are affected by physiological, though not by psychological, conditions in ourselves. The sense datum, however, though affected by the nervous system and brain, is not affected by the mind, nor is it part of the mind. It is an entity independent of mind and known by mind exactly as it is. Thus Idealism forms no part of the view of perception we are considering.

Universals. If we are to limit the activity of the mind in perceiving to bare awareness—if, in fact, the mind knows sense data just as they are, differences between people's perceptions being explained in terms of differences between the sense data perceived—there seems to be no good ground for attributing to mind a different sort of activity in knowledge. Hence, some Realists believe in the independent reality of objects known as universals. When one thinks of justice, the mind, on this view, is in direct contact with a non-mental entity called sometimes a " universal," sometimes a " subsistent object," the relation of the mind to this object being one of direct awareness. A theory of thinking and, in particular, of the part played by the mind in thinking, has been worked out in America by Prof. Montagu and others on this basis.

LESSON 22

The Theory of Sense Data

THE following considerations are offered in favour of the view that what we directly apprehend in the external world are not physical objects, but sets of sense data ; that these, and not objects, are directly perceived. The arguments are mainly taken from C. D. Broad's " The Mind and Its Place in Nature."

(1) If I am looking at a bell, nobody would maintain that what I see is, or is identical with, the whole of the surface of the bell. For example, the bell has an inside as well as an outside ; yet what I see is a coloured patch of indefinite boundaries, which, although it may be part of the outside, is certainly not part of the inside. Therefore what I see is not identical with the whole surface of the physical object which we call a bell.

(2) The bell, considered as a physical object, is extended not only in space but in time ; it has a past and a future, and the length of its history from the time of casting to that of demolition is in theory measurable. What I see is a single, comparatively short contemporary event. It may be true that the short contemporary event which is the object of my seeing is also a contemporary slice of the history of the bell, which extends backward into the past and forward into the future, but it is certainly not identical with it.

(3) A bell is more than a coloured surface, and the surface itself has qualities other than that of colour ; it is, for example, also hard and cold. What I see when I look at the bell has colour, but is neither hard nor cold. Therefore, what I see is not identical with the surface of the bell.

(4) What I touch when I touch the bell is both hard and cold, but is not coloured. The surface of the bell is coloured. Therefore what I touch is not identical with the surface of the bell. It is also different from what I see when, as I say, I look at the bell. The conclusion is that neither in visual nor in tactile experience is what I directly apprehend by means of my senses the *whole* surface of the bell.

(5) I can be the victim of what are commonly called hallucinations. A hallucination is a state of mind in which I believe

myself to see things which would in common parlance be said not to be there. A similar state of mind attends intoxication ; the drunkard sees what he calls pink rats in circumstances in which no person who is not drunk sees them, and in which consequently there would be common agreement among all sober persons that the pink rats were not there.

Accepting this argument at its face value, assuming, that is to say, that the drunkard's experience is, as we say, delusive, in the sense that there really are no pink rats there, then we are justified in saying that, whatever it is that the drunkard perceives—and he certainly does perceive something—is not identical with a physical object, since in this case no such object exists.

Nor is physical science any kinder. The information which has been obtained by physicists with regard to the nature of matter and of light, and by physiologists with regard to the machinery of perception and more particularly the workings of the nervous system, have an important bearing on the problems under discussion. It is common knowledge that many physicists deny the existence of an external world of solid material things, and are inclined to adopt views not dissimilar from those of Kant, according to which the apparently independent objects of the world outside us are really constructed by our own minds.

Heat and Sound. Heat, according to the physicist's account, is caused by or *is* the energy, both kinetic and potential, of the motion of molecules. Consider, for example, the case of a gas. It consists of molecules, of about a hundred-millionth of an inch across, with comparatively large spaces between them, moving about in all directions with an average speed measured in hundreds of yards a second. The molecules meet and collide, and in consequence of their collision the gas has a certain temperature. If the gas is placed in a flame or hot body, the molecules of which it is composed will gain in energy, moving rapidly and colliding more violently. Imperceptibly the temperature of the gas will go up ; heat, as we say, is generated. But the cause of this heat is the greater energy of motion of the molecules ; or, to put it as a text-book of physics would put it, heat *is* nothing but the energy of motion of molecules.

Similarly, sound is said to be caused by, or alternatively to *be,* waves in the atmosphere. These waves vary in length, in frequency of vibration and in mode of vibration. Variations in length determine the loudness, in frequency of vibration the pitch, and in mode of vibration the quality of the sound. Sound, then, is produced by atmospheric waves. Atmospheric waves are described as regions of pressure and rarefaction in the atmosphere moving forward with a certain velocity, and the movement of such a region of the atmosphere is the cause of, or simply *is*, sound. Thus the properties of the atmospheric waves which the sounding body gives out determine the character of the sounds.

Smell and Colour. Smell is, or is caused by, or consists of, molecules given off in the form of vapour by the substance which in ordinary language is said to smell. Smell, it is interesting to note, is not even for common sense a property which is attached to the object ; a smell, it is thought, is something *given off by* rather than something which *belongs to*. Most significant of all is the case of colour. Colour is often described as a quality of light ; it is, at any rate, intimately bound up with light, so that where there is no light, there is no colour. Now light, says the physicist, is, or is caused by, a certain set of wave-lengths of varying frequencies in the electro-magnetic spectrum. Within this section of wave-lengths which are, or which produce, light, certain subsections are earmarked for the different colours. At one end of the section, that containing waves of shortest wave-length and highest frequency, are violet rays ; at the other, red rays. Beyond violet are the ultra-violet rays, which are called violet only by courtesy, since they cannot be seen : below red, at the other end of the section, are the infra-red, which equally are red by courtesy only. Between lie the other colours. Thus, just as light-waves constitute a particular section of the waves graded according to length and frequency in the electro-magnetic spectrum, most of which are not visible, so each colour is constituted by a subsection of waves of particular frequency and wave-length falling within the light section.

These scientific descriptions of the qualities which characterize the world of our everyday experience have an important point in common ; the scientific objects in terms of which the qualities are analysed, are themselves devoid of the qualities in question. Thus physics takes the ordinary qualities of the world we perceive and analyses them into something else. The world we see is coloured, the world we hear noisy ; but the world of physics is neither coloured nor noisy. What, then, has become of colour and noise ? The obvious answer is the Idealist one that they are supplied by the mind of the perceiver.

LESSON 23

Physicist's View of Perception

MOST people would say that the physicist's world is in some sense more real than the sensory world, or at any rate that the physicist gives a truer account of the nature of things than the man in the street ; and this view is certainly shared by most physicists. It is desirable, therefore, if we are to determine whether the outside world really contains qualities or not, to consider very briefly what happens, according to the physicist, when, as we say, we see something external to ourselves.

Let us suppose, then, that I am a modern physicist who is looking at a distant object. This object I believe to be a highly complicated set of physical processes, which are electrical in character. I know further that a physical process, which I call a light ray, starts from the object and travels through the intervening medium of the atmosphere, being changed in the course of its journey into another physical process, which ultimately reaches the retina of my eye. Here it is changed into, or provokes, another physical process, which travels along my optic nerve, where it changes into yet another physical process and produces some effect on my brain about which I know very little for certain, but which I assume to be also some kind of physical process.

When this physical process occurs in the brain, there ensues a process of an entirely different kind, namely a *psychological* event which I call seeing. This is directed not upon the physical process in the brain which was the latest physical *cause* in the chain of events which preceded it, but upon what is called the object, which I know in my capacity of physicist to be a set of complicated physical processes which happened earlier in the series of processes than the brain process, this earlier set of physical processes being selected apparently arbitrarily from among the chain of physical processes which preceded the occurrence of the physical process in my brain.

Now this account involves a number of inferences, two of which in particular rest upon assumptions which may be mistaken. I am looking, let us say, at the star Sirius on a dark night. If physics is to be believed, light waves which started to travel from Sirius many months ago reach (after a specified time which astronomers calculate) the earth, impinge upon my retinas and cause me to say that I am seeing Sirius. Now the Sirius about which they convey information to me is the Sirius which existed at the time when they started. This Sirius may, however, no longer exist ; it may have disappeared in the interval taken by the travelling light ray. To say that one can see what no longer exists is absurd. It follows that, whatever it is that I am seeing, it is not Sirius. What, in point of fact, I do see is a yellow patch of a particular size, shape and intensity. I infer from my knowledge of astronomy that this yellow patch had an origin, with which it is connected by a continuous chain of physical events, several years ago and many million miles away. But this inference may be mistaken ; the origin of the yellow patch, which I call a star, may be a blow on the nose, or a lamp hanging on the mast of a ship.

Knowledge and Deduction. Nor is this the only inference involved. It is true that I *think* I am seeing a yellow patch, but am I really justified in holding this belief ? So far as physics and physiology are concerned, all that we are entitled to say is that the optic nerve is being stimulated in a certain way, as a result of which certain events are being caused to happen in the brain. Are we really justified in saying any more than this ? Possibly we are, but it is important to realize that, if we do say more than this, an inference is once again involved, and once again the inference may be mistaken. Directly we go beyond the bare statement " the optic nerve is being stimulated in such and such a way," and conclude from this fact " therefore I am seeing an object of such and such a character," we are drawing an inference and are liable to fall into error. What, then— if the physicist and physiologist are right—we, in fact, know are certain events taking place in our own brains. The outside world is not itself known ; its existence is merely an inference due to the fact that we think these events must have a cause. Perception by touch makes the matter even plainer.

If we accept the teaching of physics and physiology, what we know in perception are not the movements of matter, but certain events in ourselves connected with those movements ; not objects external to ourselves, but the effects of the impact of light-rays and other forms of energy proceeding from these objects upon our bodies. This, in general, is the view of the matter which is taken by Sir Arthur Eddington. The external world is for him not something that we perceive, but something that we construct from messages that reach the brain along the nerves. The mind, he says, " weaves an impression out of the stimuli travelling along the nerves to the brain." Illustrating this conception, he makes use of a vivid simile, which likens the mind to an editor sitting in his inner sanctum receiving messages from a number of different reporters and, with the aid of a good deal of invention, piecing them together into a story.

The material which reaches the brain along these channels, the material which the mind must utilize for its story-making or world-building, is of the scantiest. Colour, temperature, sound, texture, all are lacking. These are not qualities which are given to us from outside, but qualities with which the mind invests the material which reaches it, " fancies " which it projects into the external world. Even the structure of familiar things, their " substantiality " and apparent permanence, are bestowed upon them by the mind.

It is not difficult to see why physicists adopt idealist views. In contrast to the roundabout and indirect nature of our knowledge of the external world, there is placed the directness, the immediacy and the certainty of the mind's knowledge of itself. Our knowledge of the external world, it seems, is something which results from a long chain of messages which have travelled along intricate and roundabout lines of communication. But, to quote Sir Arthur Eddington, " there is one kind of knowledge which cannot pass through such channels—namely, knowledge of the intrinsic nature of that which lies at the far end of the lines of communication." This knowledge, which is direct knowledge of something as it is in itself, is knowledge of a mind. " Mind," he says, " is the first and most direct thing in our experience. All else is remote inference." We have, he continues, " an acquaintance with the mental and spiritual nature of ourselves, known in our minds by an intimate contact transcending the methods of physics." If the one thing which we know as it really is, turns out to be a mind, might it not also be the case that other things, if they could be known as they really are, that is to say, from inside, would turn out to be mental, too ? Thus we reach the familiar conclusion that the reality of things is probably mental, and that the material world is really a form of appearance which mental existences present to certain finite intelligences and partial points of view. Material phenomena, in fact, are the results of abstraction and selection by our own minds from a spiritual reality which underlies them.

Sir James Jeans's view of the world as a thought in the mind of its Creator conceived as a Mathematician, is a product of the same line of thought reached by not very dissimilar arguments. Nor are these views, as is sometimes suggested, peculiar to English scientists. Famous Continental physicists, such as Einstein, Schrodinger and Planck, incline to think of consciousness as fundamental, and matter as something derived from consciousness.

It should, however, be strongly emphasized that these conclutions are not in any way necessitated. Nor can it be said that they have won much general favour among philosophers. What has happened is that, owing to certain recent developments in physics, many scientists have come to adopt those views of the external world which are to be found either in Berkeley's philosophy or in Kant's. The fact that scientists have come to share the views of these philosophers does not necessarily prove them to be true ; nor does it remove the very serious objections to which idealist interpretations of the universe are exposed, which have frequently been pointed out by philosophers in the past.

The state of physics is at the moment too transitional to enable any definite philosophical conclusions to be based upon the theories of physicists. Three main positions which may be regarded rather as starting points for further inquiry than as established conclusions are permissible, and any of them may be adopted. (1) We may take, as Sir Arthur Eddington does, an idealist line and hold that the only thing we directly know is our own experience, that this is continuous with an all-pervading spiritual reality, and that the apparent world of matter is the result of an arbitrary selection from this spiritual reality. (2) We may hold that the only events that we can possibly know are those taking place in our own bodies and brains—this is known sometimes as the " under-hat philosophy "—and that the external world is merely an inference from these events. (3) We may hold that what we directly know are sense data, and that the worlds both of scientific objects and physical objects are somehow constructed out of sense data. The difficulty on this view is to work out a satisfactory theory of the relations between these different worlds.

LESSON 24

The Philosophy of Materialism

MATERIALISM has its roots in the science of the late 19th century, and in order to follow its rise we must retrace our steps some little distance in time and consider the speculations and controversies which began with the publication of Darwin's " Origin of Species." Materialism, or the belief that matter, however defined, is the sole type of existence in the universe and that the laws which govern the movements of matter are, therefore, fundamental and all-embracing, was backed by all the contemporary science of the late 19th century. Its main support was, however, derived from biology and psychology.

Darwin's work had shown that the evolution of life upon this planet was a continuous process from the amoeba and jellyfish, in which it first manifested itself, to its culmination in the human race. This development was achieved by means of a process of natural selection. Variations in species occurred ; the off-spring would be either more or less suited to their environments than their parents ; those that were suited to their environment prospered, chose mates in whom a similarly advantageous variation had appeared, and handed on the variation to their offspring. Creatures that varied in a manner unsuited to their environment died off. As to the cause of the initial variations upon which the law of natural selection operated, Darwin confessed agnosticism. It must be presumed, therefore, that the initial variations were to be ascribed to chance.

The other main theory in the field, that of Lamarck, ascribed the changes in and development of living organisms to the effects upon them of changes in their external environment. As the environment changed, living organisms either succeeded in adapting themselves to it, or they did not. If they were successful, the variation in the organisms resulting from the adaptation gradually became established so that a new species came into being. If they were not, the non-adaptable creature died out.

Both theories had an important point in common. In order to explain the whole process of development that has led from the amoeba to Man, including also the development of intelligence in Man, they found it necessary to invoke neither mind nor purpose, neither creative force nor divine agency; they relied solely upon the operation of natural forces. Darwin ascribed the development to chance variations of which the fittest survived; Lamarck to the automatic adaptation of creatures to their environment. Complete determinism results in either case, since all changes in living organisms, including human beings, will be the result of prior changes in the external environment to which the human being responds. It is obvious, if this view is correct, that, just as the body is relegated to dependence upon its external environment, so a particular theory of the status and function of mind, a theory which equally relegated mind to complete dependence upon the body, is required. This theory was supplied by 19th century psychology.

If body and mind be conceived as completely different sorts of entities, the question of how they manage to interact presents serious difficulties. The attributes of the body are those of any piece of matter—weight, size, mass, occupancy of space and so forth—and the movements of the body obey the laws of physics. None of these attributes belongs to the mind. The mind has neither weight nor size nor shape, it does not occupy space, and its contents are not atoms and electrons, but the stream of thoughts, images, volitions, etc., which make up consciousness. If it has no single quality in common with the body, how can it establish that contact with the body that interaction implies? How can it influence the body or be influenced by it?

Descartes solved the difficulty by regarding the apparent synchronization between mental events and bodily events as due to divine intervention. There was, he held, no causal connexion between mind and body, but God had so arranged matters that any event in the one was accompanied by a corresponding event in the other. This view, known as psycho-physical parallelism, was unacceptable to science, and, since the difficulty of conceiving interaction between entities completely different in kind seemed insurmountable, science met the situation by denying the difference. The body obviously was material; the mind, then, it was inferred, must be material, too. Hence arose a conception of consciousness as a very attenuated form of matter, a sort of glow surrounding the brain, whose function was limited to registering or lighting up the events which occur in the

FLORENCE NIGHTINGALE (1820–1910). Born in Florence, she became interested in hospital work when quite young. In 1854 she sailed for the Crimea and remained with the troops until the end of the war. The "lady of the lamp," as she was called by the soldiers, received the O.M. in 1907.

MODERN HISTORY 26

MAKERS OF THE GERMAN EMPIRE. Left, William I (1797–1888), who succeeded his brother as king of Prussia in 1861, and was proclaimed first German emperor ten years later. Right, Prince Otto von Bismarck (1815–98) came of Prussian Junker stock, and first came into political prominence as an opponent of the liberal movement in 1848. From 1862 to 1871 he was premier of Prussia, and thenceforth until 1890, when he was dismissed by the young Kaiser William II, chancellor of the Reich. His policy of " blood and iron " was inspired throughout by the determination to make Germany a united and powerful military empire.

MODERN HISTORY 26

FATHERS OF UNITED ITALY. Count Camillo di Cavour (left; 1810–61) was born in Turin. In 1848 he started a liberal newspaper and was soon recognized as a leader of the Italian nationalists. Four years later he became premier, and remained so with short intervals until his death. Giuseppe Mazzini (centre; 1805–72), born at Genoa, was early exiled for republican activities. In 1849 he set up a short-lived republic in Rome. He would have nothing to do with the new Italian kingdom, and was still plotting for a republic when he died. Right, Giuseppe Garibaldi (1807–82) was born at Nice, a fisherman's son, and in 1834 joined Mazzini's Young Italy movement. During 1836–48 he was in South America, but from 1848 onwards he led an army of irregulars in all the campaigns in Italy.

MODERN HISTORY 26

Plate 58   Volume **V**

brain. Since the glow of consciousness could not light up events which were not there, it followed that nothing could occur in the mind which had not previously occurred in the brain. Hence all mental events were dependent upon and determined by preceding bodily events, and free will was a delusion.

If the mind, a particular sort of emanation from the body, is determined by the body, and the body by events in the external world, the chain of cause and effect leading from movements of matter in the material universe to the thoughts of human beings is complete. We live in a cast-iron universe which develops according to necessary laws, which are ultimately of the same kind as those studied by physics. Mind and spirit are not fundamental, but late and unimportant arrivals in a material universe, the products of material conditions. Causation proceeds always from the less living to the more. Living organisms are determined by the external environment in which they are placed, and within the living organism the mind is determined by the bodily and nervous system of which it is the mere reflection. Hence, the laws which are appropriate to happenings of every kind are those which govern the movements of small particles of matter. To quote Professor Whitehead : " Little lumps of material moving in space according to necessary and inevitable laws have produced our hopes, our fears, the scent of the rose, the colours of the sunset and the mystic's experience of God. They have also produced our knowledge of the little bits. Mind, in short, is merely the consciousness of the bits by themselves." When the conditions favourable to living organisms have passed away, we may expect life to disappear, finishing its pointless journey with as little noise and significance as in the person of the amoeba it began it. Meanwhile, the universe as a whole may be conceived after the model of a gigantic clock, functioning as the result of the automatic interaction of its parts.

The philosophical implications of the materialist view of the universe are : (1) Free will is an illusion. (2) Mind is an emanation from the body, and the body a product of material forces. (3) There is no purpose or plan in the universe. (4) There is no Creator. (5) The law of cause and effect which operates in the world of matter is ultimate, and applies also to life. The following books are suggested : " Materialism Restated," Chapman Cohen ; " History of Materialism," F. A. Lange (Eng. trans.).

Our Course in Philosophy is continued in Volume 6.

LESSON 17

The Wave Nature of Light

(See Colour Frontispieces)

WE have seen that the visible octave which constitutes the range of electromagnetic waves that affect the retina of the eye only forms part of a large family of waves which may be detected because they affect one or more of the senses, or which may be detected by special apparatus (e.g. wireless waves). There is no doubt that the radiations are waves, and that their wave-lengths may be measured.

A source of white light sends out a band of wave-lengths from one value to double that value in all directions about the source ; a monochromatic source sends out a very limited range of wave-lengths, which we might say has one value only, just as the London wireless station sends out one wave-length only, whereas the old spark transmitting station used to send out a band of waves which affected a wireless receiver over a wide range of tuning. To study the wave nature itself it is much easier, in almost every case, to consider a " monochromatic " source and see what happens, and then see how this is modified when we use white light. We discussed waves in Lesson 13 (Volume 4, page 528) and saw that, when conditions were right, two sets of waves act on each other, producing interference effects and diffraction or bending, and we were led to anticipate similar results with *any* wave motion.

In strings and the like, the conditions are easy to produce, because, in the first place, it is relatively easy to have two identical sources of vibration, and, again, the wave-motions produced are readily visible. In light, even in a monochromatic source, we are dealing with a complex thing. What happens is that any particular point in the source sends out a train of waves for a short interval of time and then repeats this ; in other words, the source is not giving a straightforward, continuous output. To get interference we must reproduce the same source in duplicate and so get identical origins for two wave trains, and in these circumstances we are able to produce a large variety of interference and allied effects.

Let us see how this was done by Fresnel. A source of light illuminated a narrow slit S, and the light was allowed to fall on an arrangement (shown in Fig 1) of two identical prisms placed base to base. This arrangement is called a biprism, and the refracting angles of the prisms were equal and very small. The

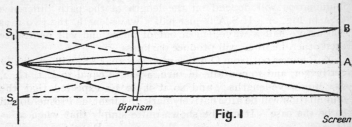

Fig. 1

Biprism

Screen

light falling on the prism was refracted as shown, and appeared to come from S_1 and S_2, but in the region AB the two beams overlapped. Considered as waves, we have in the region AB two sets of identical waves in the same space, and we can, therefore, predict interference effects in this region. Where the waves from the two beams fit together, crest to crest and trough to trough, we expect double the amplitude and, in point of fact, four times the brightness of the one beam; but where the waves emerge together with a crest of the one joining a trough of the other, the waves destructively interfere, and, although the light beams are both there, the net result is zero illumination. This experiment was made, and the interference resulted in a set of parallel fringes of alternately bright and dark bands. (There is no real difficulty in repeating the experiment, using, say, sodium light; it is done by students as a routine experiment in the laboratories.)

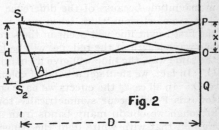

Fig. 2

The distance apart of these bands can be measured by viewing them by means of a microscope, and if d and D (see Fig. 2) are also measured, we can calculate quite easily the wave-length of the light used. Fig. 2 shows the essentials of the optical paths.

S_1 and S_2 are the equivalent sources, and OP is the screen or eye-piece of the microscope. It seems clear that rays of light from S_1 and S_2 have the same length of path to O, and, therefore, arrive in phase (i.e. crest to crest) and so produce an addition of their individual amplitudes. As we pass up the screen to P, the illumination will depend on the length of the path difference (S_2A in Fig. 2). If S_2A is just half a wave-length, the two rays will arrive half a wave-length out of phase and will neutralize each other, i.e. they will produce darkness.

As P moves out from O it is fairly clear that AS$_2$ will gradually get bigger, and so contain, in turn, a length equal to $\frac{1}{2}$, 1, $1\frac{1}{2}$, 2, $2\frac{1}{2}$, etc. wave-lengths; and so it is to be expected that the illumination will be alternatively dark and light, as Fresnel found to be the case. It can be shown quite simply that when $x = \frac{D}{d} \cdot \frac{\lambda}{2}$ there is the first dark band, and when $x = \frac{D}{d} 2 \left(\frac{\lambda}{2}\right)$ there is the first bright band, and so on. Therefore, if D, d and x are measured λ, the wave-length, can be calculated. In this way the value is found to be $5\cdot89 \times 10^{-5}$cm. $= \cdot0000589$ cm. for the yellow sodium light (actually this is composed of two wave-lengths: $5\cdot8899 \times 10^{-5}$ and $5\cdot8959 \times 10^{-5}$cm.). In all the above we have assumed a monochromatic source, but if we use white light, which is a mixture of wave-lengths, to illuminate the biprism, the maximum and zero illumination produced by the yellow component will be precisely in the same place as when that colour only was used as source. But, in addition, each colour in the white light beam will produce its own effect, which is similar in nature, but differs in magnitude because of the difference in wave-length.

It seems obvious that, when we consider the large red rays, the first bright line will occur in the screen when AS$_2$ is equal to one wave-length of the red, i.e. will be farther away from O. In the same way, the blue will give its maximum at a point nearer to O. In fact, we shall get a band of colour about the white centre at O. In all cases the effects we have considered in the direction towards P will occur symmetrically towards O, of course, but, although we obtain many bands from a monochromatic source, we find that with white light the fringes soon cease because we have overlapping of the colours, producing a general white illumination, in a very small distance after the first set.

One might be rather tempted to suggest that these results seem very like those of ordinary refraction through a prism, as considered in Lesson 15, volume 4, page 539, but the positions of these colours do not agree with such an explanation, and, further, the same scheme of things can be produced by other means without prisms, which, in this case, were simply used to obtain two similar sources. For example, in Fig. 3, another method of producing two identical sources is shown. Two mirrors OA and OB are slightly inclined to each other, and the source S is reproduced by reflection at S_1 and

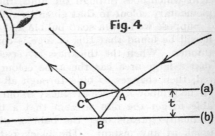

Fig. 3

S_2 as far behind the mirrors as S is in front of them. At XY the two beams interfere and produce results similar to those described above.

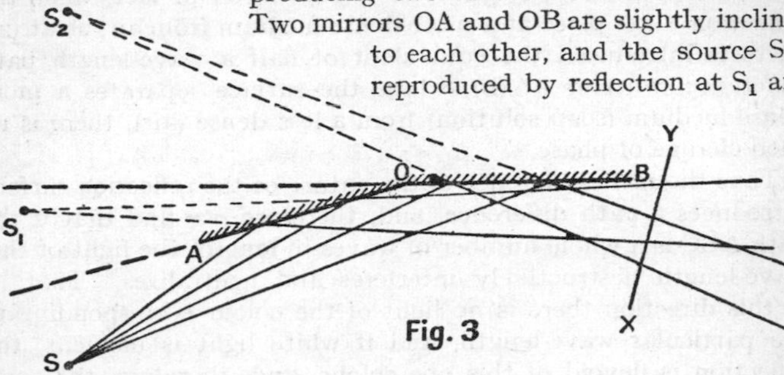

Perhaps the best-known example of the effects of the interference of light is the colour produced in soap films and soap bubbles. The magnificent hues seen on the bubbles blown from a pipe, or on the bubbly surface of soapy water, are brought about by the interference of the white light which falls on the very thin films. If we consider a very much magnified section of a soap film, we see that light falling on it can suffer reflection at the first surface (Fig. 4); then, of the light which is refracted into the soap film, some is reflected at the surface (b) and will emerge, as shown, parallel to the first ray. When we think of a wide beam of light as being incident, instead of one ray, we

Fig. 4

find that the reflected beam is made up of millions of rays, some of which have been simply reflected at (a) and an equal number reflected at (b). What an eye sees by these reflected rays depends largely on the way in which the two sets of rays behave when they unite. If the extra path, ABC, which the one set of rays have to travel, is equal to a whole number of waves, we should expect that the two sets of rays would reinforce, crest to crest, and produce a brightness. As a matter of fact, when the reflection takes place at a more dense medium from air, as at (a), there is introduced the equivalent of half a wave-length path difference, whereas at (b), where the surface separates a more dense medium (soap solution) from a less dense (air), there is no such change of phase.

Thus the mere difference in the nature of the reflection surface introduces a path difference, and, therefore, we find that if the path ABC is a whole number of waves in length, the light of this wave-length destructively interferes and neutralizes. That is, in this direction there is no light of the colour corresponding to the particular wave-length, and if white light is incident, the reflection is devoid of this one colour, and, therefore, the complementary colour (i.e. white minus this particular colour) is produced and the film appears to be coloured. The colour will, of course, change when the thickness of the film changes, because the extra path ABC is thereby changed, and so is the wave-length which interferes at this particular path difference.

Again, if the path difference is a whole number of waves' lengths plus a half-wave of one colour, this will be reinforced at the particular angle which gives this condition, and there will thus be an excess of one colour on a white background. In both ways the reflected light gives rise to colours. In the case of the light which goes through the films, the colour seen is the complementary colour to that given by reflection.

Suppose we blow a soap bubble and watch the colour change, it will be found that this change is continuous as the film gets thinner. When the thickness is very greatly reduced, we find that a large area has the same colour, which in turn becomes red, then changes to blue through all the intermediate colours of the rainbow. If we are lucky in our soap solution we may be able to get the film so thin that a black patch appears and gradually spreads over the bubble, which at this stage might break at any instant. The black patch means that we have reduced the thickness of the bubble to something much less than the wave-length of blue light, i.e. of the order of much less than

·00004 cm. In fact, the path difference between the two reflected rays is negligibly small (only a minute fraction of the wave-length of blue light), and all that is happening is that the difference in phase caused by reflection at the upper surface, as we saw above, introduced a path difference of half a wave and all waves, therefore, interfere, and we obtain the perfectly black spot. The film is only a few molecules thick at this stage. A certain amount of patience is required to produce this effect, but the experiment can easily be tried with a clay pipe and a soap solution.

The same explanation accounts for many well-known beautiful colour schemes, such as those produced by thin oil films on the surface of water. The colours of opals and many gems of the same kind, butterfly's wings, peacock feathers and the like can all be explained in terms of interference, as such, or in terms of an allied effect, which is called *diffraction*. The difference between interference and diffraction is quite arbitrary : the methods are similar, as we shall see.

Before we go on to consider this other interesting phenomenon, there is one particular form of interference fringe system which is worth consideration because of its wide application. If we take a curved surface and put it in contact with a perfectly plane surface, we find that beautiful coloured rings appear when illuminated with white light. These rings are called Newton's rings. Many elaborate instruments, called interferometers, have been devised to produce them, and to measure by their aid the dimensions of small objects and the change in length of longer objects when subjected to change of physical conditions.

If we take a piece of good plate glass and rest a weak convex spectacle lens on it and illuminate with white light, the rings appear. If the light enters at right angles to the plane, as at o.1.2 in Fig. 5, it is clear that ray 1 can reflect at AOB or at CD. These reflected rays, coming together, reinforce or interfere

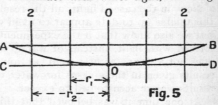

Fig. 5

if the path difference is half a wave or a whole wave, and so produce rings of light or darkness about O, as the path difference is the same in a circle about O. If we use monochromatic light we get bright and dark rings of the colour used. Now, if CD moves away parallel to itself, we find that the rings appear to move in or out. For a movement of CD equal to half a wave, the path difference made is a whole wave, and so the rings seen move so that they take the place of their former neighbouring rings. This is used to measure small movements in physical and engineering practice. It has the virtue of enabling an accurate measurement to ·000005 cm. without using anything more harmful to the apparatus than a beam of light, which is reflected from the apparatus itself.

LESSON 18

More About the Wave Theory of Light

WHEN we discussed the properties of waves in Lesson 13 (volume 4, page 528), we saw that, in cases of water waves, the motion was able to go round a small obstacle, Fig. 1 (b), whereas a long breakwater casts shadows, Fig. 1 (a). If water waves are directed to an opening between two obstacles, they pass through, not only in the original direction, but in a fan-like direction, spread outwards, as shown in Fig. 1 (c).

If, now, we make the opening small, as in Fig. 1 (d), we find that water waves pass outwards in circles, as shown in the figure. The student can easily repeat these experiments by using a bath as an experimental tank and making waves with a piece of stick. It will be found that the smaller the opening in the experiment shown in Fig. 1 (d) the more complete are the circular waves which are set up on the side remote from the disturbance.

Now, in the case of light, all the results which we have seen in this Course up to date appear to fit in with a wave propagation, but we also know that if the experiments shown in Fig. 1 be performed with light, instead of water, waves, the type of result does not appear—at first sight, at any rate—to agree with the results given in these cases for water waves. Fig. 2 shows the results we are accustomed to expect.

At one time it was believed that this apparent disagreement was a decided blow to a wave theory for light. It was, therefore, a matter of great scientific interest to see whether light by any chance behaved as in Fig. 1, to some degree, and to explain the bulk disagreement. Now there is a very important difference between the two waves. Water waves are long; light waves are very small. In the water waves in Fig. 1 (b), for example, the size of the obstacle is comparable with the wave-length,

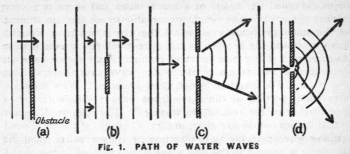

Fig. 1. PATH OF WATER WAVES

whereas in Fig. 2 (b) the obstacle is some hundred thousand times as great as the wave-length. The same may be said of the opening between the obstacles in Figs. 1 (d) and 2 (d).

To make a fair comparison, therefore, it seems desirable so to reduce the size of the obstacle, or the opening, as to be at any rate of the same *order* as the wave-length of the light used, and then to see if the bending of the light waves takes place, as shown in Fig. 1 for water waves.

We are so accustomed to recognizing that light travels in

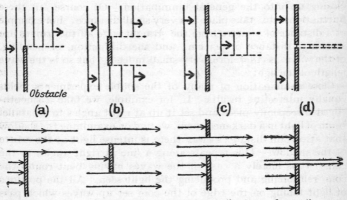

Fig. 2. The upper figures represent wave fronts, the lower figures the corresponding rays of light using obstacles and apertures the same size as in Fig. 1; (a) a long obstacle. (b) a short obstacle. (c) a wide opening. (d) a narrow opening.

straight lines that it comes as a mild shock to find that, when we deal with extremely small openings, there appears to be a variation from this rule. For example, if the sun is shining on a room darkened by means of a black blind and there is a very minute pin-prick in the blind, we are able to see the sun shining at the small pin-prick even when the eye is not in a straight line with it and the sun—in fact, the light will reach us in almost all directions if the hole is small enough ; and so we have an experimental realization of the water wave case illustrated in Fig. 1 (d). The question which then arises is, " Why should a very small portion of the wave front behave differently when separated from the rest of the wave ? " The suggested answer is that it does not do so ; that, in fact, all points of the wave send out new waves but, owing to interference, all we realize when the full wave is present is the new wave front, parallel to the old.

If we look more carefully into the shadow cast by an object with a straight edge in a darkened room, for example, we find, using a low-power microscope to study the shadow produced, that there is no sharp line of demonstration from brightness to darkness, but that a gradual shading off to zero light takes place within the shadow. Further, we find that near the edge of the shadow, in the part which appears to be bright to the naked eye, there is a fluctuation of intensity of the light, forming a set of straight line fringes parallel to the straight edge and rapidly closing up into the general illumination. Of course, all these fluctuations, etc., take place in a very small distance. For example at a distance of 1 metre from the straight edge all the fringes are seen in a distance of 0·3 cm., and the diffraction, or bending, of the waves is, therefore, very small indeed ; but so is the wave length of the light.

Close examination of many of the simple experiments yields equally interesting results. If, for example, we take a smooth-edged threepenny piece and set it up at right angles to a parallel beam of light in a darkened room, we find on examining the shadow that at certain distances away there is intense light at the centre of the shadow. This repeats along a line at right angles to the coin. It is merely a case of the waves having bent round the coin, reinforcing and producing the light seen. All the portions of light falling on the edge of the coin set up waves which pass into the shadow, but in most directions these waves destructively interfere, and darkness results. The point is, perhaps, best studied in the case of a narrow slit on which a parallel beam of light is falling. As seen in Fig. 3, there is no doubt that a direct beam goes through, but if each point across the slit AB sends out waves, as in Fig. 1 (d), the illumination in any other direction simply depends on what is the result of all the secondary waves from AB in the direction chosen. It can be shown that if BC is equal to half a wavelength of the light used there is reinforcement, and the light so formed can be viewed by means of a telescope. When BC $=\lambda$ there is darkness; when BC $=1\frac{1}{2}\lambda$ there is a second bright light, and so on. In other words, there are

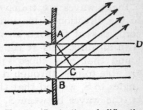

Fig. 3. Production of diffraction fringes.

bright and dark *diffraction* fringes arranged symmetrically about the " straight through position " shown. The positions of these fringes depend on the colour of the light used, the red light diffraction fringe being at a greater angle than the violet. Once more we produce colours when white light is used to illuminate the slit.

Measuring Wave-Length. At the National Physical Laboratory at Teddington there is a machine which is able to rule a very large number of lines per cm. on glass and metal, and so produces what is called a *diffraction grating*. This ruling of lines makes alternate transmitting slits and opaque lines of the order of 14,000 lines per inch. Light falling on these gratings is diffracted at an angle which depends on the colour of the light used ; the angles are bigger for the longer wave-lengths. The result is the production of a spectrum : the same thing occurs at an angle almost double the first, and the colours are practically twice as far apart. If conditions permit, this is again repeated and we have *spectra of the 1st, 2nd and 3rd, etc., order*.

The diffraction grating provides an excellent means of measuring the wave-length of the light falling on it, and it is often used instead of a prism as a means of analysing the spectra of light sources.

This brief discussion of diffraction, taken in conjunction with what we saw in Lesson 17 (page 514) on interference, leads us to believe that light is undoubtedly a wave motion. Of course, there are two kinds of wave motion, as we saw in Lesson 13 (volume 4, page 528); and the experiments we have described so far do not differentiate between the two, as both exhibit interference and diffraction. However, there are many very beautiful experiments which decide the point for us.

Light waves are transverse, i.e., they vibrate at right angles to the direction of motion of the wave. If we take a stretched cord, pass it through two slits, S_1 and S_2, and vibrate the end A in all directions at right angles to the cord (*see* Fig. 4), it is found that only those vibrations which are parallel to slit S_1 are able to pass through it ; and if we arrange the slit S_2 at right angles to S_1 we find that the cord at C is not moving. We speak of the waves between S_1 and S_2 as being *plane polarized*, i.e., vibrating in one plane only. Now, if light is a *transverse* vibration it may vibrate as does the string at A, and it should be possible to produce plane polarization.

Polarization of Light. Various ways have been found to accomplish this. There is a green crystal called tourmaline, which has the property of splitting light up into two vibrations at right angles, and further, absorbs one of the vibrations and only transmits light vibrations in one plane, like the string at B

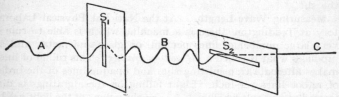

Fig. 4. A practical experiment to show how light waves vibrate at right angles to the direction of motion of the wave. Direction of vibration at A in all directions, B in one plane, and C no vibration.

in Fig. 4. It is to be noticed that the tourmaline is *not a slit*, but merely acts to light as the slit S_1 does to the string. When ordinary light has passed through such a crystal and becomes plane polarized, it does not appear different from ordinary light. If, however, a second crystal of tourmaline is placed in the path of the plane polarized light it is found that, as the second crystal is rotated, it comes to a position when its axis is at right angles to the first (the crystals are said to be " crossed ") and all the light is cut off. It seems remarkable that a strong beam of light from an arc lamp cannot penetrate through these two crossed crystals, which are transparent separately or when arranged together with their axes parallel : and it forms a striking example of the transverse character of the wave motion which we call light.

A crystal called Iceland spar has also the property of splitting ordinary light up into two components or parts which vibrate in planes at right angles to each other. In this case the spar does not absorb one half like the tourmaline. However, it is found that the two rays in the crystal are plane polarized in planes at right angles to each other, and that one ray obeys the ordinary laws of refraction as we discussed them. The other ray does not follow the same laws, and is aptly called the " extraordinary ray." In general, the two rays separate in going through the crystal, and when the light comes out it is doubled. If such a crystal is placed on this print a double set of images is seen through the clear crystal, as shown in Fig. 5. If these images are again viewed through tourmaline it is found that they disappear in turn when the axis of the tourmaline is turned through a right angle. By a simple method, too long to describe here, it is possible to construct a Nicol prism with a rhomb of calcite ; this allows the extraordinary light to pass through, but cuts off the ordinary ray ; and so ordinary light, when passed through the " prism," is plane polarized, and is not tinted green, as when a tourmaline crystal is used.

Fig. 5.

Using a Nicol prism to analyse the light reflected and transmitted through a sheet of glass, we find that the light is split up into two beams which are polarized at right angles.

When plane polarized light is passed through sugar solutions the plane of polarization is turned through an angle which depends on the concentration and length of the column of solution. This is so definite that it forms a method of testing concentrations of organic solutions, and is widely used in commerce and pure scientific work where the measurements of rotation are carried out with a *saccharimeter*.

There are many experiments which we might consider in connexion with polarization, but we must leave this branch of physics with a feeling of confidence that the polarization experiments have at least established the fact that our light waves are transverse in character.

LESSON 19

Physical Aspects of Sound

CONTINUING our survey of the elements of Physics, we will now consider some of the physical aspects of sound—how it is produced and propagated, and something of its nature.

The first essential for a sound is, of course, the source or starting point. Whether we think of musical notes produced by a tuning fork, a piano, an organ, a violin, a saxophone, or simply a noise such as is produced by a pneumatic drill, we realize that one common feature in these sources is vibration. The vibration of the prong of a tuning fork, the string of a piano or a violin is fairly apparent, but in wind instruments the only possible substance to vibrate is the air within the tubes—which, in fact, does vibrate and so produces the characteristic note of this type of instrument.

Sound Sources. Assuming that the vibration in the source is the starting point of the sound, the question which arises is, how does the vibration change to produce the different notes which are emitted, on the one hand, or the mere *noise*, on the other ? We find that the size of the source determines the pitch of a musical note heard, and we may be inclined to ask, why does this change in the size of the source produce the difference in pitch ?

In the first place, all sources of musical notes give out regular vibration of a definite frequency (i.e. number of vibrations per second). One definite pitch corresponds to a definite frequency. For example, if a source vibrates in a regular manner 256 times per second, the note given out is what we call middle C (on some scales this number is modified slightly). In other words, we associate pitch with the frequency of vibration of the source. Mathematically, we can calculate the frequency of vibration of a string of a given material of known thickness and length when stretched with a known tension, and we find that the frequency (n) is proportional to the square root of the tension and is inversely proportional to the length and the square root of the mass per centimetre In other words, if the tension of the given string of a fixed material is constant, we find that the frequency is inversely proportional to the length, i.e. if we double the length we halve the frequency and make the pitch an octave lower. Similar rules can be deduced to apply to columns of air, vibrating plates such as telephone diaphragms, etc. When some sources vibrate they do so in a complex manner. Consider the case of a violin string, for example. In addition to the simple vibration there is a possibility of other waves of half and other simple fractions of the length of the first being superimposed on it. These *overtones* give the distinctive note of the violin. In a noise there is no *regular* vibration, and the frequency emitted is an assortment of a vast number of individual frequencies, each of which alone would produce a musical note, but which together result in *noise* only.

Sound Waves. We have seen that the source of sound is a vibrating body, and we will now consider how the vibration sets up what we call " sound waves," which travel from the source to the listener. If we consider a tuning fork vibrating in a regular manner, it is clear that the prongs of the fork will compress the air as they move outwards and endeavour to rarefy the air as they move inwards, thus giving rise to a pressure wave in the air. In this way the maintained movement of the fork is communicated to the air.

The fork itself vibrates in S.H.M. (*see* Lesson 13, volume 4, page 528), and so does the air particle next to it. The air particles in the neighbourhood gradually take up a S.H.M., but the phase of the vibration differs as we consider particles more removed from the source. In other words, we realize that we have here all the conditions for the production of wave motion, as we discussed it in Lesson 13. The great difference which we notice between this wave and light waves is that the air particles vibrate in the direction in which the wave is moving.

We have seen that the alternative way of regarding this is to consider the pressure set up by the moving air particles. No *transverse* S.H.M. movement is possible because, of course, there is no force set up in air or liquids to restore such a transverse displacement ; but a movement in the line of propagation can be propagated, for the movement itself sets up a force, which restores the particles to their original position.

Our picture of a sound wave in air, therefore, is one in which the propagation is brought about by the movement of the individual air particles, each about a position of rest ; the particles have a phase difference in their movement which results in compressions and rarefactions of the particles. Under no circumstances do we visualize transverse movement. It is to be noticed that for a sound wave in air it is the *air* which moves. The same in water, wood, wires, etc. This is again different from light. We are here stating that the material medium is the transmitting agent.

We can easily show that sound requires a material medium for its transmission, for if we hang an electric bell in a glass vessel, using the wires as support, and then apply an air pump (*see* Lesson 5, volume 2, p. 584) to withdraw all the air from the vessel, we find that the noise of the ringing bell gets fainter and fainter as the air is withdrawn. When we have almost a vacuum in the glass vessel the sound is almost inaudible. All the time we can *see* the hammer of the bell hitting the gong, i.e. light can be transmitted through the vacuum, but sound cannot.

Velocity of Sound. Sound travels through air at 0° C. with a velocity of about 1,090 ft. per second or 331 metres per second, and not with the tremendous velocity of light. The early determinations of velocity were made by observing a distant flash of a gun firing, and by noting the time which elapsed before the explosion of the charge was heard a measured distance away. It is the reverse process to that we use as a method of estimating the distance of a thunderstorm, in which the number of seconds between seeing a flash of lightning and hearing the corresponding roll of thunder is recorded. In each 5 seconds the sound has travelled 5,450 ft., which may be taken as approximately one mile (5,280 ft.), which is the distance from the storm, assuming that light travels so quickly that its time is negligible.

Sound travels in different substances with very different speeds, as may be seen in the following table :

Substance.	Velocity of sound (approx.).
Air at 0° C.	331 metres per sec.
Water	1400 ,, ,, ,,
Steel	5000 ,, ,, ,,
Wood, pine deal	3300 to 4900 ,, ,, ,,

It will be seen from these figures that it is possible for an observer to see at a distance a hammer strike a railway line, then to hear the sound which has travelled along the steel, and then, a little later, hear the sound carried through the air.

The relation between wave-length (λ), frequency (n) and velocity (v) is $v = n\lambda$, as before; therefore in air the wave-length of middle C (n = 256) is 33,000/256 cm., i.e. almost 129 cm. In other words, the wave-length is fairly long. Such things as reflection, refraction, interference and diffraction are to be expected with these waves, of course, and we realize that the general order of results are those we anticipate with long waves. If we remember the effects discussed in Lesson 18 (page 520) we shall realize that the bending or diffraction of sound round buildings is what is to be expected with the waves, and that the lower the note, the longer the wave and, therefore, the bigger these effects will be. We have an example of reflection in echoes, when sound is reflected at walls and faces of mountains, etc.

Interference of sound waves can be demonstrated by using the apparatus illustrated in the accompanying diagram. It con-

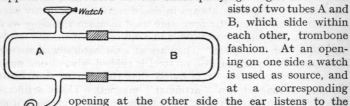

sists of two tubes A and B, which slide within each other, trombone fashion. At an opening on one side a watch is used as source, and at a corresponding opening at the other side the ear listens to the sounds. When B is pushed in so that the sound has an equal path each way, i.e. via A or B, a loud tick is heard, but when B is pulled out a position is reached when practically no noise is heard. The path via B has been increased by half a wave-length of the note given out, and interference of the waves has been operative in dimming the intensity. The experiment is more successful, of course, when a source of one frequency is used.

From what has been said it appears that, as it exhibits so many of the wave properties, sound is undoubtedly a wave motion in material media. That no polarization is possible indicates that the wave is longitudinal. It appears to be produced by vibrating bodies, and takes on a frequency of those bodies. Scales of musical notes have frequencies simply related, and are used in musical composition because to our ear they form pleasing combinations.

LESSON 20

Magnetism in Physics

IN the preceding Lessons in this Course we have considered in turn the outlines of mechanics, properties of matter, heat, light and sound ; now to complete the survey of the widespreading subject of physics we will investigate some of the chief properties of magnetism and electricity. This allied pair of subjects is of great importance to the physicist because of the very far-reaching nature of the results of practical investigation and theoretical speculation.

Magnetism. The text books recall that the beginnings of magnetism are to be found in a discovery of great antiquity ; this is that certain magnetic oxides of iron were observed to have the property of setting always in one direction when freely suspended. These magnetic ores were used in much the same way in which a compass is now used, and acquired the name of " leading stone " or lode stone. They are at least naturally occurring magnets. If a piece of iron or steel is rubbed, always one way, with such a lodestone, it is found that the iron or steel itself becomes a magnet (an " artificial " magnet). These artificial magnets in turn can impart their magnetic power to pieces of iron and steel by exactly the same process.

One common feature of both sorts of magnet is that they attract to themselves small pieces of iron and steel. No doubt the earliest memory most of us have of magnetism is this very property. Most schoolboys used to have a horse-shoe magnet as a very cherished possession and performed the experiment just referred to by using pins or tin tacks as the small iron objects (Fig. 1a). Large numbers adhere to the ends marked N and S when brought near the magnet. In a laboratory the ordinary " bar magnet " is most often used. This is made from a straight piece of steel instead of the horse-shoe shape. If this is placed on a sheet of paper and then entirely covered with iron filings, it is found that when the bar is lifted, the filings adhere in two tufts, round the two ends of the bar magnet, just as the tacks remained only at the ends of the horse-shoe magnet (Fig. 1b). We say that at the ends we have the *poles* of the magnet.

When a bar magnet is hung so that it can swing freely in a horizontal plane we find that one end always points north. The pole at this end we call the north-seeking pole (often contracted to N pole) ; the pole at the other end is called the south-seeking pole (or S pole).

We find that if we bring the N pole of a magnet near the N pole of the suspended magnet, the latter turns away ; we say it is

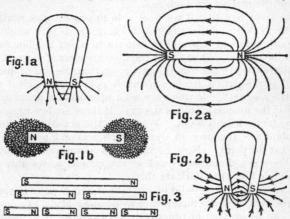

Fig. 1a

Fig. 2a

Fig. 1b

Fig. 2b

Fig. 3

repelled. If we bring a S pole near the S pole of this suspended magnet, this also is repelled ; but we find that a N and S attract each other. This is usually summarized by saying that " like poles repel, unlike poles attract."

Obviously the force of repulsion or attraction depends on how strong the two poles are and how far apart they are. As in all physics we like to have a definition of the units in which to measure, so we define a unit pole in terms of the force : " A unit north pole is such that if we place it one centimetre away from another unit N pole, in air, the force of repulsion is one dyne."

If two north poles are of strengths m and m^1 and are separated by a distance of d cm. of air, it has been found that the force of repulsion (F) is given by

$$F = \frac{mm^1}{d^2}$$

This expresses what we call the *inverse square law*.

To account for the fact that one magnet usually tends to turn another, we say that, in the space around a magnet, there is a magnetic field. If we take a bar magnet and cover it with a sheet of glass and scatter iron filings on the glass, we find that after tapping the glass gently in order to allow the filings to turn, a very definite picture is obtained. The iron filings take on the form of Fig. 2a. If we used a horse-shoe magnet, the result is shown in Fig. 2b. We say that the filings map out the *magnetic fields* of the magnets in each case.

It is clear, too, that if we were able to place a unit north pole near the N pole of either magnet in Fig. 2, the N pole would go to the south pole and it would in fact travel along the line marked out in the figure. We say that the lines are *lines of magnetic force*, and alternative to the iron filings we say that the line of magnetic force " is the path a freely moving N pole would take if placed near the magnet." If there are a lot of lines in a given area we say that the magnetic field is strong. If there are few lines we say the magnetic field is weak. We define the actual magnetic field at a point as " the force in dynes which acts on a unit north pole placed at the point." Now, like all forces on unit poles or anything else, there is a direction as well as magnitude, so we always put arrows (*see* Fig. 2) to indicate this.

However useful and valid it is to talk of unit N poles in theoretical problems, and as convenience in defining fields, etc., no such thing can be isolated in practice. For example, if we magnetize a steel hack saw blade and then break it into two in an attempt to isolate the N pole and the S pole, we find that we have two complete magnets. Again, if each half is broken to make two quarters, each quarter is itself a complete magnet, as shown in Fig. 3.

We are led to the conclusion that in iron and steel the molecules are magnets which are in general arranged in a haphazard fashion. When stroked with a magnet the molecules align themselves in one direction, so that however small the portion which we break away from the main magnet, the molecules, being in alignment, show north and south polarity in the segment of steel detached.

But to return to the question of the magnetic fields, we now assume that whenever a field is applied to a magnet, it causes a force to act on the magnet. In terms of this definition we say that in the first place a magnet sets in the meridian because there is a magnetic field *due to the earth*. In fact, the earth produces magnetic effects which are the same as if a huge magnet had its S seeking pole near the north geographic pole and its N seeking pole near the south geographic pole. No such magnet exists, of course, but the magnetic field around the earth is similar to that which would be produced by such a distribution of magnetic poles. Naturally over an area so small as England (compared with the area of the earth) the magnetic line of force may be taken as parallel, and the field is said to be uniform. Suppose the strength of this magnetic field is H dynes per unit pole (or H *gauss*) and that a magnet is pivoted so that it can rotate in a horizontal plane, it is clear that when the magnet is not setting in the magnetic meridian (i.e. the direction of the earth's line of force) it is acted on by a pair of forces which tend to turn it to there. For example, in Fig. 4, suppose H is the direction of the earth's horizontal magnetic field, and NS is the position of the magnet. We have in the magnet two poles at N and S each of the same pole strength, say *m* units. The force at N on the pole there is H × m (since by definition H is the force on *unit* pole). A similar force acts at S in the opposite direction and so these forces produce a turning couple which will tend to

Fig. 4

move the magnet round until it lies along N¹S¹, where the two forces act in the same line and opposite in direction.

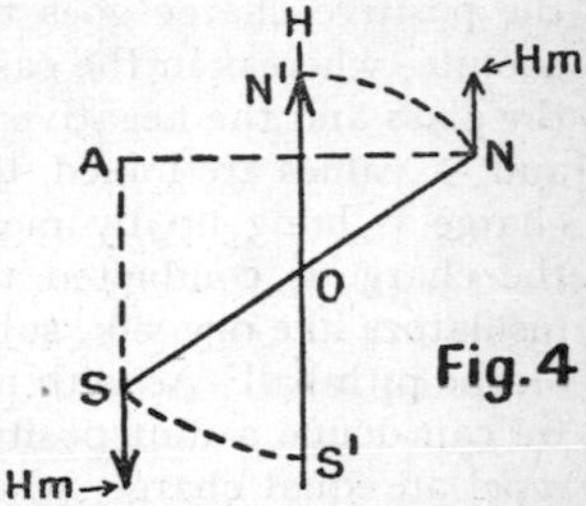

If a uniform magnetic field of strength F now acts on the magnet, in a direction at right angles to that of H, the magnet will turn round through some angle, say $\theta°$, from the meridian, and it can be shown that F and H are related by the expression

$$F = H \tan \theta.$$

We can use this relation to compare field strengths whether the fields are due directly to magnets, or, as we shall see later, to electric currents.

Electricity. The name electricity is derived from the Greek *elektron*, which means amber. This is a constant reminder of the fact that the earliest recorded method of producing electricity is by rubbing amber. When any two different substances are rubbed together, electricity is produced by the friction. For example, if an ebonite fountain-pen is rubbed on the coat or on the hair it is found that the pen acquires the property of attracting light pieces of tissue paper towards it. If we suspend a light gilded ball of elder pith by means of a dry silk thread and hang near to it a glass rod which has been rubbed with silk, we find that the ball is attracted to the rod and then is repelled. Any attempt to take the rod near the charged pith ball results in repulsion.

The same sequence of events is witnessed if an ebonite rod rubbed with flannel replaces the glass rod. But it is found that the ball, when charged from the glass rod, is subsequently attracted by the ebonite rod. We recognize two kinds of charges : the one on the glass is now called positive, the one on the ebonite is called negative, and we find that " like charges repel and unlike charges attract." In the process of producing a charge by friction, we manufacture equal positive and negative charges from the two uncharged bodies. In the case of rubbing ebonite with flannel the positive charge goes to the flannel and the negative to the ebonite, whereas in the case of glass and silk the positive goes to the glass and the negative to the silk. If two equal charges of + and — values are mixed, the net result is no net charge. When a charge is hung up by means of a wire or a damp silk thread, the charge is conducted to the support and leaks away. Using insulators like dry silk, sulphur, ebonite, etc., the charge remains on the pith ball. As with magnetic poles which obey similar laws, we can define a unit positive charge as " that charge which will repel an equal charge, when one centimetre away in air, with a force of one dyne," and also we deduce a similar inverse square law, viz. : if two charges of q and q^1 are d cms. apart in air the force (F) of repulsion in dynes is given by

$$F = \frac{q\ q^1}{d^2}$$

In the same way we define *electric-field strength* at a point as " the force in dynes which acts on a unit positive charge placed at that point " ; e.g. if a charge of + 10 units is placed in a uniform electric field of 50 dynes/unit pole, the force acting on it is $10 \times 50 = 500$ dynes.

Another useful electrical conception may be obtained from this introductory account of electricity, produced by friction and remaining as a stationary charge, namely, *potential*. If we have two charges of opposite kind, positive and negative, and we join them together by a conducting path, e.g. a wire, we find that positive electricity flows from the positive to the negative, and we say we have an electric current flowing. This only lasts for a very small interval of time. If a positive charge is joined by a wire to the earth, a current of electricity flows to the earth and the body loses its charge, whereas when we join a negative charge, by means of a wire, to the earth, the current flows from the earth to the body, and the flow, which is almost instantaneous, discharges the body. We take the earth as our zero in these cases. We say the free negative charge has a negative potential and the free positive, a positive potential, and the earth is said to be at zero potential.

In the same way, if we have two bodies charged with positive electricity and join them together by means of a wire, there will in general be a flow of electricity (a current) from the body at the higher potential to the body at the lower potential. In the case of a sphere we can find that the potential is equal to the charge on it divided by the radius of the sphere. This is deduced by defining potential in a quantitative manner as being equal to the work done in bringing up a unit positive charge to the body from a long way away (infinity). We may take it as axiomatic that if an electric potential difference exists on a conductor, there will be a flow of electricity from the place at the higher to the place at the lower potential, which tends to equalize potential.

Our Course in Physics is continued in Volume 6.

LESSON 19

Nervous System of the Human Body

(See plate 59)

THE great central nerve exchange communicates with the whole organism by a series of nerve cables consisting of bundles of nerve fibres bound together by connective tissue—the cranial and spinal nerves. Within the skull 12 pairs of cranial nerves emerge from the brain-stem, and of these four pairs transmit incoming messages which convey the sensations

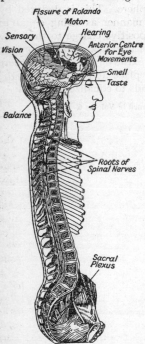

Fissure of Rolando
Motor
Sensory
Hearing
Vision
Anterior Centre for Eye Movements
Smell
Taste
Balance
Roots of Spinal Nerves
Sacral Plexus

NERVOUS SYSTEM. The brain and spinal cord, with their nerves, form the central nervous system.

of sight, hearing, taste and smell. They are in communication through various relay stations with the cortex of the brain, the impulses they convey passing to the special areas where perception in consciousness arises. Other pairs of cranial nerves convey outgoing messages to the muscles of the face, of the eyeball and the neck. These work in close collaboration with the special sense organs. One pair, the two great vagus nerves, forms the connecting link between the brain and the vital organs, the heart, the lungs, the stomach and intestines. The nerve centres from which they convey messages are in the bulb.

From the spinal cord emerge 31 pairs of spinal nerves, the main cables for the innervation of each half of the body and the limbs attached to them. These nerves have two roots lying one in front of the other as they pass out from the spinal cord between the bodies of the vertebrae, the small bones composing the spinal column. The anterior root contains

(536)

nerve fibres arising from cells in the anterior part of the grey matter of the cord, and these fibres pass direct to muscles in all parts of the body. They convey outgoing (efferent) messages from the cortex, relayed to them by cells in the cord having previously crossed the mid-line of the body as they passed down through the brain. The posterior roots contain fibres which end in communication with nerve cells in a small mass of grey matter lying on each root.

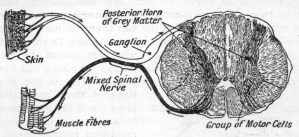

EFFERENT NERVE. The fibres shown here in black carry impulses from the spinal cord to a muscle fibre, and are termed efferent

These little masses are the posterior root ganglia. They are relay stations for the reception and transference to the higher centres of incoming messages, afferent or sensory impulses. They, too, cross the middle line before they reach their destination in the cortex or the grey matter deep in the brain substance. The fibres of the posterior root arise in the cells of the ganglia. Some of them go no farther than to communicate with cell stations close to their entry into the cord ; others pass to the cerebellum, others by a long uninterrupted route to the cortex. Anterior and posterior roots unite close to the spinal column to form trunk lines which, as they pass to their destination, give off smaller branches to supply different groups of muscles or sensory end-organs. The nerve trunks opposite the limbs are of greatest size, since these parts naturally call for a generous nerve supply. Five pairs of nerves enter the arms and seven pairs the legs.

Structure of a Nerve. We now pass on to look at the more intimate structure of the nerve machine and its methods of working. The entire mechanism consists of a vast number of nerve units, each unit consisting of a nerve cell with its processes—the various units being held together and supported by a special and peculiar tissue made up of cells and fibres, the neuroglia. Nerve cells vary in shape and size, but are mostly angular or star-shaped. Branches radiate from the angles of the cell, and while most of these divide up into a number of tiny twigs or fibrils, one process, and one only, becomes the axis-cylinder of a nerve fibre. Soon after it leaves the cell this process becomes invested with a sheath of fatty material, and when it reaches its destination it breaks up into ramifying twigs. Every unit is independent of every other unit. There is no actual contact—but the dendrons and the terminal twigs of the axis-cylinder intermingle and interlace, the nerve impulses passing across the gap from one unit to another. The habitual passage of impulses from one unit to another forms

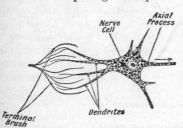

what are known as "nerve-paths"—a kind of beaten track. This is the physical basis of the "association of ideas" and the performance of habitual movements which by repetition become instinctive.

The axis-cylinder depends on the well-being of the cell of which it is a part for its efficiency as a conductor. If it becomes severed from the parent cell it undergoes degeneration and dies. A new axis-cylinder then slowly grows outward from the cell to replace it.

The entire nervous system consists of these units collected in larger or smaller masses and stations. A unit arranged to carry incoming messages to the central exchange has a transmitter or receptor—a special end-organ which may be in the skin, in a tendon, or in a special sense organ, such as the eye, or ear, or tongue. From the end-organ the nerve fibre passes to the first

NERVE CELL AND NEURON CONNEXION. Below, parts of one type of nerve cell. The main process becomes the axis-cylinder of a nerve carrying impulses from the cell, while the dendrites carry impulses into the cell. Above, a nerve fibre from a distant nerve cell ends in fine filaments (left), which intertwine with the fine processes of a nerve cell (right); a nerve impulse is thus sent into the cell.

relay station, its parent cell. From the cell the message is then relayed through its dendrons to a neighbouring cell, and so through other stations to its final reception in the cortex. Units carrying outgoing messages consist of the cell in which, maybe, the impulse arises *de novo*, or is received from another cell, the conducting fibre ending in branching twigs interlacing with the dendrons of the next relay cell ; and, finally, the end-organ lying amid the fibres of a muscle whence the stimulus to contract is conveyed to the actual fibres.

Sympathetic Nervous System. In preceding Lessons frequent allusion has been made to sympathetic nerves. This part of the nervous system governs the processes in the body over which we have no conscious control. Under normal conditions the sympathetic nerves keep the central nervous system informed of the conditions obtaining in the vital organs without bringing these conditions to the notice of the conscious self. Necessary adjustments are made in the higher centres of the brain to meet changing conditions, by means of messages sent out by the sympathetic route, and these are equally unconscious. The stopcock action of the smaller arteries, the rate and force of the heart-beat and the muscular contractions in the walls of the hollow organs of the body, such as the stomach, intestine and bladder, are brought about and controlled through the medium of this system. The secretory activity of the digestive glands is also under its control and regulation, and it is closely linked up with the activity of the internal secreting glands, especially with the adrenals. In disease or disorder the messages from the vital organs arouse conscious disturbance and produce " symptoms." The sympathetic system consists of a chain of ganglia, or collections of nerve cells, lying on each side of the vertebral column and also of other outlying ganglia, the chief of which is the large coeliac ganglion in the upper part of the abdomen.

The sympathetic ganglia are connected to the spinal nerves by bundles of nerve fibres. They form a relay station for messages which pass to and from the spinal cord from and to the vital organs, the hollow organs, and the blood vessels. The fibres running between the periphery and the ganglia accompany the nerve trunks derived from the spinal nerves, but differ from the fibres of the latter in having no fatty sheath. The sympathetic ganglia are also linked together by bundles of nerve fibres, and so ensure cooperation between all organs and systems.

LESSON 20

The Nervous System in Action

HAVING now looked at the general make-up of the nervous mechanism, it remains briefly to study it in action. The simplest example of nervous activity is the phenomenon of a reflex action. For this, two nerve units are required, one to convey an ingoing nerve impulse, the other an outgoing one, though in actual happening several units of a similar kind are usually concerned. If a nerve-ending in the skin of a decapitated frog is irritated, the limb is immediately withdrawn from the source of irritation. There is here no question of conscious action—it is an unconscious reflex response. An ingoing impulse has passed along sensory nerve fibres to their relay cells in a posterior root ganglion to be there relayed through its neurons to the neurons of cells in the anterior grey matter of the cord in the immediate neighbourhood. From thence it passes along the axis cylinders of these cells to the muscles necessary to produce the requisite action.

Let us see now what happens to ourselves in our waking life when a similar response is called for. We suddenly touch something that is too hot to be comfortable. In the skin are special touch structures whose business it is to receive the impression of a sudden change of temperature. From them nerve fibres convey the impulse to the relay centres in the cord and thence, after various relays, to the cells of the grey matter in the brain. Meanwhile some of the nerve energy of the impulse has spread in various directions. Some of it has influenced motor nerve cells in the immediate neighbourhood of the cord and set going a motor impulse to the muscles whose contraction removes the injured part almost before we have become conscious of the discomfort. Some of it passes into the sympathetic system, impulses then going to the blood vessels of the part, causing them to dilate and to produce the reddened appearance familiar after a burn—a protective mechanism to ensure quick repair. Some of the nervous energy is relayed to the cortex of the brain and is there converted into conscious sensation which is recognized at once as undesirable and unpleasant. It gives rise to an instinctive desire to escape from something harmful. The impulse is reinforced, spreads into other nerve channels, and some of these set going further motor and sensory impulses, the effect of which is to bring about further muscular action with the object of removing ourselves from the danger or removing the danger itself. In this way what began as a simple reflex action is built up into a series of complex nervous phenomena.

Take again what happens when we are suddenly startled by a loud noise. The auditory receptors in the inner ear receive a powerful stimulus. This passes by the auditory nerve to the hearing centre in the brain cortex and there gives rise to an unpleasant sensation. Again, some of the nerve

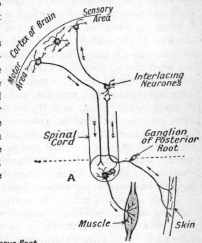

energy overflows into other channels, notably into the sympathetic system, to record its influence on the heart, respiration and the adrenal glands. The heart may momentarily "stand still" and then take on a more rapid action. The breathing is disturbed and the adrenals secrete more actively, causing a free flow of sugar from the bodily reserves in preparation for necessary muscular activity.

NERVOUS SYSTEM. A. Diagram showing general structure of the nervous system, arrows indicating the direction in which impulses travel. **B.** A spinal reflex arc; a painful prick on the hand causes the latter to be drawn away quickly, apart from any deliberate intention. This comes about by the mechanism shown, through spinal cord centres.

These bodily disturbances are conveyed to the lower levels of consciousness and give rise to a sense of discomfort and a more or less painful desire to escape from danger. The whole re-action forms what is called an "instinctive nervous pattern." The part of it which gives rise to conscious distress, together with the impulse to escape, is the "emotional" aspect of the instinct. Animal conduct is characterized by reaction patterns —Man is more teachable, i.e. new reaction patterns are readily set up and modes of reaction become subject to deliberate choice through the action of the highest level cells of the frontal cortex.

Here we enter the realm of the pure psychologist. But the student of physiology should realize how many of the activities of everyday life are carried on beneath the level of consciousness. An unending stream of nervous impulses is continually passing from the special sense organs, the muscles and tendons, the internal organs, the arteries and the skin to the lower level stations in the brain, and thence in an outgoing stream to the vital organs, the muscles, tendons, arteries, etc. We carry out complex muscular actions ; we sit down and get up, we walk, we balance the body on the feet and operate even highly skilled actions while our field of consciousness may be entirely occupied elsewhere. Most of these actions have, however, to be learned by practice and experience. Later they acquire an instinctive or highly elaborate reflex character.

Many of the so-called "intelligent" actions in animals have been shown by Pavloff to be of the nature of "conditioned reflexes." One kind of stimulus becomes by repetition closely linked up with the reaction pattern of a previously acting stimulus, so that the animal reacts to the new one in the same manner.

We must conclude this Lesson with a few words about the cerebellum. This part of the brain has for its main function the maintenance of the equilibrium of the body and the co-ordination of the action of the various groups of muscles brought into play in the performance of various movements. It is connected to the spinal cord and brain by three stalks containing nerve fibres passing to and from the muscles and the higher motor centres of the cortex. The mass of the cerebellum consists of myriads of nerve fibrils and relay cells and it is partly divided into two main lobes, each lobe being in connexion with its own side of the body and not, as in the case of the cerebrum, with the opposite side. It is this part of the brain that takes over the automatic control of the muscle groups that subserve habitual and more or less unconscious movements.

Nerve Links of Mind and Body

IN the preceding three Lessons in this Course a general sketch has been given of the two great divisions of the nervous system. On the one hand we have the voluntary or central nervous system, the function of which is to keep the organism in touch with its external environment and to allow it to respond to changes in that environment ; and on the other the involuntary or vegetative system whose function it is to control the vital mechanisms of the body in such a way as to enable it to respond in the most effective manner, in other words, to act on what may be called the internal environment. We become acquainted with the external world through the medium of our sense organs, i.e. organs possessing groups or layers of special cells sensitive to the action of specific external agents. These cells include the touch corpuscles in the skin, some influenced by contact and others sensitive to heat and cold, smell corpuscles in the nose, taste buds in the tongue (both the two latter being stimulated by chemical substances), cells in the internal ear sensitive to sound waves, and cells in the retina of the eye sensitive to waves of light.

Sensory nerve fibres, central relaying station and outgoing motor impulses to the muscular engines, provide the mechanism for suitable response to the stimuli so received, and enable the organism to adjust itself to the demands of the external world. No less important is the adjustment of the internal environment. The activities of the viscera, the heart, lungs, stomach and bowels, the urinary bladder and the sex organs, the digestive glands, liver and pancreas—all these must be not only under constant control but their activities must be accurately adjusted to meet the varying demands of the external world on the organism as a whole. Every demand from without calls for an adjustment, great or small, in the working of the various organs specially concerned in the responsive activity. We have seen in Lesson 19 that the vegetative nervous system, whose office it is thus to control the viscera, is made up of fibres leaving the brain and spinal cord, linked together by communicating strands, and having their own relay cell stations as they pass to the organs.

The vegetative system is divided into three main parts, cranial, thoracico-lumbar (leaving the cord between the levels of the great nerve trunks to the upper and lower limbs), and sacral, i.e. those emerging from the lower end of the cord. Reference to the diagram will give the reader a general idea of the distribution of

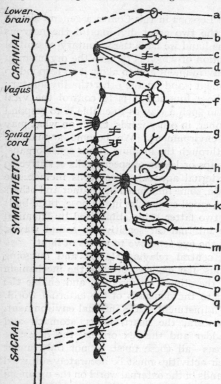

the vegetative nerve supply, and it will be noted that the most vital organs receive a double supply, one from the cranial or sacral set, and the other from the central or, as it is usually called the " sympathetic " division. The main distribution of cranial fibres originating in cells in the lower brain (the vital centres) is through the great vagus nerves passing down the neck to the thorax and abdomen. It will also be noted how closely linked up together are the sympathetic fibres, and how wide is their distribution. The impulses conveyed by the sympathetic group, and those conveyed by the cranial and sacral groups, lead to opposed types of action. Thus vagus action slows and strengthens the heart's action, sympathetic action makes it beat more rapidly. Vagus

AUTONOMIC NERVOUS SYSTEM. Diagram showing general arrangement of the vegetative system. The broken lines indicate nerve fibres before they reach the ganglions; the solid lines are fibres issuing from the ganglions. a, iris; b, salivary gland; c, hair; d, sweat gland; e, surface artery; f, heart; g, liver; h, stomach; j, spleen; k, visceral artery; l, small intestine; m, adrenal medulla; n, hair; o, sweat gland; p, artery; q, bladder; r, colon.
Based on diagram in W. B. Cannon's " The Wisdom of the Body," Kegan Paul

action is localized in its action, sympathetic action is organized for producing diffuse effects.

It is the sympathetic group that comes widely into action in response to every stimulus from without, that gives rise to " feeling," i.e. emotional disturbance. Take, for example, a state of fear. The heart and respiration take on more rapid action, the activities of the digestive organs are slowed down, the blood vessels in the internal parts become constricted, the adrenal glands pour out an increased amount of secretion and, in an animal, the hair becomes erect. Vagus control is a more steady and constant influence of an inhibitory nature and tending all the time to counteract sympathetic disturbance.

The functions of the cranial group are mainly protective, conservative and upbuilding. Narrowing of the pupil of the eye protects it from the damaging effect of bright light ; gastric and bowel peristalsis, controlled by the vagus nerves, serve the purposes of nutrition ; and vagus control over the glandular activities of the liver and pancreas serves to stoke the fires of life. The sacral division has for its main function the emptying of hollow organs which become periodically filled. The principal of these organs are the urinary bladder and the colon and rectum. The sexual function is also under its control. Voluntary control is here closely linked to the automatic action, but can be submerged under the stress of overpowering emotion.

Sympathetic action is thus mainly protective in its purposes. The effects outlined above will be seen to be mainly directed towards enabling the organism to escape from, or to combat, the danger to which it seems exposed. Blood supply to the voluntary muscles is increased, oxygenation is speeded up and the increased outflow of adrenalin releases a more rapid output of sugar to serve as fuel for unusual muscular effort. While nature has arranged so admirable a provision for meeting emergencies it is nevertheless a mechanism that is capable of, and, under conditions of ultra-civilization, undergoes, much abuse. Lack of emotional control, a too ready emotional response to everyday circumstances, worry, lack of sufficient mental and bodily rest and relaxation, all those factors which go to make up the badly balanced mentality, these are the cause of a strained and overworked vegetative nerve system. They lead to functional disorder of the body machinery and are a very common cause of ill-health.

Our Course in Physiology is continued in Volume 6.

LESSON 1

First Principles in the Pitman System

PITMAN'S Shorthand can be acquired easily by anyone of ordinary intelligence. It is a phonetic system; that is to say, words are written according to sound, ordinary spelling being ignored. For instance, *cat* is represented by *kăt*; *cough* by *kŏf*; *knee* by *nē*, and so on. This point is most important, and must be thoroughly understood from the outset.

Consonants. Words are composed of consonants and vowels. Let us consider the first group of consonants, composed of eight straight strokes, as follows:

\ *p*, \ *b*, | *t*, | *d*, / *ch*, / *j*, — *k*, — *g*.

The horizontal strokes are written from left to right, and the others are written downwards. The consonant *ch* (called *chay*) is the sound heard in such words as *cheek* and *march*, and *g* (called *gay*) the sound heard in *give*, *bag*, etc. These consonants should be practised until they can be written correctly and without hesitation. The size and thickness of the strokes shown above should not be exceeded. A pen with a fairly fine flexible nib and a ruled notebook should be used.

Consonants are joined, as in longhand, without lifting the pen, thus:

\ *pp*, \ *pt*, \ *bt*, \ *bb*, L *tb*, L *tk*, ⟨ *ch p*,

L *ch k*, L *jk*, \ *kb*, ⌐ *gt*.

Vowels. Vowels are represented by dots and dashes written alongside the strokes.

Long *ā*, as in *Tay*, is represented by a heavy dot, thus, |· Tay, — Kay, .— ache, |‹ tape, |· take.

Short *ĕ*, as in *bet*, is represented by a light dot, thus, –· egg, \ bet, \— peck, /· cheque *or* check.

Long ō, as in *toe*, is represented by a heavy dash, thus, — Coe, ˌ oak, ⊢ toe, ⊢ Joe, ⊢ joke.

Short ŭ, as in *up*, is represented by a light dash, thus, ⟍ up, ⊢ tub, ⊢ duck.

Note that the above vowel signs are written at the middle of strokes.

When a vowel is sounded before a consonant, the dot or dash is placed before the stroke; when a vowel is sounded after a consonant, the dot or dash is placed after the stroke. In the case of the horizontal strokes, a vowel which occurs before the consonant is written above, and a vowel which occurs after the consonant is written underneath. The consonant outline is written first, and then the vowel sign.

The learner will find that, if he has mastered the foregoing simple rules, he can already write in Pitman's Shorthand quite a wide range of words. The words and shorthand forms in the following Exercise should be carefully studied and copied several times, until they can be written without hesitation.

EXERCISE 1
READ AND WRITE

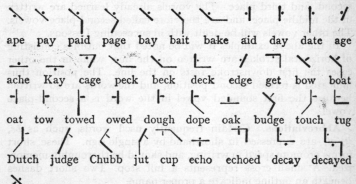

ape pay paid page bay bait bake aid day date age

ache Kay cage peck beck deck edge get bow boat

oat tow towed owed dough dope oak budge touch tug

Dutch judge Chubb jut cup echo echoed decay decayed

obey coke cocoa.

When the student has become thoroughly acquainted with the consonant and vowel signs above explained, he should proceed with the study of a further group of consonants. In contrast to the eight straight strokes already given, the new group of consonants consists of shallow curves. Here they are:—

◟ *f,* ◟ *v,* (*ith,* (*thee,*) *s,*) *z,* ╯ *ish,* ╯ *zhee,* ⌒ *m,* ◡ *n,* ◡ *ing.*

The first eight strokes are written downwards, and the remaining three from left to right. Careful study of the following words will reveal the exact consonantal value of these signs:—

◟ foe, ◟ folk, ◟ Fay, ◟ fade, ◟ vote, ◟ vague, ⤙ oath, ⤚ both, ⤙ faith, (they, ⤚ bathe,) ace,) say,) essay, ⤳ owes, ╱ show, ╱ showed, ╱ shake, ⌒ aim, ⌒ may, ⌒ make, ◡ neigh, ◡ name, ◡ came, ⌐ tongue, ◟ bunk, ◠ monk.

The difference in the sounds represented by the strokes (and (, as heard in the words *both* and *bathe*, should be specially noted.

Vowels. There are three places alongside a stroke in which vowels may be written; beginning, middle, and end; or first, second, and third place. The vowels already learned are written in the middle place, and are therefore called second-place vowels. The other vowels will be dealt with in succeeding Lessons.

In the above examples it will be noted that outlines consisting of horizontal strokes are written on the line, while in the other cases the first downstroke rests on the line. The position thus indicated is termed second position, and the words are so written because the first sounded vowel in the word is a second-place vowel.

Abbreviations. Certain frequently used words, such as *be, it, of,* are expressed in shorthand by a single sign. These short forms promote speed in writing, and should be thoroughly memorized. A small cross represents a full stop. Two short dashes beneath an outline indicate a proper name.

ABBREVIATIONS

─ a *or* an, . the, ╲ all, ╲ too *or* two, ╌ of, ╲ to, ╌ on, | but, ╌ and, ╱ should, ╲ be, | it, | do.

(548)

FIRST PRINCIPLES

The signs for *and* and *should* are always written *upwards*.

The following Exercise should be carefully read and afterwards copied.

EXERCISE 2

1. Do they know the name of the Dutch boat?

2. The debt should be paid on Monday the tenth of May.

3. Joe and Ted both say the cheque came on the tenth of the month.

4. It should be the aim of all of us to make the show pay.

In order to test his knowledge of the rules so far explained, the reader should attempt to put into shorthand the following short Exercise, the key to which is given in the next Lesson.

EXERCISE 3

(Abbreviations are shown in italic type)

1. They say they may change *the* name *of the* boat.
2. *All but two of* us came up *on* Monday *to the* show.
3. They *should* take *it on the* coach.

LESSON 2

Writing the Vowels

THE key to Exercise 3 given in our first Lesson appears below, and the student should carefully note any errors. The correct forms should be written out several times in order that they may be impressed on the memory.

KEY TO EXERCISE 3

1. [shorthand symbols]

2. [shorthand symbols]

3. [shorthand symbols]

We will now consider the third and last group of consonants, namely :—

[shorthand symbols]

| l, | r, | ray, | w, | y, | h. |

In the above group ⟍ *r* and ⟋ *h* are written downward. The others are written upward. All of them are light strokes.

The following words should be studied carefully, so that the exact value of these consonants may be appreciated.

EXERCISE 4

READ AND WRITE

[shorthand symbols] lay lake low loam pay pale fellow jay jail air oar

[shorthand symbols] tow tore door dare may mare show shore ray rate raid

[shorthand symbols] row road rogue burrow furrow Murray weigh woe

(550)

wedge yo yoke head headache hedge hay Haig hug.

It will be seen that there are two forms of *r*, namely, downward *r* ⟍ and *ray* ⟋ (always written upward).

When a word begins with vowel-r, as air, oar, earl, or when *r* ends a word, use ⟍ , thus, air, oar, earl, core, pair, tear, share.

When *r* begins a word or when a word ends with r-vowel, use ⟋ , thus, row, rake, rug, rush, borough.

The above is the general rule for the writing of *r*, but in a few cases, in order to avoid awkward joinings, the rule is not strictly adhered to, as in (*a*) Rome, rum, firm; (*b*) urge, earth; (*c*) roar, rare.

The rule for the use of the strokes *h* is simple. Use ⟋ when it stands alone, or is followed by ___ *k*, ___ *g*, and the upward form ⟋ in other cases, thus, hay, hake, hoe, hope, hub, head, hung.

Here are the four vowels which are written in the first place, that is, at the beginning of a stroke :—

Long *ah*, as in *pa*, is represented by a heavy dot, thus, pa, palm, tar, far, farm.

Short *ă*, as in *at*, is represented by a light dot, thus, at, tap, back, lack, rack.

Long *aw*, as in *saw*, is represented by a heavy dash, thus, saw, jaw, bought, talk, law.

Short *ŏ*, as in *top*, is represented by a light dash, thus, top, shop, got, lock, wash.

An examination of the above outlines will show that when the first sounded vowel in a word is a first-place vowel, the outline is written in the first position, that is, the first downstroke or upstroke in the outline is written above the line.

ABBREVIATIONS

⌐ ought, ⟋ who, ⟍ put, ⟍ to be, ⎸ had, ⊣ different-ce, ⟋ much, ⟋ which, ⟋ large, ― can, ― come, ― go, ― give-n, ⌐ for, ⌐ have.

When the foregoing rules and abbreviations have been mastered Exercise 5 should be attempted. The key is given in the next Lesson.

EXERCISE 5

1. Murray *and* Farrow *can come to the* show *to be given on* Monday.
2. *The* head *of the* firm may *have to go to* Assam *for a* month or *two*.
3. They *had a large* lock *put on, which ought to* make *much* difference.

The remaining four vowels are written in the third place.

Long *ē*, as in *eat*, is represented by a heavy dot, thus, ⊣ eat, ⊣ tea, ⟍ eke, ― key, ⌐ teak, ⌐ team, ⌐ lea, ⌐ leak.

Short *ĭ*, as in *if*, is represented by a light dot, thus, ⟍ if, ⟍ bit, ⟍ bill, ⟍ bilk, ⟋ chill, ⟋ mill, ⟋ milk.

Long *ōō*, as in *chew*, is represented by a heavy dash, thus, ⟋ chew, ⟋ Jew, ⟋ cool, ⟍ move, ⟍ food, ⟍ boot.

Short *ŏŏ*, as in *book*, is represented by a light dash, thus, ⟍ book, ⌐ look, ⌐ took, ⟍ pull, ⟍ push.

It should be noted that when a third-place vowel occurs between two strokes the vowel sign is placed before the second stroke.

The following tables set out clearly the long and the short vowels.

	LONG				SHORT	
1.	ah	⎤	aw	⎤	1.	ă	⎤	ŏ	⎤
2.	ā	.	ō	―	2.	ĕ	.	ŭ	―
3.	ē	.	ōō	―	3.	ĭ	.	ŏŏ	―

The long vowels are heard in the sentence: Pa, may we all go too; and the short vowels in the sentence: That pen is not much good.

It should be remembered that the places of the vowels are counted from the point where the stroke begins: thus,

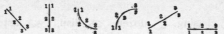

When a third-place vowel is the first-sounded vowel in a word, the outline is written in the *third* position, that is, the first down-stroke or the first upstroke is written through the line. Outlines consisting of horizontals taking third position are written on the line, as ⌣— ink.

EXERCISE 6
READ AND WRITE

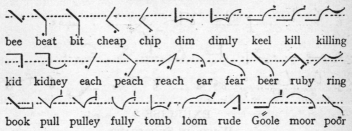

bee beat bit cheap chip dim dimly keel kill killing

kid kidney each peach reach ear fear beer ruby ring

book pull pulley fully tomb loom rude Goole moor poor

The very frequently occurring consonant *s*, and its correspond-ing heavy sound *z*, are represented by a small circle as well as by the strokes) *s* and) *z*. This small circle joins easily to other consonants at the beginning, middle, or end of a word, and is a great aid to speed. At the beginning of a stroke the circle is read first; at the end of a stroke it is read last. Used initially, the circle represents *s* only, but in the middle or at the end of an outline it may represent *s* or *z*. The following simple rules should be carefully studied.

Circle *s* is written inside a curve, thus, ⦕ safe, ⌒ seem, ⦖ sole, ⦗ slow, ⌣ nose, ⌣ snows, ⌣ insane.

Circle *s* is written with the *left* motion ⟲ to straight strokes, thus, ⌐ sat, ⎰ said, ⎰ set, ⎰ sets, ⟋ such, ⌐ soak, ⌐ soaks.

Circle *s* is written outside of the angle formed by two straight strokes, thus, ⌐ desk, ⊣ sixty, ⟨ opposite, ⟨ justice, ⌐ dispose.

Note ⟨ chasing, ⟨ dozen, ⌢ lisp, ⌣ fasten, in which the angle is not formed by two straight strokes.

ABBREVIATIONS

⌒ as *or* has, o is *or* his, ⊣ itself, ⌒ because, ⟨ those, (this, ⟨ thus, ⟍ special-ly, ⟍ speak.

EXERCISE 7
COPY AND TRANSCRIBE

1. [shorthand outlines]

2. [shorthand outlines]

3. [shorthand outlines]

EXERCISE 8
WRITE IN SHORTHAND

1. *The* books *should be put on the* ledge *and thus* save space.
2. *Because of the special* packing case *the* car came safely.
3. He *has a large* salary *because of his special* abilities.

(Keys to the above Exercises are given in the next Lesson.)

LESSON 3

Circles and Loops

TOWARDS the end of our last Lesson we saw how sometimes *s* and *z* are represented by a small circle. We now pass to consider the loops representing *st* and *str*, and the important distinction between the uses of the circle and stroke forms.

KEY TO EXERCISE 5

KEY TO EXERCISE 7

1. Those at the city office seldom speak of the case.
2. Six of the sixty desks chosen had special locks.
3. Thomas Johnson has hopes of selling his business this month.

KEY TO EXERCISE 8

Loops. A small loop, written in the same direction as the circle *s*, ⟨ represents the light or heavy sound of *st* (named stee), thus, ⟨ sop, ⟨ stop, ⟨ said, ⟨ stead, ⟨ Tess, ⟨ test, ⟨ raise, ℓ raised, ℓ face, ℓ faced, ⌐ lace, ℓ laced, ℓ last, ℓ ballast.

A large loop, also written in the same direction as the circle *s*, represents the sound of *str*, thus, ⌐ dust, ⌐ duster, ⌐ coast, ⌐ coaster, ⌐ mass, ⌐ master, ⌐ less, ⌐ lest, ⌐ Lester.

The circle *s* may be added to these loops, thus, ⌐ cost, ⌐ costs, ⌐ coster, ⌐ costers, ⌐ nest, ⌐ nests.

The *str* loop is never used at the beginning of a stroke. Note, therefore, such forms as ⌐ sterling, ⌐ stirrup.

EXERCISE 9
READ AND WRITE

state states stayed steady stitch stage seem steam store

story sole stole steal sane stain stun stunning Bess best

taste taster tastes tasters chest chests jest jester jests

jesters suggest suggests suggesting minister ministers invest

investor investors must muster musters.

Initial and Final Vowels. As a circle or loop at the beginning of a stroke is always read first, and at the end of a stroke is always read last, it follows that when a word begins or ends with a vowel sound we must use the alternative stroke consonants to accommodate the vowel signs. For example, in the words ⌐ sack, ⌐ sleep, the circle is used because the word begins with *s*; but in such words as *ask*, *asleep*, which begin with a vowel sound, the stroke form of *s* must be used in order to provide a place for the vowel sign, thus, ⌐ ask, ⌐ asleep.

CIRCLES AND LOOPS

In the same way, in ⟨symbol⟩ race, ⟨symbol⟩ police, ⟨symbol⟩ honest, the circle or loop is used because *s* or *st* is the last sound. Compare ⟨symbol⟩ racy, ⟨symbol⟩ policy, ⟨symbol⟩ honesty, where the vowel at the end makes a stroke consonant necessary.

In ⟨symbol⟩ deposit, ⟨symbol⟩ visit, ⟨symbol⟩ beset, the vowel between the *s* and *t* makes it necessary to write the circle *s* and *t*. For the sake of distinction from ⟨symbol⟩ cost, the word caused is written ⟨symbol⟩

ABBREVIATIONS

0 first, ⟨symbol⟩ most, ⟨symbol⟩ thank-ed, (think, ⟨symbol⟩ though, (them,) was, ⟨symbol⟩ whose.

EXERCISE 10
COPY AND TRANSCRIBE

1. ⟨shorthand symbols⟩ x

2. ⟨shorthand symbols⟩ x

3. ⟨shorthand symbols⟩ x

4. ⟨shorthand symbols⟩ x

EXERCISE 11
WRITE IN SHORTHAND

1. Honesty *is the* best policy.
2. *Whose* job *is it* to see *to the* registers?
3. *It is to be* supposed they *thanked the* lad *for* adjusting *the* lists.
4. *Though the* costs may *be* heavy *the* barrister suggests they *should* appeal.

(Keys to the above Exercises are given in the next Lesson.)

A large circle written at the beginning of a word, in the same direction as the circle *s*, represents the sound of *sw*, as heard in the following words: ⟋ sweep, ⟋ sweet, ⟋ switch, ⌒ swim, ⟍ swing, ⟋ swell, ⟍ swear.

A similar large circle, written at the end of a stroke, represents the sound of *s-s* having a light or heavy sound, with the intervening vowel *ĕ*, as heard in the following words: ⟍ paces, ⟍ pieces, ⟋ chases, ⟍ taxes, ⟍ boxes, ⟍ laces, ⟍ misses.

The large circle *ses* may be used in the middle of words, thus, ⟍ necessary, ⟍ necessity, ⟍ successive, ⟍ excessive.

Should any vowel other than short *ĕ* occur between the two *s's*, it may be indicated by writing the sign inside the circle, thus, ⟍ insist, ⟍ resist, ⟍ Texas, ⟍ basis, ⟍ census, ⟍ Mississippi, ⟍ exhaust.

Final *s* is added thus, ⟍ successes.

EXERCISE 12
READ AND WRITE

swab Swede swayed Swiss swam swim swimming swinging

omnibus omnibuses doze dozes case cases guess guesses

face faces terrace terraces mix mixes fence fences

emphasis Genesis paralysis synopsis exist axis.

For purposes of distinction the large circle is not used in a few words ending in *s-s*. The following outlines should be carefully noted: ⟍ possess, ⟍ access, ⟍ recess.

As ⟍ policy, ⟍ jealousy, ⟍ Lucy, and other similar words are written with the stroke *s*, the stroke is retained in derived words, thus, ⟍ policies, ⟍ jealousies, ⟍ Lucy's.

CIRCLES AND LOOPS

ABBREVIATIONS

↗ shall, ↗ wish, ↗ usual-ly, ⌒ me, ⌢ him, ‿ in *or* any, ‿ own, ‿ language *or* owing, ‿ thing, ‿ young, ϐ themselves, ╱ are, ↗ our *or* hour, ○ ourselves, ╱ we.

EXERCISE 13
COPY AND TRANSCRIBE

1.

2.

3.

4.

EXERCISE 14
WRITE IN SHORTHAND

1. *All the* boxes *are* ready, *and should be put on the* 8.50 a.m. *to* Manchester.
2. *In our own* case *we think our* policy *should* lead *to* success.
3. *Come and* see *me on* Monday or Wednesday, *and we shall* discuss *young* Swain's case.
4. *It is* no easy *thing to* master *a language*, a fact *on which* they *themselves* lay emphasis.

(Keys to the above Exercises are given in the next Lesson.)

LESSON 4

Methods of Phrasing

THE following are the keys to the Exercises given in the previous Lesson. Any errors made should be carefully noted and the correct forms written several times each to impress them on the memory.

KEY TO EXERCISE 10

1. The thief who stole the minister's car posed as a guest at the party.
2. The speed of the car and the state of the road caused the skid.
3. The investors think the first step must be to stop waste.
4. Most of them seem to think the judge's summing-up was just and fair.

KEY TO EXERCISE 11

1.

2.

3.

4.

KEY TO EXERCISE 13

1. We ourselves think it is necessary to despatch the notices on the fourth.
2. The police state the speed of the omnibuses in such a busy thoroughfare was excessive.
3. We wish to see the young lady who came to our offices on Monday.
4. It is usual for me to look in at the shop for an hour or so each day.

1. [shorthand symbols] 8.50 a.m.

[shorthand symbols]

2. [shorthand symbols]

3. [shorthand symbols]

[shorthand symbols]

4. [shorthand symbols]

[shorthand symbols]

Diphthongs. There are four common diphthongs, or double vowels, namely, *ī, oi, ow*, and *ū*, as heard in the words *I enjoy loud music*. These diphthongs are represented as follows:—

[symbols] ī, [symbols] oi, [symbols] ow, [symbols] ū.

Note carefully, in the following words, how these signs are used: [symbol] tie, [symbol] my, [symbol] joy, [symbol] boy, [symbol] loud, [symbol] rowdy, [symbol] beauty, [symbol] cure.

The signs *ī* and *oi* are written in the first vowel place; *ow* and *ū* are written in the third vowel place.

In a few cases, when an easy and facile joining can be made at the beginning or end of words, the diphthong signs may be joined to consonants, thus, [symbol] ice, [symbol] eyes, [symbol] item, [symbol] isle, [symbol] nigh, [symbol] oiled, [symbol] bow, [symbol] due, [symbol] few, [symbol] new, [symbol] value, [symbol] review, [symbol] now.

Note that, for greater convenience in joining, the *ū* sign may sometimes be tilted, as in *value*; and the signs for *ī* and *ow* abbreviated to a single tick, as in *isle* and *now*.

A small tick added to a diphthong sign indicates another vowel immediately following the diphthong, thus, 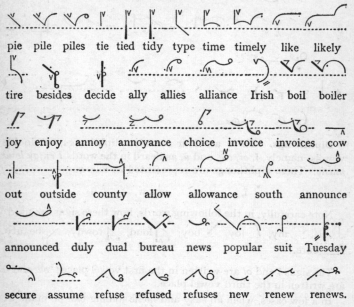 buying, ⌇ diary, ⌇ loyal, ⌇ towel, ⌇ annuity.

EXERCISE 15
READ AND WRITE

pie pile piles tie tied tidy type time timely like likely

tire besides decide ally allies alliance Irish boil boiler

joy enjoy annoy annoyance choice invoice invoices cow

out outside county allow allowance south announce

announced duly dual bureau news popular suit Tuesday

secure assume refuse refused refuses new renew renews.

A small semicircle is used for an abbreviation for w at the beginning of — k, — g, ⌒ m, ＼ r, ／ ray, thus, ⌇ week, ⌇ weeks, ⌇ walk, ⌇ wig, ⌇ Wemyss, ⌇ war, ⌇ warm, ⌇ wire, ⌇ worry, ⌇ worth, ⌇ worthy.

This semicircle is always read first. If a vowel begins a word, the stroke w must be used, thus, ⌇ wake, but ⌇ awake, ⌇ ware, but ⌇ aware.

(562)

METHODS OF PHRASING

1. [shorthand outlines]

2. [shorthand outlines]

3. [shorthand outlines]

Phrasing. A most interesting feature of Pitman's Shorthand is what is termed phrasing, that is, the joining of two or more words together as an aid to fluency in writing. For instance, the forms for the words *we have* ⟋ ⟍ may be joined easily and without any loss of legibility, thus, ⟋⟍ In the same way, *it should be* ❘ ⟋ ⟍ may be joined, thus ⟨ The increase in speed which must result from judicious phrasing will be obvious. Other examples of simple phrasing are ⟨ it may be, ⟨ it is, ⟩ it was.

The extent to which phrasing is adopted is optional, but in joining words the following points must be kept in mind: (1) A phrase should be easy to write; (2) it should not ascend too far above or too far below the line; (3) it must be easy to read.

The first word in a phrase should occupy the position in which it would be written if standing alone. For example, a phrase beginning with the word *for* must start above the line, thus, ⟍ for which; while a phrase beginning with *may* must start on the line, thus, ⟋ may be. (It is seldom necessary, by the way, to vocalize phrases.)

A small tick at the end of a word represents *the*. It is written either upward or downward, whichever forms the better angle from a speed point of view, thus,

(Down) ⟍ of the, › to the, ⟋ and the, ⟍ by the, ⟍ have the.

(Up) ⌐ at the, ⟋ which the, ⟩ was the.

This tick is never used initially or for *the* standing alone.

Note ⟋ on the, and ⟋ but the, which are slightly tilted to give a better angle.

Before studying the following list of phrases, the reader should learn the following abbreviations:—

⌐ why, ∧ how, ⌢ you, ⌐ beyond, ⟋ I, ⌐ with, ⊂ when, ⌐ what, ⟩ would, ⌐ oh *or* owe, ⎸ he.

In phrasing, the sign ⟋ may be shortened to one tick before ⟍ ⌢ and ⌐, thus, ⌐ I can, ⌐ I am, ⟋ I will (I'll).

The word *he* standing alone, or at the beginning of a phrase, is written ⟋ ; but in the middle of a phrase it is represented by the abbreviation ⎸ ; thus, ⟋ he may, ⟍ if he may.

Phrases. The list of phrases given below should be carefully studied and copied until they can be fluently and accurately written. A light smooth style of writing should be aimed at.

After they have been memorised, the student should endeavour to write the phrases from dictation at a suitable speed.

Further examples of phrasing will be given in later Lessons.

⟩ I think		⟍ I will		⟋ you will be
⟍ I think you should be		⟍ I will be		⟍ how can they
⟍ I have		⟍ you should be		⟍ why do you
⟍ I have the		⟍ you can		⟍ why have you
⟍ I have had		⟍ you may		⟍ for him
⟍ I am		⟍ you may be		⟍ for me

EXERCISE 17
COPY AND TRANSCRIBE

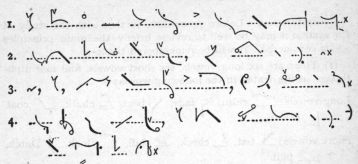

(Keys to the above Exercises are given in the next Lesson.)

LESSON 5

A Brief Review of Our Progress

WHEN the student has corrected his rendering of Exercises 16 and 17 from the Keys given below, he should have each exercise dictated to him several times. Vowel signs may be omitted in this practice. A light touch is essential in speed work.

KEY TO EXERCISE 16

1. The excuse given by the boy seems to me to be weak.
2. The youth in charge of the lorry states he was on the right side of the road at the time of the smash.
3. The failure of the firm, which was announced last week, was due, in my view, to the poor work of the buying staff.

KEY TO EXERCISE 17

1. I think the time has come for the affairs of the firm to be looked into.
2. If you will be at the office by five, I shall be happy to see you.
3. You should, I think, renew the back tyres of the car, as they show signs of wear.

4. If he desires to have our advice, I think it will be wise for him to see us by Monday at the latest.

Recapitulation. Before proceeding further with the study of the system it may be well to review briefly the main principles so far considered. It will be remembered that:—

(1) There are six long vowels, six short vowels, and four diphthongs, as illustrated in the following words:—

Long vowels : ⌒ calm, ⌐ fade, ⌐ beat, ⌐ chalk, ⌐ coal, ⌐ doom.

Short vowels : ⌐ bat, ⌐ check, ⌐ chill, ⌐ lock, ⌐ Dutch, ⌐ pull.

Diphthongs : ⌐ dye, ⌐ like, ⌐ choice, ⌐ boil, ⌐ rowdy, ⌐ couch, ⌐ duty, ⌐ Bute.

(2) When a word begins with a vowel followed by *r*, or when a word ends with the sound of *r*, the downward form is generally employed, thus, ⌐ oar, ⌐ ark, ⌐ early, ⌐ pier, ⌐ jeer, ⌐ share. Contrast these words with ⌐ row, ⌐ rack, ⌐ rally, ⌐ Pirrie, ⌐ jury, ⌐ sherry.

(3) The above rule is not strictly adhered to if an awkward form would result. Note ⌐ Rome, ⌐ remedy, ⌐ earth, ⌐ rage, ⌐ roar, ⌐ officer, ⌐ razor.

(4) *H* standing alone, or followed by *k* or *g*, is written downward, thus, ⌐ hay, ⌐ he, ⌐ hockey, ⌐ Haig.

(5) A small circle at the beginning of a stroke represents the sound of *s*, and at the end of a stroke it represents *s* or *z*, thus, ⌐ sat, ⌐ sight, ⌐ same, ⌐ sane, ⌐ sell, ⌐ sells, ⌐ smile, ⌐ smiles, ⌐ task, ⌐ desk, ⌐ desks, ⌐ risk, ⌐ risks.

This circle is written with the left motion to straight strokes, inside curves, and outside an angle formed by two straight strokes.

Where a word begins with the sound of *z*, the stroke *z* is used, thus, ⟍ zeal, ⟍° zealous.

(6) A shallow loop, written in the same direction as circle *s*, represents the sound of *st*, and a large loop represents the sound of *str*, thus, ⟋ state, ⟋ stood, ⟋ stitch, ⟋ stitches, ⌒ stem, ⟋ stole, ⟋ roast, ⟋ roaster, ⊢ dust, ⊢ duster, ⊢ dusters, ⌒ minister, ⌒ Axminster.

The *str* loop is never used at the beginning of a stroke. Thus we write ⟋ sterling, ⟋° sterilize.

(7) A large circle at the beginning of a stroke represents *sw*, and at the end of a stroke *sez* or *ses*, thus, ⟋ sweep, ⟋ switch, ⟋ cause, ⟋ causes, ⟋ race, ⟋ races, ⟋ census, ⟋ exist.

ABBREVIATIONS

⟍ subject-ed, ⟍ several-ly, ⟍ your, ⟍ year, ⌣ influence, ⌣ influenced, ⌣ next, ⟋ Lord.

EXERCISE 18
WRITE IN SHORTHAND
(Phrases are indicated by hyphens)

1. Five *of-the* six cases were tied *with* thick rope.
2. I-*think-it-is* likely *you*-may see Davis *when you-are in* Leicester.
3. *A* few *of-the* guests *are* leaving early *on*-Monday, *and-the* rest *on* Tuesday.
4. "*The Influence of-the* Cinema" *is-the first of-the several subjects to be* discussed *next* season.
5. *Lord* Johnson used *his influence in several* ways *this year, and our next* appeal *should-be a* big success.

EXERCISE 19
COPY AND TRANSCRIBE

1.

2. [shorthand symbols]

3. [shorthand symbols]

Double Consonants. Up to this stage we have considered single consonants, i.e. simple straight and curved strokes. We now come to what are termed double consonants, formed by the blending of *r* and *l* with other consonants. For instance, in the words *pray*, *break*, *Fred*; *play*, *Blake*, *fled*, it will be noticed that the *r* and the *l* blend with the preceding consonants to form one sound, *pray* being equal to the sounds *pr-a*, *break* to *br-a-k*, *play* to *pl-a*, and so on. The added letters are represented by initial hooks, thus :—

A small hook at the beginning of a straight stroke, and written with the left motion, ◯, adds *l* :—

   ⟍ *pl*,   ⟍ *bl*,   ⎰ *tl*,   ⎰ *dl*,   ⎰ *chl*,   ⎰ *jl*,   ⌒ *kl*,   ⌒ *gl*.

These consonants are named *pel*, *bel*, etc., and are pronounced as a single sound. The vowels are placed as they would be to single consonants. A careful study of the following examples will show the real sound value of the hooked strokes.

play   place   replace   Blake   bloom   total   peddle   meddle

fickle   local   buckle   treacle   legal   single   terrible   doubling.

A small hook at the beginning of a straight stroke, and written with the right motion, ◯, adds *r* :—

   ⟍ *pr*,   ⟍ *br*,   ⎰ *tr*,   ⎰ *dr*,   ⎰ *chr*,   ⎰ *jr*,   — *kr*,   — *gr*.

Thus we have:—

pry　pride　press　repress　break　broom　branch　better

brighter　dream　teacher　dredge　dredger　maker　meagre.

It is, of course, essential that outlines should be formed without lifting the pen. Special attention should be given to the manner in which the hooked forms are joined to preceding strokes. In one or two cases, as, for instance, in reply, and tiger, it is necessary to modify the shape of the hook slightly for the sake of a facile joining.

ABBREVIATIONS

principle *or* principal-ly; liberty, member *or* remember-ed, number-ed; truth; Dr. *or* doctor, dear, during; chair, cheer; larger; care.

EXERCISE 20
COPY AND TRANSCRIBE

1.

2.

(Keys to the above Exercises are given in the next Lesson.)

LESSON 6

Double Consonants

THE following are the keys to the three Exercises which were set in Lesson 5. When these have been corrected where necessary, the study of the double consonants may be continued.

KEY TO EXERCISE 18

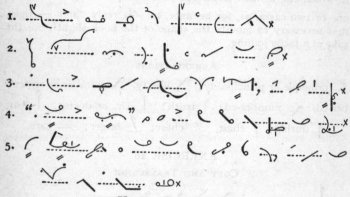

KEY TO EXERCISE 19

1. When the case was put to the jury by the counsel they took but forty minutes to decide the case.
2. For the work of taking the census two months ago it was necessary to engage a large staff.
3. Many officers were on duty at the Epsom races last week, and they had a busy time.

KEY TO EXERCISE 20

1. Dr. Grace is still remembered by all who play cricket.
2. The large increase in the number of members of the club during the last few months is largely due to the care with which Dr. Draper has carried out his duties, and we think the numbers should steadily grow larger.

Double Consonants: Curves. It has been shown how initial hooks representing *l* and *r* are added to straight strokes, the *l* hook being written with the left motion and the *r* hook with the right motion. As hooks cannot conveniently be written on the outside of a curved stroke, the method of representing the addition of *r* and *l* to curves is to employ a small hook for *r*, and a large hook for *l*, both hooks being written inside the curve, thus, ⌣ *fr*, ⌣ *vr*, (*thr*, (*THr*,) *shr*,) *zhr*, ⌒ *mr*, ⌣ *nr*, ⌣ *fl*, ⌣ *vl*, (*thl*,) *shl* (up), ⌒ *ml*, ⌣ *nl*. Note that the form) *shr* is always written downward and) *shl* is always written upward.

EXERCISE 21.

READ AND WRITE

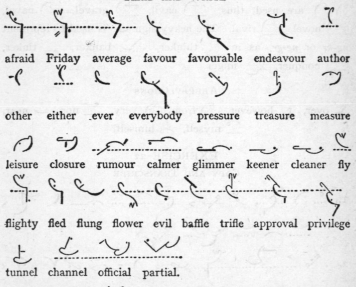

afraid Friday average favour favourable endeavour author

other either ever everybody pressure treasure measure

leisure closure rumour calmer glimmer keener cleaner fly

flighty fled flung flower evil baffle trifle approval privilege

tunnel channel official partial.

The strokes))) are not hooked for the addition of *r* or *l*. With a small initial hook attached they are used as alternative forms for *fr*, *thr*, *THr*, thus, ⌐ *fr*, ⌐ *vr*,) *thr*,) *THr*. When the double consonant stroke *fr*, *vr*, *thr*, or *THr* is the only stroke in a word the second, or reverse, form is used in cases where the word does not begin with a vowel, thus, ⌒. free, ⌒ fry, ⌐ fray, ⌐. three,)- throw, but ⌐ offer, ⌐ ever, ⌐ every, ⌐ author, -(other.

When joined to another stroke the forms are used which join most conveniently. As a general rule it will be found that the reverse forms are joined to strokes written towards the right. Note the following forms :—

⌐ frame, ⌐ frail, ⌐⌐ freak,) thread, ⌐ throb, ⌐ thrive, ⌐ coffer, ⌐ lever, ⌐ verb, ⌐ verbal, ⌐ river.

After *k*, *g*, *n*, or a straight upstroke the reverse forms for *fl*, *vl*, ⌐ ⌐ are used, thus, ⌐ cavil, ⌐ gravel, ⌐ naval, ⌐ novel, ⌐ rival. The heavy sign ⌣ is used to represent *ng-kr* or *ng-gr*, as in ⌐ thinker, ⌐ banker, ⌐ tinker, ⌐ conquer, ⌐ finger.

ABBREVIATIONS

⌐ over, ⌐ however, ⌐ from, ⌐ very, ⌐ nor, ⌐ near, ⌐ myself, ⌐ himself.

EXERCISE 22
COPY AND TRANSCRIBE

DOUBLE CONSONANTS

The circle *s* may be prefixed to the *pl*, *fr*, and *fl* series of double consonants by writing the circle inside the hook, thus, ⟍ supple, ⟍ supply, ⟍ sable, ⟍ settle, ⟍ subtle, ⟍ saddle, ⟍ cycle, ⟍ safer, ⟍ sever, ⟍ summer, ⟍ sooner, ⟍ civil, ⟍ civility.

In the case of straight strokes hooked for *r* all that is necessary is to write the circle or loop on the same side as the *r* hook, the *r* being included in the circle or loop. This applies also to the *sw* circle, thus, ⟍ upper, ⟍ supper, ⟍ super, ⟍ spring, ⟍ sober, ⟍ stray, ⟍ strange, ⟍ strong, ⟍ strength, ⟍ eater, ⟍ sweeter, ⟍ swagger, ⟍ ochre, ⟍ stoker.

It will be seen from the above outlines that the initial circle or loop is read first, in accordance with the invariable practice.

Both hook and circle must be shown in the middle of a word, thus, ⟍ extra, ⟍ extreme, ⟍ extremely, ⟍ express, ⟍ expressed, ⟍ possible, ⟍ traceable, ⟍ bicycle, ⟍ tricycle.

In order to obtain briefer or more convenient forms, the double consonant strokes are occasionally used even when a distinct vowel comes between a consonant and *l* or *r*. In cases where this special use of the double consonant stroke is made, a dot vowel is shown between a stroke and the *l* or *r* by writing a small circle instead of the usual vowel sign after (preferably) or before the stroke, thus, ⟍ parcel, ⟍ dark, ⟍ darker, ⟍ direct, ⟍ directly, ⟍ sharp, ⟍ sharply.

In words like ⟍ term, ⟍ perceive, ⟍ nervous, ⟍ mercury, the hooked form sufficiently represents the first syllable, and the circle representing short *ĕ* may be omitted.

An intervening dash vowel or diphthong is shown by writing the vowel or diphthong sign through, or at the beginning, or at the end of the stroke, thus, ⟍ corner, ⟍ Burmah, ⟍ tolerable, ⟍ former, ⟍ North, ⟍ Norfolk, ⟍ coarse, ⟍ coarsely,

⤳ before, ⟩ purchase, ⊥⊥ occur, ⊥⊥○ occurrence, ⅂ church,

⌐⌐ lecture, ⌐⌐ lectures, ⌐⌐ capture, ⌐⌐ literature. Note

the distinctive forms ⤸ regard, ⤹⌐ regret.

This form of vocalization is not generally used for one-syllable words, where the consonants are separated by a strongly-sounded vowel. Note, for instance, ⟍ pare, ⩗ pale, ⌐ dare, ⩗ pole, ⊦ dole.

ABBREVIATIONS

⟩ their, there, ⌒ more, remark-ed, ⌒ mere, Mr.; ⤸ sure, ⟩ pleasure; ⌒ valuation; ⤸ people, ⤸ belief-believe-d; ⌐ tell, ⌐ till, ⌐ deliver-ed-y; ⟋ largely; ⌒ call, ⌒ equal-ly; ⤸ surprise, ⤸ surprised.

EXERCISE 23
WRITE IN SHORTHAND

1. *This* summer *Mr.* North *is to-deliver* a course *of* lectures *on* "Ciphers *and* Codes."
2. *We-have-pleasure* in enclosing a few *more* copies *of-the* brochure on "*The Valuation of*-Property," which, *we-are-sure*, *should-be* of service *to Mr.* Strange.
3. Many *people* expressed *their surprise* at-the strong *remarks of Mr.* Soper.

Our Course in Pitman's Shorthand Is continued in Volume 6.

LESSON 10

Another Step in Grammar

THE conditional mood is formed by adding the terminations *ía, ías, ía, íamos, íais, ían* to the infinitive of all regular verbs. Note that in English the word " should " means an *obligation*, which the conditional in Spanish does not imply. E.g. I would buy it, *Lo compraría* ; but " I *should* buy it " would be translated with the verb *Deber—Debería de comprarlo.* Again, " Should you think so ? " does not imply " Would you think so ? " Therefore the conditional of think must be given in English as " would."

CONDITIONAL MOOD OF *Comprar.*

Singular.	Plural.
comprar-*ía*, I would buy	comprar-*íamos,* we would buy
comprar-*ías*	comprar-*íais*
comprar-*ía*	comprar-*ían*

Second Conjugation : *beber-ía, beber-ías,* etc., I would drink.
Third Conjugation : *cumplir-ía, cumplir-ías,* etc., I would fulfil.

When the future tense of a verb is irregular, the conditional mood is formed by adding the above terminations to the stem of the future.

Infinitive.	Future.	Conditional.
saber, to know	sabré	sabría
poder, to be able	podré	podría
decir, to say	diré	diría
salir, to go out	saldré	saldría

The conditional mood of *ser* and *estar* is regular—*sería, estaría ;* that of *tener* and *haber* is irregular—*tendría, habría.*

VOCABULARY.

the failure	el fracaso	the excess	el exceso
a port	un puerto	expenses	gastos
to imply	implicar	to appoint	nombrar
consignee	consignatario	on any account	de ningún modo
	representative	agente representante	
	by sailing vessels	por barcos de vela	

Exercise I.

TRANSLATE INTO SPANISH : 1. Would you sell it at that price ?
2. No ; it would be a failure. 3. What would you advise me ?
4. I would explain it to him again. 5. The consignees would not
pay the excess on any account. 6. Do you think that it would
be cheaper to send the goods by sailing vessels ?

Indefinite Adjectives and Pronouns. To distinguish the
interrogative from the relative adjectives and pronouns, the
former class take the accent. The following indefinite adjectives
and pronouns take the gender and number of the substantive
to which they refer :

how much	*¿ cuánto ?*	much	*mucho*
too much	*demasiado*	little	*poco*
any, some	*alguno*	none	*ninguno*
same	*mismo*	all, the whole	*todo*
	other, another	*otro*	

" How many " is rendered by *cuánt-os, -as ;* " many," by
much-os, -as ; " too many," by *demasiad-os, -as ;* and " few "
by *poc-os, -as.*

" Any " and " some " used as partitive adjectives in front of
a singular noun are either omitted or translated by *un poco de*
(lit., a little of)—*compre Vd. carne* (or *un poco de carne*), buy
some meat. When the following noun is in the pural " some "
and " any " are either omitted or rendered by *algunos* or *unos*—
¿ tiene hermanos ? has she (or he) any brothers ?

The words *algo*, something ; *nada*, nothing ; *alguien*, anybody,
somebody ; and *cada*, each, every, are invariable. After a negation, " anybody " and " any " are respectively rendered by
nadie and *ninguno*—*no ha escrito a nadie*, she (or he) has not
written to anybody.

VOCABULARY.

to meet	*encontrar*	the frontier	*la frontera*
to stop	*parar*	an armchair	*un sillón*
the circular	*la circular*	comfortable	*cómodo*
a branch	*una sucursal*	printed	*impreso*
the things	*las cosas*	I think so	*creo que sí*
the garden	*el jardin*	by post	*por correo*
Scotland	*Escocia*	Columbia	*Colombia*
both	*ambos*	the back	*la espalda*
a handkerchief	*un pañuelo*	the opinion	*la opinión*

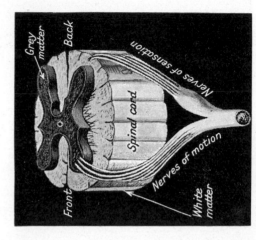

SPINAL CORD. Section showing the grey and white matter of which it is composed, with bundles of descending motor nerves and ascending sensory nerves. PHYSIOLOGY 19

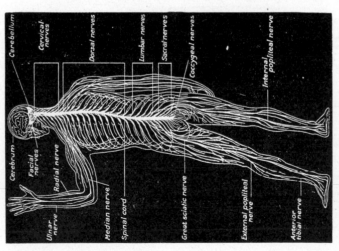

NERVOUS SYSTEM. Diagram of the network of nerves of the human body seen from the back. PHYSIOLOGY 19

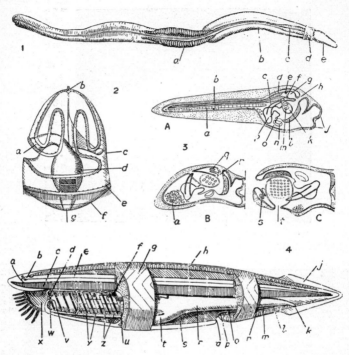

SIMPLE VERTEBRATES. 1. Balanoglossus or acorn-worm, entire animal : a,
prominences formed by "liver" caeca ; b, genital ridges ; c, branchial region ; d,
collar ; e, proboscis. **2.** Larval form (Tornaria), lateral view ; a, mouth ; b, eye ;
c. proboscis-pore ; d intestine ; e, ciliated band ; f, hinder ciliated ring ; g, anus.
3. Diagrams of metamorphosis of ascidian larva ; A, larva at time of fixation ; B,
midway in the metamorphosis ; C metamorphosis complete ; a, notochord ; b, dorsal nerve cord ; c, intestine ; d, trunk ganglion ; e, eye ; f, statolith ; g, cerebral
vesicle ; h, mouth . i fixation papillae ; k, right rudiment of atrium ; l, endostyle ;
m. gill slits : n, heart ; o, epicardium ; p, stomach ; q, adult ganglion : r ciliary
tunnel , s. ganglion : t, atrial opening. **4.** Diagram of anatomy of Amphioxus ; a,
eye-spot : b, brain ; c, notochord ; d, velum ; e, nerve cord ; f, l and p, coelom ; g,
myotomes ; h, dorsal fin-ray : j, tail fin ; k, anus ; m and o, posterior prolonga-
tion of atrium : n, ventral fin-ray ; q, atriopore : r, intestine ; s, atrium : t, liver :
u gonad : v. velar tentacles ; w, mouth ; x, oral hood ; y. gills : z. gill-bars.
ZOOLOGY 21

1, 2 and 4, from Parker & Haswell, "A Text-book of Zoology," Macmillan & Co ;
3. from Borradaile, Potts, Eastham & Saunders, "The Invertebrata," Cambridge
University Press

Plate 60   Volume V

ANOTHER STEP IN GRAMMAR

EXERCISE II.

TRANSLATE INTO SPANISH : 1. How many printed circulars did you send by post ? 2. I have not sent any today. 3. Has anybody been here this morning ? 4. No, sir ; nobody has come. 5. He used to spend too much money. 6. That bank has too many branches in Colombia. 7. Please give me some more milk. 8. Do you wish anything ? 9. No ; I do not wish anything. 10. Do they sell (any) German newspapers ? 11. I think so. 12. Where did you buy those handkerchiefs ? 13. I bought all the things at the same shop. 14. Each house has a small garden at the back. 15. All (the) trains stop at the frontier. 16. He has given me something. 17. We met some friends at the theatre. 18. The other armchair is more comfortable. 19. We receive very few orders from Scotland. 20. Both are of the same opinion.

There are many adjectives which can be used as nouns and then become subject to all the rules governing substantives, as, for instance, *joven*, young ; *un joven*, a young man ; *francés*, French ; *un francés*, a Frenchman.

Grande, great, when it implies merit, loses the final syllable and is placed before the noun—*un gran pintor*, a great painter. When it refers to size, it is placed after the noun—*un edificio grande*, a large building.

The masculine adjective *santo*, saint, drops the last syllable before all proper names, except *Domingo*, *Toribio*, and *Tomás*—*San José*, Saint Joseph ; *Santo Tomás*, Saint Thomas. The feminine *santa* is invariable—*Santa Lucía*, Saint Lucy ; *Santa Isabel*, Saint Elizabeth.

Suffixes. Diminutive and augmentative suffixes are terminations applied to nouns and adjectives, qualifying their original meaning. Their correct use is rather difficult, and can only be learned properly by practice. Students should therefore refrain from using them until they master the language. In the meantime, adjectives should always be used in their place.

Diminutives express smallness, fondness, and sometimes pity or contempt. The chief diminutive terminations are *ico*, *ito*, *illo*, *uelo*. All these terminations change the final *o* into *a* in the feminine.

The principal augmentative terminations are *ón*, *azo*, *ote* in the masculine, and *ona*, *aza*, *ota* in the feminine. These terminations simply imply largeness, but *achón* further expresses clumsiness and contempt. Diminutives are frequently applied to proper names. Examples of both types of suffixes are : *una casita*, a little house ; *un perrazo*, a big dog ; *la callejuela*, the narrow lane ; *una mujerona*, a big woman ; *el cigarillo*, the cigarette ; *un borrachón*, a drunkard ; *un muchachote*, a big boy ; *un hambrón*, a hungry fellow ; *un poquito*, a little bit ; *Pepito*, Joe ; *Anita*, Nancy.

KEYS TO EXERCISES IN LESSON 9.

(I). 1. ¿ Comprendió Vd. la canción ? 2. No ; cantó en italiano aquella noche. 3. Esperamos dos horas por lo menos ; ¿ qué hora llegó el tren ? 4. Más tarde que nunca. Casi a las ocho y media. 5. ¿ Cuanto le costó (a Vd.) el viaje ? 6. Tomé un billete de ida y vuelta que es mucho más barato. 7. ¿ Cuando comenzaron los contratistas a construir el muelle ? 8. Creo que comenzaron poco después de Pascua. 9. ¿ Comprobó Vd. todas las facturas ? 10. No : no tuve tiempo para comprobarlas todas. 11. ¿ Llovió ? 12. Solamente por la noche. 13. ¿ Esperaron en casa ? 14. No ; salieron a saludarle. 15. ¿ Dónde ancló el vapor ? 16. En medio de la bahía. 17. No comprendo por qué no contestaron mi telegrama en el acto.

(II). 1. Veinte buques. 2. Cincuenta y tres chelines. 3. Setenta y nueve páginas. 4. Cuarenta y cinco cajas de azúcar. 5. Ciento siete libras. 6. Trescientos sesenta y cinco días. 7. Seiscientos trece árboles. 8. ¿ Cuántos años tiene ahora ? 9. Tiene setenta y cinco. A los veintitrés años de edad mandaba una fragata de ochenta y cuatro cañones. 10. ¿ Qué edad tenía Vd. entonces ? 11. Tenía quince años. 12. En mil setecientos Davenant calculó la producción anual de todas las minas de Inglaterra entre setecientas y ochocientas mil libras. 13. El área del Canadá es de tres millones quinientas diez mil millas cuadradas, lo cual es casi equivalente a la superficie territorial de Europa. 14. Las bajas del enemigo fueron mil cincuenta hombres muertos, mil setecientos heridos y dos mil quinientos prisioneros. 15. En mil ochocientos cuarenta y cuatro, el ingreso líquido de las aduanas de Liverpool ascendió a cuatro millones trescientas sesenta y cinco mil quinientas veintiseis libras, un chelín y ocho peniques.

(III). 1. Fuma un par de pipas después de la comida. 2. Yo viajaba en tercera clase. 3. Están viviendo ahora en el quinto piso del mismo edificio. 4. Lo leí en el primer capítulo. 5. ¿ Lo prestó Vd. el tomo veinte de la Biblioteca Española ?

6. Desembarcamos en Valparaíso el veintiano de Diciembre de mil ochocientos setenta y nueve. 7. Su mujer nació el seis de Enero de mil ochocientos ochenta y seis. 8. El treinta de Agosto será el cumpleaños de su primer hijo. 9. ¿ Qué fecha es hoy ? 10. El diecinueve de Febrero. 11. Felipe Tercero ascendió al trono de España en mil quinientos noventa y ocho. 12. En mil cuatrocientos noventa y tres, el Papa Alejandro Sexto concedió a los reyes Católicos derechos exclusivos sobre el Nuevo Mundo. 13. El Emperador Carlos Quinto expiró el veintiuno de Septiembre de mil quinientos cincuenta y ocho, a la edad de cincuenta y ocho años, seis meses y veinticinco días. 14. Al final del siglo diecisiete la población de Inglaterra era de cinco millones doscientas mil almas. 15. El arqueo de los vapores del puerto de Londres ascendió, al final de mil ochocientos cincuenta y cuatro, a ciento treinta y ocho mil toneladas, sin contar los buques de menos de cincuenta toneladas. 16. En el reinado de Carlos Segundo—escribe Macaulay—ni una sola ciudad provinciana del reino contenía treinta mil habitantes y solamente cuatro tenían diez mil. 17. Durante un cuarto de siglo, la proporción de nacimientos en Italia permaneció casi estacionaria a treinta y siete por mil. 18. Una pulgada es igual a un doceavo de pie. 19. Cuatro mil quinientas sesenta y tres cienmilésimas.

LESSON 11

Reflexive Verbs and Pronouns

A VERB is called reflexive when its object is a person or thing identical with the subject—*yo me lavo*, I wash myself. The reflexive personal pronouns " myself," " thyself," " himself," " herself," and " yourself " are rendered by *me*, *te*, *se ;* and " ourselves," " yourselves," " yourselves " (familiar form), and " themselves " are respectively translated by *nos*, *se*, *os*, and *se*. The position of these reflexive forms with regard to their verb is the same as that of the conjunctive personal pronouns. Not all verbs which are reflexive in Spanish must be assumed to be so in English. The infinitive of a reflexive verb may be easily recognized, because it is invariably composed of the usual form of the infinitive and the termination *se* (oneself) —*esconderse*, to hide oneself. The final *s* or *d* of the first and second persons plural of the affirmative imperative is dropped in all reflexive verbs—*escondámonos*, let us hide ourselves ; *escondeos*, hide yourselves.

As a model for the conjugation of reflexive verbs, *levántarse*, " to get up," may be taken ; it must be noted that such verbs are exceedingly common in Spanish.

PRESENT INDICATIVE.

Singular	*Plural*
me levanto, I get up	*nos levantamos*, we get up
te levantas	*os levantáis*
se levanta	*se levantan*

IMPERFECT.

no me levantaba, I used not to get up
no se levantaba, he (she) used not to get up
no nos levantábamos, we used not to get up

PAST DEFINITE.

se levantó, he (she) got up
nos levantamos, we got up
se levantaron, they got up

FUTURE.

no me levantaré, I shall not get up
no te levantarás, thou shalt not get up
no os levantaréis, you will not get up

CONDITIONAL MOOD.

se levantaría, he would get up
nos levantaríamos, we would get up
se levantarían, they would get up

IMPERATIVE MOOD.

levántate, get up (thou)
levántese Vd, get up (you)
levantémonos, let us get up
no se levanten Vds, do not get up

VOCABULARY.

to be like	*parecerse a*	to sit down	*sentarse*
to be glad	*alegrarse*	to alight	*bajarse*
to go to bed	*acostarse*	to wake up	*despertarse*
to get angry	*enfadarse*	to swim	*nadar*

REFLEXIVE VERBS AND PRONOUNS

to get tired	*cansarse*	to laugh	*reirse*
to retire	*retirarse*	to refuse	*negarse*
to bathe	*bañarse*	to lodge	*alojarse*
to move	*mudarse*	to walk	*andar*
to know how	*saber*	the demand	*la demanda*
to hope	*esperar*	increase	*aumento*
until	*hasta*	the seaside	*la playa*
during	*durante*	the village	*la aldea*

to make up one's mind	*decidirse*
to take advantage	*aprovecharse*
to establish oneself	*establecerse*
to make a mistake	*equivocarse*
to raise the price	*subir el precio*
to enjoy oneself	*divertirse*
to trouble oneself	*molestarse*
to get married to	*casarse con*
to catch a cold	*resfriarse*
to praise oneself	*alabarse*
to say good-bye	*despedirse*
to wash oneself	*lavarse*
the daughter	*la hija*
the royal palace	*el palacio real*
the central market	*el mercado central*

EXERCISE I.

TRANSLATE INTO SPANISH. 1. He was glad to (trans. *de*) see me. 2. I hope (that) you will enjoy yourselves. 3. They went to bed so late because they had to wait for their father. 4. We did not sit down during the whole evening. 5. It would be so easy to make a mistake. 6. Do not trouble yourself. 7. The cashier gets very (trans. *mucho*) angry when we make a mistake. 8. Alight in front of the Royal Palace 9. They will soon get tired if they walk so quickly. 10. We used not to wake up until half-past seven. 11. Do you think he will retire from (the) business next year ? 12. I think he will retire if his daughter gets married to his partner. 13. Make up your mind. 14. I caught a cold at the seaside. 15. Did you bathe ? 16. No ; I do not know how (*no sé*) to swim. 17. We would establish ourselves near the central market. 18. They took advantage of the great increase in the demand to raise their (trans. *los*) prices. 19. She used to praise herself too much. 20. I had to say good-bye to (trans. *de*) all my friends. 21. They would laugh. 22. We refuse to accept their terms. 23. Where can I (*puedo*) wash myself ? 24. He is like a friend of mine. 25. The soldiers were lodged in the houses of the village. 26. We moved to this house a few (*algunos*) days afterwards.

When a reflexive verb used in the plural refers to two or more persons separately it is called *reciprocal*, and the reflexive pronoun *se* must be translated into English by " each other " if only two persons are meant, and by " one another " when the subjects of the verb are several—*se comprenden*, they understand each other ; *se ayudan*, they help one another.

As sometimes the meaning of the sentence may be doubtful, it is usual in such cases to make it clearer by some addition—*se conocen a sí mismos*, they know themselves ; *se conocen el uno al otro*, or *mútuamente*, they know each other ; *se conocen los unos a los otros*, they know one another.

Verbs expressing a state of transition are very frequently reflexive in Spanish. Thus, to become, *convertirse ;* to fall asleep, *dormirse.* Sometimes the reflexive form is used to denote a modification of the idea expressed by the original verb—*abonar*, to pay ; *abonarse*, to subscribe.

Impersonal Sentences. Many impersonal sentences which in English are constructed in the passive voice, or with the aid of words like " people," " they," used in a general sense, must be rendered into Spanish by the reflexive form of the verb—*se decía*, it was said, people said ; *se dan lecciones*, lessons given ; *se habla español*, Spanish spoken (here).

VOCABULARY.

to comment	*comentar*	to omit	*suprimir*
to admit	*admitir*	to serve	*servir*
to request	*suplicar*	to apply	*solicitar*
to prohibit	*prohibir*	to issue	*despachar*
to let	*alquilar*	to make	*hacer*
to do	*hacer*	to repair	*componer*
to take time	*tardar tiempo*	by land	*por tierra*
to continue	*continuar*	by sea	*por mar*
page	*página*	silence	*silencio*
yearly	*al año*	dog	*perro*
rent	*alquiler*	the result	*el resultado*
ballot	*votación*	to measure	*a medida*

site	*solar*	vowel	*vocal*
suit	*traje*	to want	*necesitar*
nowadays	*hoy dia*	on horseback	*a caballo*
public works	*obras públicas*	how long ?	*¿ cuánto tiempo ?*
second hand	*de segunda mano*	shorthand writer	*taquígrafo*
everywhere	*en todas partes*	to collect (cash)	*cobrar*
	furnished flat	*piso amueblado*	

Exercise II.

TRANSLATE INTO SPANISH. 1. It is believed that they are more than ten. 2. People commented (on) the news. 3. Second-hand books bought, sold, and exchanged. 4. Is English spoken there ? 5. I do not think so, but French is spoken everywhere. 6. No dogs admitted. 7. Silence requested. 8. People travel more nowadays. 9. The journey was then done on horseback. It took (imp.) twenty or thirty days. 10. How long does it take (*se tarda*) from here to Barcelona ? 11. It takes one day and a half by land and seven or (*u*) eight days by sea. 12. Money lent. 13. The result of the ballot is not yet known. 14. Sold everywhere. 15. Two millions are yearly spent in public works. 16. It will be continued next week. 17. Spanish shorthand writer wanted. 18. Smoking prohibited.

Keys to Exercises in Lesson 10.

I. 1. ¿ Lo vendería Vd. a ese precio ? 2. No, sería un fracaso. 3. ¿ Qué me aconsejaría Vd. ? 4. Yo se lo explicaría otra vez. 5. Los consignatarios no pagarían el exceso de ningún modo. 6. ¿ Cree Vd. que sería más barato enviar los géneros por barcos de vela ?

II. 1. ¿ Cuántas circulares impresas envió Vd. por correo ? 2. No he enviado ninguna hoy. 3. ¿ Ha estado alguien aquí esta mañana ? 4. No, señor ; no ha venido nadie. 5. Gastaba demasiado dinero. 6. Ese banco tiene demasiadas sucursales en Colombia. 7. Haga el favor de darme más leche. 8. ¿ Desea Vd. algo ? 9. No ; no deseo nada. 10. ¿ Venden periódicos alemanes ? 11. Creo que sí. 12. ¿ Dónde compró Vd. esos pañuelos ? 13. Compré todas las cosas en la misma tienda. 14. Cada casa tiene un jardín pequeño a la espalda. 15. Todos los trenes paran en la frontera. 16. Me ha dado algo. 17. Encontramos a algunos amigos en el teatro. 18. El otro sillón es más cómodo. 19. Recibimos muy pocos pedidos de Escocia. 20. Ambos son de la misma opinión.

LESSON 12

Impersonal Verbs

IMPERSONAL verbs are those which can only be conjugated in the third person singular of each tense, such as *tronar*, to thunder; *nevar*, to snow. The various tenses of the form "there is" are rendered by the third person of *haber*, with the single exception of the present indicative, which is translated by *hay* instead of *ha*. The student must bear in mind that *haber*, being in this case an impersonal verb, cannot be conjugated in the plural. Thus "there is" and "there are" are both rendered by *hay;* "there was" and "there were" by *habia*, and so on. As, however, *haber* thus conjugated only implies existence, whenever "there is" or "there are" expresses the place where persons or things are, *alli está, alli están* must be used instead of *hay*: *alli está mi libro*, there is my book.

When "any," "some" or "none," used in connexion with any tense of the impersonal form of "be," refer to a previous noun, those words are generally rendered by *lo, la, los, las,* according to the gender and number of that noun : *beberé vino español si lo hay*, I shall drink Spanish wine if there is some.

"To be cold, hot, sunny, windy," and so on are translated by *hacer frío, calor, sol, viento*, and so on : *hace demasiado calor*, it is too hot ; *hacía viento*, it was windy. The past definite, future and conditional of *hacer* are irregular, the third person singular of these tenses being *hizo, hará, haría*.

"Ago" is rendered by *hace : hace tres semanas*, three weeks ago.

"To be necessary" may be translated either by *ser necesario, ser menester, ser preciso*, or by the impersonal verb *haber que : para aprender un idioma extranjero hay que* (or *es preciso, menester, necesario*) *estudiar muchísimo*, in order to learn a foreign language it is necessary to study very hard.

The defective auxiliary "must" may be rendered either by *deber, tener que*, or *haber de ; debo* (*tengo que* or *he de*) *terminarlo hoy*, I must finish it today.

"Ought" is translated by the conditional tense of *deber : debería cambiarlo*, he ought to exchange it.

IMPERSONAL VERBS

Vocabulary.

the people	*la gente*	the deck	*la cubierta*
free	*libre*	cabin	*camarote*
to hail	*granizar*	often	*a menudo*
seldom	*raramente*	splendid	*espléndido*
to dawn	*amanecer*	almanac	*almanaque*
umbrella	*paraguas*	to drizzle	*lloviznar*
in time	*a tiempo*	fog	*niebla*
reply	*respuesta*	fault	*culpa*
gold	*oro*	affair	*asunto*
safe	*seguro*	to grow dark	*anochecer*
it looks like rain	*parece que va*	all the same	*de todos modos*
	a llover	on the fore-deck	*a proa*
it does not matter	*no importa*	of course	*naturalmente*
summer holidays	*vacaciones de*	to rise (the sun,	*salir (el sol, la*
	verano	the moon)	*luna)*

Exercise.

TRANSLATE INTO SPANISH : 1 There are many reasons to
(trs. *para*) suppose that. 2. There were too many people on
(the) deck. 3. Is there anybody in that cabin ? 4. I think
so, but there are several free on the foredeck. 5. There is no
time to (trs. *que*) lose. 6. There will be more the day after to-
morrow. 7. It only rained the two first evenings. 8. Does it
hail often in your country ? 9. Very seldom ; the last time that
it hailed was five years ago. 10. Yesterday was (*hizo*) a splendid
day. 11. At what time does it dawn now ? 12. According to
the almanac, the sun rises at a quarter to six. 13. In winter it
grows dark earlier than in summer. The days are very short.
14. It is too hot in this room ; please open that window. 15.
With pleasure, but it will be too cold. 16. It does not matter.
I thank you very much, all the same. 17. Please lend me an
umbrella. It looks like rain. 18. I think it is drizzling already.
19. Was it sunny during your summer holidays ? 20. On the
contrary, we had fog almost every day. 21. There is your
friend's motor-car. 22. It will be necessary to explain it to him
again. 23. He must have forgotten it.

There are some Spanish verbs like *gustar*, " to like " or " to
please," *faltar*, " to want " or " to be in want of," *pesar*, " to be
sorry," and a few others, which require a construction of the
phrase absolutely different from that which is used in English.

In sentences of this kind the person, who in English is the subject, becomes the object, while this latter becomes, in a manner, the subject, of the Spanish verb. Thus, for instance, " I like that book " must be rendered by *aquel libro me gusta* (lit., that book pleases me) ; " he wants time " by *le falta tiempo* (lit., time is wanting to him) ; and " I am sorry to have written to him " by *me pesa haberle escrito*.

" How," used in questions formed with the verb " to like," is always omitted in Spanish, and the present participle, which sometimes represents the object of the sentence, must be translated by the infinitive : *¿ Le gusta a Vd. viajar ?* How do you like travelling ?

Hacer falta is very frequently employed instead of *faltar :* *me hace falta otro empleado*, I want another clerk.

A present participle immediately preceded by a preposition must be rendered in Spanish by the infinitive : *después de haber comprado el billete*, after having bought the ticket ; *sin pronunciar una palabra*, without uttering a word.

The words " so " and " very " are translated by *tan* and *muy* in front of adjectives, adverbs, and past participles preceded by *ser* and *estar*, but they are rendered by *tanto* and *mucho* whenever they qualify a noun or a verb : *no estoy tan cansado como Vd.*, I am not so tired as you ; *no hace tanto frío como ayer*, it is not so cold as yesterday.

" Very much " must be rendered by *muchísimo* and " so much " by *tanto*.

Keys to Exercises in Lesson 11.

(I). 1. Se alegro de verme. 2. Espero que se divertirán Vds. 3. Se acostaron tan tarde porque tuvieron que aguardar a su padre. 4. No nos sentamos durante toda la noche. 5. ¡ Sería tan fácil equivocarse ! 6. No se moleste Vd. 7. El cajero se enfada mucho cuando nos equivocamos. 8. Bájense Vds. enfrente del Palacio Real. 9. Pronto se cansarán si andan tan de prisa. 10. No nos despertábamos hasta las siete y media. 11. ¿ Cree Vd. que se retirará del negocio el año que viene ? 12. Creo que se retirará si su hija se casa con su socio. 13. Decídase Vd. 14. Me resfrié en la playa. 15. ¿ Se bañó Vd. ? 16. No, no sé nadar. 17. Nos estableceríamos cerca del Mercado Central. 18. Se aprovecharon del gran aumento en la demanda para subir los precios. 19. Ella se alababa demasiado. 20.

Tuve que despedirme de todos mis amigos. 21. Se reirían. 22. Nos negamos a aceptar sus condiciones. 23. ¿ Dónde puedo lavarme ? 24. Se parece a un amigo mío. 25. Los soldados se alojaron en las casas de la aldea. 26. Nos mudamos a esta casa algunos días después.

(II). 1. Se cree que son más de diez. 2. Se comentó la noticia. 3. Se compran, se venden y se cambian libros de segunda mano. 4. ¿ Se habla inglés allí ? 5. Creo que no, pero se habla francés en todas partes. 6. No se admiten perros. 7. Se suplica el silencio. 8. Se viaja más hoy día. 9. El viaje se hacía entonces a caballo. Se tardaban veinte o trienta días. 10. ¿ Cuanto se tarda de aquí a Barcelona ? 11. Se tardan día y medio por tierra y siete u ocho días por mar. 12. Se presta dinero. 13. El resultado de la votación no se sabe todavía. 14. Se vende en todas partes. 15. Se gastan dos millones al año en obras públicas. 16. Se continuará la semana que viene. 17. Se desea un taquígrafo español. 18. Se prohibe fumar.

LESSON 13

Conjunctions and the Subjunctive

IN Spanish " to," meaning " in order to," in front of an infinitive is generally translated by *para*, unless it is preceded by part of a verb of motion, when it is always rendered by *a* : it is too late to protest, *es demasiado tarde para protestar ;* he has gone to protest, *ha ido a protestar*. Other important verbs after which " to " is rendered by *a* are :

to learn	*aprender*	to teach	*enseñar*
to compel	*obligar*	to commence	*comenzar*
to begin	*empezar*	to authorize	*autorizar*
to submit	*someterse*	to get used	*acostumbrarse*
to refuse	*negarse*	to invite	*invitar, convidar*

There are certain verbs after which " to " is not translated at all. The principal are :

to promise	*prometer*	to like	*gustar*
to hope	*esperar*	to want	*querer*
to be able	*poder*	to be sorry	*sentir, pesar*
to wish	*desear*	to know how to	*saber*
to allow	*permitir*	to intend	*intentar*

Whenever the conjunction *y* (and) occurs immediately before a word beginning with *i* or *hi*, it is changed into *e* for the sake of euphony : *España e Inglaterra*, Spain and England. For the same reason *o* (or) becomes *u* in front of a word beginning with *o* or *ho* : *setenta u ochenta casas*, seventy or eighty houses.

The conjunction *pero* (but) after a negative sentence must be changed into *sino*, unless it is followed by a verb : *no he recibido el dinero, sino solamente los intereses*, I have not received the money, but only the interest ; *no ha recibido el dinero todavía, pero ya ha cobrado los intereses*, he has not received the money yet, but he has already cashed the interest.

Vocabulary.

a street	*una calle*	the square	*la plaza*
to walk	*pasear*	to pay a visit	*visitar*
besides	*además*	to consult	*consultar*
to finish	*acabar*	to skate	*patinar*
ice	*hielo*	magazine	*revista*
to take	*tomar*	bookcase	*estante*
the fiancé	*el novio*	to ask for	*pedir*
certainly	*naturalmente*	tramway	*tranvía*
a cousin	*un primo*	to undertake	*emprender*
Do you ? Did you ?		*¿ y Vd.?*	
to be very pleased to		*tener mucho gusto en*	
the address		*la dirección, las señas*	
to keep waiting		*hacer aguardar*	
the information		*los informes*	
a long time		*mucho tiempo*	

Note. Bookcase is more correctly *biblioteca*, though *estante*, which literally means shelf, is also used.

Exercise I.

Translate into Spanish : 1. How would you like to live in Paris ? 2. I should like it very much. 3. What is he in want of ? 4. He wants more money to undertake a new business. 5. Do you know your cousin's address in Madrid ? 6. His address used to be 106, Murillo Street (*trs.* Street of Murillo, number 106). 7. Mine is 24, Hernán Cortés Square, where I hope to see you soon. 8. Many thanks. I shall be very pleased to pay you a visit next summer. 9. Do you like walking ? 10. Yes, but not today ; it is very hot, and, besides, I am too tired (fem.). 11. He is now sorry to have accepted the offer without consulting his partners. 12. She always keeps us waiting a long time. 13. How much time do they still want to finish their work ? 14 They want another hour. 15. They do not work so quickly as they promised us. 16. Do you know (how) to skate ? 17. No ; do you ? 18. I like skating on the ice.

Subjunctive Mood. The subjunctive mood is more strictly observed in Spanish than in English ; it generally implies that the action or state expressed by the verb is not quite certain, as it is when the indicative mood is employed, but merely contingent or doubtful. The following examples will make clearer the import of the subjunctive : Indicative : *cuando lo veo le hablo*, when(ever) I see him I speak to him ; Subjunctive : *cuando lo vea le hablaré*, when I may see him I shall speak to him. Indicative : *aunque ha estudiado mucho sabe muy poco*, although he has studied a great deal he knows very little ; Subjunctive : *aunque haya estudiado mucho sabe muy poco*, although he may have studied a great deal, he knows very little. As will be seen, the actions which in these sentences are positively expressed by the indicative mood (*veo* and *ha estudiado*) become at once doubtful when the subjunctive is used.

The simple tenses of the subjunctive mood are three : present, imperfect, and future. Although a construction of the infinitive with the auxiliaries " may," " might," " would," is sometimes an exact equivalent of the Spanish subjunctive, this is far from being the case always. It would therefore be utterly misleading to attach any general or permanent translation to the above tenses, whose employment must be regulated by certain fixed principles which are stated at a later stage.

The first conjugation verbs form their present subjunctive by adding to the stem the terminations *e, es, e, emos, éis, en*. Verbs of the second and third conjugations add the terminations *a, as, a, amos, áis, an*.

SUBJUNCTIVE MOOD.

Singular.	Plural.
1. *compr-e*	*compr-emos*
compr-es	*compr-éis*
compr-e	*compr-en*
2. *beb-a*	*beb-amos*
beb-as	*beb-áis*
beb-a	*beb-an*

(589)

Singular.		Plural.	
3. cumpl-a		cumpl-amos	
cumpl-as		cumpl-áis	
cumpl-a		cumpl-an	

The present subjunctive of *ser*, *estar*, *haber* and *tener* is as follows :

sea	esté	haya	tenga
seas	estés	hayas	tengas
sea	esté	haya	tenga
seamos	estemos	hayamos	tengamos
seáis	estéis	hayáis	tengáis
sean	estén	hayan	tengan

Note that the third person singular and the first and third persons plural of the present subjunctive are the same as the corresponding ones of the imperative. This is also the case when the imperative of a verb happens to be irregular.

EXERCISE II.

Form the present subjunctive of the following verbs : 1. *cambiar*. 2. *coser*. 3. *vivir*. 4. *vender*. 5. *alquilar*. 6. *haber*. 7. *escribir*. 8. *ser*. 9. *contestar*. 10. *comer*.

KEY TO EXERCISE IN LESSON 12.

1. Hay muchas razones para suponer eso. 2. Había demasiada gente en la cubierta. 3. ¿ Hay alguien en ese camarote ? 4. Creo que sí, pero hay varios libres (*or* desocupados) a proa. 5. No hay tiempo que perder. 6. Habrá más pasado mañana. 7. Solamente llovió las dos primeras noches. 8. ¿ Graniza a menudo en su país ? 9. Muy raramente ; la última vez que granizó fué hace cinco años. 10. Ayer hizo un día espléndido. 11. ¿ A qué hora amanece ahora ? 12. Según el almanaque, sale el sol a las seis menos cuarto. 13. En el invierno anochece más temprano que en el verano. Los días son muy cortos. 14. Hace demasiado calor en esta habitación ; haga Vd. el favor de abrir esa ventana. 15. Con mucho gusto, pero hará demasiado frío. 16. No importa ; muchas gracias de todos modos. 17. Haga el favor de prestarme un paraguas ; parece que va a llover. 18. Creo que ya está lloviznando. 19. ¿ Hacía sol durante sus vacaciones de verano ? 20. Al contrario ; teníamos niebla casi todos los días. 21. Ahí está el automóvil de su amigo. 22. Será necesario explicárselo otra vez. 23. Debe haberlo olvidado

LESSON 14

On the Use of the Subjunctive

I N the subjunctive mood, the imperfect and future tenses are formed by dropping the termination -*ron* from the third person plural of the past definite, and then affixing to the stem thus obtained the terminations -*ra*, -*ras*, -*ra*, -*ramos*, -*rais*, -*ran*, or -*se*, -*ses*, -*se*, -*semos*, -*seis*, -*sen*, for the imperfect, and -*re*, -*res*, -*re*, *remos*, -*reis*, -*ren*, for the future.

IMPERFECT SUBJUNCTIVE.

Singular		*Plural*	
1. *compra* -	ra / se	*comprá* -	ramos / semos
compra -	ras / ses	*compra* -	rais / seis
compra -	ra / se	*compra* -	ran / sen
2. *comie* -	ra / se	*comié* -	ramos / semos
comie -	ras / ses	*comie* -	rais / seis
comie -	ra / se	*comie* -	ran / sen
3. *cumplie*-	ra / se	*cumplié*-	ramos / semos
cumplie-	ras / ses	*cumplie*-	rais / seis
cumplie-	ra / se	*cumplie*-	ran / sen

FUTURE SUBJUNCTIVE.

1. *compra-re*	2. *comie-re*	3. *cumplie-re*
compra-res	*comie-res*	*cumplie-res*, etc.

EXERCISE I.

Form the imperfect subjunctive of the following verbs: 1. *entregar* (on -*ra*). 2. *aprender* (on -*se*). 3. *embarcar* (-*ra*). 4.

cancelar (-se).   5. *emitir* (-ra).   6. *escribir* (-se).   7. *ser* (-ra).
8. *temer* (-se).

EXERCISE II.

Form the following subjunctive tenses : 1. Present of *estar*.
2. Future of *cantar*.   3. Imperfect of *perder*.   4. Future of *pro-meter*.   5. Present of *haber*.   6. Imperfect of *viajar*.   7. Future
of *discutir*.   8. Imperfect of *surtir*.   9. Present of *responder*.
10. Future of *firmar*.

When the infinitive or present participle which sometimes
represents the second verb in an English compound phrase can
by means of the conjunction " that " be changed, without
altering the meaning of the sentence, into the subjunctive mood,
this latter construction must always be adopted in Spanish.
Thus, the phrases " he wants you to reply at once," and " I did
not like their smoking in the office," may be transformed into
" he wants (wishes) that you should reply at once," and " I did
not like that they should have smoked in the office." These
phrases must, therefore, be rendered in Spanish by the following :
desea que conteste Vd. enseguida, and *no me gustó que fumaran en
la oficina*.

When the subjects of the two sentences which form the phrase
are identical, the infinitive of the second verb must be used
instead of the subjunctive mood : *deseo ver al gerente*, I want to
see the manager.

The subjunctive mood must be employed :

(1) After most conjunctions formed with *que*, among which
the principal are :

a fin de que	so that	*para que*	in order that
antes que	before	*no sea que*	lest
en caso que	in case	*a menos que*	unless
sin que	without	*hasta que*	until
después que	after	*dado que*	granted that
con tal que	provided that		

Examples are : *con tal que escriba*, provided he writes ; *a menos
que envíen los géneros enseguida*, unless they send the goods at
once.

(2) After the conjunction *si* (if) when it does not mean
" whether," and the other verb in the sentence is in the conditional.
In this case the imperfect subjunctive must be employed : *si
tuviera más dinero lo compraría*, if I had more money I should
buy it.

USE OF THE SUBJUNCTIVE

(3) After the words *aunque* (even if) and *cuando* (when), in sentences implying contingency : *escribiré aunque no tenga noticias suyas*, I will write even if I have no news from him ; *iremos cuando lo terminemos*, we shall go when we finish it. If, however, a positive statement is made, *cuando* (whenever) and *aunque* (although) must be followed by the indicative mood : *escribiré aunque no tengo noticias suyas*, I will write although I have no news from him ; *estudio cuando tengo tiempo*, I study whenever I have time.

(4) After the adverbial expression *tan pronto como* (as soon as) in sentences which refer to the future : *los compraré tan pronto como reciba sus instrucciones*, I shall buy them as soon as I receive his instructions.

(5) After many impersonal sentences, such as " it is probable, possible, strange, necessary," and the like : *es extraño que no haya venido todavía*, it is strange that he should not have come yet ; *es probable que telefonée antes de las seis de la tarde*, it is probable that she may telephone before 6 p.m.

Note that, when in sentences of this kind the subject of the second verb is not mentioned, the infinitive is used instead : *sería mejor aguardar*, it would be better to wait.

(6) After most verbs implying emotion such as *alegrarse*, to be glad ; *sentir*, to be sorry ; *temer*, to be afraid, and the like : *me alegro de que hayan encontrado lo que deseaban*, I am glad they have found what they wanted ; *tememos que no reciban el aviso a tiempo*, we are afraid they will not receive the advice in time.

(7) After certain verbs expressing a state of mind such as *desear*, to want ; *dudar*, to doubt, and so on : *¿ desea Vd. que cambiemos los billetes de banco ?* do you want us to change the bank-notes ? *dudo que lo hayan vendido tan pronto*, I doubt their having sold it so soon.

(8) After verbs expressing command, demand, surprise, ignorance, permission, prohibition, satisfaction, supplication, advising, counselling, soliciting, entreating, and conveniency : *nos prohibió que saliéramos*, he forbade us to go out.

(9) After superlatives or any word used in a superlative sense : *compraré el mejor que tenga*, I will buy the best one he may have ; *estoy seguro de que se concederá al primer inglés que lo solicite*, I am sure it will be granted to the first Englishman who may apply for it.

(10) In exclamations implying a wish : *¡ Dios le ampare !* May
God protect him ! *¡ Viva el Rey !* Long live the King !

KEYS TO EXERCISES IN LESSON 13.

(I) 1. ¿ Cómo le gustaría a Vd. vivir en París ? 2. Me
gustaría muchísimo. 3. ¿ Que le hace falta ? 4. Le hace falta
más dinero para emprender un nuevo negocio. 5. ¿ Sabe Vd.
las señas de su primo en Madrid ? 6. Sus señas eran : Calle de
Murillo número 106. 7. Las mías son : Plaza de Hernán Cortés,
24, donde espero verle pronto. 8. Muchas gracias, tendré mucho
gusto en visitarle el verano que viene. 9. ¿ Le gusta a Vd pasear ?
10. Sí pero no hoy : hace mucho calor, y además, estoy demasiado
cansada. 11. Ahora le pesa haber aceptado el ofrecimiento sin
consultar con sus socios. 12. Siempre nos hace aguardar mucho
tiempo. 13. ¿ Cuánto tiempo les falta todavía para terminar su
trabajo ? 14. Les falta otra hora. 15. No trabajan tan de prisa
como nos prometieron. 16. ¿ Sabe Vd patinar ? 17. No ; ¿ y
Vd. ? 18. Me gusta patinar en el hielo.

(II) 1. cambie, cambies, cambie, cambiemos, cambiéis, cambien.
2. cosa, cosas, cosa, cosamos, cosáis, cosan. 3. viva, vivas,
viva, vivamos, viváis, vivan. 4. venda, vendas, venda, vendamos,
vendáis, vendan. 5. alquile, alquiles, alquile, alquilemos,
alquiléis, alquilen. 6. haya, hayas, haya, hayamos, hayáis,
hayan. 7. escriba, escribas, escriba, escribamos, escribáis,
escriban. 8. sea, seas, sea, seamos, seáis, sean. 9. conteste,
contestes, conteste, contestemos, contestéis, contesten. 10. coma,
comas, coma, comamos, comáis, coman.

LESSON 15

Subjunctive Mood and Passive Voice

THE tense of the subjunctive mood to be used when translating into Spanish the subordinate clause of a compound
phrase is generally determined by the tense used in the
principal clause. Thus : (1) If the leading verb is in the present or future indicative, the present or compound past of the
subjunctive (according to the original sentence) should be
employed : *probablemente le aconsejarán a Vd. que les escriba*

(594)

SUBJUNCTIVE MOOD AND PASSIVE VOICE

lo antes posible, they will probably advise you to write to them as soon as possible ; *me alegro de que haya venido Vd.,* I am glad you have come.

(2) If the principal verb is in the compound past or compound future of the indicative, the verb of the dependent clause should be conjugated in the present of the subjunctive ; *el gerente le ha ordenado que los envíe inmediatamente,* the manager has ordered him to send them at once ; *ya le habrán ordenado que regrese a Londres,* they will have already ordered him to return to London.

(3) If the verb in the principal sentence is in the past indicative or conditional, the second verb should be employed in the imperfect subjunctive : *no le permitimos que saliese,* we did not permit him to go out ; *temía que no llegara a tiempo,* I was afraid he might not arrive in time ; *me habían aconsejado que lo aceptase,* they had advised me to accept it ; *le hablaría si lo conociese,* I would speak to him if I knew him.

(4) When the first verb is in the imperfect subjunctive preceded by the conjunction *si,* the subordinate verb must be employed in the conditional : *si lo vendiera lo compraría,* should he sell it, I would buy it.

(5) If the leading verb is in the pluperfect subjunctive, the second verb must be conjugated in the same tense : *si lo hubiera sabido yo también hubiera ido,* had I known it, I should also have gone.

The future subjunctive can be ignored as it is very seldom met with in literature, and never in ordinary conversation.

VOCABULARY.

a term	*un plazo*	postcard	*tarjeta postal*
to request	*rogar*	the parcel	*el paquete*
disengaged	*desocupado*	to call	*llamar*
to come down	*bajar*	the mistake	*la equivocación*
to let one know	*avisar*	to keep one's word	*cumplir la palabra*

EXERCISE I.

TRANSLATE INTO SPANISH : 1. We shall not pay unless you give us the receipt. 2. Please send me a telegram as soon as you receive the parcels. 3. The cashier will check the books again so that there may be no mistakes. 4. They will not sign the contract, although they have promised to do so (*hacerlo*). 5. It is a pity he has not come today. 6. If he asks for me, tell him to wait at (en) the station. 7. Let me know when she comes down. 8. She will not learn it unless it is very easy. 9. At what time do you want us to call you ? 10. Please call me at seven o'clock sharp. 11. If they were in London I would (intention, not obligation) pay them a visit. 12. I think your friends will arrive before we finish the letter. 13. I doubt whether they will keep their word. 14. We would rent that house if it were not so expensive.

Passive Voice. The Spanish passive voice is formed, as in English, by placing the different tenses, single or compound, of the verb *ser* (to be) in front of the past participle of all transitive verbs. Thus, from the active verb *castigar* (to punish) the passive verb *ser castigado* (to be punished) is obtained.

In all passive sentences the past participle takes the gender and number of the substantive or substantives to which it refers : *los prisioneros fueron canjeados al amanecer,* the prisoners were exchanged at daybreak. In compound tenses only the past participle of the transitive verb undergoes the change, that of the verb " to be " being unchangeable : *las mejoras han sido realizadas sin grandes gastos,* the improvements have been carried out without great expense. In phrases of this kind the preposition " by " is generally translated *por,* unless the verb expresses an act of the mind, in which case it is often rendered by *de.*

Many impersonal sentences which in English are constructed in the passive voice must be translated into Spanish by the reflexive form of the verb (*see* Lesson II, page 579), a construction which is not so often used when the verb expresses a mental action and its object is a person : *las vocales del idioma inglés no siempre se pronuncian del mismo modo,* the vowels of the English language are not always pronounced in the same manner ; *en esa casa, el padre es mucho más respetado que la madre,* in that house the father is much more respected than the mother. *En esa casa se respeta mucho más al padre que a la madre* would also be correct.

VOCABULARY.

to reward	*recompensar*	to praise	*elogiar*
to treat	*tratar*	to employ	*emplear*
to acclaim	*aclamar*	to avoid	*evitar*
to sentence	*sentenciar*	to improve	*mejorar*
to promote	*ascender*	to recognize	*reconocer*

to hate	*odiar*	to admire	*admirar*
to elect	*elegir*	to deserve	*merecer*
to legalize	*legalizar*	to forge	*falsificar*
to dismiss	*despedir*	to applaud	*aplaudir*
to defeat	*derrotar*	to amount	*ascender*
to love	*amar*	the kindness	*la bondad*
the protest	*la protesta*	the minister	*el ministro*
a tenor	*un tenor*	the troop	*la tropa*
a war	*una guerra*	a marquis	*un marqués*
a picture	*un cuadro*	the owner	*el dueño*
the will	*el testamento*	a colony	*una colonia*
the service	*el servicio*	the coast	*la costa*
a casualty	*una baja*	a viceroy	*un virrey*
an Indian	*un indio*	municipal	*municipal*

the consideration	*la consideración*
the generosity	*la generosidad*
the behaviour	*la conducta*
to communicate	*comunicar*
the imprisonment	*la prisión*
the independence	*la independencia*
everybody	*todo el mundo*
cordially	*cordialmente*
silver mines	*minas de plata*
in due form	*en debida forma*
the authority	*la autoridad*
a forger	*un falsificador*
utterly	*completamente*
bloody	*sangriento*
revolutionary	*revolucionario*
both of them	*los dos, ambos*
a member of Parliament	*un diputado*
a provincial governor	*un gobernador de provincia*
in his progress through	*a su paso por*
an accomplished fact	*un hecho consumado*
South American republics	*Républicas Sud-Americanas*

NOTE. As a " Member of Parliament " refers to the English Legislative Power, it is also translated by *Miembro de Parlamento*. *Diputado* is a Deputy, i.e. Member of the Chamber of Deputies. Most Republican countries have a " Congress " composed of a House of Deputies and the Senate, members of which are called *Senadores*, Senators.

SPANISH 15

Exercise II.

TRANSLATE INTO SPANISH : 1. They (fem.) have not been
rewarded by the owners with as much generosity as they hoped.
2. His last picture was admired and praised by everybody.
3. The new members of Parliament were elected in the (al)
following year   4. The protest was signed by all the officials of
the company. 5. She has not been treated with all the consideration and kindness (that) her behaviour deserves. 6. They
would have been employed in the colonies. 7. All the Ministers
were called to the palace. 8. The news was communicated by
telegraph to all the provincial governors. 9. The documents
were legalized in due form, so as to (para) avoid their being forged.
10. The king was acclaimed in his progress through the streets of
the town. 11. The forgers of the first will were then sentenced to
five years (de) imprisonment. 12. His sister will be dismissed one
of these days. 13. All the municipal services have been improved in the last ten months.

KEYS TO EXERCISES IN LESSON 14.

I. 1. entregara, entregaras, entregara, enregáramos, entre-
garais, entregaran. 2. aprendiese, aprendieses, aprendiese,
aprendiésemos, aprendieseis, aprendiesen. 3. embarcara,
embarcaras, embarcara, embarcáramos, embarcarais, embar-
caran. 4. cancelase, cancelases, cancelase, cancelásemos, cancel-
aseis, cancelasen. 5. emitiera, emitieras, emitiera, emitiéramos,
emitierais, emitieran. 6. escribiese, escribieses, escribiese,
escribiésemos, escribieseis, escribiesen. 7. fuera, fueras, fuera, fuér-
amos, fuerais, fueran. 8. temiese, temieses, temiese, temiésemos,
temieseis, temiesen.

II. 1. esté, estés, esté, estemos, estéis, estén. 2. cantare,
cantares, cantare, cantáremos, cantareis, cantaren. 3. perdiera or
perdiese, perdieras or perdieses, perdiera or perdiese, perdiéramos
or perdiésemos, perdierais or perdieseis, perdieran or perdiesen.
4. prometiere, prometieres, prometiere, prometiéremos, prome-
tiereis, prometieren. 5. haya, hayas, haya, hayamos, hayáis,
hayan. 6. viajase, viajases, viajase, viajásemos, viajaseis, viajasen.
7. discutiere, discutieres, discutiere, discutiéremos, discutiereis,
discutieren. 8. surtiera, surtieras, surtiera, surtiéramos, surtierais,
surtieran. 9. responda, respondas, responda, respondamos,
respondáis, respondan. 10. firmare, firmares, firmare, firmáremos,
firmareis, firmaren.

LESSON 16

Some Exercises in Revision

BEFORE beginning the study of the Spanish irregular verbs, and in order the more thoroughly to master the application of the rules given in the previous Lessons, the student should first learn the two vocabularies and then translate the two following Exercises. With regard to the first vocabulary here given, it should be noted that *cuán* is the abbreviated form of *cuanto*, how ; that *el mar*, the sea, is both masc. and fem. gender ; that *el nombramiento*, the appointment, means appointment to an office and not arrangement for meeting.

VOCABULARY.

to word	*redactar*	to declare	*declararse* (reflexive)
to come in	*entrar*	to help	*ayudar*
to happen	*suceder*	to hear	*oír*
to find out	*averiguar*	to find	*encontrar*
to resign	*dimitir*	to return	*regresar*
to approve	*aprobar*	to pass	*pasar*
to trouble	*molestar*	to cause	*causar*
to throw	*echar*	to bear	*soportar*
to fight	*pelear*	to incline	*inclinarse*
to overcome	*vencer*	the water	*el agua (f.)*
to suffer	*sufrir*	a leaf	*una hoja*
to have just	*acabar de*	the lift	*el ascensor*
the sea	*el mar*	the noise	*el ruido*
the cup	*la taza*	dismay	*espanto*
the staircase	*la escalera*	a concert	*un concierto*
the rustling	*el susurro*	the strike	*la huelga*
horror	*horror*	weary	*fatigado*
a place	*un sitio*	hostilities	*hostilidades*
Castilian	*castellano*	a guest	*un invitado*
a relation	*un pariente*	the choice	*la elección*
the solitude	*la soledad*	the passion	*la pasión*
the avarice	*la avaricia*	destitute	*desprovisto*
how	*cuán*	campaign	*campaña*

severities	*rigores*	the hotel	*el hotel*
the capital	*la corte*	the army	*el ejercito*
the first time	*la primera vez*	fond of	*aficionado a*
notwithstanding	*sin embargo,*		
	no obstante	patiently	*pacientemente*
not anywhere	*en ninguna*	exactly	*exactamente*
	parte	the privation	*la privación*
His Majesty	*Su Majestad*	through train	*tren directo*
the ambassador	*el embajador*	the visiting-	*la tarjeta de*
the appointment	*el nombramiento*	card	*visita*
an explosion	*una explosión*	base-minded	
plenty of time	*tiempo de sobra*	people	*villanos*
the darkness	*la obscuridad*	Christmas Eve	*Noche Buena*
to approach	*acercarse*	the advertise-	
to have lunch	*almorzar*	ment	*el anuncio*
to ride (a horse)	*montar a caballo*	Chamber of	*Cámara de*
to shoot, to hunt	*cazar*	Deputies	*Diputados*
to confer benefits	*hacer bien*	The Minister	*El Ministro de*
the damage	*el desperfecto,*	for Foreign	*Relaciones*
	el daño	Affairs	*Extranjeros*
a treaty of	*un tratado de*		or *Negocios*
commerce	*comercio*		*Extranjeros*

Exercise 1.

Translate : 1. Los invitados eran, en su mayor parte, parientes y amigos suyos. 2. Acababan de almorzar cuando nosotros entramos. 3. Yo le ayudé a redactar la solicitud. 4. No deje Vd. de ir el día de Noche Buena. 5. Al oir (*on hearing*) la explosión nos acercamos a la fábrica para ver que había sucedido. Los desperfectos fueron importantísimos, calculándose las pérdidas en varios miles de libras. 6. ¿ Averiguaron Vds. el nombre del viajero que comió con nosotros en la estación de Valladolid ? 7. Me dió su tarjeta de visita pero debo haberla perdido pues no he podido encontrarla en ninguna parte. 8. Aquella fué la primera y última vez que lo vi. Algunos meses después me escribió mi hermano para decirme que lo había visto en un hotel de Nápoles. 9. Era alemán pero hablaba castellano tan bien como un español. 10. ¿ Le gusta a Vd. vivir en el campo ? 11. Sí, soy muy aficionado a cazar y montar a caballo. 12. Se cree que el Gobierno dimitirá tan pronto como su Majestad el Rey regrese a la Corte.

EXERCISES IN REVISION

Vocabulary.

to attempt	*intentar*	to prefer	*preferir*
to command	*mandar*	to fall	*caer*
to go round	*dar la vuelta*	to capture	*capturar*
to sack	*saquear*	to render	*prestar*
to leave	*salir*	a comedy	*una comedia*
to lead	*orientar*	the critic	*el crítico*
a task	*una tarea*	a caravel	*una carabela*
the art	*el arte* (m. and f.)	a victor	*un vencedor*
		a habit	*un hábito*
the world	*el mundo*	the appeal	*la apelación*
a pension	*una pensión*	blind	*ciego*
the object	*el objeto*	the aim	*el objetivo*
a ditch	*una zanja*	the loyalty	*la lealtad*
serious	*serio*	recovered	*restablecido*
beautiful	*bello*	due	*debido*
a ducat	*un ducado*	the empire	*el imperio*
cents	*céntimos*	the admiral	*el almirante*
whatever	*lo que*	the dew	*el rocío*
a colonel	*un coronel*	to commemor-	
the clouds	*las nubes*	ate	*conmemorar*
to become	*convertirse*	to remember	*acordarse*
to demoralize	*desmoralizar*	the degradation	*la degradación*
the retrogression	*el retroceso*	the impatience	*la impaciencia*
the vanquished	*los vencidos*	the animalism	*la animalidad*
all others	*todos los demás*	unfortunate	*desgraciado*
the memory	*la memoria*	the commander	*el comandante*
the regiment	*el regimiento*	a masterpiece	*una obra de arte*
the brute force	*la fuerza bruta*	the green grass	*la hierba verde*
the blue sky	*el cielo azul*	to be bored	*aburrirse*
to conquer	*conquistar*	to undertake	*emprender*
to settle	*cancelar*	to agree with	*estar de acuerdo*
the coat-of-arms	*el escudo de armas*	it is the same for me	*me es igual*
seriously ill	*gravemente enfermo*	a matter of taste	*una cuestión de gusto*
to spend the time	*pasar el tiempo*	an immense booty	*un inmenso botín*
the return journey	*el viaje de vuelta*		

Exercise II.

TRANSLATE INTO SPANISH : 1. We have come by (the) train.
2. Where did you spend the night ? 3. We have been travelling
since yesterday afternoon. 4. How much do I owe you ? 5. You
owe me seven pesetas and 25 cents. 6. How many pence are there
in a peseta ? 7. A peseta has 100 cents, which are about tenpence.
8. Did my friends pay you ? 9. They settled their account before
you arrived. 10. Have you (got) change for (*de*) a five-pound
note ? 11. I think so. Do you want silver or gold ? 12. It is the
same for me. Whatever may be better for you. 13. Pizarro
conquered the Empire of the Incas with less than 200 men.
14. Have you ever been in Peru ? 15. Last year I spent two
months at Lima. It was an extremely interesting journey.

Keys to Exercises in Lesson 15.

(I) 1. No pagaremos a menos que nos dé Vd. el recibo. 2.
Haga Vd. el favor de enviarme un telegrama, tan pronto como
reciba los paquetes. 3. El cajero comprobará los libros otra vez
a fin de que no haya equivocaciones. 4. No firmarán el contrato
aunque hayan prometido hacerlo. 5. Es lástima que no haya
venido hoy. 6. Si pregunta por mí dígale que espere en la estación.
7. Avíseme cuando baje. 8. Ella no lo aprenderá a menos que
sea muy fácil. 9. ¿ A que hora desea Vd. que lo llamemos ?
10. Hagan el favor de llamarme a las siete en punto. 11. Si
estuvieran en Londres los visitaría. 12. Creo que sus amigos
llegarán antes que terminemos la carta. 13. Dudo que cumplan
su palabra. 14. Alquilaríamos esa casa si no fuese tan cara.

(II) 1. No han sido recompensadas por sus dueños con tanta
generosidad como esperaban. 2. Su último cuadro fué admirado
y elogiado por todo el mundo. 3. Los nuevos diputados fueron
elegidos al siguiente año. 4. La protesta fué firmada por todos
los funcionarios de la compañía. 5. No ha sido tratada con toda
la consideración y bondad que su conducta merece. 6. Hubieran
sido empleados en las colonias. 7. Todos los ministros fueron
llamados al palacio. 8. La noticia fué comunicada por telégrafo
a todos los gobernadores de provincia. 9. Los documentos
fueron legalizados en debida forma para evitar que fueran falsi-
ficados. 10. El rey fué aclamado a su paso por las calles de la
ciudad. 11. Los falsificadores del primer testamento fueron
entonces sentenciados a cinco años de prisión. 12. Su hermana
será despedida uno de estos días. 13. Todos los servicios
municipales han sido mejorados en los diez últimos meses.

LESSON 17

Irregular Verbs

VERBS are called irregular when in some of their tenses they either deviate from the general rules already given for their conjugation, or, when following these rules, they alter or omit some of the letters forming the stem of the infinitive. These last-mentioned changes in the stem of verbs, which are otherwise perfectly regular, have, in general, no other object than to retain the same pronunciation of the stem throughout the conjugation. Thus, for instance, in the first person singular of the past definite of *colocar* (to place), the last *c* of the stem *coloc* is changed into *qu* in order to preserve the hard sound of that letter. Should this alteration not be made, the word obtained in the ordinary way would have a sound quite alien to the original infinitive. To avoid this, *coloqué* (*koh-loh-kay*) and not *colocé* (*kol-loh-thay*) is, therefore, to be used as the first person singular of the past definite of *colocar*. Other examples are : *venzo* instead of *venco* in *vencer* (to vanquish) ; *pagué* instead of *pagé* in *pagar* (to pay).

The verbs that, in order to retain the original sound of the stem throughout all the tenses, require some alteration in their radical letters are as shown in the table in page 604.

The stem of a few verbs undergoes, from custom, a similar change. Thus :

1. Verbs ending in *zar* change the *z* into *c* before *e*—*rezar*, to pray, *recé*, I prayed ; *gozar*, to enjoy, *gocé*, I enjoyed.

2. Verbs ending in *guar* take the diaeresis on the *u* before *e* : *averiguar*, to investigate, *averigüemos*, let us investigate.

3. Verbs ending in *acer*, *ecer*, *ocer*, or *ucir* take *z* before the radical *c* when this letter is followed by the vowels *a* or *o* : *ofrecer*, to offer, *ofrezco*, I offer ; *conducir*, to lead, *que nos conduzcan*, let them lead us. Important exceptions to this rule are : *hacer*, to make ; *cocer*, to cook ; *torcer*, to twist, and a few others.

4. Verbs of the second and third conjugations whose stem ends in *ch*, *ll*, or *ñ* drop the vowel *i* whenever the diphthongs *ie* or *io* occur in their termination : *tañer*, to play a musical

instrument, *tañendo la guitarra*, playing the guitar; *zambullirse*, to plunge into water, *se zambulleron en el río*, they plunged into the river.

5. Verbs of the second and third conjugations whose stems end in *a*, *e*, or *u* change the *i* of a termination into *y* whenever that vowel is immediately followed by *a*, *e*, or *o*: *caer*, to fall,

FORMATION OF SOME SPANISH IRREGULAR VERBS			
Verbs whose infinitive ends in	Change Into	When the first letter of the termination is	Examples
car	*c* *qu*	*e*	*atacar*, to attack; *ataquemos*, instead of *atacemos*
cer or *cir*	*c* *z*	*o* or *a*	*esparcir*, to scatter; *esparzo*, instead of *esparco*
gar	*g* *gu*	*e*	*halagar*, to flatter; *halagué*, instead of *halagé*
ger or *gir*	*g* *j*	*o* or *a*	*escoger*, to choose; *escojo*, instead of *escogo*
guir	*gu* *g*	*o* or *a*	*distinguir*, to distinguish; *distinga*, instead of *distingua*
quir	*qu* *c*	*o* or *a*	*delinquir*, to transgress; *delinco*, instead of *delinquo*

cayó, he fell; *huir*, to flee, *huya Vd.*, flee; *proveer*, to supply, *proveyendo* supplying.

Important exceptions to this rule are those verbs ending in *guir* in which the *u* is not pronounced, as in *distinguir*, to distinguish; *seguir*, to follow; *perseguir*, to pursue, etc.; *distinguieron*, they distinguished. When the *u* is sounded, as in *argüir*, to argue, the stem follows the rule and takes the *y* after the *u* in all terminations beginning with *o*, *e*, or *a*. Thus: *arguyo*, I argue, *arguyeron*, they argued.

IRREGULAR VERBS

VOCABULARY.

to mark	*marcar*	to touch	*tocar*
to look for	*buscar*	to destroy	*destruir*
to obey	*obedecer*	to cause	*causar*
to translate	*traducir*	to punish	*castigar*
to judge	*juzgar*	to correct	*corregir*
to protect	*proteger*	to demand	*exigir*
to escape	*escabullirse*	to solemnize	*solemnizar*
to authorize	*autorizar*	to bustle	*bullir*
to be afraid	*tener miedo*	a list	*una lista*
a picture	*un cuadro*	around	*alrededor*
twice	*dos veces*	the right	*el derecho*
the rebel	*el rebelde*	bridge	*un puente*
the honesty	*la honradez*	the energy	*la energía*
a victim	*una víctima*	the maid	*la doncella*
yourself	*Vd. mismo*	easily	*fácilmente*
nevertheless	*sin embargo*	simply	*sencillamente*
the delight	*la delicia*	midnight	*media noche*
Titian	*el Ticiano*	Greek	*griego*
to be thankful	*agradecer*	a subscription	*una subscripción*
to acknowledge	*reconocer*	therefore	*por consiguiente*
to disguise one-		the flood	*la inundación*
self	*disfrazarse*	extraordinary	*extraordinario*
to gather, to		the where-	
catch	*coger*	abouts	*el paradero*
to fade, to decline	*decaer*	the express	
to show oneself	*mostrarse*	train	*el tren expreso,*
to bear witness			*rápido*
to	*atestiguar*	a perfect thing	*un cosa perfecta*
in advance	*por adelantado*	a statue	*una estatua*
the suffering	*el sufrimiento*	to extinguish,	
the deception	*el desencanto*	to quench	*extinguir*

EXERCISE.

TRANSLATE INTO SPANISH : 1. Do you know his name ? 2.
I marked it on the list. 3. Do not touch any of those pictures.
4. Let them look for their papers. 5. I explained it to him twice.
6. I do not think the troops will vanquish the rebels so easily
as the Government hope. 7. He simply has done it in order
that I may be thankful to him. 8. Obey and translate those
documents. 9. I do not acknowledge his authority, and therefore

I do not obey his orders. Punish me if you think I deserve it.
10. No; I have no right to judge your conduct. Judge it
yourself. 11. It is very probable that the fire may be extinguished
before midnight. 12. Take a tram and catch the express train.
13. Let us protect her. 14. I am sure he will not correct her
exercises. 15. Ask (demand) to be paid a month in advance.
16. I did not authorize him to cancel the contract. 17. Let us
solemnize her birthday. 18. We did not disguise ourselves.
19. I bore witness to his honesty. 20. Let him investigate her
whereabouts. 21. They escaped from the hands of the police.

KEYS TO EXERCISES IN LESSON 16.

(I) 1. The guests were for the most part relations and friends
of his. 2. They had just had their lunch when we came in.
3. I helped him to word the application. 4. Do not fail to go on
Christmas Eve. 5. On hearing the explosion we approached
the factory in order to see what had happened. The damage
was most important, the losses being estimated at several thousand pounds. 6. Did you find out the name of the traveller
who dined with us at Valladolid station ? 7. He gave me his
visiting-card, but I must have lost it, for I have not been able
to find it anywhere. 8. That was the first and last time I saw
him. Several months afterwards my brother wrote to tell me
that he had seen him at a Naples hotel. 9. He was a German, but
he spoke Castilian as well as a Spaniard. 10. Do you like living
in the country ? 11. Yes ; I am very fond of shooting and riding.
12. It is believed that the Government will resign as soon as
his Majesty the King returns to the capital.

(II) 1. Hemos venido por tren. 2. ¿ Dónde pasaron Vds.
la noche ? 3. Hemos estado viajando desde ayer tarde. 4.
¿ Cuánto le debo a Vd. ? 5. Me debe Vd., siete pesetas y veinticinco céntimos. 6. ¿ Cuántos peniques hay en una peseta ?
7. Una peseta tiene cien céntimos, que son aproximadamente
diez peniques. 8. ¿ Le pagaron a Vd. mis amigos ? 9. Can-
celaron su cuenta antes de que Vd. llegase. 10. ¿ Tiene Vd.
cambio de un billete de cincolibras ? 11. Creo que sí. ¿ Desea
Vd. plata u oro ? 12. Me es igual. Lo que sea mejor para Vd.
13. Pizarro conquistó el imperio de los Incas con menos de
doscientos hombres. 14. ¿ Ha estado Vd. alguna vez en el
Perú ? 15. El año pasado pasé dos meses en Lima. Fué un
viaje interesantísimo.

Our Course in Spanish is continued in Volume 6.

LESSON 20

Sea-Urchins, Sea-Cucumbers and Lilies of the Sea

A N ordinary or regular sea-urchin is of spherical form and covered with spines which give it the appearance of the hedgehog rolled up and with prickles erected. Hidden in the spines, near the lower pole of the body, is a small mouth surrounded by soft skin, and at the upper pole the anus. The spines are attached by ball and socket joints and muscles to calcareous plates in the skin, arranged very regularly in twenty rows or meridians, and disposed in ten double sets. Five of these sets are perforated by minute pores, through which the tube feet project. The sucker-like action of the tube feet is greatly enhanced in sea-urchins, which can climb over steep rocky slopes and even remain there for long periods. The writer has seen captive edible urchins (*Echinus esculentus*) remain perched upon vertical rocks on the Cornish coast for months on end. These climbing adventures are partially facilitated by the action of the movable spines. In some tropical species of sea-urchin the spines also serve as weapons, and can inflict poison wounds upon the enemies of these forms. Many of the spines of the ordinary sea-urchin are modified into minute pincers or pedicellariae, with three jaws instead of the two of the starfish. The pedicellariae of the sea-urchin are of several kinds. Some are " snappers," which seize and kill minute creatures attempting to settle on the skin (tridactyl type) ; others are " cleansers," which sweep away sandy particles that fall on the body (trifoliate type) ; many have bulbous heads and are armed with poison glands for use in defence (gemmiform type) ; and, finally, one type, the ophio cephalous, has jaws resembling the head of the snake, and these are fringed with teeth, which hold prey until the tube feet can reach it to convey it to the mouth.

The regular urchin commonly browses upon seaweed and feeds on small organisms attached thereto, and to cope with these a complicated biting mechanism has been developed. This consists of five V-shaped jaws, each carrying a long pointed tooth that grows continuously like the front teeth of the rabbit, and numerous plates for the attachment of masticatory muscles. The entire arrangement, when dissected out, looks remarkably like an antique lantern, and is known as " Aristotle's lantern."

We saw in the preceding Lesson that in the starfish and brittle-star tube feet are confined to the lower or ambulacral surface of

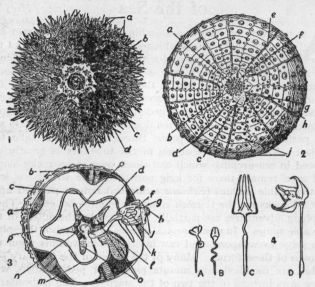

SEA-URCHINS. 1. Echinus miliaris from oral side ; a, ambulacrum ; b, inter-ambulacrum ; c, gill ; d, peristome. **2.** Diagram of aboral view of dried shell of Echinus : the spines, pedicellariae and tube feet have been removed ; a, anus ; b, leathery skin around anus ; c, madreporic plate ; d, ambulacrum ; e, pores through which tube feet protrude ; f, genital plate with genital pore ; g, ocular plate ; h, line of junction of ambulacral and interambulacral plates ; j, base of spine. **3.** Sea-urchin, part of shell removed to show alimentary canal ; a, ampullae at base of tube feet ; b, dorsal blood vessel ; c, ventral blood vessel ; d, rectum ; e, blood ring ; f, jaw ; g, lantern of Aristotle (displaced) ; h, mouth, surrounded by five teeth (j) ; k, arch ; l, oesophagus, coiled intestine and rectum ; m, siphon ; n, fold of peritoneum supporting genital rachis ; o, ovaries with oviducts. **4.** Pedicellariae of Echinus miliaris ; A, trifoliate ; B, ophiocephalous ; C, tridactyl ; D, gemmiform.

From Borradaile, Potts, Eastham & Saunders, " The Invertebrata,"
Cambridge University Press

the body, and that this surface is no more extensive than the opposite or adambulacral one. In the spherical sea-urchin, as also in the sausage-shaped sea-cucumber, the body is compact and almost completely covered with tube feet. In other words, the ambulacral surface has been developed extensively with

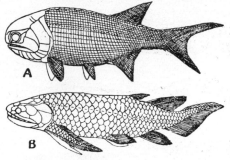

ANCESTORS OF BONY FISHES. A, restoration of a primitive Palaeopterygian, an elongated fish with heterocercal tail and a single dorsal fin. **B,** primitive Crossopterygian with two small dorsal fins and long blade-like pectorals, similar to the 127 lb. Latimeria chalumnae caught alive off S. Africa in December, 1938.

From J. R. Norman, " A History of Fishes," Ernest Benn, Ltd.

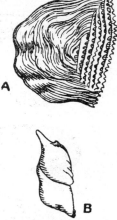

TYPICAL SCALES. A, ctenoid or comb-like scale of the carp ; **B,** ganoid scales, as found in primitive fishes and in the sturgeon.

From Parker & Haswell, " Text-book of Zoology," Macmillan & Co.

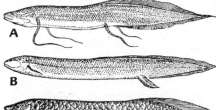

SPECIES OF LUNG-FISH. A, African mud-fish (Protopterus). **B,** South American Lung-fish (Lepidosiren). **C,** Australian lung-fish (Epiceratodus).

From J. R. Norman, " A History of Fishes," Ernest Benn, Ltd.

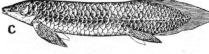

STAGE OF METAMORPHOSIS in Leptocephalus, the larval form of the European fresh-water eel.

From Norman, " A History of Fishes "

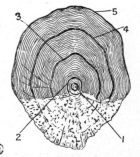

SALMON SCALE. Cycloid scale from large spring-fish ; 1 and 2 show two years' river-life ; 3–5, three years' sea-life.

From Norman, " A History of Fishes "

ZOOLOGY 24

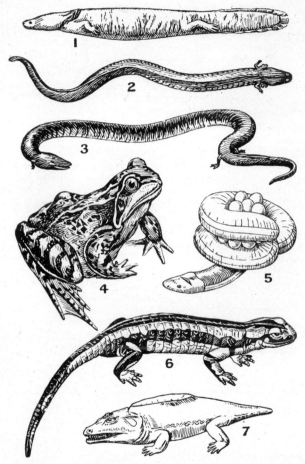

TYPES OF AMPHIBIA. **1.** Necturus (Perennibranchiata). **2.** Siren (Sirenoidea). **3.** Amphiuma (Caducibranchiata). **4.** Rana (Anura). **5.** Ichthyophis (Apoda). **6.** Salamandra (Caducibranchiata). Nos. 1–3 and 6 belong to the order Urodela **7.** Cacops (Stegocephalia): this form is allied to the primitive reptiles. ZOOLOGY 25

1–6, from Parker & Haswell, " Text-book of Zoology," Macmillan

Plate 62   *Volume V*

great reduction of the adambulacral surface, here represented solely by a very small area, on which the anus is found. The form of the sea-urchin has been obtained from the starfish form by coalescence of the arms with the disk, and by the great development of their lower surfaces. The diagram will help to make this perfectly clear.

So-called irregular sea-urchins are of a more specialized nature than regular urchins. One type of irregular urchin, the cake-urchin, has a centrally situated mouth and a much flattened body. These forms live at or near the surface of sandy expanses, and walk on numerous tube feet like the ordinary urchin. Aristotle's lantern is preserved in a modified condition, and the teeth are used for shovelling sand and mud into the mouth. Another type of irregular urchin is the heart-urchin, in which both mouth and anus are eccentrically placed. These animals dwell deeply buried in sand or mud, through which they move, not by means of tube feet, but by ploughing with much curved and modified spines. Aristotle's lantern has completely disappeared, and a novel mode of feeding has been devised. Special tube feet are developed which are capable of great extension and bear fringed adhesive disks at their extremities ; these collect sand containing food organisms and convey it to certain short and stout " buccal " tube feet which push it into the mouth.

Sea-Cucumbers. These creatures are elongated, tough-skinned and not unlike the cucumber in form. They crawl on the sea floor or burrow in its deposits, and are by far the most muscular of all echinoderms. The mouth lies at one end of the animal, an is surrounded by short blunt tentacles, really modified tube fee which serve to shovel mud containing organisms into the foc canal. The skin is hardened by lime to a slighter extent than types we have considered so far, and contains peculiar plates characteristic forms, resembling anchors and wheels.

The body is five-sided, and the tube feet are generally arrang in five double rows, one along each side of the body, though tl are often scattered irregularly, and may be absent. In sc forms which creep on the sea-floor there may be a well-mar distinction between upper and lower surfaces, the creeping sur comprising three of the five sides of the body. These sides cc spond to the ambulacral and adambulacral areas of the urchin, so that the sea-cucumber in its natural position confc to a sea-urchin laid on its side.

Behind the bases of the tentacles and around the first part of the food canal is the ring canal of the water vascular system. This gives off five radial vessels, exactly as in the sea-urchin, which run along bands of muscular tissue marking the ambulacral areas. A short winding canal, ending in a perforated plate, hangs from the ring canal ; this is the stone canal, which opens, not to the exterior, as in star-fish and urchin, but into the coelomic cavity. A nerve-ring surrounds the mouth and gives off five radial nerves, which pass along the ambulacra.

The alimentary canal is a simple cylindrical tube, which forms several coils within the coelom and terminates near the end of the animal farthest removed from the mouth in a relatively wide chamber, the cloaca. A pair of remarkable organs open into the cloaca. These are tree-like and receive the name " respiratory trees." Each starts behind as a tubular stem, but becomes branched in an elaborate manner, some of the branches reaching almost to the front end of the animal. These ramifications end in minute vesicles, through the walls of which sea-water, filling the trees, passes into the coelom. The stream which passes into the body of the animal in this way conveys oxygen to the coelomic fluid, and so to the organs. In some Holothurians the main branches of the respiratory trees have been transformed into filamentous tubes, the Cuvierian organs, which secrete a sticky substance that swells up in sea water and forms long silky threads. The irritated animal contracts its body muscles violently, and the pressure set up in the fluid-filled coelomic cavity tears the cloaca and expels the Cuvierian organs, as also sometimes the entire alimentary canal. If the cause of irritation is an enemy, this is entangled by the adhesive threads. Animals which have discharged their food canals immediately set about the task of re-forming (regenerating) a new one.

The sea-cucumber, like the starfish and sea-urchin, is either male or female. The ovaries and testes are very similar to one another and resemble bunches of minute grapes ; they open to the surface of the animal by a fine canal opening on the supper surface some short distance back from the mouth.

Early development of the sea-cucumber leads to the formation of a free-swimming larva known as an *auricularia*.

Sea-Lilies. These are creatures of the deep sea, once numerous and flourishing, but now comparatively rare, and obtained only by dredging the depths of ocean. They are attached by a long

jointed stalk, which bears circlets of sensitive feelers and which ends in a cup. The mouth is found in the centre of the cup and is directed upwards, not downwards towards the substratum, as in all other types of echinoderms. Radiating from the margin of the cup are five branching arms of feathery appearance. These are grooved above, the grooves uniting and converging towards the mouth. The grooves are traps for the fine organisms living near the sea-lily, for they bear innumerable fine cilia, which sweep currents towards the mouth. The sea-lilies have not made a success of this easy-going life, and are on the way to extinction.

Feather-stars. Very closely related to the sea-lilies, feather-stars are in a much more flourishing condition at the present time, owing no doubt to their having relinquished sedentary life. They have rid themselves of the stalk, and are able to swim actively by bending and straightening their five branched and feathery arms. When occasion demands they can hold fast to rocks or sea-weeds, or even climb by means of a whorl of jointed threads, which spring from the under side and correspond to one of the numerous circlets found on the stalk of the sea-lily.

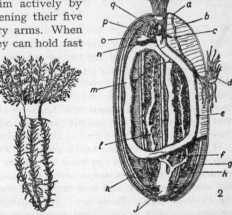

SEA-CUCUMBERS. 1. Cucumaria planci; entire animal seen from ventral surface. 2. Internal organs of Holothurian as seen when body-wall is divided along middle of dorsal surface; a. genital aperture; b, genital duct; c, madreporic canal; d, gonad; e and m, intestine; f and l, respiratory trees; g, circular layer of muscle; h, longitudinal band of muscle; j, cloaca; k, Cuvierian organs; n, stomach; o, Polian vesicle; p, ring strand of haemal system; q, ring-vessel of ambulacral system.

From Parker & Haswell, " Textbook of Zoology," Macmillan & Co.

The life history of the individual feather-star—*Antedon*, for instance —affords us a valuable clue to the past history of the group to which it belongs. It commences life as a microscopic free-swimming larva, this stage being followed by one in which fixation occurs. The stalked or pentacrinoid larva gets its name from the resemblance it bears to the adult *Pentacrinus*, one of the permanently fixed members of the Crinoidea. After a time the stalk is cast off and fixed life exchanged for an active one. With this change comes the development of anchoring organs and great elongation of the arms. It is interesting to know that the adult Pentacrinus often makes an effort to live the free life, breaking from its moorings and swimming by waving movements of its arms. But it is compelled to trail its long stalk behind it. *Rhizocrinus* is a permanently rooted relative of *Pentacrinus* found at great depths in the Atlantic.

LESSON 21

Simplest Members of the Vertebrata

(See plate 60)

VERTEBRATES, or backboned animals, are distinguished from all other animals by three important characters : (1) the sides of the throat are perforated by slits, called gill-slits, or visceral clefts , (2) a long, tubular nerve cord extends along the body near its upper edge ; (3) a longitudinal supporting rod, the notochord, lies immediately below the nerve cord, and in most vertebrates forms the basis of the backbone. These characters are not necessarily seen in adult vertebrates, but they occur at some time during the life history of the individual.

If these characters are taken severally as criteria of relationship, the *Vertebrata*, or, as they are better called, the *Chordata*, include not only fishes, amphibians, reptiles, birds and mammals, but also three other and less familiar classes, collectively called the *Protochordata*. These are : (1) *Enteropneusta*, characterized by acorn-headed worms, and sometimes called *Hemichordata ;* (2) *Tunicata* or *Urochordata*, containing sea-squirts or ascidians ; (3) *Cephalchordata* or lancelets.

Chordata are Metazoa with a well-developed coelom, and the manner in which the coelom develops in *Protochordata* provides us with a key to the ancestry of the phylum. We should scarcely search among the radially symmetrical *Echinodermata* for the probable ancestor of the *Chordata* were we to use adult characters alone as evidences of affinity. But, as we have emphasized in earlier Lessons, ontogeny, or the development of the individual, greatly assists us in our search for animal affinities. And here we meet a most unsuspected fact. The larva of *Balanoglossus*, a typical member of the *Enteropneusta*, bears remarkable resemblance to the larva of *Echinodermata*. The *tornaria*, as this larva is called, has the looping ciliated band and the form of the generalized sea-hedgehog larva. There are certain additions, however—a terminal tuft of cilia and a pair of minute eye-spots, for instance. In both types of larvae the coelom rudiment develops as three sets of outgrowths at the sides of the food canal. In the adult *Balanoglossus* these three primary coelom segments are retained in definite, externally visible regions of the body.

According to the recapitulation theory, which is upheld by the majority of zoologists, the individual in its development to some extent repeats the history of the race to which it belongs. The fact that both echinoderm and protochordate develop from such closely similar larvae suggests at once that these great animal stocks arose from closely allied, if not identical, ancestors. If the chordate characters possessed by the protochordate are reliable criteria of relationship between these animals and higher *Chordata*, then all *Chordata* arose from a free-swimming ancestor bearing some resemblance to the typical echinoderm larva.

Acorn-Worms. The best known member of the *Enteropneusta* is the acorn-worm, *Balanoglossus*, a small burrowing worm-like creature found in the sea. Near relatives, called *Cephalodiscus* and *Rhabdopleura*, are also marine, but live at great depths in tubular dwellings, which they construct for themselves from secretions of the front end of their bodies. These creatures differ from *Balanoglossus* in certain features ; the proboscis is small, the collar bears numerous " arms " from which tentacles arise, and the food canal is U-shaped so that in this case the anus lies close to the mouth.

We recognize three regions in the body of *Balanoglossus*. In front there is a large, club-shaped organ, the *proboscis*, which is an efficient burrowing organ. Embracing the stalked base of the proboscis is a narrow, circular fold, the *collar*, and behind this is the long, cylindrical *trunk* region of the body. The proboscis appears flaccid at times, but becomes turgid and hard as a preliminary to burrowing operations, owing to the entry of sea-water into a cavity within it. The cavity is the first division of the coelom. The collar region contains the second division of the coelom, while the remaining division of this cavity is found in the trunk.

A double series of small slits open on the upper surface of the front part of the trunk. These are the gill-slits which increase in number throughout life. This part of the body is given over largely to respiration, and for this reason is called the *branchial* region. The slits lead into a special respiratory part of the food canal, which is sharply marked off from the digestive part. The food canal commences at the slit-like mouth between proboscis and collar, and ends at the hinder extremity of the elongated body. It is an almost straight tube, which gives off pouches believed to function as a liver.

Blood vessels and nerves run along upper and lower sides of the body. The latter are thicker on the upper side, but have not sunk below the surface of the body, as in higher vertebrates, being little more than strips of sensitized skin. The notochord is very rudimentary, being confined to the front end of the animal and serving as a support for the proboscis alone. It is on account of this short notochord that *Balanoglossus* is sometimes called a Hemichordate. The reproductive organs are simple bags of cells arranged in a double row in the branchial region. Ovaries and testes are found in different animals, so that *Balanoglossus* affords a contrast with the hermaphrodite ascidian.

Ascidians or Sea-Squirts. These animals are familiar objects—not easily recognized as animals, however—attached to rocks and weeds on the seashore. The bag-like body is enclosed in a covering or test of tunicine, a secreted substance chemically related to the cellulose of plants. The animal is normally distended with water, but contracts when touched by emitting two fine jets of water from small apertures near its upper end. One of these openings leads into the first part of the food canal, which is modified for breathing and feeding purposes in much the same way as are the ctenidia of molluscs. Numerous microscopic perforations (derived from gill-clefts) conduct water through the pharynx into cavities overlying it, and thence to the exterior by the second opening seen outside the animal's body. The water current conveys oxygen and small organisms into the pharynx, oxygen being absorbed by the blood, while the organisms are swept along into the digestive part of the food canal, entrapped in mucus.

Most of the organs of the ascidian's body are degenerate, but the blood vascular system is a well-developed set of irregular spaces. Circulation of blood shows a phenomenon unique in the animal kingdom. The heart, which is found below the body wall near the point of attachment of the animal, pulsates regularly and drives blood into small vessels at one end. After a number of beats the pulse becomes slower, and finally ceases. When the beats are renewed, blood is driven in the *opposite* direction for a time, after which comes reversal again. By means of this reversal of heart-beat, blood is passed alternately to the gills, as in fishes, and to the viscera.

The fertilized egg of the ascidian develops into a peculiar tailed larva not unlike the tadpole of the frog. It has a notochord which extends throughout the tail region, but is absent from the body ; hence the name *Urochordata*. Near the upper side of the ascidian tadpole's body is a tubular nerve cord, and the presence of two gill-clefts further marks the young animal as a member of the *Chordata*. After a relatively short, free-swimming life, however, these chordate characters are lost during the course of swift degenerative changes constituting a metamorphosis. The tail, with its nerve cord and notochord, is absorbed completely, only a single ganglion of the nervous system persisting in the adult. The gill-slits become multiplied in number as the pharynx rapidly increases in size. In short, the active larva becomes transformed so completely that even the expert would be hard pressed to classify the adult if he knew nothing of its previous history. The habit possessed by most ascidians of budding off new individuals repeatedly from a creeping stem or stolon, would further perplex him. But the larva makes perfectly clear the true affinities of the apparently lowly animal.

The Lancelet. This animal, known to zoologists as *Branchiostoma* and also as *Amphioxus*, is the commonest member of the *Cephalochordata*, a class of chordates in which the notochord extends through the length of the body and into the head region, and persists throughout life. It is a small fish-like creature found burrowing in sand or fine gravel not far from the seashore. The elongated body is compressed from side to side and pointed at both ends, to which fact it owes the name *Amphioxus*. When feeding, the animal lies buried in sand in a vertical position, with only the tip of its body protruding. Water is drawn into the bell-shaped, jawless mouth by the action of cilia on the pharynx wall. The mouth serves both for breathing and feeding.

Amphioxus shows all the characters of the typical chordate animal. Over the long notochord lies a tubular nerve cord, and in the pharynx region we encounter numerous perforations, which are the gill-clefts. These slits are not visible externally, but this is simply because they have been overgrown by special folds of the body wall which forms a distinct cavity, the *atrium*, that opens to the exterior by a single pore, situated some way back along the body and on its lower surface. Water entering the mouth passes through the gill-clefts into the atrium and leaves the body by the atriopore.

The blood vascular system shows interesting features. The vessels composing it are all of one kind, but, because of undoubted homologies with the more complex vessels of higher chordates, they are called arteries and veins. The arrangement of these vessels is remarkably like that found in the fish. A single contractile vessel, regarded as the heart, lies near the lower surface of the body, and drives blood forwards, giving off branches to the gills. Here blood is charged with oxygen and collected into larger and larger vessels for circulation to the food canal and other parts of the body. Two main arterial trunks lie near the upper surface of the body in front, uniting into a single vessel at a point farther back. This is called the *dorsal aorta*, and from it small branches pass off to the food canal. If we were to substitute a true heart for the contractile tube of *Branchiostoma* and, further, were to reduce the number of gill arteries to five, we should be left with a fairly good picture of the circulation of a shark. Another resemblance to the fish is a second system of blood capillaries, which pass through the substance of an outgrowth of the food canal that is believed to serve as a liver. Such a system is called a hepatic portal system, about which we shall have more to say in later Lessons.

The nerve cord of *Branchiostoma* is, obviously, of the same pattern as that of the fish, though greatly simpler in nature. It is slightly expanded in front to form a rudimentary brain, and from it paired nerves arise at regular intervals along the body. The organization of the lancelet is definitely fish-like, but at a low level. The animal is jawless, like the lamprey and hagfish, has neither skull, nor ears, nor paired eyes. It is simpler than the most primitive fish, as this is simpler than a bird. Moreover, it has excretory organs which are at the level of those of the annelid. But the lancelet shows the three general characters of the chordate animal throughout life, and thus links up with the higher *Chordata*, with which we shall deal in later Lessons.

LESSON 22

Characteristics of the Craniates

FISHES, amphibians, reptiles, birds and mammals are chordate animals collectively called the *Craniata*. These animals agree in possessing a skull, a complex brain and highly organized nervous system, red blood containing special cells or corpuscles, and a heart consisting of three or four chambers. At first sight we might deem animals like the shark, frog, pigeon and dog unrelated in their differences, but a striking fundamental unity of plan runs through the entire craniate series. Not only are similar organs arranged in the same general way, but the finer structure of the organs is decidedly uniform. Such uniformity does not prevail in the invertebrate groups we have so far studied. We shall do well, therefore, to examine the general characters of the typical craniate animal before proceeding to study the various types of the *Craniata*.

One side of the craniate body is, externally, the mirror image of the opposite side. Symmetry is bilateral, as in Arthropoda. The body is elongated from front to back, and divisible into three regions, called head, trunk and tail. The head accommodates the brain and principal sense organs, bears the mouth and contains the pharynx ; the trunk contains the coelom, in which the chief organs of digestion, circulation, excretion and reproduction are located ; and the tail, which lies behind the anus and the coelom, is a region devoid of more important organs. In aquatic *Craniata* the tail is large and merged with the trunk ; it is the chief organ of locomotion. In terrestrial forms such a tail would be a hindrance and, accordingly, we find it greatly reduced. In the most highly organized craniates a narrow neck is interpolated between the trunk and the head. This is a relatively recent acquisition in the racial history of the group, and one that fishes and amphibians lack.

The mouth is a transverse slit at or near the front end of the body, and near it are paired nostrils leading to the organ of smell. The paired eyes lie at the sides of the head, and on top of the head is a vestigial sense organ, the *pineal* organ, which may show the typical structure of an eye. For this reason it is sometimes referred to as a third eye. Behind the eyes are the paired organs of hearing (auditory organs)—in lower forms, as much concerned with the function of balancing as with that of hearing. At the sides of the head is a series of openings, the gill-slits, which rarely exceed seven in number. In terrestrial air-breathing forms they disappear in the adult, and are given the name visceral clefts. The gill-slits of sharks are open to the exterior ; those of bony fishes are covered by a fold of skin supported by bone, the operculum, which grows out from the side of the head, just in front of the foremost gill-cleft, and extends backwards.

The openings of excretory and reproductive systems may be distinct (they are found near the anus), though sometimes there is a single *urino-genital* opening, and the ducts of these systems may open into the terminal part of the food canal, so that there is but a single aperture for the exit of faeces, urine and eggs or sperms. The compartment thus formed is called a *cloaca*, and its opening the cloacal aperture.

Fins and Limbs. In fishes, and in amphibians like the newt, a single median fin runs along the upper side of trunk and tail, and is continued over the tip of the tail on to its lower surface. In fishes this fin is broken up into distinct fins of back (*dorsal*), belly (*ventral*) and tail (*caudal*). Fishes also have paired fins, of which the pectorals lie close behind the last gill-slit and the pelvics at the sides of the anus. All craniates higher than fishes have replaced the paired fins by limbs, of which the fore-limb corresponds to the pectoral fin and the hind-limb to the pelvic. The hands and feet of terrestrial craniates have five fingers and toes, this *pentadactyl* limb being very characteristic of the group's higher members. Beneath the two-layered skin are muscle segments or myotomes of cone-like form. The muscles enclose the coelom, which is more widely separated from the upper surface of the animal than from the lower. In this mass of muscle near the upper surface of the animal lies the backbone and, within it, the nerve cord. In fishes the coelom is divided into two compartments—a pericardium, containing the heart, in front and a peritoneal cavity, containing the viscera, behind.

Supporting or skeletal structures fall into two categories. The *exoskeleton* takes the form of deposits in the skin, but is never a secretion, like the shells of molluscs. Scales, feathers, hairs, nails, claws, hooves and horns are exoskeletal structures. The *endoskeleton*, or true skeleton, of bone or gristle, is very complex, and varies considerably in different classes of Craniata. The basis of the skeleton is an axial rod, the notochord, found only in the early stages of development in the majority of the craniates. It lies between the nerve cord and the coelom.

Structure of the Skull. The backbone consists of a chain of many pieces, or vertebrae, through which the notochord passes. The skull is attached to the front end of the vertebral column, and consists of a brain case, or cranium, with capsules containing the organs of smell and hearing, and a number, varying from four to nine, of elements called visceral arches. The first lies close behind the mouth, and is called the *mandibular* arch ; the second is called the *hyoid* arch ; and the rest are called *branchial* arches, because they support the gills of aquatic forms. In all craniates, except the lamprey and its allies, the upper and lower halves of the *mandibular* arch (palatine bar and Meckel's cartilage) form the support of upper and lower jaws. The second or *hyoid* arch is similarly divided ; its upper part (the hyomandibular), in lower craniates, serves to connect the jaws with the skull. This is the *hyostylic* mode of jaw suspension. In all craniates higher than the fish the jaws are suspended from the skull either by the *quadrate* or by the *squamosal*, forming the *autostylic* suspension. The lower part of the hyoid arch forms a support for the muscles of the tongue. The branchial arches of water-living forms lie in the walls of the gill-clefts, which they help to strengthen.

Alimentary Canal. The food canal, like most viscera, lies chiefly in the peritoneal cavity. It is seen in its simplest form in the sharks, where it is divisible into the buccal cavity, pharynx, gullet or oesophagus, stomach and intestine. This last often opens into a cloaca, which receives also the ducts of the excretory and reproductive organs. Many characteristic structures are developed in connexion with the food canal. The lining of the mouth develops a ridge along each jaw on which teeth are formed. A tooth is typically constructed from three tissues—enamel, dentine and cement. Dentine builds up the bulk of the tooth, and occurs in a variety of forms, some of which approach bone in strength and structure. The exposed surface of the tooth is capped with a dense layer of enamel, the hardest substance in the body. Cement material serves to fix the tooth in the tissue of the jaws, and is almost indistinguishable from bone.

In connexion with the alimentary canal digestive glands are developed. Salivary glands open into the mouth, and secrete a fluid, saliva, which converts starch into sugar. Two large glands develop in relation to the intestine, and lie in the peritoneal cavity. These are the liver and the pancreas. The ducts open into the intestine and that of the liver has a blind reservoir, the gall-bladder, in which the bile secreted by this organ is stored until required for use. Other important glands are the ductless glands, which pour their secretions not into canals leading to a definite part of the animal, but into the blood stream. Of these the spleen, thyroid, thymus, pituitary and suprarenal body are all important, each playing an intricate part in the economy of the body.

Circulation of the Blood. The blood vascular system is more complex than that of any animal type we have so far studied.

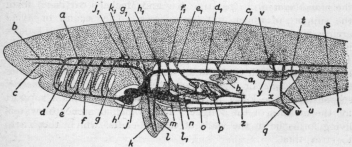

VASCULAR SYSTEM OF A FISH. a, efferent branchial artery ; a_1, spermatic artery b, carotid artery ; b_1 gonad ; c jugular vein ; c_1, spermatic artery ; d, first gill opening ; d_1, cardinal vein e, afferent branchial artery e_1, mesenteric artery ; f, ventral aorta . f_1, coeliac artery ; g, last gill opening g_1, hepatic vein ; h ventricle of heart ; h_1, hepatic artery ; j_1 auricle of heart j_1 precaval vein ; k subclavian vein k_1 dorsal aorta . l, subclavian artery ; l_1, stomach , m, liver ; n, hepatic portal vein ; o, lateral vein ; p, spleen , q, iliac vein ; r, caudal vein ; s, caudal artery ; t and u, renal portal vein ; v. renal artery ; w, iliac artery x, kidney ; y, renal vein ; z, intestine.

From Parker & Haswell

It can be best understood in the fish, as shown in the diagram above. The muscular heart—the pumping organ of the system —is composed of three chambers, *sinus venosus, auricle* and *ventricle,* of which the last is foremost. These chambers are separated from one another by apertures guarded by valves opening in one direction only, a forward direction. This arrangement prevents back-flow of the blood. An elastic blood vessel, the ventral aorta, arises from the ventricle, and gives off paired branches to each of the gills, where a network of minute capillaries is formed, in which purification occurs.

After leaving the gills the blood passes into vessels in the pharynx roof, and is discharged into a median vessel, the *dorsal aorta*, lying just below the vertebral column. From this vessel arteries are given off to the limbs and viscera, while the reduced main trunk passes to the tail region. From capillary networks in the organs, blood is returned to the heart along a second set of vessels, called veins. Those from the head are *jugulars* and *cardinals*. Blood from the tail may pass directly to the heart by a second and hinder (*posterior*) cardinal, or may pass by an alternative route through the substance of the kidney, as the *renal portal* veins. Blood loaded with digested food materials passes to the liver—where storage occurs—by the *hepatic portal* vein, and thence to the heart by the hepatic vein.

Nervous System. The nervous system arises as a groove along the back of the embryo. Later, the edges of the groove are rolled up, so that a tube, lined by ectoderm, is formed. As growth proceeds, the front end of the tube is dilated and forms the brain rudiment, the rest becoming spinal or nerve cord, from which spinal nerves grow out towards the muscles of the body wall. The brain undergoes complication by division into a series of chambers or ventricles, and by unequal thickening of its walls. From the brain, cranial nerves, paired like the spinal nerves, are given off. There are ten pairs in fishes and amphibians, and two more in higher craniate types. The first supplies the organ of smell, the second that of sight, and the eighth that of hearing. The third, fourth and sixth nerves supply the six muscles which move each eye. The fifth and seventh are distributed to the jaw muscles, mouth, palate and teeth, while the ninth serves the first pair of gills. Perhaps the most important nerve is the tenth, which sends branches to the remaining gills, to the heart and viscera, and to a series of organs of balance at the sides of the body. In higher craniates an eleventh cranial nerve runs to certain shoulder muscles, and a twelfth sends branches to the neck and tongue. Nerves vary in function. Some (one, two and eight) convey messages from sense organs to the brain : these are called *sensory* nerves. Others (three, four and six) carry impulses to muscles from the brain ; these are *motor* nerves. A few (ten, for instance) have both sensory and motor fibres ; these are the so-called *mixed* nerves.

(621)

LESSON 23

Lampreys, Sharks and Rays

THE term " fish " is not uncommonly used to denote any animal which lives habitually in water. To define a fish as an aquatic vertebrate would be more accurate. but this definition leaves much to be desired. Many animals with backbones living their lives in water are definitely not fishes. The newt or eft possesses the characters of amphibia, and the seal, whale and otter are mammals. We get closer to the mark in extending the definition of a fish to include aquatic vertebrates which breathe by means of gills—delicate folds or filaments connected with openings or gill-clefts in the sides of the throat—and which balance and propel themselves through water by special paddle-like limbs called fins. These characters are true piscine ones. Fins are flattened expansions of the body, some of which lie in the middle line and are unpaired, while others are paired and correspond to the limbs of higher vertebrates. All fins are supported by firm rods of horn or gristle or bone, called fin-rays. In most fishes the body is clothed in a defensive armour of scales or bony plates embedded in the skin.

Though it was at one time believed to be the case, all animals which answer our definition of a fish cannot be regarded as constituting a single class of vertebrate, of equal standing with the class of birds or that of reptiles. More detailed study of the structure and evolutionary history of such animals has led to the formation of entirely different conclusions. The lampreys and hagfishes (Cyclostomes) possess pouchlike gills and mouths devoid of biting jaws, but more like suckers ; they resemble true fishes superficially in shape, in habits and in their mode of breathing, but differ in certain characters as much as true fishes differ from amphibians, being regarded as a separate class. The creatures we recognise as sharks, dogfishes and rays (Selachians) have skeletons composed of gristle or cartilage, and were separated from true fishes with a bony skeleton (Pisces) very early during the history of living things of the earth. Our definition of fishes, therefore, applies to three distinct classes of vertebrates.

Cyclostomes. Lampreys and hags (*Cyclostomata*) are eel-like creatures distinguished from all other vertebrates by a jawless sucking mouth, a single organ of smell, and their lack of paired appendages or fins. The sea-lamprey (*Petromyzon marinus*), which attains a length of over one yard, and the fresh-water lamprey or lampern (*P. fluviatilis*), which is somewhat smaller, are common species in the northern hemisphere. *Petromyzon* has a cylindrical head and trunk and a tail which is flattened from side to side. In front of and below the head is a basin-like hollow, the mouth funnel, beset with horny teeth. At the bottom of the funnel is a horny tongue, also carrying sharp teeth, and close beside it is the relatively small mouth. The mouth acts like a sucker, enabling the lamprey to fix itself to the body of a fish, while the armed tongue rasps off flesh to serve as food. The organ of smell has only a single nostril, which is found on top of the head immediately in front of an area of transparent skin ; this is a vestigial third eye. The paired functional eyes lie at the sides of the head, and are seen to lack eyelids, but are covered by a thin transparent protective covering of skin. Seven pairs of small apertures situated at the sides of the head (the first being close behind the eyes) are the gill-clefts, and the region in which they occur is the respiratory or branchial region. When fixed

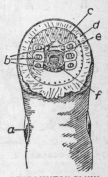

PETROMYZON FLUVI-ATILIS. Ventral view of the head of the common fresh - water lamprey : a, eye ; b, teeth of buccal funnel ; c, buccal funnel ; d, papillae ; e, mouth.

From *Parker & Haswell*, "*Textbook of Zoology*" Macmillan

to a stone the lamprey cannot take water in at the mouth, as does the true fish, but pumps water into and out of the gill apertures by muscular action. This accounts for the alternate rise and fall of the wall of the body in the branchial region of the fixed animal.

Petromyzon has an interesting larva, the *ammocoete*, which feeds very much like the adult lancelet. The thyroid gland resembles its homologue, the endostyle of *Amphioxus*, in opening on the floor of the pharynx and in secreting mucus threads in which food organisms caught up in the respiratory stream are entangled and passed into the food canal. The buccal funnel is not yet formed, and the rudimentary eyes lie under the skin.

Elasmobranchs. Selachians differ from true or bony fishes in lacking bone in the skeleton—which is entirely gristly, with limy deposits in certain elements—in not having an air bladder and in possessing naked gill-clefts. The name given to the Selachians by the zoologist, *Elasmobranchii*, refers to the strap-like gills. The surface of the dog-fish's body is rough and prickly when stroked from the tail towards the head. This is due to the presence in the skin of numerous tooth-like elements, *dermal denticles* (sometimes called placoid scales). Each denticle consists of two parts, a basal plate of bone-like material and a superficial spine coated with the substance (enamel) which covers the teeth of higher animals. The denticles are admirably shown in a commercial preparation of shark skin (shagreen). The teeth of the shark are neither more nor less than modified placoid

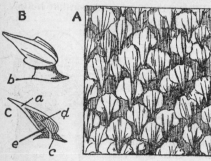

PLACOID SCALES. A, portion of the skin of the rough hound as seen under a hand-lens; **B,** a single scale removed from the skin; **C,** the same in section (diagrammatic); a, enamel; b, base of the scale; c, the same in section; d, dentine; e, pulp cavity.

From Borradaile, "Elementary Zoology"

scales arranged in regular rows in the mouth and on the lips. Such teeth are continually replaced, as they break off, by younger growing teeth within the mouth cavity. The teeth and the spines of the scales contain a cavity in which blood circulates, carrying food materials to the denticles.

The dog-fish's body is spindle-shaped and well adapted to life in water. It is divisible into three regions, called head, trunk and tail. A small aperture immediately behind each eye, the spiracle, marks the hinder limit of the head, beneath which is the wide crescentic mouth, while the *cloaca*, or common opening of the food canal, excretory system and reproductive system, marks the limits of trunk and tail. The gill-slits, of which there are five on each side of the throat, and the spiracle open internally into the pharynx, and serve as outlets for water taken in by way of the mouth.

The body of the fish is flattened not from above downwards

like the head, but from side to side. Two pairs of fins and four median fins are found on trunk and tail. The paired *pectoral* fins lie close behind the head. They correspond to the fore-limbs of higher types. The hinder paired fins, *pelvics*, which are the homologues of the hind limbs of land animals, are smaller and lie just in front of the cloaca. In males they are united in the middle line and bear each a grooved rod, the *clasper*, used in the reproductive act. Two single fins lie on the back, these being the fore and hind *dorsal fins*, while one lies on the under side, the *ventral fin*, and another follows the outline of the tail. This last, the *caudal fin*, has two lobes, and the tip of the tail passes into the upper lobe.

Such a fin is different from that of the bony fish, and is given the name *heterocercal*.

The body wall is ex-tremely muscular, and the muscles represent segments of the body. These *myotomes* are ar-ranged in the form of a W throughout trunk

CAUDAL FINS. Diagrams showing structure of caudal fins : **A** (heterocercal), sturgeon (Acipenser sp.) ; **B** (homocercal), haddock (Gadus aeglefinus).

From Norman, " History of Fishes," Ernest Benn, Ltd.

and tail regions. The alternate contractions of the myotomes of opposite sides pull the tail from side to side and serve to propel the fish, while the fins are used for balancing and steering. The muscles alternate with the vertebrae, which lie buried in the myotome mass.

Rays and Skates. These well-known and important food fishes have a rhomboidal body and a long cylindrical tail, and are closely related to sharks and dog-fishes, with which they are connected by a series of transitional forms. The edible parts are the triangular sides of the body, which are the enormously enlarged pectoral fins. The whip-like tail of sting-rays bears a formidable weapon in the form of a spine—from eight to fifteen inches long—which is serrated along both margins and which has arisen, in all probability, by fusion or enlargement of certain dermal denticles. These spines are shed periodically and replaced by new ones growing beneath them.

Skates and rays live on the floor of the sea, and the mouth, being situated on the lower surface, is not favourably placed for taking in water needed in respiration. Accordingly, we find that water enters the pharynx by way of the spiracle, which is more suitably placed on top of the head. Water leaves the pharynx through the gill-slits located on the lower surface of the head near the mouth. The spiracle is thus more important in rays and skates than in the dog-fish, which is better able to draw water into the mouth.

Organs in which electricity is generated, to be discharged at the will of the fish, are found in the torpedo or electric ray, occurring in tropical and temperate seas. One organ runs through the entire thickness of the body between the head and the enlarged pectoral fins on either side. Each organ is made up of numerous vertical columns, filled with clear jelly, and is divided into a number of minute compartments, each of which has a flattened electric plate. A cluster of nerve fibrils is attached to one side of each plate. These unite with a main nerve for the entire organ, which runs to a special part of the brain. The side of the plate possessing nerve endings is negative to the opposite side, and the entire organ is positive on its upper surface and negative on its lower one. By means of the electric organs the torpedo ray is able to kill or paralyse its enemies or prey.

One group of the *Elasmobranchii* deserves special mention. This is the *Holocephali* in which *Chimaera*, sometimes called " king of the herrings," is placed. The head is blunt and there is no spiracle. Only one external gill aperture is seen, for the gills are intermediate between those of shark and bony fish, being covered by an opercular fold. The paired fins occupy the same relative position as those of the dog-fish, and the cells of the dorsal fin secrete a virulent venom, which causes painful wounds. The tail is sometimes an enormously elongated filament. The few existing members of the *Holocephali* known to zoology are the degenerate descendants of a once important group.

The eggs of Elasmobranchs contain large reserves of food yolk used by the developing embryo, and are enclosed in horny pillow-shaped cases known popularly as " mermaid's purses." Each corner of the case has either a short horn or a cluster of.twisted threads projecting from it. These serve to fix the egg-case firmly in crevices or attach them to seaweeds until the young animal hatches out. The young, on hatching, resembles its parents and soon commences to feed. Many months are spent, however, in the shelter of the capsule.

LESSON 24

True or Bony Fishes

(See plate 61)

THE class of bony fishes (*Pisces*), a large and dominant group which appears still to be on the up grade, contains so many species that considerable difficulty is experienced in arranging them into sub-classes and orders, about which experts disagree. Three sub-classes are recognized by some authorities : *Palaeopterygii, Crossopterygii and Neopterygii.* The three names mean respectively " ancient fins," " fringed fins " and " new fins." The groups differ in characters of a technical kind, chiefly in the nature of the skeleton, the form of the scales and the structure of the fins. The first and second groups together contain less than fifty species, while the last contains three hundred times this number. Long before the bony fishes we know came into existence the first two groups were dominant fishes and populated all waters of the earth.

During early Devonian times the earliest members of the *Palaeopterygii* appeared as a family of fishes now known as the Palaeoniscids. Before this group became extinct it gave rise to the ancestor of modern bony fishes included in the *Neopterygii.* The Palaeoniscids were elongated fishes with heterocercal tails and one dorsal fin. The body was enclosed in an armour of shining and elaborately sculptured *ganoid* scales. Such scales are the most primitive type found in bony fishes. Each consists of a rhomboidal plate made up of three layers : on the surface, a layer of an enamel-like substance (ganoine) ; below this, a thick layer of bone ; and, between the two, a third layer containing blood vessels. The scales articulate with one another by a peg and socket joint. Such scales occur in the bichirs (*Polypterus*), which live in tropical African swamps and rivers, and the sturgeons (*Acipenser*) among living fishes. In the sturgeon, which is clearly descended from the Palaeoniscids, the only part of the armour remaining is a small cluster of ganoid scales on the upper part of the tail. Five rows of bony plates run along each side of the body from head to tail, however, and these have a similar structure to the rhomboid scales.

The *Crossopterygii* include existing lung-fishes, like the Queensland *Ceratodus* or Burnett salmon and the African (*Protopterus*) and South American (*Lepidosiren*) lung-fishes. One of the earliest forms is *Dipterus*, found as a fossil in the Old Red Sandstone of Scotland. Starting with this interesting fish, it would be possible to arrange a series of forms illustrating the probable line of descent of existing forms. The bones encasing the cranium have been reduced in number, the body has become more eel-like, and the ganoid scales have been replaced by the type of scale found in higher fishes, called *cycloid* scales. One group of Crossopterygians, we might observe in passing, is the probable ancestor of the amphibians and of all other four-footed terrestrial vertebrates ; this is the *Osteolepidae*.

The taxonomist recognizes thirty-one orders of *Neopterygii*. To attempt to enumerate their characters or even the common names of their representatives appears futile and unprofitable. The orders vary in size and importance. One contains a single species, the bow-fin (*Amia*), from the rivers of the United States. Another includes the fresh water gar-pikes (*Lepidosteus* and its allies), also from the New World. A third and more important order includes a large assemblage of modern fishes, the salmon, trout, herring, and also peculiar oceanic fishes with phosphorescent organs, the *Stomias* family. These agree in having the pelvic fins placed in the abdominal position (in the middle of the belly), and in having an air-bladder connected with the gullet.

The air-bladder, or swim-bladder, of the fish is a cylindrical sac with silvery walls, lying just below the backbone in the body cavity. It varies in size and form in different fishes, and may be present in one form and absent in a near relative. If punctured with a sharp instrument it collapses at once, which indicates that it normally contains a gas of one kind or another. In most fishes it is a simple bag filled with a mixture of different gases, but in *Amia* and *Lepidosteus* and in the lung-fishes, all of which are air-breathers, the walls are richly vascularized and much folded. In these fishes it bears a remarkable resemblance to the lungs of terrestrial vertebrates, being divided into two lobes. Blood is conveyed to the bladder in these instances by vessels similar to those connected with the lungs of Amphibia.

Functions of the Air-bladder. Probably no single vertebrate organ performs so wide a variety of functions as the air-bladder of the bony fish. In most fishes it serves as an organ of flotation, by means of which the animal can accommodate itself to varying pressures met with at different depths. Fine blood vessels in its walls are aggregated in certain areas to form the red glands, believed to secrete gases into the bladder. It is interesting to observe that such glands are found in fishes with " blind " air-bladders. In addition to the red glands, another structure (the oval) occurs, which possesses the power of absorbing excess gas when required. As a fish rises towards the surface the pressure of the surrounding water decreases, and, consequently, the gas in the bladder expands and the body tends to rise too rapidly. But gas is absorbed by the appropriate parts of the bladder wall, so that equilibrium is restored. Similarly, when the fish swims downwards the pressure increases, gas in the bladder is compressed, the body becomes heavier and tends to sink over rapidly. The secretion of gas by the red glands counteracts this tendency.

In some fishes the bladder is an organ for the production of sounds. Mr. Norman reports (in his " A History of Fishes," Benn, 1931, which all interested in fishes should read) that in some cat-fishes there is a mechanism, called the elastic mechanism, whose action causes the wall of the bladder to vibrate, giving rise to sounds. The cat-fish, *Doras*, emits a deep growl audible a hundred feet away when the fish is out of water. The fishes known as drums (*Sciaenidae*) are said to hum, purr and whistle loud enough to be heard by persons listening on the deck of a ship. This does not exhaust the functions of the air-bladder. In some fishes it is an auxiliary organ of hearing, being intimately connected with the inner ear. An aperture in the hinder wall of the ear is closed by a fine skin or membrane, which is in contact with a narrow tubular outgrowth of the air-bladder. In cat-fishes the first four vertebrae behind the skull form a chain of bones connecting the air-bladder with fluid-filled spaces round the inner ear. This *Weberian* mechanism cannot be concerned with pressure regulation, since it occurs only in fresh water fishes (and, therefore, shallow water forms) and is probably connected with hearing.

The air-bladder is intimately associated with the digestive canal, and develops as a small outgrowth of the gullet. As the size of the bladder increases this connexion becomes more and more insignificant, until at length it is an extremely narrow tube called the pneumatic duct. In some forms this remains open, though in others it closes and may disappear. Our own lungs develop in a similar manner. For this and other reasons it is believed that the original function of the air-bladder was respiratory, and that its pressure-regulating function is a secondary one. In the earliest fishes, many of which swarmed in shallow water, air breathing was probably unnecessary, but later competition forced many fishes to ascend rivers. Some would find shelter in ponds and swamps, where pollution due to decaying vegetation induced them to take up air-breathing owing to the difficulty of gill-breathing under these conditions. From these forms were derived the ancestor of land vertebrates, which found the conquest of land a means of escape from enemies or an assurance of abundant food.

Growth of Scales. The scales of bony fishes differ considerably from the dermal denticles of the *Elasmobranchii* and lack the enamel covering. Typical scales, such as those of the carp, are shaped each like a finger nail. The front end is deeply embedded in the skin, while its hinder end, which has minute serrations, is free and overlaps the scale behind. This type of scale is comb-like or *ctenoid*. Another type (*cycloid*) lacks the hinder toothed margin, and is found in fishes with soft rayed fins—the herring and salmon, for instance. Examined under the microscope the scales reveal the age of the fish. This is because the scales are constant in number, and must grow in order to cover the increasing surface of the growing fish. With high magnification we see a number of concentric rings, resembling the rings of growth shown in a cross section of a tree. Like the tree, the fish grows more rapidly during one season of the year than during another. Spring and summer are times of plenty and the fish grows more rapidly then than at other times. The scales grow with corresponding rapidity. In autumn and winter growth slows down, and may ultimately cease. So also does the growth of scales. The result is that close rings (of winter) alternate in the scale with wider rings (of summer), and a count of the close rings tells us how many winters the fish has lived through. Age determination can be made also by examination of small limy concretions found within the ear cavity, and used as agents of balance, for these ear-stones, or otoliths, also show alternate zones of summer and winter growth.

Larval Fish. Young or larval fishes differ greatly from their parents. The interesting larva of the common eel was long unrecognized, and was given a different name, *Leptocephalus*, because regarded as belonging to a different group of fishes. It is a glassy, leaf-like creature, so much flattened from side to side that we can read print through its transparent body. The black pigment of its eyes alone betrays the young animal. The whole story of the European eel was elucidated by the late Dr. Johannes Schmidt, who tracked the Leptocephali on their extensive journey across the Atlantic. Mature eels migrate across the bed of the ocean and spawn in its western part, south-east of Bermuda. The Leptocephali hatch out in the spring and travel in the Gulf Stream towards our shores. They possess needle-like teeth, by means of which they can capture minute organisms that serve as food. They spend two years in travel, and arrive on this side of the Atlantic about three inches in length. They then undergo transformation—becoming smaller and more slender—into tiny elvers or grass-eels. The larval teeth are lost and new peg-like teeth are developed, and the elvers are ready to ascend the rivers, where they seek ponds and there grow to maturity. Truly one of the most romantic life histories known to Zoology !

LESSON 25

Some Amphibians of Yesterday and Today

(See plate 62)

SOME classes of the Vertebrata are very well defined : we recognize mammals by their covering of hairs ; we identify birds by their feathers ; and we separate fishes from all other vertebrates on account of their fins, scales and breathing apparatus. For the remaining vertebrates, reptiles and amphibia, we can find no such easy distinction. Both types are backboned ; and both, speaking generally, have adopted a creeping mode of life. Examining the two types more carefully, however, we find criteria which enable us to distinguish between them. One type breathes by means of lungs from the time of birth onwards ; all animals belonging to this type—lizards, snakes, crocodiles, tortoises, and turtles—we group together as Reptilia.

The remaining animals, including frogs, toads, tritons, newts and mud-puppies, form the Amphibia.

Amphibians are small, weak creatures, which meet with much persecution from the higher and more formidable vertebrates. To avoid this, the terrestrial forms hide in holes or make burrows underground, venturing out for food under the protection of darkness. The skin is soft and moist; in all, except a few burrowing forms, it is devoid of scales, and in these exceptions the scales lie completely hidden within the skin. The young animal differs from its parents in that it lives in water and breathes like a fish. Later, however, it is transformed into the adult by a series of extensive changes which constitute a metamorphosis, and for the rest of its life is an air-breathing creature. A frog, as is well known, does not hatch out of the egg as a miniature adult, but as a limbless tadpole, breathing by means of gills and presenting other resemblances to a fish. Later it comes to resemble the parent by metamorphic changes ; the fore and hind limbs sprout out, the air-breathing lungs are developed, while the gills entirely disappear. The young animal possesses the characteristics of a fish ; the adult, those of a reptile. There are exceptions to this general rule. Some amphibians metamorphose before hatching from the egg, and some, notably the mud-eels (*Proteus and Siren*), retain their gills throughout life. The narrow plan on which the amphibian body is built is modified in a rich variety of ways in different members of the class.

We might feel justified in thinking that the air-breathing habit of adult amphibians sufficiently marks them off from fishes. We saw in previous Lessons that some fishes possess a sort of lung and can breathe air, while some amphibians continue to use their gills and rarely leave the water. What, then, is the real criterion of distinction between fishes and amphibians ? It is not the nature of the respiratory mechanism, but the structure of the limbs. Fishes possess fins, whereas amphibians, in common with higher vertebrates, have modified these appendages into five-fingered or pentadactyl limbs. The basal joint of such a limb is formed of a single elongated bone (in the thigh or upper arm), its middle part consists of two elongated bones (in the shin or lower arm), while the part most distant from the body is built up of a series of small bones arranged in diverging rows (and forming the skeleton of toes and fingers). This last part is most subject to modification, chiefly by fusion of parts.

Extinct Amphibians. The earliest known four-legged creatures lived in early Palaeozoic times. The remains of these now extinct animals are found in Carboniferous strata of Europe and North America and are the fossilized skeletal parts. Of the soft tissues of their bodies we know practically nothing, because such parts have not been preserved. From these primitive backboned animals which first took possession of the land, not only the Amphibia but also the Reptilia and higher groups have evolved. The upper side of the cranium was roofed over by bones resembling the body plates of armoured fishes, and for this reason such animals are grouped together as the *Stegocephalia*. Some were very small, but others attained a huge size, and became extinct as a result of their own unwieldiness during the earlier stages of the Secondary epoch, being apparently unable to compete successfully with types well on the way to becoming reptiles. These creatures possessed pentadactyl limbs and a skeleton so generalized that it is not difficult to derive from it the skeleton of a typical newt. The vertebrae are distinctive, and the manner in which the skull is slung to the backbone is definitely amphibian. In some Stegocephalia two bony projections or condyles on the skull fit into depressions in the foremost vertebra ; in others a simple joint is effected without condyles.

Present-day Amphibia. These are grouped in three orders : the *Apoda* or Caecilians ; the *Urodela*, or tailed amphibians ; the *Anura*, or tailless amphibians. *Caecilia*, a snake-like amphibian which lacks limbs and tail, forms an example of the first order ; newts and salamanders belong to the second order ; and frogs and toads are included in the third order. Caecilians are not of especial interest to us. They are widely distributed in the tropical regions of both hemispheres, where they are found burrowing in damp earth. Their distribution, and the fact that they are devoid of any means of rapid dispersal, suggest that they are of great antiquity. And these curious creatures, though much specialized in some respects, come nearer to the primitive extinct forms in some characters than do other existing amphibians. Numerous small bony plates lie embedded in their skin, representing the armour once characteristic of the class.

Most country dwellers are familiar with the little efts, or newts, commonly seen in ponds or ditches or crawling over the damp ground in their vicinity. In appearance they are not unlike lizards, but their movements are much more sluggish, while the slimy, scaleless skin and the clawless digits at once show them to be amphibia. The animal sprawls even more than reptiles do, and the thumb is absent. In addition, we remark on the fact that newts lay their eggs in water, and tadpoles hatch out from them. These larvae possess filamentous gills, which sprout out from the sides of the throat, and, later, gill-clefts, which open to the exterior by an opercular aperture, as in bony fishes. In the adult the gill filaments have disappeared and the gill-clefts have closed. There are exceptions, however, which will be mentioned later.

Salamanders resemble newts, but are mostly larger. When adult they are better suited to life on land. The spotted salamander, *Salamandra maculosa*, common in damp woods in parts of central Europe, is of striking colour, being black with orange markings. In such terrestrial urodeles the limbs stand out from the trunk, and the soles of feet and hands are pressed close to the ground with the digits directed forwards. The body is assured of better support in consequence. The saw-edged crest, found in the male newt, is not present and the tail is slender and cylindrical.

With a solitary exception, all the members of the sub-order containing newts and salamanders (*Caducibranchiata*) have functional eyes provided with movable eyelids. This exception is *Amphiuma*, an eel-like creature with greatly reduced limbs, which lives in the ditches of rice fields in the U.S.A. Closely related to this creature is *Cryptobranchus*, one species of which, *C. japonicus*, is the giant salamander of Japan. This amphibian, which lives in mountain streams, is the largest known and attains a length of five feet.

Another sub-order of the Urodela, the *Perennibranchiata*, contains forms with three pairs of fringed external gills which spread out transversely from the sides of the throat. Periodically they contract and become pale, and alternately become red as they are filled with blood. *Necturus*, the mud-puppy, with species living in the Mississippi basin and the Canadian lakes, a voracious nocturnal creature, belongs to this group. It has functional eyes covered with thin folds of transparent skin, four fingers and four toes, and two gill-clefts. Another member of the group is *Proteus*, a European form which lives entirely in the subterranean waters of caves. The eyes of this creature are completely hidden beneath folds of opaque skin and are degenerate. It has three fingers and two toes, and the white or pinkish skin of its body, if subjected to light, is as sensitive as a photographic plate, becoming jet black.

The third sub-order of the Urodela, *Sirenoidea*, contains forms with persistent gills and lidless eyes, but with fore-limbs only, the hind limbs having disappeared. To this group belongs *Siren*, the mud-eel, which occurs in the southern U.S.A. The fore-limb is short and has three or four digits, and the toothless jaws have horny sheaths. The animal lies buried in the mud of ponds and ditches, occasionally crawling over the ground and swimming with arms folded to the sides of the body.

The elongated body of the Urodela is supported by a varying number of vertebrae in different types. The entirely aquatic forms have the largest number, while truly terrestrial types have fewest. Thus the vertibral column of the eel-like *Amphiuma* is built up of about 100 vertebrae, that of *Siren* and *Proteus* of about 60, that of *Triton* about 50, while that of *Salamandra* comes last with about 40. Terrestrial amphibia have far fewer vertebrae, this reduction of the number being an adaptation to life on land. The modern Urodela have been derived from amphibians which had made a conquest of land only to revert to the old aquatic environment ; they have become readapted to aquatic life without regaining the primitive elongation of the backbone. In Anura the trunk has been shortened and made more rigid, to suit life on land, by reducing the number of supporting vertebrae.

LESSON 26

Frogs and Toads

FROGS and toads (*Anura*), the most successful of all amphibians, are found in almost every part of the world. Our first glance at the common frog, *Rana temporaria*, reveals to us a short, tailless body with disproportionately long limbs, characters that we associate with the leaping habit. The frog is also an expert swimmer, and the hind feet are webbed. They execute movements closely resembling those of the human swimmer, but the fore limbs take no part in aquatic progression, being folded on the breast.

The skin is moist and soft, being kept in this condition by numerous glands, which lie immediately beneath it and open on to its surface, discharging quantities of mucus from time to time. Frogs—and, in fact, all tailless amphibians—breathe solely by means of lungs and the skin, the gills and gill-slits of the tadpole being entirely lost in the adult. At first the newly hatched and limbless tadpole breathes by three pairs of plume-like gills, much like those of the mud-puppy, *Necturus*. Later on these are replaced by so-called "internal" gills, vascular folds on the walls

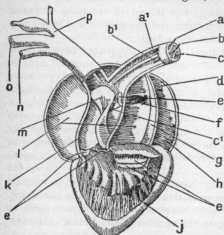

of gill-slits, which place the cavity of the throat in communication with the exterior. A fold then grows back over the external gills (now shrivelling up) and the gill-slits, the edge of which fuses with the body wall, except at one point on the left side, where a small round opening (the spiracle) remains. Through this passes water which has entered the mouth, traversed the gill-slits and bathed the gills for the purpose of breathing. Meanwhile, the lungs are growing out as pouches from the

HEART OF A FROG, from the ventral aspect, with the cavities laid open; a, a¹, bristle in left carotid trunk; b, b¹, bristle in left systemic trunk; c, c¹, bristle in left pulmo-cutaneous trunk; d. aperture of pulmonary veins; e, e, valves; f, sinu-auricular aperture; g, auricular septum; h, left auricle; j, ventricle; k, conus arteriosus; l, right auricle; m, longitudinal valve; n, pulmo-cutaneous arch; o, systemic arch; p, carotid arch.

*From Parker & Haswell, "Textbook of Zoology,"
Macmillan*

hinder part of the mouth floor, and begin to share the work of respiration, gradually supplanting the gills as these dwindle, ultimately to disappear, and as the gill-slits close. These alterations involve profound changes in the heart and blood vessels.

Blood Supply. To begin with, the heart agrees in all its essentials with that of the fish, consisting of two principal chambers: an *auricle*, which receives the impure blood of the body, and a muscular *ventricle*, which pumps it to the gills for purification, and on to the tissues of the body. As the lungs commence to function, blood from them is poured into the auricle, which becomes divided by a fleshy partition into two chambers, right and left auricles. This oxygenated blood passes into the left auricle, the right one serving as a receptacle for non-oxygenated blood. The two chambers open into the ventricle, and, since this remains undivided, the pure and impure blood is mixed in its cavity. Owing to the extreme sponginess of the ventricle wall, however, the mixing is only partial. And when the ventricle contracts, first pure blood, then mixed blood, and, finally, impure blood is pumped forwards into the single vessel leaving it. Pure blood is directed into vessels serving the head region, impure blood is sent to the lungs and skin, while mixed blood supplies the rest of the body.

From amphibia upwards to reptiles, birds and mammals, evolution has brought about a gradual perfecting of the arrangements for keeping pure and impure blood separate. But only in birds and mammals is this end completely attained and the entire body supplied by perfectly pure blood; to this we may attribute the marked success of these two classes of backboned animals.

Visceral Arches. The gill system of a primitive vertebrate, like the fish, is related to six visceral arches. The first and second are the mandibular and hyoid arches, the last four are branchial arches. Each arch is supplied by an artery (the afferent branchial) which branches from the main vessel or ventral aorta from the heart. Blood in the afferent branchial arteries passes through blood capillaries in the filaments of the gills, after which it is collected by another set of arteries, the efferent branchials; these unite to form the dorsal aorta in the roof of the throat.

In the tadpole, of Urodela as well as Anura, the first two visceral arches are not concerned with oxygenation of the blood, the four branchial arches alone being functional in this way. The efferent branchial arteries leading out of these arches join to form two main vessels, which unite behind into the dorsal aorta, but have arterial extensions in front leading to the head. At metamorphosis, when the lungs function, changes occur in these arteries. As the gills atrophy their capillaries disappear, so that afferent and efferent arteries become continuous. The first branchial artery becomes the *carotid* arch, carrying pure blood to the head; the second becomes the *systemic* arch, conveying blood to the body generally; the third branchial artery disappears completely; and the last branchial artery forms the *pulmo-cutaneous* arch, along which impure blood passes to the lungs and skin. These are the three channels mentioned previously. The piece of artery connecting the first two branchial arches of the tadpole becomes closed and persists as a fibrous strand, the *ductus caroticus*. One reservation must be made for the majority of Urodela, in which, alone of all four-footed animals (tetrapods), the third branchial artery persists.

In the frog, as in the dogfish, a chamber behind the heart and opening into it, the *sinus venosus*, receives three large veins,

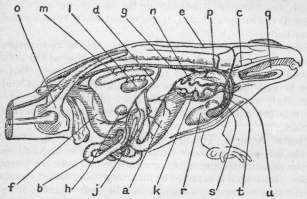

ARTERIAL SYSTEM OF MALE FROG, from right side; a, stomach; b, small intestine; c, carotid artery; d, coeliaco-mesenteric artery; e, cutaneous artery; f, large intestine; g, dorsal aorta; h, spleen; j, hepatic artery; k, right lung; l, testis; m, kidney; n, pulmonary artery; o, pelvic girdle; p, subclavian artery; q, tongue; r, ventricle; s, carotid arch; t, systemic arch; u, pulmo-cutaneous arch.

From A. M. Marshall, " The Frog." David Nutt

paired *superior vena cava* (draining blood from the head, forelimb and skin) and a single *inferior vena cava* (bringing blood from the liver and the kidney). Connected with the latter are two important systems of veins, the *hepatic portal system*, developed in connexion with the liver, and the *renal portal system*, associated with the kidney. Blood from the hind limbs, which has already passed through one set of capillaries, must pass by one of these channels in order to reach the heart. In doing so it must pass through a second set of capillaries in the one organ or the other. The term *portal system* is given to veins such as these which terminate at both extremities in capillaries.

Blood from the dorsal aorta passes to the digestive canal by a number of branches from a single artery, the *coeliaco-mesenteric*. These various branches pass to the stomach and intestine, in the walls of which they break up into capillaries. Digested food materials are absorbed into the blood contained within the capillaries, which is collected into larger and larger veins, ultimately forming the single hepatic portal vein, which receives a vein draining blood from the hind limb. One of the functions of the liver is to remove food materials from the blood for storage until required. The hepatic portal is the channel along which blood proceeding to this store-house is carried. When blood leaves the liver it flows out by a pair of hepatic veins, and these join the inferior vena cava.

Tongueless Species. Frogs and toads, in the widest sense, are as cosmopolitan as they are abundant in species. Some anurans possess a tongue and are known as the *Phaneroglossa* ; others lack a tongue and are grouped together as the *Aglossa*. The most archaic and also the most specialized tailless amphibians are included in the latter group, though lack of a tongue does not necessarily show that the animal is archaic. One of the Aglossa, *Hymenochirus*, has the shortest vertebral column among vertebrates, there being only five vertebrae in front of that carrying the hip bone or pelvic girdle. The lungs have developed spongy strands, which cross their cavities, greatly reducing them ; in this they have reached a higher grade than the lungs of any other amphibia. The part of the body cavity containing the heart and lungs is partially cut off from the part containing the other viscera by a fan-like muscle, which simulates the diaphragm or muscular partition between thorax and abdomen in the mammal.

Another tongueless form is *Pipa*, the Surinam toad, found in Brazil. In the skin of the female's back small pouches provided with lids are developed, and in these the eggs are deposited, here to remain throughout development and until metamorphosis. In both sexes the skin is covered with small tubercles, each of which carries a small horny spine and a poison gland, while larger poison glands are found on the upper and lower surfaces.

Frogs and toads belonging to the Phaneroglossa, though not readily distinguished externally, are differentiated by certain internal characters. Of these the nature of the shoulder or pectoral girdle, which carries the forelimbs, is distinctive. **In** the toad group the girdle consists of halves that overlap on the lower side ; in the frog group the halves meet below to form a strong bar. It is of interest to note that not all toads have a thickset frame and warty appearance, as popularly understood ; since, in addition, some frogs have this appearance, such characters are not diagnostic. But most toads are terrestrial, and many burrow in the ground. They are nocturnal hunters, which kill large numbers of snails and other harmful creatures ; hence they are not the pestilential nuisances some superstitious people believe them to be. Among other evils, they have been supposed to spit venom, to suck the udders of cows and to poison milk kept in cellars—which reports are, of course, absolutely fanciful.

Edible and Tree-climbing Frogs. The common frog is too well known to call for comment here. Its large green relative, the edible frog, *R. esculenta*, occurs almost as commonly on the Continent, and is cultivated for its edible properties. With one exception (*Rhacophorus*, the flying frog), all the many species of the frog family (*Ranidae*) found in North America, Europe and Asia belong to the one genus, *Rana*. The greatest number of genera occur in Africa and the Indo-Malayan countries. *Rhacophorus* lives in tree tops in Japan, India, Malaya and N. Australia. Both fingers and toes are strongly webbed, and their terminal joints are provided with adhesive disks. These characters enable the animal to glide considerable distances in a slanting direction and to seek a hold on the foliage of fresh trees.

Tree frogs proper (*Hylidae*) occur in South America, with a few species in Europe and Asia, but not in Africa, India or Malaya. Typical members of the family have finger disks, and green is the usual colour, though most forms possess the power to change their colour when necessary. Most of them lay numerous eggs in long strings, which are attached to various parts of the body. Some tree frog mothers construct nests in which to deposit their eggs, the most remarkable case being that of *Hyla faber*, the South American ferreiro. The female builds a circular mud wall in the shallow part of a pond, and in this the eggs are laid. The success of many Anura in the struggle for existence is partly due to their possessing strong parental instincts.

Our Course in Zoology is continued in Volume **6**

END OF VOLUME FIVE